BEGINNING
Algebra

Fourth Edition

James Streeter
Late Professor of Mathematics
Clackamas Community College

Donald Hutchison
Clackamas Community College

Louis Hoelzle
Bucks County Community College

WCB McGraw-Hill

Boston, Massachusetts   Burr Ridge, Illinois   Dubuque, Iowa
Madison, Wisconsin   New York, New York   San Francisco, California   St. Louis, Missouri

WCB/McGraw-Hill

A Division of The **McGraw·Hill** *Companies*

Beginning Algebra

Instructor's Edition for Beginning Algebra

This book is printed on acid-free paper.

6 7 8 9 0   VNH VNH 9 0 0

ISBN 0-07-063271-5 (Student Edition)

ISBN 0-07-0632276-6 (Instructor's Edition)

Publisher: Thomas L. Casson
Sponsoring editor: Jack Shira
Marketing manager: Michelle Sala
Project manager: Eva Marie Strock
Production supervisor: Michelle Lyon
Designer: Wanda Kofax
Cover designer: Linear Design Group
Compositor: York Graphic Services, Inc.
Typeface: Times New Roman
Printer: Von Hoffmann

Library of Congress Cataloging-in-Publication Data

Streeter, James (James A.)
    Beginning algebra/James Streeter, Donald Hutchison, Louis
Hoelzle.— 4th ed.
       p.   cm.
    Includes index.
    ISBN 0-07-063271-5 (SE).—ISBN 0-07-063276-6 (TE)
    1. Algebra.   I. Hutchison, Donald, 1948–   .   II. Hoelzle, Louis F.
III. Title.
QA152.2.S77   1997
512.9—dc21
                                                                    97–20718
                                                                    CIP

http://www.mhhe.com

ABOUT THE AUTHORS

While a graduate student at the University of Washington, **James Streeter** paid for his education as a math tutor. It was here that he began to formulate the ideas that would eventually become this package. Upon graduation, he taught for 2 years at Centralia Community College. In 1968 he moved on to Clackamas Community College to become the school's first mathematics chair.

At the college, Jim recognized that he faced a very different population than the one he had tutored at the University of Washington. Jim was convinced that to reach the maximum number of these students, he would have to utilize every medium available to him. Jim opened a math lab that included CAI, original slides and tapes (which were eventually published by Harper & Row), and original worksheets and text materials. With the assistance of the people at McGraw-Hill, that package has been refined to include media and supplements that did not even exist when this project began.

Donald Hutchison spent his first 10 years of teaching working with disadvantaged students. He taught in an intercity elementary school and an intercity high school. He also worked for 2 years at Wassaic State School in New York and 2 years at the Portland Habilitation Center. He worked with both physically and mentally disadvantaged students in these two settings.

In 1982, Don was hired by Jim Streeter to teach at Clackamas Community College. In 1989, Don became Chair of the Mathematics Department at the college. It was here at Clackamas that Don discovered two things that, along with his family, form the focus for his life. Jim introduced Don to the joy of writing (with the first edition of *Beginning Algebra*), and Jack Scrivener converted him to a born-again environmentalist.

Don is also active in several professional organizations. He was a member of the ACM committee that undertook the writing of computer curriculum for the 2-year college. From 1989 to 1994 he was the Chair of the Technology in Mathematics Education Committee for AMATYC. He was President of ORMATYC from 1996 to 1998.

Louis Hoelzle has been teaching at Bucks County Community College for 27 years. In 1989, Lou became Chair of the Mathematics Department at Bucks County Community College. He has taught the entire range of courses from Arithmetic to Calculus, giving him an excellent view of the current and future needs of developmental students.

Over the past 34 years, Lou has also taught Physics courses at 4-year colleges, which has enabled him to have the perspective of the practical applications of mathematics. In addition, Lou has extensively reviewed manuscripts and written several solutions manuals for major textbooks. In these materials he has focused on writing for the student.

Lou is also active in professional organizations. He has served on the Placement and Assessment Committee for AMATYC since 1989.

This book is dedicated to the family I've lived with and loved for the past 25 years. Claudia, my beautiful and loving partner, and Trinh, Micol, Jake, and Christine. They are the essence of my being.

Don Hutchison

This book is dedicated to my wife and children, who have shared my joys, sorrows, successes, and failures over 32 years. Rose, my friend, my inspiration, and part of my very being, and Beth, Ray, Amy, Oscar, Meg, Johanna, and Patrick, the joys of my life.

Louis Hoelzle

THIS SERIES IS DEDICATED TO THE MEMORY OF JAMES ARTHUR STREETER, AN ARTISAN WITH WORDS, A GENIUS WITH NUMBERS, AND A VIRTUOSO WITH PICTURES FROM 1940 UNTIL 1989.

CONTENTS

PREFACE

Statement of Philosophy

We believe that the key to learning mathematics, at any level, is active participation. When students are active participants in the learning process, they have the opportunity to construct their own mathematical ideas and make connections to previously studied material. Such participation leads to understanding, success, and confidence. We developed this text with this philosophy in mind and integrated many features throughout the book to reflect this philosophy. The *Check Yourself* exercises are designed to keep students involved and active with every page of exposition. The calculator references involve students actively in the development of mathematical ideas. Many exercise set have application problems, challenging exercises, writing exercises, and/or collaborative exercises. Each exercise is designed to awaken interest and insight within students. Not all the exercises will be appropriate for every student, but each one provides another opportunity for both instructor and student. Our hope is that every student who uses this text will be a better mathematical thinker as a result.

Changes from the Third Edition

As we set out to revise *Beginning Algebra,* we had to keep in mind that this is a successful text with a very supportive group of adopters. Our goal in this revision was to incorporate new elements to enhance an already proven system. In order to accomplish this goal, we regularly communicated with both current and potential users of the text. We also solicited contributions from professionals with considerable experience in the implementation of collaborative and writing activities in the classroom. We worked hard to incorporate these ideas throughout the text. Every potential change was sent to a set of reviewers. We were very pleased with the support we received from these reviewers. We believe collaborating with so many adept professionals (see the acknowledgments section) has greatly enhanced this text.

Writing in Mathematics

Almost every section includes a set of writing exercises. These exercises encourage students to both research and communicate mathematical ideas. We tried to build a model that helps students understand that being able to solve a problem is useful only if you first understand the problem and then are able to communicate your solution.

Collaborative Projects

Although we use group projects as a regular part of our curriculum at both Clackamas Community College and Bucks County Community College, we felt we needed to turn to an individual with specialized experience in writing collaborative exercises. As a result, we worked with Bobby Righi of Seattle Central Community College to develop this new feature. Bobby has given many presentations and written articles focused on the use of collaborative material. She provided excellent activities for nearly every section of the text.

Integration of Probability and Statistics

Implementation of the NCTM and AMATYC standards across the country has resulted in an increased focus on data analysis in mathematics courses. Students in Precalculus, College Algebra, and even Intermediate Algebra are being exposed to elements of statistics, including curve fitting and simple regression, for which they have little or no preparation. We built a foundation for assimilation of this material that is integrated into the topics normally associated with Beginning Algebra. The statistical topics we introduced include data types, extremes, summation notation, median, mean, and range.

Abbreviated Topics

Everything that we teach in mathematics has value. Not everything that students learn must have obvious application to their lives. Having said that, there is still room to reassess the amount of time we spend on each topic. Two topics in particular, factoring and simplification of radicals, are often cited as overly developed in algebra textbooks. Emerging technology is making it less critical for students to master the intricacies of these topics. As a result, we reduced our coverage of these two areas.

CHAPTER 4

POLYNOMIALS

INTRODUCTION

The U.S. Post Office limits the size of rectangular boxes it will accept for mailing. The regulations state that "length plus girth cannot exceed 108 inches." "Girth" means the distance around a cross section; in this case, this measurement is $2h + 2w$. Using the polynomial $l + 2w + 2h$ to describe the measurement required by the Post Office, the regulations say that $l + 2w + 2h \leq 108$ inches.

The volume of a rectangular box is expressed by another polynomial:

$$V = lwh$$

A company that wishes to produce boxes for use by postal patrons must use these formulas as well as do a statistical survey about the shapes that are useful to the most customers. The surface area, expressed by another polynomial expression, $2lw + 2wh + 2lh$, is also used so each box can be manufactured with the least amount of material, in order to help lower costs.

Pedagogical Features

This edition has taken nine major directions. The changes are presented below, with examples of each one.

Application Areas

Each chapter now opens with a real-world vignette that showcases an example of how mathematics is used in a wide variety of jobs and professions. Problem sets for each section then feature one or more modeling/word problems that relate to the chapter-opening vignette. The application areas and the chapter each area appears in are:

Application Area	Chapter
Archeology	1. The Language of Algebra
Anthropology	2. Signed Numbers
Environmental Science	3. Equations and Inequalities
Postal Work	4. Polynomials
Encoding	5. Factoring
Dietary Science	6. Algebraic Fractions
Pediatric Medicine	7. Graphing Linear Equations and Inequalities
Electrical Engineering	8. Systems of Linear Equations
Civil Engineering	9. Radicals
Pyrotechnics	10. Quadratic Equations

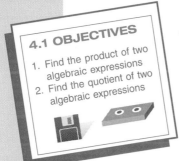

Section Objectives

Objectives for each section are clearly identified in the margin. Related media icons are included in these boxes.

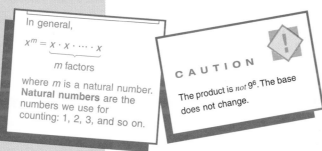

Marginal Notes and Caution Icons

Marginal notes are provided throughout and are designed to help the students focus on important topics and techniques. Caution icons point out potential trouble spots.

Check Yourself Exercises

These exercises have been the hallmark of the text; they are designed to actively involve students throughout the learning process. Each example is followed by an exercise that encourages students to solve a problem similar to the one just presented. Answers are provided at the end of the section for immediate feedback.

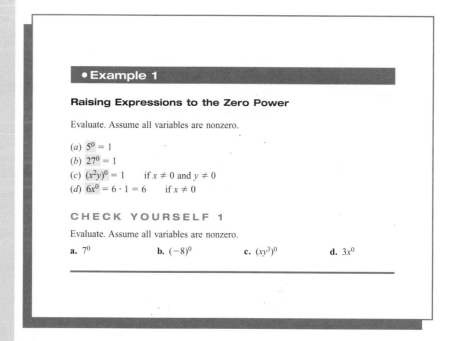

• Example 1

Raising Expressions to the Zero Power

Evaluate. Assume all variables are nonzero.

(a) $5^0 = 1$
(b) $27^0 = 1$
(c) $(x^2y)^0 = 1$ if $x \neq 0$ and $y \neq 0$
(d) $6x^0 = 6 \cdot 1 = 6$ if $x \neq 0$

CHECK YOURSELF 1

Evaluate. Assume all variables are nonzero.

a. 7^0 **b.** $(-8)^0$ **c.** $(xy^3)^0$ **d.** $3x^0$

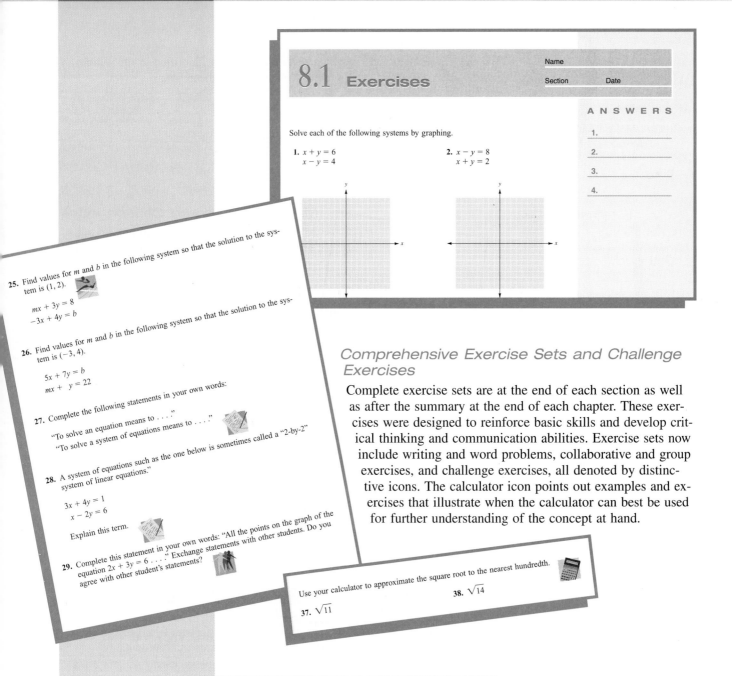

8.1 Exercises

Name

Section   Date

ANSWERS

1. _____
2. _____
3. _____
4. _____

Solve each of the following systems by graphing.

1. $x + y = 6$
$x - y = 4$

2. $x - y = 8$
$x + y = 2$

25. Find values for m and b in the following system so that the solution to the system is $(1, 2)$.

$mx + 3y = 8$
$-3x + 4y = b$

26. Find values for m and b in the following system so that the solution to the system is $(-3, 4)$.

$5x + 7y = b$
$mx + y = 22$

27. Complete the following statements in your own words:

"To solve an equation means to . . . ."

"To solve a system of equations means to . . . ."

28. A system of equations such as the one below is sometimes called a "2-by-2" system of linear equations.

$3x + 4y = 1$
$x - 2y = 6$

Explain this term.

29. Complete this statement in your own words: "All the points on the graph of the equation $2x + 3y = 6$ . . . ." Exchange statements with other students. Do you agree with other student's statements?

Use your calculator to approximate the square root to the nearest hundredth.

37. $\sqrt{11}$

38. $\sqrt{14}$

Comprehensive Exercise Sets and Challenge Exercises

Complete exercise sets are at the end of each section as well as after the summary at the end of each chapter. These exercises were designed to reinforce basic skills and develop critical thinking and communication abilities. Exercise sets now include writing and word problems, collaborative and group exercises, and challenge exercises, all denoted by distinctive icons. The calculator icon points out examples and exercises that illustrate when the calculator can best be used for further understanding of the concept at hand.

● Getting Ready for Section 5.2
[Section 4.7]

Multiply.

a. $(x - 1)(x + 1)$
b. $(a + 7)(a - 7)$
c. $(x - y)(x + y)$
d. $(2x - 5)(2x + 5)$
e. $(3a - b)(3a + b)$
f. $(5a - 4b)(5a + 4b)$

Answers

1. 2   **3.** 8   **5.** x^2 **7.** a^3 **9.** $5x^4$ **11.** $2a^4$ **13.** $3xy$ **15.** $5b$
17. $3abc^2$ **19.** $(x + y)^2$ **21.** $4(2a + 1)$ **23.** $8(3m - 4n)$
25. $4m(3m + 2)$ **27.** $5s(2s + 1)$ **29.** $12x(x + 2)$ **31.** $5a^2(3a - 5)$
33. $6pq(1 + 3p)$ **35.** $7mn(m^2 - 3n^2)$ **37.** $6(x^2 - 3x + 5)$

Getting Ready Exercises

These exercises draw on problems from previous sections of the text and are designed to help students review concepts that will be applied in the following section. This preview helps students make important connections with upcoming material.

Summary

Algebraic Equations [3.1–3.3]

$3x - 5 = 7$ is an equation

Equation A statement that two expressions are equal.

4 is a solution for the
equation because
$3 \cdot 4 - 5 = 7$
$12 - 5 = 7$
$7 = 7$ (True)

Solution A value for the variable that will make an equation a true statement.

Equivalent Equations Equations that have exactly the same solutions.

Writing Equivalent Equations There are two basic properti~~...~~
equivalent equations.

Summary and Summary Exercises

These comprehensive sections give students an opportunity to practice and review important concepts at the end of each chapter. Answers are provided with section references to aid in summarizing the material effectively.

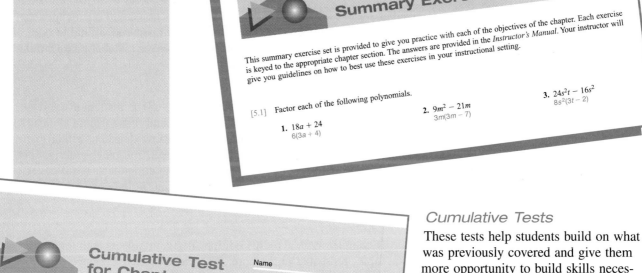

Summary Exercises

This summary exercise set is provided to give you practice with each of the objectives of the chapter. Each exercise is keyed to the appropriate chapter section. The answers are provided in the *Instructor's Manual*. Your instructor will give you guidelines on how to best use these exercises in your instructional setting.

[5.1]   Factor each of the following polynomials.

1. $18a + 24$
$6(3a + 4)$

2. $9m^2 - 21m$
$3m(3m - 7)$

3. $24s^2t - 16s^2$
$8s^2(3t - 2)$

Cumulative Test
for Chapters 1-6

Name _____

Section _____   Date _____

This test covers selected topics from the first six chapters.

Perform the indicated operation.

1. $x^2y - 4xy - x^2y + 2xy$

2. $\dfrac{12a^3b}{9ab}$

3. $(5x^2 - 2x + 1) - (3x^2 + 3x - 5)$

4. $(5a^2 + 6a) - (2a^2 - 1)$

A N S W E R S

1. _____
2. _____
3. _____
4. _____
5. _____

Cumulative Tests

These tests help students build on what was previously covered and give them more opportunity to build skills necessary in preparing for midterm and final exams.

Self-Tests

Each chapter ends with a self-test to give students confidence and guidance in preparing for in-class tests. Answers are at the back of the book.

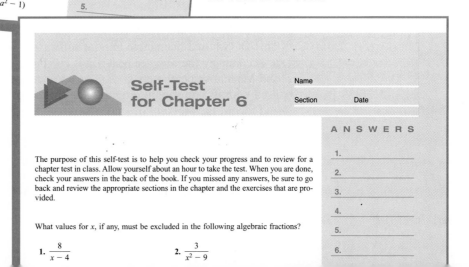

Self-Test
for Chapter 6

Name _____

Section _____   Date _____

A N S W E R S

The purpose of this self-test is to help you check your progress and to review for a chapter test in class. Allow yourself about an hour to take the test. When you are done, check your answers in the back of the book. If you missed any answers, be sure to go back and review the appropriate sections in the chapter and the exercises that are provided.

What values for x, if any, must be excluded in the following algebraic fractions?

1. $\dfrac{8}{x - 4}$

2. $\dfrac{3}{x^2 - 9}$

1. _____
2. _____
3. _____
4. _____
5. _____
6. _____

Supplements

A comprehensive set of ancillary materials for both the student and the instructor is available with this text.

Instructor's Edition

This ancillary includes answers to all exercises and tests. These answers are printed in a second color for ease of use by the instructor and are located on the appropriate pages throughout the text.

Instructor's Solutions Manual

The manual provides worked-out solutions to all of the exercises in the text.

Instructor's Resource Manual

The resource manual contains multiple-choice placement tests for three levels of testing: (1) a diagnostic pretest for each chapter and three forms of multiple-choice and open-ended chapter tests; (2) two forms of multiple-choice and open-ended cumulative tests; and (3) two forms of multiple-choice and open-ended final tests. Also included is an answer section and appendixes that cover collaborative learning and the implementation of the new standards.

Print and Computerized Testing

The testing materials provide an array of formats that allow the instructor to create tests using both algorithmically generated test questions and those from a standard testbank. This testing system enables the instructor to choose questions either manually or randomly by section, question type, difficulty level, and other criteria. Testing is available for IBM, IBM-compatible, and Macintosh computers. A softcover print version of the testbank provides most questions found in the computerized version.

Streeter Video Series

The video series is completely new to this edition. It gives students additional reinforcement of the topics presented in the book. The videos were developed especially for the Streeter pedagogy, and features are tied directly to the main text's individual chapters and section objectives. The videos feature an effective combination of learning techniques, including personal instruction, state-of-the-art graphics, and real-world applications.

Multimedia Tutorial

This interactive CD-ROM is a self-paced tutorial specifically linked to the text and reinforces topics through unlimited opportunities to review concepts and practice problem solving. It requires virtually no computer training on the part of the students and supports IBM and Macintosh computers.

MathWorks

This DOS-based interactive tutorial software is available and specifically designed to accompany the Streeter pedagogy. The program supports IBM, IBM-compatible, and Macintosh computers as well as a variety of networks. MathWorks can also be used with its companion program, the Instructor's Management System, to track and record the progress of students in the class.

In addition, a number of other technology and Web-based ancillaries are under development; they will support the ever-changing technology needs in developmental mathematics. For further information about these or any supplements, please contact your local McGraw-Hill sales representative.

Acknowledgments

In the process of writing four editions of this text, we learned much more than we could ever have taught. The faculty we work with, the students who do us the honor of signing up for our classes, and the staff at McGraw-Hill have all been part of our education. The first two groups are the most important, but the most difficult to identify. The totality of their contributions is overwhelming. Every student who has sat in our offices struggling to learn this material has helped us write the next edition. Every story that another teacher has told us, every AMATYC session we've attended, and every reviewer comment that we've read has become part of the fabric of this text. A great deal of thanks certainly goes to Bobby Righi, who contributed mightily to the vignettes and problem sets in this text, as well as Norma James, who served as accuracy reviewer. In addition, our thanks goes to the following people for their important contributions to the development of this edition:

Richard Butterworth, Massasoit Community College (MA)

Charles Clare, Diablo Valley College (CA)

John DeCoursey, Vincennes University (IN)

David Donaldson, Northwest State Community College (OH)

Cheryl Groff, Florida Community College, South Campus

Mel Hamburger, Laramie County Community College (WY)

Paul Wayne Lee, Saint Philip's College (TX)

Carl Mancuso, William Paterson College (NJ)

Robert Mooney, Salem State College (MA)

Larry Pontaski, Pueblo Community College (CO)

Donna Russo, Quincy College (MA)

Randy Sowell, Central Virginia Community College

Gene Steinmeyer, Doane College (NE)

Mary Thurow, Minneapolis Community College

Annette Wiesner, University of Wisconsin–Parkside

But, it is the McGraw-Hill staff who has suffered with me the most, so it is from this group we would like to select a few individuals who deserve recognition. Special thanks go to Denise Schanck for her support and confidence, Karen Minette for her considerable organizational skills, Jack Maisel for his patience in interpreting our scrawls, Michael Johnson for his vision; Nancy Evans for her clarity; Jack Shira for his ability to anticipate the next hurdle; and Maggie Rogers for her thoroughness.

We also express much appreciation to Zanae Rodrigo for her attention to detail.

Donald Hutchison
Louis Hoelzle

TO THE STUDENT

You are about to begin a course in algebra. We made every attempt to provide a text that will help you understand what algebra is about and how to effectively use it. We made no assumptions about your previous experience with algebra. Your progress through the course will depend on the amount of time and effort you devote to the course and your previous background in math. There are some specific features in this book that will aid you in your studies. Here are some suggestions about how to use this book. (Keep in mind that a review of *all* the chapter and summary material will further enhance your ability to grasp later topics and to move more effectively through the text.)

1. If you are in a lecture class, make sure that you take the time to read the appropriate text section *before* your instructor's lecture on the subject. Then take careful notes on the examples that your instructor presents during class.

2. After class, work through similar examples in the text, making sure that you understand each of the steps shown. Examples are followed in the text by *Check Yourself* exercises. Algebra is best learned by being involved in the process, and that is the purpose of these exercises. Always have a pencil and paper at hand, and work out the problems presented and check your results immediately. If you have difficulty, go back and carefully review the previous exercises. Make sure you understand what you are doing and why. The best test of whether you do understand a concept lies in your ability to explain that concept to one of your classmates. Try working together.

3. At the end of each chapter section you will find a set of exercises. Work these carefully in order to check your progress on the section you have just finished. You will find the solutions for the odd-numbered exercises following the problem set. If you have had difficulties with any of the exercises, review the appropriate parts of the chapter section. If your questions are not completely cleared up, by all means do not become discouraged. Ask your instructor or an available tutor for further assistance. A word of caution: Work the exercises on a regular (preferably daily) basis. Again, learning algebra requires becoming involved. As is the case with learning any skill, the main ingredient is practice.

4. When you have completed a chapter, review by using the *Summary*. You will find all the important terms and definitions in this section, along with examples illustrating all the techniques developed in the chapter. Following the Summary are *Summary Exercises* for further practice. The exercises are keyed to chapter sections, so you will know where to turn if you are still having problems.

5. When finished with the *Summary Exercises,* try the *Self-Test* that appears at the end of each chapter. This test will give you an actual practice test to work as you review for in-class testing. Again, answers with section references are provided.

6. Finally, an important element of success in studying algebra is the process of regular review. We provided a series of *Cumulative Tests* throughout the textbook, beginning at the end of Chapter 3. These tests will help you review not only the concepts of the chapter that you have just completed but those of previous chapters. Use these tests in preparation for any midterm or final exams. If it appears that you have forgotten some concepts that are being tested, don't worry. Go back and review the sections where the idea was initially explained, or the appropriate chapter summary. That is the purpose of the cumulative tests.

We hope that you will find our suggestions helpful as you work through this material, and we wish you the best of luck in the course.

Donald Hutchison
Louis Hoelzle

THE LANGUAGE OF ALGEBRA

INTRODUCTION

Cultures from all over the world have developed number systems and ways to record patterns in their natural surroundings. The Mayans in Central America had one of the most sophisticated number systems in the world in twelfth century AD. The Chinese numbering and recording system dates from around 1200 BC. The oldest evidence of numerical record is in Africa, where a bone notched in numerical patterns and dating from about 35,000 BC was found in the Lebembo Mountains near modern-day Swaziland in southern Africa.

The roots of algebra developed among the Babylonians 4000 years ago in an area now part of the country of Iraq. The Babylonians developed ways to record useful numerical relationships so that they were easy to remember, easy to record, and helpful in solving problems. Archeologists have found many tables, such as one giving successive powers of a given number, 9^2, 9^3, 9^4, ..., 9^n, analogous to our modern tables of logarithms. The tables include instructions for solving problems in engineering, economics, city planning, and agriculture. The writing was on clay tablets. Some of these formulas developed by the Babylonians are still in use today.

You are about to embark on an exciting and useful endeavor: learning to use algebra to help you solve problems. It will take some time and effort, but do not be discouraged. Everyone can master this topic—people just like you have used it for many centuries! Today algebra is even more useful than it has been in the past because it is used in nearly every field of human endeavor. ⬛

© B. Daemmrich/The Image Works

From Arithmetic to Algebra

1.1 OBJECTIVES

1. Represent the operations of addition, subtraction, multiplication, and division by using the symbols of algebra
2. Identify algebraic expressions

In arithmetic, you learned how to do calculations with numbers by using the basic operations of addition, subtraction, multiplication, and division.

In algebra, you will still use numbers and the same four operations. However, you will also use letters to represent numbers. Letters such as x, y, L, or W are called **variables** when they represent numerical values.

Here we see two rectangles whose lengths and widths are labeled with numbers.

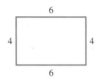

If we need to represent the length and width of *any* rectangle, we can use the variables L and W.

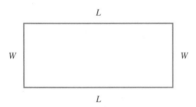

In arithmetic:
+ denotes addition
− denotes subtraction
× denotes multiplication
÷ denotes division.

You are familiar with the four symbols (+ , − , × , ÷) used to indicate the fundamental operations of arithmetic.

Let's look at how these operations are indicated in algebra. We begin by looking at addition.

Addition

$x + y$ means the *sum* of x and y or x *plus* y.

● Example 1

Writing Expressions That Indicate Addition

Some other words that tell you to add are "more than" and "increased by."

(*a*) The *sum* of a and 3 is written as $a + 3$.
(*b*) L *plus* W is written as $L + W$.
(*c*) 5 *more than* m is written as $m + 5$.
(*d*) x *increased by* 7 is written as $x + 7$.

● ● ● **CHECK YOURSELF 1***

Write, using symbols.

a. The sum of y and 4   **b.** a plus b
c. 3 more than x **d.** n increased by 6

Let's look at how subtraction is indicated in algebra.

> **Subtraction**
>
> $x - y$ means the *difference* of x and y or x *minus* y.

● Example 2

Writing Expressions That Indicate Subtraction

Some other words that mean to subtract are "decreased by" and "less than."

(*a*) *r minus s* is written as $r - s$.
(*b*) The *difference* of m and 5 is written as $m - 5$.
(*c*) *x decreased by* 8 is written as $x - 8$.
(*d*) 4 *less than a* is written as $a - 4$.

● ● ● **CHECK YOURSELF 2**

Write, using symbols.

a. w minus z
b. The difference of a and 7
c. y decreased by 3
d. 5 less than b

You have seen that the operations of addition and subtraction are written exactly the same way in algebra as in arithmetic. This is not true in multiplication because the sign $\times$ looks like the letter x. So in algebra we use other symbols to show multiplication to avoid any confusion. Here are some ways to write multiplication.

Note: x and y are called the **factors** of the product xy.

> **Multiplication**
>
> | | | |
> |---|---|---|
> | A raised dot | $x \cdot y$ | |
> | Parentheses | $(x)(y)$ | These all indicate the *product* of x and y or x times y. |
> | Writing the letters next to each other | xy | |

*Check Yourself Answers appear at the end of each section throughout the book.

• Example 3

Writing Expressions That Indicate Multiplication

Note: You can place letters next to each other or numbers and letters next to each other to show multiplication. But you *cannot* place numbers side by side to show multiplication: 37 means the number "thirty-seven," not 3 times 7.

(*a*) The product of 5 and *a* is written as $5 \cdot a$, $(5)(a)$, or $5a$. The last expression, $5a$, is the shortest and the most common way of writing the product.

(*b*) 3 times 7 can be written as $3 \cdot 7$ or $(3)(7)$.

(*c*) Twice *z* is written as $2z$.

(*d*) The product of 2, *s*, and *t* is written as $2st$.

(*e*) 4 more than the product of 6 and *x* is written as $6x + 4$.

● ● ●   **CHECK YOURSELF 3**

Write, using symbols.

a. *m* times *n*
b. The product of *h* and *b*
c. The product of 8 and 9
d. The product of 5, *w*, and *y*
e. 3 more than the product of 8 and *a*

Before we move on to division, let's look at how we can combine the symbols we have learned so far.

Not every collection of symbols is an expression.

> An **expression** is a meaningful collection of numbers, variables, and signs of operation.

• Example 4

Identifying Expressions

(*a*) $2m + 3$ is an expression. It means that we multiply 2 and *m*, then add 3.

(*b*) $x + \cdot + 3$ is not an expression. The three operations in a row have no meaning.

(*c*) $y = 2x - 1$ is not an expression. The equals sign is not an operation sign.

(*d*) $3a + 5b - 4c$ is an expression. Its meaning is clear.

● ● ●   **CHECK YOURSELF 4**

Identify which are expressions and which are not.

a. $7 - \cdot x$
b. $6 + y = 9$
c. $a + b - c$
d. $3x - 5yz$

To write more complicated products in algebra, we need some "punctuation marks." Parentheses ( ) mean that an expression is to be thought of as a single quantity. Brackets [ ] and braces { } are used in exactly the same way as parentheses in algebra. Look at the following example showing the use of these signs of grouping.

• Example 5

Expressions with More Than One Operation

(*a*) 3 times the sum of *a* and *b* is written as

This can be read as "3 times the quantity *a* plus *b*."

$3(a + b)$

The sum of *a* and *b* is a single quantity, so it is enclosed in parentheses.

No parentheses are needed here since the 3 multiplies *only* the *a*.

(*b*) The sum of 3 times *a* and *b* is written as $3a + b$.
(*c*) 2 times the difference of *m* and *n* is written as $2(m - n)$.
(*d*) The product of *s* plus *t* and *s* minus *t* is written as $(s + t)(s - t)$.
(*e*) The product of *b* and 3 less than *b* is written as $b(b - 3)$.

● ● ● ●   CHECK YOURSELF 5

Write, using symbols.

a. Twice the sum of *p* and *q*
b. The sum of twice *p* and *q*
c. The product of *a* and the quantity *b* − *c*
d. The product of *x* plus 2 and *x* minus 2
e. The product of *x* and 4 more than *x*

In algebra the fraction form is usually used.

Now let's look at the operation of division. In arithmetic, you use the division sign ÷, the long division symbol $\overline{)}$, and the fraction notation. For example, to indicate the quotient when 9 is divided by 3, you could write

$9 ÷ 3$ or $3\overline{)9}$ or $\dfrac{9}{3}$

Division

$\dfrac{x}{y}$ means *x divided* by *y* or the *quotient* of *x* and *y*.

• Example 6

Writing Expressions That Indicate Division

Write, using symbols.

(*a*) *m* divided by 3 is written as $\dfrac{m}{3}$.

(b) The quotient of a plus b divided by 5 is written as $\dfrac{a+b}{5}$.

(c) The sum p plus q divided by the difference p minus q is written as $\dfrac{p+q}{p-q}$.

● ● ● **CHECK YOURSELF 6**

Write, using symbols.

a. r divided by s
b. The quotient when x minus y is divided by 7
c. The difference a minus 2 divided by the sum a plus 2

Notice that we can use many different letters to represent variables. In Example 6 the letters m, a, b, p, and q represented different variables. We often choose a letter that reminds us of what it represents, for example, L for *length* or W for *width*.

● Example 7

Writing Geometric Expressions

Write each geometric expression, using symbols.

(a) *Length* times *width* is written $L \cdot W$.

(b) One-half of *altitude* times *base* is written $\dfrac{1}{2}\, a \cdot b$.

(c) *Length* times *width* times *height* is written $L \cdot W \cdot H$.

(d) Pi (π) times *diameter* is written πd.

● ● ● **CHECK YOURSELF 7**

Write each geometric expression, using symbols.

a. Two times *length* plus two times *width*   **b.** Two times pi (π) times *radius*

● ● ● **CHECK YOURSELF ANSWERS**

1. (a) $y + 4$; **(b)** $a + b$; **(c)** $x + 3$; **(d)** $n + 6$.   **2. (a)** $w - z$; **(b)** $a - 7$; **(c)** $y - 3$;
(d) $b - 5$.   **3. (a)** mn; **(b)** hb; **(c)** $8 \cdot 9$ or $(8)(9)$; **(d)** $5wy$; **(e)** $8a + 3$.
4. (a) Not an expression; **(b)** not an expression; **(c)** an expression; **(d)** an expression.
5. (a) $2(p + q)$; **(b)** $2p + q$; **(c)** $a(b - c)$; **(d)** $(x + 2)(x - 2)$; **(e)** $x(x + 4)$.

6. (a) $\dfrac{r}{s}$; **(b)** $\dfrac{x - y}{7}$; **(c)** $\dfrac{a - 2}{a + 2}$.   **7. (a)** $2L + 2W$; **(b)** $2\pi r$.

Name

Section   Date

Write each of the following phrases, using symbols.

1. The sum of c and d

2. a plus 7

3. w plus z

4. The sum of m and n

5. x increased by 2

6. 3 more than b

7. 10 more than y

8. m increased by 4

9. a minus b

10. 5 less than s

11. b decreased by 7

12. r minus 3

13. 6 less than r

14. x decreased by 3

15. w times z

16. The product of 3 and c

17. The product of 5 and t

18. 8 times a

19. The product of 8, m, and n

20. The product of 7, r, and s

21. The product of 3 and the quantity p plus q

22. The product of 5 and the sum of a and b

23. Twice the sum of x and y

24. 3 times the sum of m and n

25. The sum of twice x and y

26. The sum of 3 times m and n

27. Twice the difference of x and y

28. 3 times the difference of c and d

29. The quantity a plus b times the quantity a minus b

30. The product of x plus y and x minus y

1.
2.
3.
4.
5.
6.
7.
8.
9.
10.
11.
12.
13.
14.
15.
16.
17.
18.
19.
20.
21.
22.
23.
24.
25.
26.
27.
28.
29.
30.

A N S W E R S

31.

32.

33.

34.

35.

36.

37.

38.

39.

40.

41.

42.

43.

44.

45.

46.

47.

48.

49.

50.

51.

52.

53.

54.

55.

56.

31. The product of *m* and 3 less than *m*

32. The product of *a* and 7 more than *a*

33. *x* divided by 5

34. The quotient when *b* is divided by 8

35. The quotient of *a* plus *b*, divided by 7

36. The difference *x* minus *y*, divided by 9

37. The difference of *p* and *q*, divided by 4

38. The sum of *a* and 5, divided by 9

39. The sum of *a* and 3, divided by the difference of *a* and 3

40. The difference of *m* and *n*, divided by the sum of *m* and *n*

Write each of the following phrases, using symbols. Use the variable *x* to represent the number in each case.

41. 5 more than a number

42. A number increased by 8

43. 7 less than a number

44. A number decreased by 10

45. 9 times a number

46. Twice a number

47. 6 more than 3 times a number

48. 5 times a number, decreased by 10

49. Twice the sum of a number and 5

50. 3 times the difference of a number and 4

51. The product of 2 more than a number and 2 less than that same number

52. The product of 5 less than a number and 5 more than that same number

53. The quotient of a number and 7

54. A number divided by 3

55. The sum of a number and 5, divided by 8

56. The quotient when 7 less than a number is divided by 3

57. 6 more than a number divided by 6 less than that same number

58. The quotient when 3 less than a number is divided by 3 more than that same number

Write each of the following geometric expressions using symbols.

59. Four times the length of a side (s).

60. $\dfrac{4}{3}$ times π times the cube of the radius (r)

61. The radius (r) squared times the height (h) times π

62. Twice the length (L) plus twice the width (W)

63. One-half the product of the height (h) and the sum of two unequal sides (b_1 and b_2)

64. Six times the length of a side (s) squared

Identify which are expressions and which are not.

65. $2(x + 5)$ **66.** $4 + (x - 3)$

67. $4 + \div m$ **68.** $6 + a = 7$

69. $2b = 6$ **70.** $x(y + 3)$

71. $2a + 5b$ **72.** $4x + \cdot 7$

73. Population growth. The Earth's population has doubled in the last 40 years. If we let x represent the Earth's population 40 years ago, what is the population today?

74. Species extinction. It is estimated that the Earth is losing 4000 species of plants and animals every year. If S represents the number of species living last year, how many species are on Earth this year?

75. Interest. The simple interest (I) earned when a principal (P) is invested at a rate (r) for a time (t) is calculated by multiplying the principal times the rate times the time. Write a formula for the interest earned.

57. _____

58. _____

59. _____

60. _____

61. _____

62. _____

63. _____

64. _____

65. _____

66. _____

67. _____

68. _____

69. _____

70. _____

71. _____

72. _____

73. _____

74. _____

75. _____

76. _____

77. _____

a. _____

b. _____

c. _____

d. _____

e. _____

f. _____

76. **Kinetic energy**. The kinetic energy of a particle of mass m is found by taking one-half of the product of the mass and the square of the velocity (v). Write a formula for the kinetic energy of a particle.

77. Rewrite the following algebraic expressions in English phrases. Exchange papers with another student to edit your writing. Be sure the meaning in English is the same as in algebra. These expressions are not complete sentences, so your English does not have to be in complete sentences. Here is an example.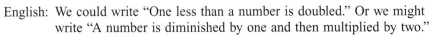

Algebra: $2(x - 1)$

English: We could write "One less than a number is doubled." Or we might write "A number is diminished by one and then multiplied by two."

(a) $n + 3$ (b) $\dfrac{x + 2}{5}$ (c) $3(5 + a)$

(d) $3 - 4n$ (e) $\dfrac{x + 6}{x - 1}$

● *Getting Ready for Section 1.2 [Appendix 1]

Perform each of the indicated operations.

a. $3 + 3 + 3$ b. $3 \cdot 3 \cdot 3$ c. $5 + 5 + 5 + 5$

d. $5 \cdot 5 \cdot 5 \cdot 5$ e. $4 + 4 + 4 + 4 + 4$ f. $4 \cdot 4 \cdot 4 \cdot 4 \cdot 4$

Answers

We provide the answers for the odd-numbered exercises at the end of each exercise set.

1. $c + d$ **3.** $w + z$ **5.** $x + 2$ **7.** $y + 10$ **9.** $a - b$ **11.** $b - 7$
13. $r - 6$ **15.** wz **17.** $5t$ **19.** $8mn$ **21.** $3(p + q)$ **23.** $2(x + y)$
25. $2x + y$ **27.** $2(x - y)$ **29.** $(a + b)(a - b)$ **31.** $m(m - 3)$ **33.** $\dfrac{x}{5}$
35. $\dfrac{a + b}{7}$ **37.** $\dfrac{p - q}{4}$ **39.** $\dfrac{a + 3}{a - 3}$ **41.** $x + 5$ **43.** $x - 7$
45. $9x$ **47.** $3x + 6$ **49.** $2(x + 5)$ **51.** $(x + 2)(x - 2)$ **53.** $\dfrac{x}{7}$
55. $\dfrac{x + 5}{8}$ **57.** $\dfrac{x + 6}{x - 6}$ **59.** $4s$ **61.** $\pi r^2 h$ **63.** $\dfrac{1}{2}h(b_1 + b_2)$
65. Expression   **67.** Not an expression   **69.** Not an expression
71. Expression   **73.** $2x$ **75.** $I = Prt$ **77.** 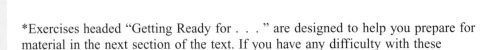   **a.** 9   **b.** 27   **c.** 20
d. 625   **e.** 20   **f.** 1024

*Exercises headed "Getting Ready for . . . " are designed to help you prepare for material in the next section of the text. If you have any difficulty with these exercises, please review the section referred to in brackets.

1.2 Exponents and the Order of Operations

1.2 OBJECTIVES

1. Write a product of factors in exponential form
2. Determine the order in which the operations should be done

$5 + 5 + 5 = 15$
and
$3 \cdot 5 = 15$

A factor is a number or a variable that is being multiplied by another number or variable.

Since an exponent represents repeated multiplication, 5^3 is an expression.

CAUTION

Be careful: 5^3 is *not* the same as $5 \cdot 3$. Notice that $5^3 = 5 \cdot 5 \cdot 5 = 125$ and $5 \cdot 3 = 15$.

In Section 1.1, we showed how symbols are used to denote the four basic operations. Often in mathematics we define other symbols that will allow us to write expressions in a more compact or "shorthand" form. This is an idea that you have encountered before. For example, an expression with repeated addition, such as

$$5 + 5 + 5$$

can be rewritten as

$$3 \cdot 5$$

Thus multiplication is shorthand for repeated addition.

In algebra, we frequently have a number or variable that is repeated in an expression several times. For instance, we might have

$$5 \cdot 5 \cdot 5$$

To abbreviate this product, we write

$$5 \cdot 5 \cdot 5 = 5^3$$

This is called **exponential notation** or **exponential form.** The exponent or power, here 3, indicates the number of times that the factor or base, here 5, appears in a product.

$$5 \cdot 5 \cdot 5 = 5^3 \quad \begin{array}{l} \nearrow \text{Exponent or power} \\ \searrow \text{Factor or base} \end{array}$$

• Example 1

Writing Expressions in Exponential Form

(*a*) Write $3 \cdot 3 \cdot 3 \cdot 3$, using exponential form. The number 3 appears 4 times in the product, so

$$3 \cdot 3 \cdot 3 \cdot 3 = 3^4 \quad \begin{array}{l} \text{Four factors} \\ \text{of 3} \end{array}$$

This is read "3 to the fourth power."

(*b*) Write $x \cdot x \cdot x$, using exponential form. The same idea works for letters or variables, so since x appears 3 times in the product, you can write

$$x \cdot x \cdot x = x^3$$

This is read "x to the third power" or "x cubed."

● ● ● **CHECK YOURSELF 1**

Write in exponential form.

a. $4 \cdot 4 \cdot 4 \cdot 4 \cdot 4 \cdot 4$ **b.** $y \cdot y \cdot y \cdot y$

If a product involves a combination of numbers and letters or different letters, the exponential form can also be used.

● Example 2

Writing Expressions in Exponential Form

Write each of the following, using exponents.

(a) $5 \cdot m \cdot m$

Two factors
of *m*

$5 \cdot m \cdot m = 5m^2$

Note that the exponent applies *only* to *m*, *not* to 5. There is only one factor of 5.

This is read "5 times *m* to the second power" or "5 times *m* squared."

(b) $a \cdot a \cdot b \cdot b \cdot b \cdot b$

Two factors   Four factors
of *a*   of *b*

If more than one letter appears, we usually write the product in alphabetical order.

$a \cdot a \cdot b \cdot b \cdot b \cdot b = a^2 b^4$

(c) $3 \cdot x \cdot x \cdot y \cdot y \cdot y$

$3 \cdot x \cdot x \cdot y \cdot y \cdot y = 3x^2 y^3$

One factor   Two   Three
of 3   factors factors
         of *x*   of *y*

● ● ● **CHECK YOURSELF 2**

Write in exponential form.

a. $6 \cdot b \cdot b \cdot b$ **b.** $p \cdot p \cdot p \cdot q \cdot q \cdot q \cdot q \cdot q$ **c.** $5 \cdot m \cdot m \cdot m \cdot n \cdot n$

There also may be situations in which it will be useful to change an expression from exponential form to an expanded form (written as a product of factors).

• Example 3

Writing Expressions in Expanded Form

Write each expression in expanded form.

(a) $4x^3$

The exponent 3 applies *only* to *x*.

$4x^3 = 4 \cdot x \cdot x \cdot x$

(b) $(4x)^3$

Now the exponent applies to *4x* because of the parentheses. So *4x* is repeated as a factor 3 times.

$(4x)^3 = (4x) \cdot (4x) \cdot (4x)$

(c) $5x^2y^3$

$5x^2y^3 = 5 \cdot x \cdot x \cdot y \cdot y \cdot y$

● ● ● CHECK YOURSELF 3

Write each expression in expanded form.

a. $5x^4$ **b.** $(5x)^4$ **c.** $3a^3b^3$

An expression will have different values depending on the number assigned to the variables in the expression. Finding the value of an expression is called **evaluating an expression.** This involves replacing each variable with a given value, as illustrated in our next example.

• Example 4

Evaluating Expressions

Evaluate each expression.

(a) $5x^2$ when $x = 2$

We replace *x* with the value 2.

$5x^2 = 5(2)^2 = 5 \cdot 2 \cdot 2$ 2 appears as a factor 2 times

$\qquad = 20$

(b) $2xy^3$ when $x = 2$, $y = 3$

Now let *x* be 2 and *y* be 3. Then

$2xy^3 = 2(2)(3)^3$

$\qquad = 2 \cdot 2 \cdot 3 \cdot 3 \cdot 3$

$\qquad = 108$

● ● ●   **CHECK YOURSELF 4**

Evaluate each expression.

a. $3a^3$ when $a = 2$

b. $5m^2n$ when $m = 3$ and $n = 4$

You have now seen all the parts that make up arithmetic expressions. In order to evaluate those expressions, you need to know the order in which the operations are done. To see why, simplify the expression $5 + 2 \cdot 3$.

CAUTION

Only one of these results can be correct.

Method 1   or   *Method 2*

$\underbrace{5 + 2} \cdot 3$ $5 + \underbrace{2 \cdot 3}$

Add first.   Multiply first.

$= 7 \cdot 3$ $= 5 + 6$

$= 21$ $= 11$

Since we get different answers depending on how we do the problem, the language of algebra would not be clear if there were no agreement on which method is correct. The following rules tell us the order in which operations should be done.

Parentheses and brackets are both grouping symbols. Later we will see that fraction bars and radicals are also grouping symbols.

> **The Order of Operations**
>
> **STEP 1** Evaluate all expressions inside grouping symbols first.
> **STEP 2** Evaluate all expressions involving exponents.
> **STEP 3** Do any multiplication or division in order, working from left to right.
> **STEP 4** Do any addition or subtraction in order, working from left to right.

● **Example 5**

Evaluating Expressions

Evaluate $5 + 2 \cdot 3$.

There are no parentheses or exponents, so start with step 3: First multiply and then add.

$5 + 2 \cdot 3$

  ——— Multiply first.

$= 5 + 6$

  ——— Then add.

$= 11$

Note: Method 2 shown above is the correct one.

● ● ●   **CHECK YOURSELF 5**

Evaluate the following expressions.

a. $20 - 3 \cdot 4$

b. $9 + 6 \div 3$

When there are no parentheses, evaluate the exponents first.

• Example 6

Evaluating Expressions

Evaluate $5 \cdot 3^2$.

$$5 \cdot 3^2 = 5 \cdot 9$$

Evaluate the power first.

$$= 45$$

● ● ● ●   CHECK YOURSELF 6

Evaluate $4 \cdot 2^4$.

Both scientific and graphing calculators correctly interpret the order of operations. This is demonstrated in Example 7.

• Example 7

Using a Calculator to Evaluate Expressions

Use your scientific or graphing calculator to evaluate each expression.

(*a*) $24.3 + 6.2 \cdot 3.5$

When evaluating expressions by hand, you must consider the order of operations. In this case, the multiplication must be done first, then the addition. With a scientific calculator, you need only enter the expression correctly. The calculator is programmed to follow the order of operations.

Entering   24.3 $\boxed{+}$ 6.2 $\boxed{\times}$ 3.5 $\boxed{\text{ENTER}}$

yields the evaluation 46.

(*b*) $(2.45)^3 - 49 \div 8000 + 12.2 \cdot 1.3$

Some calculators use the carat ($\wedge$) to designate powers. Others use the symbol x^y (or y^x).

Entering $\boxed{(}$ 2.45 $\boxed{)}$ $\boxed{\wedge}$ 3 $\boxed{-}$ 49 $\boxed{\div}$ 8000 $\boxed{+}$ 12.2 $\boxed{\cdot}$ 1.3

or $\boxed{(}$ 2.45 $\boxed{)}$ $\boxed{y^x}$ 3 $\boxed{-}$ 49 $\boxed{\div}$ 8000 $\boxed{+}$ 12.2 $\boxed{\cdot}$ 1.3

yields the evaluation 30.56.

● ● ● ●   CHECK YOURSELF 7

Use your scientific or graphing calculator to evaluate each expression.

a. $67.89 - 4.7 \cdot 12.7$ **b.** $4.3 \cdot 55.5 - (3.75)^3 + 8007 \div 1600$

Operations inside grouping symbols are done first.

• Example 8

Evaluating Expressions

Evaluate $(5 + 2) \cdot 3$.

Do the operation inside the parentheses as the first step.

$$(5 + 2) \cdot 3 = 7 \cdot 3 = 21$$

    ⌐——————— Add.

● ● ● **CHECK YOURSELF 8**

Evaluate $4(9 - 3)$.

The principle is the same when more than two "levels" of operations are involved.

• Example 9

(a) Evaluate $4(2 + 3)^3$.

    ←——— Add inside the parentheses first.

$$4(2 + 3)^3 = 4(5)^3 ←$$

    ⟍ Evaluate the power.

$$= 4 \cdot 125$$

    ⌐——— Multiply.

$$= 500$$

(b) Evaluate $5(7 - 3)^2 - 10$.

    ⟍ Evaluate the expression inside the parentheses.

$$5(7 - 3)^2 - 10 = 5(4)^2 - 10$$

    ⌐——— Evaluate the power.

$$= 5 \cdot 16 - 10$$

    ⌐——— Multiply.

$$= 80 - 10 = 70$$

    ⌐——— Subtract.

● ● ● **CHECK YOURSELF 9**

Evaluate

a. $4 \cdot 3^3 - 8 \cdot 11$.

b. $12 + 4(2 + 3)^2$.

● ● ● **CHECK YOURSELF ANSWERS**

1. (a) 4^6; **(b)** y^4.　**2. (a)** $6b^3$; **(b)** p^3q^5; **(c)** $5m^3n^2$.　**3. (a)** $5 \cdot x \cdot x \cdot x \cdot x$;
(b) $5x \cdot 5x \cdot 5x \cdot 5x$; **(c)** $3 \cdot a \cdot a \cdot a \cdot b \cdot b \cdot b$.　**4. (a)** 24; **(b)** 180.　**5. (a)** 8;
(b) 11.　**6.** 64.　**7. (a)** 8.2; **(b)** 190.92.　**8.** 24.　**9. (a)** 20; **(b)** 112.

Write each expression, using exponential form.

1. $7 \cdot 7 \cdot 7 \cdot 7$

2. $2 \cdot 2 \cdot 2 \cdot 2 \cdot 2 \cdot 2$

3. $6 \cdot 6 \cdot 6 \cdot 6 \cdot 6$

4. $8 \cdot 8 \cdot 8 \cdot 8$

5. $m \cdot m \cdot m \cdot m \cdot m$

6. $2 \cdot 2 \cdot 2 \cdot 2 \cdot 2 \cdot 2 \cdot 2$

7. $2 \cdot x \cdot x \cdot x$

8. $3 \cdot y \cdot y \cdot y \cdot y$

9. $a \cdot a \cdot a \cdot a \cdot b \cdot b$

10. $m \cdot m \cdot n \cdot n \cdot n$

11. $9 \cdot r \cdot r \cdot r \cdot s \cdot s \cdot s$

12. $6 \cdot a \cdot b \cdot b \cdot b \cdot b$

13. $5 \cdot w \cdot z \cdot z \cdot z \cdot z \cdot z$

14. $7 \cdot x \cdot x \cdot x \cdot x \cdot y \cdot y \cdot y$

Write each expression in expanded form.

15. $5x^3$

16. $2y^5$

17. $2x^2y$

18. $3ab^3$

19. $12a^3b^4$

20. $9x^5y^2$

21. $(3x)^4$

22. $(2y)^4$

23. $(4q)^5$

24. $(7t)^3$

Evaluate each expression if $x = 3$ and $y = 4$.

25. $3x^2$

26. $2y^2$

27. $(3x)^2$

28. $(2y)^2$

29. $3xy^2$

30. $2x^3y$

1.
2.
3.
4.
5.
6.
7.
8.
9.
10.
11.
12.
13.
14.
15.
16.
17.
18.
19.
20.
21.
22.
23.
24.
25.
26.
27.
28.
29.
30.

A N S W E R S

31. _____

32. _____

33. _____

34. _____

35. _____

36. _____

37. _____

38. _____

39. _____

40. _____

41. _____

42. _____

43. _____

44. _____

45. _____

46. _____

47. _____

48. _____

49. _____

50. _____

51. _____

52. _____

53. _____

54. _____

55. _____

56. _____

57. _____

58. _____

59. _____

60. _____

61. _____

62. _____

63. _____

64. _____

Evaluate each expression if $a = 2$ and $b = 5$.

31. a^2b^2 **32.** a^3b^3

33. $(ab)^2$ **34.** $(ab)^3$

Evaluate each of the following expressions.

35. $7 + 2 \cdot 6$ **36.** $10 - 4 \cdot 2$

37. $(7 + 2) \cdot 6$ **38.** $(10 - 4) \cdot 2$

39. $12 - 8 \div 4$ **40.** $10 + 20 \div 5$

41. $(12 - 8) \div 4$ **42.** $(10 + 20) \div 5$

43. $8 \cdot 7 + 2 \cdot 2$ **44.** $48 \div 8 - 4 \div 2$

45. $8 \cdot (7 + 2) \cdot 2$ **46.** $48 \div (8 - 4) \div 2$

47. $3 \cdot 5^2$ **48.** $5 \cdot 2^3$

49. $(3 \cdot 5)^2$ **50.** $(5 \cdot 2)^3$

51. $4 \cdot 3^2 - 2$ **52.** $3 \cdot 2^4 - 8$

53. $7(2^3 - 5)$ **54.** $4(3^2 - 7)$

55. $3 \cdot 2^4 - 6 \cdot 2$ **56.** $4 \cdot 2^3 - 5 \cdot 6$

57. $(2 \cdot 4)^2 - 8 \cdot 3$ **58.** $(3 \cdot 2)^3 - 7 \cdot 3$

59. $4(2 + 6)^2$ **60.** $3(8 - 4)^2$

61. $(4 \cdot 2 + 6)^2$ **62.** $(3 \cdot 8 - 4)^2$

63. $3(4 + 3)^2$ **64.** $5(4 - 2)^3$

65. $3 \cdot 4 + 3^2$

66. $5 \cdot 4 - 2^3$

67. $4(2 + 3)^2 - 25$

68. $8 + 2(3 + 3)^2$

69. $(4 \cdot 2 + 3)^2 - 25$

70. $8 + (2 \cdot 3 + 3)^2$

Evaluate each of the following expressions if $a = 2$, $b = 3$, $c = 5$, and $d = 6$.

71. $6bd$

72. $3ac$

73. $a + d$

74. $c - a$

75. $5a + 2b$

76. $3d - 7a$

Evaluate using your calculator. Round your answer to the nearest tenth.

77. $(1.2)^3 \div 2.0736 \cdot 2.4 + 1.6935 - 2.4896$

78. $(5.21 \cdot 3.14 - 6.2154) \div 5.12 - .45625$

79. $1.23 \cdot 3.169 - 2.05194 + (5.128 \cdot 3.15 - 10.1742)$

80. $4.56 + (2.34)^4 \div 4.7896 \cdot 6.93 \div 27.5625 - 3.1269 + (1.56)^2$

81. Population doubling. Over the last 2000 years, the Earth's population has doubled approximately 5 times. Write this last factor in exponential form.

82. Volume of a cube. The volume of a cube with each edge of length 9 inches (in.) is given by $9 \cdot 9 \cdot 9$. Write the volume using exponential notation.

Many of the exercise sets in this text have a set of problems marked by the hurdler logo shown here. These are particularly challenging exercises which either introduce ideas that extend the material of the section or require you to generalize from what you have learned.

83. Evaluate the expression $(3x + 2y)(3x - 2y)$ for $x = 2$ and $y = 3$.

84. Insert grouping symbols in the proper place so that the value of the expression $36 \div 4 + 2 - 4$ is 2.

65. _____
66. _____
67. _____
68. _____
69. _____
70. _____
71. _____
72. _____
73. _____
74. _____
75. _____
76. _____
77. _____
78. _____
79. _____
80. _____
81. _____
82. _____
83. _____
84. _____

85. Work with a small group of students.

Part 1: Write the numbers 1 through 25 on slips of paper and put the slips in a pile, face down. Each of you randomly draws a slip of paper until you have drawn five slips. Turn the papers over and write down the five numbers. Put the five papers back in the pile, shuffle, and then draw one more. This last number is the answer. The first five numbers are the problem. Your task is to arrange the first five into a computation, using all you know about the order of operations, so that the answer is the last number. Each number must be used and may be used only once. If you cannot find a way to do this, pose it as a question to the whole class. Is this guaranteed to work?

Part 2: Use your five numbers in a problem, each number being used and used only once, for which the answer is 1. Try this nine more times with the numbers 2 through 10. You may find more than one way to do each of these. Surprising, isn't it?

Part 3: Be sure that when you successfully find a way to get the desired answer using the five numbers, you can then write your steps using the correct order of operations. Write your 10 problems and exchange them with another group to see if they get these same answers when they do your problems.

● Getting Ready for Section 1.3

Evaluate each expression.

a. $6(2 + 3)$ **b.** $6 \cdot 2 + 6 \cdot 3$

c. $(4 + 5) + 7$ **d.** $4 + (5 + 7)$

e. $2 \cdot (3 \cdot 8)$ **f.** $(2 \cdot 3) \cdot 8$

Answers

1. 7^4 **3.** 6^5 **5.** m^5 **7.** $2x^3$ **9.** a^4b^2 **11.** $9r^3s^3$ **13.** $5wz^5$

15. $5 \cdot x \cdot x \cdot x$ **17.** $2 \cdot x \cdot x \cdot y$ **19.** $12 \cdot a \cdot a \cdot a \cdot b \cdot b \cdot b \cdot b$

21. $3x \cdot 3x \cdot 3x \cdot 3x$ **23.** $4q \cdot 4q \cdot 4q \cdot 4q \cdot 4q$ **25.** 27   **27.** 81

29. 144   **31.** 100   **33.** 100   **35.** 19   **37.** 54   **39.** 10   **41.** 1

43. 60   **45.** 144   **47.** 75   **49.** 225   **51.** 34   **53.** 21   **55.** 36

57. 40   **59.** 256   **61.** 196   **63.** 147   **65.** 21   **67.** 75   **69.** 96

71. 108   **73.** 8   **75.** 16   **77.** 1.2   **79.** 7.8   **81.** 2^5 **83.** 0   **a.** 30

b. 30   **c.** 16   **d.** 16   **e.** 48   **f.** 48

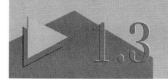

The Properties of Addition and Multiplication

1.3 OBJECTIVES

1. Recognize applications of the commutative property
2. Recognize applications of the associative property
3. Recognize applications of the distributive property

All integers, decimals, and fractions that we see in this course are real numbers.

All that we do in algebra is based on the rules for the operations introduced in Section 1.1. We call these rules **properties of the real numbers.** In this section we consider those properties that we will use in the remainder of this chapter.

The **commutative properties** tell us that we can add or multiply in any order.

The Commutative Properties

If *a* and *b* are any numbers,

1. $a + b = b + a$ Commutative property of addition
2. $a \cdot b = b \cdot a$ Commutative property of multiplication

---

• Example 1

Identifying the Commutative Properties

(*a*) $5 + 9 = 9 + 5$ and $x + 7 = 7 + x$

These are applications of the commutative property of addition.

(*b*) $5 \cdot 9 = 9 \cdot 5$

This is an application of the commutative property of multiplication.

● ● ●   CHECK YOURSELF 1

Identify the property being applied.

a. $7 + 3 = 3 + 7$ **b.** $7 \cdot 3 = 3 \cdot 7$
c. $a + 4 = 4 + a$ **d.** $x \cdot 2 = 2 \cdot x$

We also want to be able to change the grouping in simplifying expressions. This is possible because of the **associative properties.** Numbers or variables can be grouped in any manner to find a sum or a product.

The Associative Properties

If *a*, *b*, and *c* are any numbers,

1. $a + (b + c) = (a + b) + c$ Associative property of addition
2. $a \cdot (b \cdot c) = (a \cdot b) \cdot c$ Associative property of multiplication

---

• Example 2

Demonstrating the Associative Properties

(*a*) Show that $2 + (3 + 8) = (2 + 3) + 8$.

Remember, as we saw in Section 1.2, we always do the operation in the parentheses first.

$2 + \underbrace{(3 + 8)}_{\text{Add first.}}$ $\underbrace{(2 + 3)}_{\text{Add first.}} + 8$

$= 2 + 11$ $= 5 + 8$

$= 13$ $= 13$

So

$2 + (3 + 8) = (2 + 3) + 8$

(*b*) Show that $\dfrac{1}{3} \cdot (6 \cdot 5) = \left(\dfrac{1}{3} \cdot 6\right) \cdot 5$.

$\dfrac{1}{3} \cdot \underbrace{(6 \cdot 5)}_{\text{Multiply first.}}$ $\underbrace{\left(\dfrac{1}{3} \cdot 6\right)}_{\text{Multiply first.}} \cdot 5$

$= \dfrac{1}{3} \cdot (30)$ $= (2) \cdot 5$

$= 10$ $= 10$

So

$\left(\dfrac{1}{3} \cdot 6\right) \cdot 5 = \dfrac{1}{3}(6 \cdot 5)$

● ● ●   CHECK YOURSELF 2

Show that the following statements are true.

a. $3 + (4 + 7) = (3 + 4) + 7$

b. $3 \cdot (4 \cdot 7) = (3 \cdot 4) \cdot 7$

c. $\left(\dfrac{1}{5} \cdot 10\right) \cdot 4 = \dfrac{1}{5} \cdot (10 \cdot 4)$

The **distributive property** involves addition and multiplication together. We can illustrate this property with an application.

Suppose that we want to find the total of the two areas shown in the following figure.

Remember: The area of a rectangle is the product of its length and width:

$A = L \cdot W$

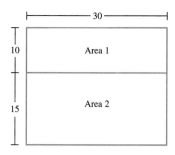

We can find the total area by multiplying the length by the overall width, which is found by adding the two widths.   [or]   We can find the total area as a sum of the two areas.

Length Overall Width

$30 \quad \cdot (10 + 15)$

$= 30 \cdot 25$

$= 750$

(Area 1)   (Area 2)
Length · Width   Length · Width

$30 \cdot 10 \quad + \quad 30 \cdot 15$

$= 300 + 450$

$= 750$

So

$30 \cdot (10 + 15) = 30 \cdot 10 + 30 \cdot 15$

This leads us to the following property.

Note the pattern.

$a(b + c) = a \cdot b + a \cdot c$

We "distributed" the multiplication "over" the addition.

The Distributive Property

If a, b, and c are any numbers,

$$a(b + c) = a \cdot b + a \cdot c \quad \text{and} \quad (b + c)a = b \cdot a + c \cdot a$$

● Example 3

Using the Distributive Property

Use the distributive property to simplify (remove the parentheses in) the following.

(*a*) $5(3 + 4)$

$5(3 + 4) = 5 \cdot 3 + 5 \cdot 4$

(*b*) $8(x + y)$

$8(x + y) = 8x + 8y$

(*c*) $2(3x + 5)$

$2(3x + 5) = 2 \cdot 3x + 2 \cdot 5$

$= 6x + 10$

Note:
$5(3 + 4) = 5 \cdot 7 = 35$

or

$5 \cdot 3 + 5 \cdot 4 = 15 + 20 = 35$

Because the variables are different, $8x + 8y$ cannot be simplified further.

Note: It is also true that

$$\frac{1}{3}(9 + 12) = \frac{1}{3}(21) = 7$$

(d) $\frac{1}{3}(9 + 12) = \frac{1}{3} \cdot 9 + \frac{1}{3} \cdot 12$

$$= 3 + 4 = 7$$

● ● ●   **CHECK YOURSELF 3**

Use the distributive property to simplify (remove the parentheses).

a. $4(6 + 7)$

b. $9(m + n)$

c. $3(5a + 7)$

d. $\frac{1}{5}(10 + 15)$

Example 4 requires that you identify which property is being demonstrated. Look for patterns that will help you remember each of the properties.

● Example 4

Identifying Properties

Name the property demonstrated.

(a) $3(x + 2) = 3x + 3 \cdot 2$ demonstrates the distributive property.
(b) $2 + (3 + 5) = (2 + 3) + 5$ demonstrates the associative property of addition.
(c) $3 \cdot 5 = 5 \cdot 3$ demonstrates the commutative property of multiplication.

● ● ●   **CHECK YOURSELF 4**

Name the property demonstrated.

a. $2 \cdot (3 \cdot 5) = (2 \cdot 3) \cdot 5$
b. $4(a + b) = 4a + 4b$
c. $x + 8 = 8 + x$

● ● ●   **CHECK YOURSELF ANSWERS**

1. **(a)** Commutative property of addition; **(b)** commutative property of multiplication; **(c)** commutative property of addition; **(d)** commutative property of multiplication.
2. **(a)** $3 + (4 + 7) = 3 + 11 = 14$ **(b)** $3 \cdot (4 \cdot 7) = 3 \cdot 28 = 84$
   $(3 + 4) + 7 = 7 + 7 = 14.$ $(3 \cdot 4) \cdot 7 = 12 \cdot 7 = 84.$
   (c) $\left(\frac{1}{5} \cdot 10\right) \cdot 4 = 2 \cdot 4 = 8$
   $\frac{1}{5} \cdot (10 \cdot 4) = \frac{1}{5} \cdot 40 = 8.$
3. **(a)** $4 \cdot 6 + 4 \cdot 7$, or 52; **(b)** $9m + 9n$; **(c)** $15a + 21$; **(d)** 5.
4. **(a)** Associative property of multiplication; **(b)** distributive property; **(c)** commutative property of addition.

Identify the property that is illustrated by each of the following statements.

1. $5 + 9 = 9 + 5$

2. $6 + 3 = 3 + 6$

3. $2 \cdot (3 \cdot 5) = (2 \cdot 3) \cdot 5$

4. $3 \cdot (5 \cdot 6) = (3 \cdot 5) \cdot 6$

5. $10 \cdot 5 = 5 \cdot 10$

6. $8 \cdot 4 = 4 \cdot 8$

7. $8 + 12 = 12 + 8$

8. $6 + 2 = 2 + 6$

9. $(5 \cdot 7) \cdot 2 = 5 \cdot (7 \cdot 2)$

10. $(8 \cdot 9) \cdot 2 = 8 \cdot (9 \cdot 2)$

11. $9 \cdot 8 = 8 \cdot 9$

12. $6 \cdot 4 = 4 \cdot 6$

13. $2(3 + 5) = 2 \cdot 3 + 2 \cdot 5$

14. $5(4 + 6) = 5 \cdot 4 + 5 \cdot 6$

15. $5 + (7 + 8) = (5 + 7) + 8$

16. $8 + (2 + 9) = (8 + 2) + 9$

17. $(10 + 5) + 9 = 10 + (5 + 9)$

18. $(5 + 5) + 3 = 5 + (5 + 3)$

19. $7(3 + 8) = 7 \cdot 3 + 7 \cdot 8$

20. $5(6 + 8) = 5 \cdot 6 + 5 \cdot 8$

Verify that each of the following statements is true by evaluating each side of the equation separately and comparing the results.

21. $7(3 + 4) = 7 \cdot 3 + 7 \cdot 4$

22. $4(5 + 1) = 4 \cdot 5 + 4 \cdot 1$

23. $2 + (9 + 8) = (2 + 9) + 8$

24. $6 + (15 + 3) = (6 + 15) + 3$

25. $5(6 \cdot 3) = (5 \cdot 6) \cdot 3$

26. $2(9 \cdot 10) = (2 \cdot 9) \cdot 10$

27. $5(2 + 8) = 5 \cdot 2 + 5 \cdot 8$

28. $3(10 + 2) = 3 \cdot 10 + 3 \cdot 2$

29. $(3 + 12) + 8 = 3 + (12 + 8)$

30. $(8 + 12) + 7 = 8 + (12 + 7)$

1. _____
2. _____
3. _____
4. _____
5. _____
6. _____
7. _____
8. _____
9. _____
10. _____
11. _____
12. _____
13. _____
14. _____
15. _____
16. _____
17. _____
18. _____
19. _____
20. _____
21. _____
22. _____
23. _____
24. _____
25. _____
26. _____
27. _____
28. _____
29. _____
30. _____

31. _____

32. _____

33. _____

34. _____

35. _____

36. _____

37. _____

38. _____

39. _____

40. _____

41. _____

42. _____

43. _____

44. _____

45. _____

46. _____

47. _____

48. _____

49. _____

50. _____

51. _____

52. _____

53. _____

54. _____

55. _____

56. _____

57. _____

58. _____

59. _____

60. _____

31. $(4 \cdot 7) \cdot 2 = 4 \cdot (7 \cdot 2)$

32. $(6 \cdot 5) \cdot 3 = 6 \cdot (5 \cdot 3)$

33. $\dfrac{1}{2} \cdot (2 + 6) = \dfrac{1}{2} \cdot 2 + \dfrac{1}{2} \cdot 6$

34. $\dfrac{1}{3} \cdot (6 + 9) = \dfrac{1}{3} \cdot 6 + \dfrac{1}{3} \cdot 9$

35. $\left(\dfrac{2}{3} + \dfrac{1}{6}\right) + \dfrac{1}{3} = \dfrac{2}{3} + \left(\dfrac{1}{6} + \dfrac{1}{3}\right)$

36. $\dfrac{3}{4} + \left(\dfrac{5}{8} + \dfrac{1}{2}\right) = \left(\dfrac{3}{4} + \dfrac{5}{8}\right) + \dfrac{1}{2}$

37. $0.1(51 + 52)$

38. $0.2(21 + 46)$

39. $\dfrac{1}{2} \cdot (2 \cdot 8) = \left(\dfrac{1}{2} \cdot 2\right) \cdot 8$

40. $\dfrac{1}{5} \cdot (5 \cdot 3) = \left(\dfrac{1}{5} \cdot 5\right) \cdot 3$

41. $\left(\dfrac{3}{5} \cdot \dfrac{5}{6}\right) \cdot \dfrac{4}{3} = \dfrac{3}{5} \cdot \left(\dfrac{5}{6} \cdot \dfrac{4}{3}\right)$

42. $\dfrac{4}{7} \cdot \left(\dfrac{21}{16} \cdot \dfrac{8}{3}\right) = \left(\dfrac{4}{7} \cdot \dfrac{21}{16}\right) \cdot \dfrac{8}{3}$

43. $2.5 \cdot (4 \cdot 5) = (2.5 \cdot 4) \cdot 5$

44. $4.2 \cdot (5 \cdot 2) = (4.2 \cdot 5) \cdot 2$

Use the distributive property to remove the parentheses in each of the following expressions. Then simplify your result where possible.

45. $2(3 + 5)$

46. $5(4 + 6)$

47. $3(x + 5)$

48. $5(y + 8)$

49. $4(w + v)$

50. $7(c + d)$

51. $2(3x + 5)$

52. $3(7a + 4)$

53. $\dfrac{1}{3} \cdot (15 + 9)$

54. $\dfrac{1}{6} \cdot (36 + 24)$

Use the properties of addition and multiplication to complete each of the following statements.

55. $5 + 7 = \underline{\quad} + 5$

56. $(5 + 3) + 4 = 5 + (\underline{\quad} + 4)$

57. $(8)(3) = (3)(\underline{\quad})$

58. $8(3 + 4) = 8 \cdot 3 + \underline{\quad} \cdot 4$

59. $7(2 + 5) = 7 \cdot \underline{\quad} + 7 \cdot 5$

60. $4 \cdot (2 \cdot 4) = (\underline{\quad} \cdot 2) \cdot 4$

Use the indicated property to write an expression that is equivalent to each of the following expressions.

61. $3 + 7$ (commutative property)

62. $2(3 + 4)$ (distributive property)

63. $5 \cdot (3 \cdot 2)$ (associative property)

64. $(3 + 5) + 2$ (associative property)

65. $2 \cdot 4 + 2 \cdot 5$ (distributive property)

66. $7 \cdot 9$ (commutative property)

Evaluate each of the following pairs of expressions. Then answer the given question.

67. $8 - 5$ and $5 - 8$
Do you think subtraction is commutative?

68. $12 \div 3$ and $3 \div 12$
Do you think division is commutative?

69. $(12 - 8) - 4$ and $12 - (8 - 4)$
Do you think subtraction is associative?

70. $(48 \div 16) \div 4$ and $48 \div (16 \div 4)$
Do you think division is associative?

71. $3(6 - 2)$ and $3 \cdot 6 - 3 \cdot 2$
Do you think multiplication is distributive over subtraction?

72. $\frac{1}{2}(16 - 10)$ and $\frac{1}{2} \cdot 16 - \frac{1}{2} \cdot 10$
Do you think multiplication is distributive over subtraction?

A N S W E R S

61. _____

62. _____

63. _____

64. _____

65. _____

66. _____

67. _____

68. _____

69. _____

70. _____

Getting Ready for Section 1.4
[Appendix 1]

a. $\dfrac{5}{2} + \dfrac{3}{2}$ **b.** $\dfrac{5}{6} + \dfrac{2}{3}$ **c.** $\dfrac{4}{3} + \dfrac{3}{5}$

d. $\dfrac{3}{8} + \dfrac{7}{12}$ **e.** $\left(\dfrac{5}{3}\right)\left(\dfrac{9}{2}\right)$ **f.** $\left(\dfrac{8}{5}\right)\left(\dfrac{5}{12}\right)$

g. $\left(\dfrac{12}{25}\right)\left(\dfrac{15}{20}\right)$ **h.** $\left(\dfrac{9}{16}\right)\left(\dfrac{24}{27}\right)$ **i.** $(3)\left(\dfrac{1}{3}\right)$

Answers

1. Commutative property of addition **3.** Associative property of multiplication
5. Commutative property of multiplication **7.** Commutative property of addition
9. Associative property of multiplication **11.** Commutative property of
multiplication **13.** Distributive property **15.** Associative property of
addition **17.** Associative property of addition **19.** Distributive property
21. $49 = 49$ **23.** $19 = 19$ **25.** $90 = 90$ **27.** $50 = 50$ **29.** $23 = 23$
31. $56 = 56$ **33.** $4 = 4$ **35.** $\dfrac{7}{6} = \dfrac{7}{6}$ **37.** $10.3 = 10.3$ **39.** $8 = 8$
41. $\dfrac{2}{3} = \dfrac{2}{3}$ **43.** $50 = 50$ **45.** 16 **47.** $3x + 15$ **49.** $4w + 4v$
51. $6x + 10$ **53.** 8 **55.** 7 **57.** 8 **59.** 2 **61.** $7 + 3$
63. $(5 \cdot 3) \cdot 2$ **65.** $2 \cdot (4 + 5)$ **67.** No **69.** No **71.** Yes **a.** 4
b. $\dfrac{3}{2}$ **c.** $\dfrac{29}{15}$ **d.** $\dfrac{23}{24}$ **e.** $\dfrac{15}{2}$ **f.** $\dfrac{2}{3}$ **g.** $\dfrac{9}{25}$ **h.** $\dfrac{1}{2}$ **i.** 1

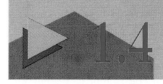

Adding and Subtracting Algebraic Expressions

1.4 OBJECTIVES

1. Add algebraic expressions
2. Subtract algebraic expressions

To find the perimeter of (or the distance around) a rectangle, we add 2 times the length and 2 times the width. In the language of algebra, this can be written as

L

W W Perimeter $= 2L + 2W$

L

We call $2L + 2W$ an **algebraic expression,** or more simply an **expression.** Recall from Section 1.1 that an expression allows us to write a mathematical idea in symbols. It can be thought of as a meaningful collection of letters, numbers, and operation signs.

Some expressions are

1. $5x^2$
2. $3a + 2b$
3. $4x^3 - 2y + 1$
4. $3(x^2 + y^2)$

In algebraic expressions, the addition and subtraction signs break the expressions into smaller parts called *terms.*

> A **term** is a number, or the product of a number and one or more variables, raised to a power.

In an expression, each sign ($+$ or $-$) is a part of the term that follows the sign.

● Example 1

Identifying Terms

(*a*) $5x^2$ has one term.
(*b*) $\underline{3a} + \underline{2b}$ has two terms: $3a$ and $2b$.
      Term   Term

Note that each term "owns" the sign that precedes it.

(*c*) $\underline{4x^3} - \underline{2y} + \underline{1}$ has three terms: $4x^3$, $-2y$, and 1.
      Term Term   Term

● ● ●   **CHECK YOURSELF 1**

List the terms of each expression.

a. $2b^4$ **b.** $5m + 3n$ **c.** $2s^2 - 3t - 6$

Note that a term in an expression may have any number of factors. For instance, $5xy$ is a term. It has factors of 5, x, and y. The number factor of a term is called the **numerical coefficient.** So for the term $5xy$, the numerical coefficient is 5.

•Example 2

Identifying the Numerical Coefficient

(a) $4a$ has the numerical coefficient 4.
(b) $6a^3b^4c^2$ has the numerical coefficient 6.
(c) $-7m^2n^3$ has the numerical coefficient -7.
(d) Since $1 \cdot x = x$, the numerical coefficient of x is understood to be 1.

● ● ● **CHECK YOURSELF 2**

Give the numerical coefficient for each of the following terms.

a. $8a^2b$ **b.** $-5m^3n^4$ **c.** y

If terms contain exactly the *same letters* (or variables) raised to the *same powers,* they are called **like terms.**

•Example 3

Identifying Like Terms

(a) The following are like terms.

$6a$ and $7a$
$5b^2$ and b^2
$10x^2y^3z$ and $-6x^2y^3z$
$-3m^2$ and m^2

Each pair of terms has the same letters, with each letter raised to the same power—the numerical coefficients can be any number.

(b) The following are *not* like terms.

Different letters
$6a$ and $7b$

Different exponents
$5b^2$ and b^3

Different exponents
$3x^2y$ and $4xy^2$

● ● ●   **CHECK YOURSELF 3**

Circle the like terms.

$5a^2b$ ab^2 a^2b $-3a^2$ $4ab$ $3b^2$ $-7a^2b$

Like terms of an expression can always be combined into a single term. Look at the following:

$$\underbrace{2x}_{x+x} + \underbrace{5x}_{x+x+x+x+x} = \underbrace{7x}_{x+x+x+x+x+x+x}$$

Rather than having to write out all those x's, try

Here we use the distributive property from Section 1.3.

$$2x + 5x = (2 + 5)x = 7x$$

In the same way,

You don't have to write all this out—just do it mentally!

$$9b + 6b = (9 + 6)b = 15b$$

and $10a - 4a = (10 - 4)a = 6a$

This leads us to the following rule.

Combining Like Terms

To combine like terms, use the following steps.

Step 1   Add or subtract the numerical coefficients.
Step 2   Attach the common variables.

● Example 4

Combining Like Terms

Combine like terms.*

(a) $8m + 5m = (8 + 5)m = 13m$

(b) $5pq^3 - 4pq^3 = 1pq^3 = pq^3$

Remember that when any factor is multiplied by 0, the product is 0.

(c) $7a^3b^2 - 7a^3b^2 = 0a^3b^2 = 0$

● ● ●   **CHECK YOURSELF 4**

Combine like terms.

a. $6b + 8b$ **b.** $12x^2 - 3x^2$

c. $8xy^3 - 7xy^3$ **d.** $9a^2b^4 - 9a^2b^4$

---

*When an example requires simplification of an expression, that expression will be screened. The simplification will then follow the equals sign.

Let's look at some expressions involving more than two terms. The idea is just the same.

● Example 5

Combining Like Terms

The distributive property can be used over any number of like terms.

Combine like terms.

(a) $5ab - 2ab + 3ab$

$= (5 - 2 + 3)ab = 6ab$

Only like terms can be combined.

(b) $\overbrace{8x - 2x} + 5y$

$= 6x \quad + 5y$

Like terms $\qquad$ Like terms

(c) $5m + 8n \quad + 4m - 3n$

Here we have used the associative and commutative properties.

$= (5m + 4m) + (8n - 3n)$

$= \quad 9m \quad + \quad 5n$

With practice you won't be writing out these steps, but doing them mentally.

(d) $4x^2 + 2x - 3x^2 + x$

$= (4x^2 - 3x^2) + (2x + x)$

$= x^2 + 3x$

As these examples illustrate, combining like terms often means changing the grouping and the order in which the terms are written. Again all this is possible because of the properties of addition that we introduced in Section 1.3.

● ● ● CHECK YOURSELF 5

Combine like terms.

a. $4m^2 - 3m^2 + 8m^2$ **b.** $9ab + 3a - 5ab$ **c.** $4p + 7q + 5p - 3q$

● ● ● CHECK YOURSELF ANSWERS

1. **(a)** $2b^4$; **(b)** $5m, 3n$; **(c)** $2s^2, -3t, -6$.   **2.** **(a)** 8; **(b)** -5; **(c)** 1.   **3.** The like terms are $5a^2b, a^2b$, and $-7a^2b$.   **4.** **(a)** $14b$; **(b)** $9x^2$; **(c)** xy^3; **(d)** 0. **5.** **(a)** $9m^2$; **(b)** $4ab + 3a$; **(c)** $9p + 4q$.

1.4 Exercises

Name

Section   Date

List the terms of the following expressions.

1. $5a + 2$

2. $7a - 4b$

3. $4x^3$

4. $3x^2$

5. $3x^2 + 3x - 7$

6. $2a^3 - a^2 + a$

Circle the like terms in the following groups of terms.

7. $5ab, 3b, 3a, 4ab$

8. $9m^2, 8mn, 5m^2, 7m$

9. $4xy^2, 2x^2y, 5x^2, -3x^2y, 5y, 6x^2y$

10. $8a^2b, 4a^2, 3ab^2, -5a^2b, 3ab, 5a^2b$

Combine the like terms.

11. $3m + 7m$

12. $6a^2 + 8a^2$

13. $7b^3 + 10b^3$

14. $7rs + 13rs$

15. $21xyz + 7xyz$

16. $4mn^2 + 15mn^2$

17. $9z^2 - 3z^2$

18. $7m - 6m$

19. $5a^3 - 5a^3$

20. $13xy - 9xy$

21. $19n^2 - 18n^2$

22. $7cd - 7cd$

23. $21p^2q - 6p^2q$

24. $17r^3s^2 - 8r^3s^2$

25. $10x^2 - 7x^2 + 3x^2$

26. $13uv + 5uv - 12uv$

27. $9a - 7a + 4b$

28. $5m^2 - 3m + 6m^2$

1.
2.
3.
4.
5.
6.
7.
8.
9.
10.
11.
12.
13.
14.
15.
16.
17.
18.
19.
20.
21.
22.
23.
24.
25.
26.
27.
28.

29. _____

30. _____

31. _____

32. _____

33. _____

34. _____

35. _____

36. _____

37. _____

38. _____

39. _____

40. _____

41. _____

42. _____

43. _____

44. _____

45. _____

46. _____

47. _____

48. _____

49. _____

50. _____

51. _____

52. _____

53. _____

54. _____

55. _____

56. _____

29. $7x + 5y - 4x - 4y$

30. $6a^2 + 11a + 7a^2 - 9a$

31. $4a + 7b + 3 - 2a + 3b - 2$

32. $5p^2 + 2p + 8 + 4p^2 + 5p - 6$

33. $\dfrac{2}{3}m + 3 + \dfrac{4}{3}m$

34. $\dfrac{1}{5}a - 2 + \dfrac{4}{5}a$

35. $\dfrac{13}{5}x + 2 - \dfrac{3}{5}x + 5$

36. $\dfrac{17}{12}y + 7 + \dfrac{7}{12}y - 3$

37. $2.3a + 7 + 4.7a + 3$

38. $5.8m + 4 - 2.8m + 11$

Perform the indicated operations.

39. The sum of $5a^4$ and $8a^4$ is

40. The sum of $9p^2$ and $12p^2$ is

41. Subtract $12a^3$ from $15a^3$.

42. Subtract $5m^3$ from $18m^3$.

43. Subtract $4x$ from the sum of $8x$ and $3x$.

44. Subtract $8ab$ from the sum of $7ab$ and $5ab$.

45. Subtract $3mn^2$ from the sum of $9mn^2$ and $5mn^2$.

46. Subtract $4x^2y$ from the sum of $6x^2y$ and $12x^2y$.

Use the distributive property to remove the parentheses in each expression. Then simplify by combining like terms.

47. $2(3x + 2) + 4$

48. $3(4z + 5) - 9$

49. $5(6a - 2) + 12a$

50. $7(4w - 3) - 25w$

51. $4s + 2(s + 4) + 4$

52. $5p + 4(p + 3) - 8$

Evaluate each of the following expressions if $a = 2$, $b = 3$, and $c = 5$. Be sure to combine terms where possible as the first step.

53. $7a^2 + 3a$

54. $11b^2 - 9b$

55. $3c^2 + 5c^2$

56. $9b^3 - 5b^3$

34

57. $5b + 3a - 2b$

58. $7c - 2b + 3c$

59. $5ac^2 - 2ac^2$

60. $5a^3b - 2a^3b$

Using your calculator, evaluate each of the following for the given values of the variable. Round your answer to the nearest tenth.

61. $7x^2 - 5y^3$ for $x = 7.1695$ and $y = 3.128$

62. $2x^2 + 3y + 5x$ for $x = 3.61$ and $y = 7.91$

63. $4x^2y \cdot 2xy^2 - 5x^3y$ for $x = 1.29$ and $y = 2.56$

64. $3x^3y - 4xy + 2x^2y^2$ for $x = 3.26$ and $y = 1.68$

65. Write a paragraph explaining the difference between n^2 and $2n$.

66. Complete the explanation: "x^3 and $3x$ are not the same because . . . ."

67. Complete the statement: "$x + 2$ and $2x$ are different because . . . ."

68. Write an English phrase for each algebraic expression below:

    (a) $2x^3 + 5x$ **(b)** $(2x + 5)^3$ **(c)** $6(n + 4)^2$

69. Work with another student to complete this exercise. Place $>$, $<$, or $=$ in the blank in these statements.

1^2 _____ 2^1 What happens as the table of numbers is extended? Try more examples.

2^3 _____ 3^2

3^4 _____ 4^3 What sign seems to occur the most in your table? $>$, $<$, or $=$?

4^5 _____ 5^4 Write an algebraic statement for the pattern of numbers in this table. Do you think this is a pattern that continues? Add more lines to the table and extend the pattern to the general case by writing the pattern in algebraic notation. Write a short paragraph stating your conjecture.

57.

58.

59.

60.

61.

62.

63.

64.

65.

66.

67.

68.

69.

70. Work with other students on this exercise.

Part 1: Evaluate the three expressions $\dfrac{n^2 - 1}{2}$, n, $\dfrac{n^2 + 1}{2}$ using odd values of n: 1, 3, 5, 7, etc. Make a chart like the one below and complete it.

n	$a = \dfrac{n^2 - 1}{2}$	$b = n$	$c = \dfrac{n^2 + 1}{2}$	a^2	b^2	c^2
1						
3						
5						
7						
9						
11						
13						
15						

Part 2: The numbers, a, b, and c that you get in each row have a surprising relationship to each other. Complete the last three columns and work together to discover this relationship. You may want to find out more about the history of this famous number pattern.

Answers

1. $5a$, 2 **3.** $4x^3$ **5.** $3x^2$, $3x$, -7 **7.** $5ab$, $4ab$ **9.** $2x^2y$, $-3x^2y$, $6x^2y$

11. $10m$ **13.** $17b^3$ **15.** $28xyz$ **17.** $6z^2$ **19.** 0 **21.** n^2 **23.** $15p^2q$

25. $6x^2$ **27.** $2a + 4b$ **29.** $3x + y$ **31.** $2a + 10b + 1$ **33.** $2m + 3$

35. $2x + 7$ **37.** $7a + 10$ **39.** $13a^4$ **41.** $3a^3$ **43.** $7x$ **45.** $11mn^2$

47. $6x + 8$ **49.** $42a - 10$ **51.** $6s + 12$ **53.** 34 **55.** 200 **57.** 15

59. 150 **61.** 206.8 **63.** 260.6

From Arithmetic to Algebra [1.1]

The sum of x and 5 is $x + 5$.
7 more than a is $a + 7$.
b increased by 3 is $b + 3$.

Addition $x + y$ means the **sum** of x **and** y or x **plus** y. Some other words indicating addition are "more than" and "increased by."

The difference of x and 3 is $x - 3$.
5 less than p is $p - 5$.
a decreased by 4 is $a - 4$.

Subtraction $x - y$ means the **difference** of x **and** y or x **minus** y. Some other words indicating subtraction are "less than" and "decreased by."

Multiplication

The product of m and n is mn.
The product of 2 and the sum of a and b is $2(a + b)$.

$$\left. \begin{array}{l} x \cdot y \\ (x)(y) \\ xy \end{array} \right\} \quad \text{These all mean the } \textit{product} \text{ of } x \text{ and } y \text{ or } x \textit{ times } y.$$

n divided by 5 is $\dfrac{n}{5}$.

The sum of a and b, divided by 3, is $\dfrac{a + b}{3}$.

Division $\dfrac{x}{y}$ means x *divided by* y or the *quotient* when x is divided by y.

Exponents and the Order of Operations [1.2]

The Notation

$5^3 = 5 \cdot 5 \cdot 5$
$\quad = 125$
$a^2 b^3 = a \cdot a \cdot b \cdot b \cdot b$
$6m^2 = 6 \cdot m \cdot m$

Exponent
$$a^4 = \underbrace{a \cdot a \cdot a \cdot a}_{4 \text{ factors}}$$
Base

The number or letter used as a factor, here a, is called the *base*. The *exponent*, which is written above and to the right of the base, tells us how many times the base is used as a factor.

The Order of Operations

1. Do any operations within grouping symbols first.
2. Evaluate all expressions containing exponents.
3. Do any multiplication or division in order, working from left to right.
4. Do any addition or subtraction in order, working from left to right.

Evaluate the power.
$5 + 3 \cdot 2^2$
Multiply.
$= 5 + 3 \cdot 4$
Add.
$= 5 + 12$
$= 17$

The Properties of Addition and Multiplication [1.3]

The Commutative Properties If a and b are any numbers,

1. $a + b = b + a$
2. $a \cdot b = b \cdot a$

The Associative Properties If a, b, and c are any numbers,

    1. $a + (b + c) = (a + b) + c$

    2. $a \cdot (b \cdot c) = (a \cdot b) \cdot c$

The Distributive Properties If a, b, and c are any numbers,

$a(b + c) = a \cdot b + a \cdot c$

Adding and Subtracting Algebraic Expressions [1.4]

Term A number, or the product of a number and one or more variables, raised to a power.

$4a^2$ and $3a^2$ are like terms.

$5x^2$ and $2xy^2$ are not like terms.

$5a + 3a = 8a$

$7xy - 3xy = 4xy$

Like Terms Terms that contain exactly the same variables raised to the same powers.

Combining Like Terms

    1. Add or subtract the numerical coefficients.

    2. Attach the common variables.

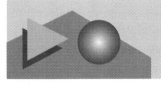

Summary Exercises

This exercise set is provided to give you practice with each of the objectives of the chapter. Each exercise is keyed to the appropriate chapter section. The answers are provided in the *Instructor's Manual*. Your instructor will give you guidelines on how to best use these exercises.

[1.1]   Write, using symbols.

    1. 5 more than y

    2. c decreased by 10

    3. The product of 8 and a

    4. The quotient when y is divided by 3

    5. 5 times the product of m and n

    6. The product of a and 5 less than a

    7. 3 more than the product of 17 and x

    8. The quotient when a plus 2 is divided by a minus 2

[1.2]   Write each of these in expanded form.

    9. x^3

    10. $y^3 \cdot y^2$

    11. $2x^3y^4$

    12. $(2x)^3y^4$

[1.2]   Evaluate each of the following expressions.

13. $18 - 3 \cdot 5$ **14.** $(18 - 3) \cdot 5$ **15.** $5 \cdot 4^2$

16. $(5 \cdot 4)^2$ **17.** $5 \cdot 3^2 - 4$ **18.** $5(3^2 - 4)$

19. $5(4 - 2)^2$ **20.** $5 \cdot 4 - 2^2$ **21.** $(5 \cdot 4 - 2)^2$

22. $3(5 - 2)^2$ **23.** $3 \cdot 5 - 2^2$ **24.** $(3 \cdot 5 - 2)^2$

[1.3]   Identify the property that is illustrated by each of the following statements.

25. $5 + (7 + 12) = (5 + 7) + 12$

26. $2(8 + 3) = 2 \cdot 8 + 2 \cdot 3$

27. $4 \cdot (5 \cdot 3) = (4 \cdot 5) \cdot 3$

28. $4 \cdot 7 = 7 \cdot 4$

[1.3]   Verify that each of the following statements is true by evaluating each side of the equation separately and comparing the results.

29. $8(5 + 4) = 8 \cdot 5 + 8 \cdot 4$ **30.** $2(3 + 7) = 2 \cdot 3 + 2 \cdot 7$

31. $(7 + 9) + 4 = 7 + (9 + 4)$ **32.** $(2 + 3) + 6 = 2 + (3 + 6)$

33. $(8 \cdot 2) \cdot 5 = 8(2 \cdot 5)$ **34.** $(3 \cdot 7) \cdot 2 = 3 \cdot (7 \cdot 2)$

[1.3]   Use the distributive law to remove parentheses.

35. $3(7 + 4)$ **36.** $4(2 + 6)$ **37.** $4(w + v)$

38. $6(x + y)$ **39.** $3(5a + 2)$ **40.** $2(4x^2 + 3x)$

Write, using exponents.

41. $5 \cdot 5 \cdot 5 \cdot 5$ **42.** $6 \cdot 6 \cdot 6 \cdot 6 \cdot 6$ **43.** $y \cdot y \cdot y \cdot y \cdot y$

44. $b \cdot b \cdot b \cdot b \cdot$ **45.** $8 \cdot a \cdot a \cdot a$ **46.** $c \cdot c \cdot d \cdot d \cdot d \cdot d$

[1.4]   List the terms of the expressions.

47. $4a^3 - 3a^2$ **48.** $5x^2 - 7x + 3$

[1.4]　Circle like terms.

49. $5m^2, -3m, -4m^2, 5m^3, m^2$

50. $4ab^2, 3b^2, -5a, ab^2, 7a^2, -3ab^2, 4a^2b$

[1.4]　Combine like terms.

51. $5c + 7c$　　　　　　　　　　**52.** $2x + 5x$

53. $4a - 2a$　　　　　　　　　　**54.** $6c - 3c$

55. $9xy - 6xy$　　　　　　　　　**56.** $5ab^2 + 2ab^2$

57. $7a + 3b + 12a - 2b$　　　　　**58.** $6x - 2x + 5y - 3x$

59. $5x^3 + 17x^2 - 2x^3 - 8x^2$

60. $3a^3 + 5a^2 + 4a - 2a^3 - 3a^2 - a$

61. Subtract $4a^3$ from the sum of $2a^3$ and $12a^3$.

62. Subtract the sum of $3x^2$ and $5x^2$ from $15x^2$.

[1.1–1.4]　Translate each of the following into an algebraic expression.

63. Carpentry. If x feet (ft) are cut off the end of a board that is 23 ft long, how much is left?

64. Money. Joan has 25 nickels and dimes in her pocket. If x of these are dimes, how many of the coins are nickels?

65. Age. Sam is 5 years older than Angela. If Angela is x years old now, how old is Sam?

66. Money. Margaret has $5 more than twice as much money as Gerry. Write an expression for the amount of money that Margaret has.

67. Geometry. The length of a rectangle is 4 meters (m) more than the width. Write an expression for the length of the rectangle.

68. Number problem. A number is 7 less than 6 times the number n. Write an expression for the number.

69. Carpentry. A 25-ft plank is cut into two pieces. Write expressions for the length of each piece.

70. Money. Bernie has x dimes and q quarters in his pocket. Write an expression for the amount of money that Bernie has in his pocket.

The purpose of this self-test is to help you check your progress and to review for a chapter test in class. Allow yourself about an hour to take the test. When you are done, check your answers in the back of the book. If you missed any problems, be sure to go back and review the appropriate sections in the chapter and the exercises that are provided.

Write, using symbols.

1. 5 less than a

2. The product of 6 and m

3. 4 times the sum of m and n

4. The quotient when the sum of a and b is divided by 3

Write, using exponents.

5. $4 \cdot 4 \cdot 4 \cdot 4$

6. $7 \cdot b \cdot b \cdot b$

Evaluate the following expressions.

7. $23 - 4 \cdot 5$

8. $4 \cdot 5^2 - 35$

9. $4(2 + 4)^2$

Identify the property that is illustrated by each of the following statements.

10. $6 \cdot 7 = 7 \cdot 6$

11. $2(6 + 7) = 2 \cdot 6 + 2 \cdot 7$

12. $4 + (3 + 7) = (4 + 3) + 7$

Use the distributive property to remove parentheses. Then simplify your result.

13. $3(5 + 2)$

14. $4(5x + 3)$

1. _____
2. _____
3. _____
4. _____
5. _____
6. _____
7. _____
8. _____
9. _____
10. _____
11. _____
12. _____
13. _____
14. _____

15. _____

16. _____

17. _____

18. _____

19. _____

20. _____

Combine like terms.

15. $8a + 7a$

16. $8x^2y - 5x^2y$

17. $10x + 8y + 9x - 3y$

18. Subtract $9a^2$ from the sum of $12a^2$ and $5a^2$.

19. Tom is 8 years younger than twice Moira's age. Write an expression for Tom's age.

20. The length of a rectangle is 4 more than twice the width. Write an expression for the length of the rectangle.

SIGNED NUMBERS

INTRODUCTION

Anthropologists and archeologists investigate modern human cultures and societies as well as cultures that existed so long ago that their characteristics must be inferred from objects found buried in lost cities or villages. When some interesting object is found, such as the Babylonian tablets mentioned in Chapter 1, often the first questions that arise are "How old is this? When did this culture flourish?" With methods such as carbon dating, it has been established that large, organized cultures existed around 3000 BC in Egypt, 2800 BC in India, no later than 1500 BC in China, and around 1000 BC in the Americas.

How long ago was 1500 BC? Which is older, an object from 3000 BC or an object from 500 AD*? Using the Christian notation for dates, we have to count AD years and BC years differently. An object from 500 AD is 1997 − 500 years old, or about 1500 years old. But an object from 3000 BC is 1997 + 3000 years old, or about 5000 years old. Why subtract in the first case but add in the other? Because of the way years are counted before the birth of Christ (BC) and after the birth of Christ (AD), the BC dates must be considered as *negative* numbers.

Very early on, the Chinese accepted the idea that a number could be negative; they used red calculating rods for positive numbers and black for negative numbers. Hindu mathematicians in India worked out the arithmetic of negative numbers as long ago as 400 AD, but western mathematicians did not recognize this idea until the sixteenth century. It would be difficult today to think of measuring things such as temperature, altitude, and money without using negative numbers. ━━━━━━━━━━━━━━━━━

*AD stands for the Latin *Anno Domini,* which means "in the year of the Lord."

© R. Lord/The Image Works

Signed Numbers and Order

2.1 OBJECTIVES

1. Understand the meaning of a negative number
2. Recognize the set of integers
3. Represent integers on a number line
4. Order signed numbers
5. Recognize extreme values
6. Evaluate a numerical expression involving the absolute value

The numbers used to count things—1, 2, 3, 4, 5, and so on—are called the **natural (or counting) numbers.** The **whole numbers** consist of the natural numbers and zero—0, 1, 2, 3, 4, 5, and so on. They can be represented on a number line like the one shown. Zero (0) is considered the origin.

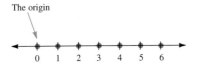

The number line continues forever in both directions.

When numbers are used to represent physical quantities (altitudes, temperatures, and amounts of money are examples), it may be necessary to distinguish between *positive* and *negative* quantities. It is convenient to represent these quantities with plus (+) or minus (−) signs. For instance,

The altitude of Mount Whitney is 14,495 feet (ft) *above* sea level (+14,495).

The altitude of Death Valley is 282 ft *below* sea level (−282).

The temperature in Chicago is 10° *below* zero (−10°).

An account could show a *gain* of $100 (+100), or a *loss* of $100 (−100).

These numbers suggest the need to extend the whole numbers to include both positive numbers (like +100) and negative numbers (like −282).

To represent the negative numbers, we extend the number line to the *left* of zero and name equally spaced points.

Numbers used to name points to the right of zero are positive numbers. They are written with a positive (+) sign or with no sign at all.

+6 and 9 are positive numbers

Numbers used to name points to the left of zero are negative numbers. They are always written with a negative (−) sign.

−3 and −20 are negative numbers

Read "negative 3."

Positive and negative numbers considered together are **signed numbers.**

Here is the number line extended to include both positive and negative numbers.

0 is not considered a signed number.

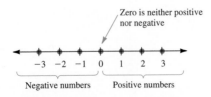

Zero is neither positive nor negative

Negative numbers   Positive numbers

The numbers used to name the points shown on the number line above are called the **integers.** The integers consist of the natural numbers, their negatives, and the number 0. We can represent the set of integers by

The dots are called *ellipses* and indicate that the pattern continues.

$$\{ \ldots, -3, -2, -1, 0, 1, 2, 3, \ldots \}$$

• Example 1

Representing Integers on the Number Line

Represent the following integers on the number line shown.

−3, −12, 8, 15, −7

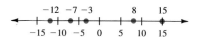

● ● ●   CHECK YOURSELF 1

Represent the following integers on a number line.

−1, −9, 4, −11, 8, 20

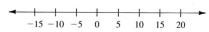

The set of numbers on the number line are *ordered*. The numbers get smaller moving to the left on the number line and larger moving to the right.

When a set of numbers are written from smallest to largest, they are said to be in *ascending order*.

• Example 2

Ordering Signed Numbers

Place each set of numbers in ascending order.

(*a*) 9, −5, −8, 3, 7

From smallest to largest, the numbers are

−8, −5, 3, 7, 9   Note that this is the order in which the numbers appear on a number line.

(*b*) 3, −2, 18, −20, −13

From smallest to largest, the numbers are

−20, −13, −2, 3, 18

● ● ● **CHECK YOURSELF 2**

Place each set of numbers in ascending order.

a. 12, −13, 15, 2, −8, −3
b. 3, 6, −9, −3, 8

The least and greatest numbers in a set are called the **extreme values.** The least element is called the **minimum** and the greatest element is called the **maximum.**

● Example 3

Labeling Extreme Values

For each set of numbers, determine the minimum and maximum values.

(*a*) 9, −5, −8, 3, 7

From our previous ordering of these numbers, we see that −8, the least element, is the minimum, and 9, the greatest element, is the maximum.

(*b*) 3, −2, 18, −20, −13

−20 is the minimum and 18 is the maximum.

● ● ● **CHECK YOURSELF 3**

For each set of numbers, determine the minimum and maximum values.

a. 12, −13, 15, 2, −8, −3
b. 3, 6, −9, −3, 8

Integers are not the only kind of signed numbers. Decimals and fractions can also be thought of as signed numbers.

● Example 4

Identifying Signed Numbers as Integers

Which of the following signed numbers are also integers?

(*a*) 145 is an integer.
(*b*) −28 is an integer.
(*c*) 0.35 is not an integer.
(*d*) $-\dfrac{2}{3}$ is not an integer.

● ● ●   CHECK YOURSELF 4

Which of the following signed numbers are also integers?

$$-23 \qquad 1054 \qquad -0.23 \qquad 0 \qquad -500 \qquad -\frac{4}{5}$$

An important idea for our work in this chapter is the **absolute value** of a number. This represents the distance of the point named by the number from the origin on the number line.

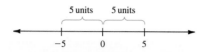

The absolute value of 5 is 5. The absolute value of -5 is also 5.
   In symbols we write

$$|5| = 5 \qquad \text{and} \qquad |-5| = 5$$

Read "the absolute   Read "the absolute
value of 5."   value of negative 5."

The absolute value of a number does *not* depend on whether the number is to the right or to the left of the origin, but on its *distance* from the origin.

● Example 5

Simplifying Absolute Value Expressions

(*a*) $|7| = 7$
(*b*) $|-7| = 7$
(*c*) $-|-7| = -7$

This is the *negative,* or opposite, of the absolute value of negative 7.

(*d*) $|-10| + |10| = 10 + 10 = 20$

Absolute value bars serve as another set of grouping symbols, so do the operation *inside* first.

(*e*) $|8 - 3| = |5| = 5$
(*f*) $|8| - |3| = 8 - 3 = 5$

Here, evaluate the absolute values, then subtract.

● ● ●   CHECK YOURSELF 5

Evaluate.

a. $|8|$　　　　　　　　**b.** $|-8|$　　　　　　　　**c.** $-|-8|$
d. $|-9| + |4|$　　　　　**e.** $|9 - 4|$　　　　　**f.** $|9| - |4|$

 All scientific calculators are able to handle negative numbers. Many of them, including all the graphing calculators, can also handle absolute value.

● Example 6

EVALUATING EXPRESSIONS WITH A CALCULATOR

Evaluate the following expression with your calculator.

$$|-34.56| - |-15.3 - 12.17|$$

First, identify whether your calculator has the ability to work with absolute values. If it does, it has a key marked ⊡ABS. To find an absolute, select the ABS and then put the expression for which the absolute value is desired inside a set of parentheses.

　　Designating a number as negative is different from subtraction! The key used to designate a negative number is either a ⊡+/− or a ⊡(−) key. Scientific calculators require that ⊡+/− be pressed after the number is entered. Graphing calculators require that ⊡(−) be selected before the number.

The following assumes that you are using a graphing calculator. Enter

ABS ⊡((⊡(−) 34.56 ⊡)) ⊡− ABS ⊡((⊡(−) 15.3 ⊡− 12.17 ⊡)) ENTER

The expression can be simplified as 7.09

● ● ●   CHECK YOURSELF 6

Evaluate the following expression with your calculator.

$$|-23.44| - |-21.2 - 15.3|$$

● ● ●   CHECK YOURSELF ANSWERS

1.

$$\xleftarrow{\quad} \underset{-20\ -15\ -10\ -5\quad 0\quad 5\quad 10\quad 15\quad 20}{\overset{-11-9\qquad -1\quad 4\quad 8\qquad\qquad 20}{\rule{6cm}{0.4pt}}} \xrightarrow{\quad}$$

2. (a) $-13, -8, -3, 2, 12, 15.$
　　(b) $-9, -3, 3, 6, 8.$

3. (a) minimum is -13; maximum is 15.
　　(b) minimum is -9; maximum is 8.

4. $-23, 1054, 0,$ and $-500.$

5. (a) 8; **(b)** 8; **(c)** -8; **(d)** 13; **(e)** 5; **(f)** 5.

6. -13.06

2.1 Exercises

Represent each quantity with a signed number.

1. An altitude of 400 feet (ft) above sea level

2. An altitude of 80 ft below sea level

3. A loss of $200

4. A profit of $400

5. A decrease in population of 25,000

6. An increase in population of 12,500

Represent the integers on the number lines shown.

7. $5, -15, 18, -8, 3$

8. $-18, 4, -5, 13, 9$

Which numbers in the following sets are integers?

9. $\left\{5, -\dfrac{2}{9}, 175, -234, -0.64\right\}$ **10.** $\left\{-45, 0.35, \dfrac{3}{5}, 700, -26\right\}$

Place each of the following sets in ascending order.

11. $3, -5, 2, 0, -7, -1, 8$ **12.** $-2, 7, 1, -8, 6, -1, 0$

13. $9, -2, -11, 4, -6, 1, 5$ **14.** $23, -18, -5, -11, -15, 14, 20$

15. $-\dfrac{1}{2}, \dfrac{3}{4}, -\dfrac{5}{6}, \dfrac{2}{3}, -\dfrac{1}{3}$ **16.** $\dfrac{3}{7}, -\dfrac{6}{7}, \dfrac{1}{7}, -\dfrac{1}{2}, \dfrac{2}{7}$

For each set, determine the maximum and minimum value.

17. $5, -6, 0, 10, -3, 15, 1, 8$ **18.** $9, -1, 3, 11, -4, 2, 5, -2$

1. _____

2. _____

3. _____

4. _____

5. _____

6. _____

7. _____

8. _____

9. _____

10. _____

11. _____

12. _____

13. _____

14. _____

15. _____

16. _____

17. _____

18. _____

A N S W E R S

19. _____

20. _____

21. _____

22. _____

23. _____

24. _____

25. _____

26. _____

27. _____

28. _____

29. _____

30. _____

31. _____

32. _____

33. _____

34. _____

35. _____

36. _____

37. _____

38. _____

39. _____

40. _____

41. _____

42. _____

43. _____

44. _____

19. $21, -15, 0, 7, -9, 16, -3, 11$

20. $-22, 0, 22, -31, 18, -5, 3$

21. $3, 0, \dfrac{1}{2}, -\dfrac{2}{3}, 5, \dfrac{3}{4}, -\dfrac{1}{6}$

22. $-3, 2, \dfrac{7}{12}, -\dfrac{3}{4}, \dfrac{5}{6}, -\dfrac{10}{3}, \dfrac{5}{2}$

Evaluate.

23. $|17|$

24. $|28|$

25. $|-10|$

26. $|-7|$

27. $-|3|$

28. $-|5|$

29. $-|-8|$

30. $-|-13|$

31. $|-2| + |3|$

32. $|4| + |-3|$

33. $|-9| + |9|$

34. $|11| + |-11|$

35. $|4| - |-4|$

36. $|5| - |-5|$

37. $|15| - |8|$

38. $|11| - |3|$

39. $|15 - 8|$

40. $|11 - 3|$

41. $|-9| + |2|$

42. $|-7| + |4|$

43. $|-8| - |-7|$

44. $|-9| - |-4|$

Label each statement as true or false.

45. All whole numbers are integers.

46. All nonzero integers are signed numbers.

47. All integers are whole numbers.

48. All signed numbers are integers.

49. All negative integers are whole numbers.

50. Zero is neither positive or negative.

Place absolute value bars in the proper location on the left side of the expression so that the equation is true.

51. $6 + (-2) = 4$

52. $8 + (-3) = 5$

53. $6 + (-2) = 8$

54. $8 + (-3) = 11$

Represent each quantity with a signed number.

55. Soil erosion. The erosion of 5 centimeters (cm) of topsoil from an Iowa corn field.

56. Soil formation. The formation of 2.5 cm of new topsoil on the African savanna.

57. Checking accounts. The withdrawal of $50 from a checking account.

58. Saving accounts. The deposit of $200 in a savings account.

59. Temperature. A temperature decrease of 10° in 1 hour.

60. Stocks. An increase of 75 points in the Dow-Jones average.

61. Baseball. An eight-game losing streak by the local baseball team.

62. Population. An increase of 25,000 in the population of the city.

45. _____

46. _____

47. _____

48. _____

49. _____

50. _____

51. _____

52. _____

53. _____

54. _____

55. _____

56. _____

57. _____

58. _____

59. _____

60. _____

61. _____

62. _____

63. _____

64. _____

a. _____

b. _____

c. _____

d. _____

e. _____

f. _____

g. _____

h. _____

i. _____

j. _____

63. Positive trade balance. A country exported $90,000,000 more than it imported, creating a positive trade balance.

64. Negative trade balance. A country exported $60,000,000 less than it imported, creating a negative trade balance.

Getting Ready for Section 2.2 [Section 1.3]

Find each sum.

a. $3 + (8 + 9)$

b. $(6 + 12) + 3$

c. $(3 + 8) + 9$

d. $6 + (12 + 3)$

e. $\dfrac{2}{3} + \left(3 + \dfrac{1}{3}\right)$

f. $\left(\dfrac{3}{4} + 1\right) + \dfrac{5}{4}$

g. $\left(\dfrac{2}{3} + \dfrac{1}{3}\right) + 3$

h. $\left(\dfrac{3}{4} + \dfrac{5}{4}\right) + 1$

i. $\left(\dfrac{1}{2} + \dfrac{1}{3}\right) + \dfrac{1}{6}$

j. $\left(\dfrac{1}{4} + \dfrac{3}{8}\right) + \dfrac{1}{2}$

Answers

1. 400 or $(+400)$ **3.** -200 **5.** $-25,000$ **7.**

$$\xleftarrow{\hspace{1em}} \underset{-20}{\bullet} \; \underset{}{\underset{-10}{\overset{-15\,-8}{\bullet}}} \; \underset{0}{\mid} \; \underset{10}{\overset{3\;5}{\bullet\bullet}} \mid \underset{20}{\overset{18}{\bullet}} \xrightarrow{\hspace{1em}}$$

9. $5, 175, -234$ **11.** $-7, -5, -1, 0, 2, 3, 8$ **13.** $-11, -6, -2, 1, 4, 5, 9$

15. $-\dfrac{5}{6}, -\dfrac{1}{2}, -\dfrac{1}{3}, \dfrac{2}{3}, \dfrac{3}{4}$ **17.** Max: 15; Min: -6 **19.** Max: 21, Min: -15

21. Max: 5; Min: $-\dfrac{2}{3}$ **23.** 17   **25.** 10   **27.** -3 **29.** -8 **31.** 5

33. 18   **35.** 0   **37.** 7   **39.** 7   **41.** 11   **43.** 1   **45.** True   **47.** False

49. False   **51.** $|6 + (-2)| = 4$ **53.** $|6| + |-2| = 8$ **55.** -5 **57.** -50

59. -10 **61.** -8 **63.** $+90,000,000$ **a.** 20   **b.** 21   **c.** 20   **d.** 21

e. 4   **f.** 3   **g.** 4   **h.** 3   **i.** 1   **j.** $\dfrac{9}{8}$

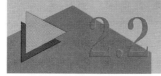

Adding Signed Numbers; Finding the Median

2.2 OBJECTIVES

1. Find the sum of signed numbers
2. Find the median of a set of signed numbers

In the previous section, we introduced the idea of signed numbers. Now we will examine the four arithmetic operations (addition, subtraction, multiplication, and division) and see how those operations are performed when signed numbers are involved. We start by considering addition.

An application may help. As before, let's represent a gain of money as a positive number and a loss as a negative number.

If you gain $3 and then gain $4, the result is a gain of $7:

$$3 + 4 = 7$$

If you lose $3 and then lose $4, the result is a loss of $7:

$$-3 + (-4) = -7$$

If you gain $3 and then lose $4, the result is a loss of $1:

$$3 + (-4) = -1$$

If you lose $3 and then gain $4, the result is a gain of $1:

$$-3 + 4 = 1$$

The number line can be used to illustrate the addition of integers. Starting at the origin, we move to the *right* for positive numbers and to the *left* for negative numbers.

• Example 1

Adding Signed Numbers

Add $\dfrac{4}{3} + \dfrac{2}{3}$.

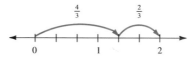

Start at the origin and move $\dfrac{4}{3}$ units to the right. Then move $\dfrac{2}{3}$ more to the right to find the sum. So we have

$$\frac{4}{3} + \frac{2}{3} = \frac{6}{3} = 2$$

● ● ● **CHECK YOURSELF 1**

Add.

a. $5 + 6$ **b.** $\dfrac{5}{4} + \dfrac{7}{4}$

The number line will also help you visualize the sum of two negative numbers. Remember, we move to the left for negative numbers.

● Example 2

Adding Signed Numbers

(*a*) Add $(-3) + (-4)$.

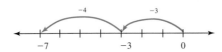

Start at the origin and move 3 units to the left. Then move 4 more units to the left to find the sum. From the graph we see that the sum is

$$(-3) + (-4) = -7$$

(*b*) Add $\left(-\dfrac{3}{2}\right) + \left(-\dfrac{1}{2}\right)$.

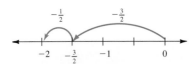

As before, we start at the origin. From that point move $\dfrac{3}{2}$ units left. Then move another $\dfrac{1}{2}$ unit left to find the sum. In this case

$$\left(-\dfrac{3}{2}\right) + \left(-\dfrac{1}{2}\right) = -2$$

● ● ● **CHECK YOURSELF 2**

Add.

a. $(-4) + (-5)$ **b.** $(-3) + (-7)$

c. $(-5) + (-15)$ **d.** $\left(-\dfrac{5}{2}\right) + \left(-\dfrac{3}{2}\right)$

You have probably noticed some helpful patterns in the previous examples. These patterns will allow you to do the work mentally without having to use the number line. Look at the following rule.

This means that the sum of two positive numbers is positive and the sum of two negative numbers is negative.

Adding Signed Numbers Case 1: Same Sign

If two numbers have the same sign, add their absolute values. Give the sum the sign of the original numbers.

•Example 3

Adding Signed Numbers

(a) $(-8) + (-5) = -13$ Add the absolute values ($8 + 5 = 13$), and give the sum the sign ($-$) of the original numbers.

(b) $[(-3) + (-4)] + (-6)$ Add inside the brackets as your first step.
$= (-7) + (-6) = -13$

● ● ● **CHECK YOURSELF 3**

Add mentally.

a. $7 + 9$

b. $(-7) + (-9)$

c. $(-5.8) + (-3.2)$

d. $[(-5) + (-2)] + (-3)$

Let's again use the number line to illustrate the addition of two numbers. This time the numbers will have *different* signs.

•Example 4

Adding Signed Numbers

(a) Add $3 + (-6)$.

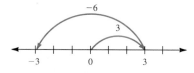

First move 3 units to the right of the origin. Then move 6 units to the left.

$3 + (-6) = -3$

(b) Add $-4 + 7$.

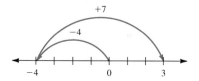

This time move 4 units to the left of the origin as the first step. Then move 7 units to the right.

$$-4 + 7 = 3$$

CHECK YOURSELF 4

Add.

a. $7 + (-5)$ **b.** $4 + (-8)$ **c.** $-4 + 9$ **d.** $-7 + 3$

You have no doubt noticed that, in adding a positive number and a negative number, sometimes the sum is positive and sometimes it is negative. This depends on which of the numbers has the larger absolute value. This leads us to the second part of our addition rule.

> **Adding Signed Numbers Case 2: Different Signs**
>
> If two numbers have different signs, subtract their absolute values, the smaller from the larger. Give the sum the sign of the number with the larger absolute value.

• Example 5

Adding Signed Numbers

(*a*) $7 + (-19) = -12$

Since the two numbers have different signs, subtract the absolute values ($19 - 7 = 12$). The sum has the sign ($-$) of the number with the larger absolute value, -19.

(*b*) $-13 + 7 = -6$

Subtract the absolute values ($13 - 7 = 6$). The sum has the sign ($-$) of the number with the larger absolute value, -13.

Remember, **signed numbers** can be fractions and decimals as well as integers.

(*c*) $-8.2 + 4.5 = -3.7$

Subtract the absolute values ($8.2 - 4.5 = 3.7$). The sum has the sign ($-$) of the number with the larger absolute value, -8.2.

CHECK YOURSELF 5

Add mentally.

a. $5 + (-14)$ **b.** $-7 + (-8)$ **c.** $-8 + 15$

d. $7 + (-8)$ **e.** $-\dfrac{2}{3} + \left(-\dfrac{7}{3}\right)$ **f.** $5.3 + (-2.3)$

There are two other properties of addition that we should mention before concluding this section. First, the sum of any number and 0 is always that number. In symbols,

---

Additive Identity Property

For any number *a*,

$$a + 0 = 0 + a = a$$

No number loses its identity after addition with 0. Zero is called the **additive identity.**

● Example 6

Adding Signed Numbers

Add.

(*a*) $9 + 0 = 9$

(*b*) $0 + (-8) = -8$

(*c*) $(-25) + 0 = -25$

● ● ●   **CHECK YOURSELF 6**

Add.

a. $8 + 0$ **b.** $0 + (-7)$ **c.** $(-36) + 0$

The opposite of a number is also called the **additive inverse** of that number.

We'll need one further definition to state our second property. Every number has an *opposite*. It corresponds to a point the same distance from the origin as the given integer, but in the opposite direction.

3 and −3 are opposites.

The opposite of 9 is −9.
The opposite of −15 is 15.

Our second property states that the sum of any number and its opposite is 0.

Additive Inverse Property

For any number *a*, there exists a number −*a* such that

$$a + (-a) = (-a) + a = 0$$

Here −*a* represents the opposite of the number *a*. The sum of any number and its opposite, or additive inverse, is 0.

•Example 7

Adding Signed Numbers

(a) $9 + (-9) = 0$

(b) $-15 + 15 = 0$

(c) $(-2.3) + 2.3 = 0$

(d) $\dfrac{4}{5} + \left(-\dfrac{4}{5}\right) = 0$

● ● ● CHECK YOURSELF 7

Add.

a. $(-17) + 17$ **b.** $12 + (-12)$

c. $\dfrac{1}{3} + \left(-\dfrac{1}{3}\right)$ **d.** $(-1.6) + 1.6$

All properties of addition from Section 1.3 apply when negative numbers are involved.

We can now use the associative and commutative properties of addition, introduced in Section 1.3, to find the sum when more than two signed numbers are involved. Example 8 illustrates these properties.

•Example 8

Adding Signed Numbers

We use the commutative property to reverse the order of addition for -3 and 5. We then group -5 and 5. Do you see why?

$(-5) + (-3) + 5$

$= (-5) + 5 + (-3)$

$= [(-5) + 5] + (-3)$

$= 0 + (-3) = -3$

● ● ● CHECK YOURSELF 8

Add.

a. $(-4) + 5 + (-3)$ **b.** $(-8) + 4 + 8$

In the previous section, we saw that the least and greatest elements of a set were called the minimum and maximum. The middle value of an ordered set is called the **median.** The median is sometimes used to represent an *average* of the set of numbers.

• Example 9

Finding the Median

Find the median for each set of numbers.

(*a*) 9, −5, −8, 3, 7

First, rewrite the set in ascending order.

−8, −5, 3, 7, 9

The median is then the element that has just as many numbers to its right as it has to its left. In this set, 3 is the median, because there are two numbers that are larger (7 and 9) and two numbers that are smaller (−8 and −5).

(*b*) 3, −2, 18, −20, −13

First, rewrite the set in ascending order.

−20, −13, −2, 3, 18

The median is then the element that is exactly in the middle. The median for this set is −2.

● ● ●   CHECK YOURSELF 9

Find the median for each set of numbers.

a. −3, 2, 7, −6, −1
b. 5, 1, −10, 2, −20

In the previous example, each set had an odd number of elements. If we had an even number of elements, there would be no single middle number.

To find the median from a set with an even number of elements, add the two middle numbers and divide their sum by 2.

• Example 10

Finding the Median

Find the median for each set of numbers.

(*a*) −3, 3, −8, 4, −1, −7

First, rewrite the set in ascending order.

−8, −7, −3, −1, 3, 4

Add the middle two numbers (-3 and -1), then divide their sum by 2.

$$\frac{(-3) + (-1)}{2} = \frac{(-4)}{2} = -2$$

The median is -2.

(b) 8, 3, -2, 4, -5, -7

Rewrite the set in ascending order.

$-7, -5, -2, 3, 4, 8$

The median is one-half the sum of the middle two numbers.

$$\frac{-2 + 3}{2} = \frac{1}{2} = 0.5$$

●●● **CHECK YOURSELF 10**

Find the median for each set of numbers.

a. $-2, -5, 15, 8, -3, -4$
b. $8, 3, -6, -8, 9, -7$

●●● **CHECK YOURSELF ANSWERS**

1. (a) 11; **(b)** 3.   **2. (a)** -9; **(b)** -10; **(c)** -20; **(d)** -4.   **3. (a)** 16; **(b)** -16;
(c) -9; **(d)** -10.   **4. (a)** 2; **(b)** -4; **(c)** 5; **(d)** -4.   **5. (a)** -9; **(b)** -15; **(c)** 7;
(d) -1; **(e)** -3; **(f)** 3.   **6. (a)** 8; **(b)** -7; **(c)** -36.   **7. (a)** 0; **(b)** 0; **(c)** 0; **(d)** 0.
8. (a) -2; **(b)** 4.   **9. (a)** -1; **(b)** 1.   **10. (a)** -2.5; **(b)** -1.5.

Add.

1. $3 + 6$

2. $5 + 9$

3. $11 + 5$

4. $8 + 7$

5. $\dfrac{3}{4} + \dfrac{5}{4}$

6. $\dfrac{7}{3} + \dfrac{8}{3}$

7. $\dfrac{1}{2} + \dfrac{4}{5}$

8. $\dfrac{2}{3} + \dfrac{5}{9}$

9. $(-2) + (-3)$

10. $(-1) + (-9)$

11. $\left(-\dfrac{3}{5}\right) + \left(-\dfrac{7}{5}\right)$

12. $\left(-\dfrac{3}{5}\right) + \left(\dfrac{12}{5}\right)$

13. $\left(-\dfrac{1}{2}\right) + \left(-\dfrac{3}{8}\right)$

14. $\left(-\dfrac{4}{7}\right) + \left(-\dfrac{3}{14}\right)$

15. $(-1.6) + (-2.3)$

16. $(-3.5) + (-2.6)$

17. $9 + (-3)$

18. $10 + (-4)$

19. $8 + (-14)$

20. $7 + (-11)$

21. $\left(\dfrac{3}{4}\right) + \left(-\dfrac{1}{2}\right)$

22. $\left(\dfrac{2}{3}\right) + \left(-\dfrac{1}{6}\right)$

23. $\left(-\dfrac{4}{5}\right) + \left(\dfrac{9}{20}\right)$

24. $\left(-\dfrac{11}{6}\right) + \left(\dfrac{5}{12}\right)$

25. $-11.4 + 13.4$

26. $-5.2 + 9.2$

27. $-3.6 + 7.6$

28. $-2.6 + 4.9$

29. $-9 + 0$

30. $-15 + 0$

ANSWERS

1. _____
2. _____
3. _____
4. _____
5. _____
6. _____
7. _____
8. _____
9. _____
10. _____
11. _____
12. _____
13. _____
14. _____
15. _____
16. _____
17. _____
18. _____
19. _____
20. _____
21. _____
22. _____
23. _____
24. _____
25. _____
26. _____
27. _____
28. _____
29. _____
30. _____

31. $18 + 0$ **32.** $14 + 0$ **33.** $7 + (-7)$

34. $12 + (-12)$ **35.** $-14 + 14$ **36.** $-5 + 5$

37. $-9 + (-17) + 9$ **38.** $15 + (-3) + (-15)$ **39.** $2 + 5 + (-11) + 4$

40. $7 + (-9) + (-5) + 6$ **41.** $(-4) + 6 + (-3) + 0$ **42.** $7 + (-3) + 5 + (-11)$

43. $1 + (-2) + 3 + (-4)$ **44.** $(-9) + 0 + (-2) + 12$ **45.** $\dfrac{5}{3} + \left(-\dfrac{4}{3}\right) + \dfrac{5}{3}$

46. $-\dfrac{6}{5} + \left(-\dfrac{13}{5}\right) + \dfrac{4}{5}$ **47.** $-\dfrac{3}{2} + \left(-\dfrac{7}{4}\right) + \dfrac{1}{4}$ **48.** $\dfrac{1}{3} + \left(-\dfrac{5}{6}\right) + \left(-\dfrac{1}{2}\right)$

49. $2.3 + (-5.4) + (-2.9)$ **50.** $-(5.4) + (-2.1) + (-3.5)$

Evaluate using your calculator. Round your answer to the nearest tenth.

51. $(-4.1967 + 5.2943) + (-3.1698)$

52. $5.3297 + 4.1897 + (-3.2869)$

53. $-7.19863 + 4.8629 + 3.2689 + (-5.7936)$

54. $-(-3.6829) + 4.5687 + 7.28967 + (-5.1623)$

Evaluate each of the following expressions.

55. $|3 + (-4)|$ **56.** $|(-11) + 9|$

57. $|-17 + 8|$ **58.** $|-27 + 14|$

59. $|-3 + 2 + (-4)|$ **60.** $|-2 + 7 + (-5)|$

61. $|2 + (-3)| + |(-3) + 2|$ **62.** $|8 + (-10)| + |-12 + 14|$

Find the median for each of the following sets.

63. $1, 3, 5, 7, 9$ **64.** $2, 4, 6, 8, 10$

65. $2, 3, 5, 7, 8, 13, 25$ **66.** $21, 23, 30, 32, 34, 37, 53$

67. $-5, -4, 2, 0, 3, 4$

68. $-7, -5, -3, 1, 5, 11$

69. $-6, -3, -2, 2, 3, 5$

70. $-8, -7, -3, -1, 2, 4$

71. $-3, 4, 9, -5, 6$

72. $-5, 11, -10, 2, 8$

73. $-15, 11, 8, -9, 4, -3$

74. $8, -17, 2, -5, 6, -11$

Label each of the following statements as true or false.

75. $-10 + 6 = 6 - 10$

76. $5 + (-9) = -9 + 5$

77. $|-3| + |2| = |-3 + (+2)|$

78. $|-8| + |3| = |-8 + 3|$

Place absolute value bars in the proper location on the left side of the expression so that the statement is true.

79. $-3 + 7 = 10$

80. $-5 + 9 = 14$

81. $-6 + 7 + (-4) = 3$

82. $-10 + 15 + (-9) = 4$

83. **Checking account.** Amir has $100 in his checking account. He writes a check for $23 and makes a deposit of $51. What is his new balance?

84. **Checking account.** Olga has $250 in her checking account. She deposits $52 and then writes a check for $77. What is her new balance?

85. **Football yardage.** On four consecutive running plays, Ricky Watters of the Philadelphia Eagles gained 23 yards, lost 5 yards, gained 15 yards, and lost 10 yards. What was his net yardage change for the series of plays?

86. **VISA balance.** Tom owes $780 on his VISA account. He returns three items costing $43.10, $36.80, and $125.00 and receives credit on his account. Next, he makes a payment of $400. He then makes a purchase of $82.75. How much does Tom still owe?

87. **Temperature.** The temperature at noon on a June day was 82°. It fell by 12° in the next 4 hours. What was the temperature at 4:00 PM?

88. **Mountain climbing.** Sharon is standing at a point 6000 feet (ft) above sea level. She descends to a point 725 ft lower. What is her distance above sea level?

67. _____

68. _____

69. _____

70. _____

71. _____

72. _____

73. _____

74. _____

75. _____

76. _____

77. _____

78. _____

79. _____

80. _____

81. _____

82. _____

83. _____

84. _____

85. _____

86. _____

87. _____

88. _____

89. _____

90. _____

a. _____

b. _____

c. _____

d. _____

e. _____

f. _____

g. _____

h. _____

89. On page 59 it is stated that "Every number has an opposite." The opposite of 9 is −9. This corresponds to the idea of an opposite in English and in English an opposite is often expressed by a prefix, for example, "un" or "ir".

(a) Write the opposite of these words: unmentionable, uninteresting, irredeemable, irregular, uncomfortable.

(b) What is the meaning of these expressions? not uninteresting, not irredeemable, not irregular, not unmentionable.

(c) Think of other prefixes that _negate_ or change the meaning of a word to its _opposite_. Make a list of words formed with these prefixes, and write a sentence with three of the words you found. Make a sentence with two words and phrases from each of the lists above. Look up the meaning of the word _irregardless_.

What is the value of −[−(−5)]? What is the value of −(−6)? How does this relate to the above examples? Write a short description about this relationship.

90. The temperature on the plains of North Dakota can change rapidly, falling or rising many degrees in the course of an hour. Here are some temperature changes during each day over a week.

Day	Mon.	Tues.	Wed.	Thurs.	Fri.	Sat.	Sun.
Temp. Change from 10 AM to 3 PM	+13°	+20°	−18°	+10°	−25°	−5°	+15°

Write a short speech for the TV weather reporter that summarizes the daily temperature change. How would you characterize the average daily midday change?

⬤ **Getting Ready for Section 2.3 [Appendix 1]**

Subtract as indicated.

a. $\dfrac{5}{2} - \dfrac{3}{2}$ **b.** $\dfrac{7}{2} - 2$ **c.** $\dfrac{4}{3} - \dfrac{1}{6}$ **d.** $\dfrac{9}{4} - \dfrac{3}{2}$

e. $5 - \dfrac{2}{3}$ **f.** $\dfrac{9}{10} - \dfrac{1}{4}$ **g.** $\dfrac{1}{5} - \dfrac{1}{7}$ **h.** $\dfrac{12}{5} - \dfrac{2}{3}$

Answers

1. 9   **3.** 16   **5.** 2   **7.** $\dfrac{13}{10}$ **9.** −5   **11.** −2   **13.** $-\dfrac{7}{8}$ **15.** −3.9

17. 6   **19.** −6   **21.** $\dfrac{1}{4}$ **23.** $-\dfrac{7}{20}$ **25.** 2   **27.** 4   **29.** −9   **31.** 18

33. 0   **35.** 0   **37.** −17   **39.** 0   **41.** −1   **43.** −2   **45.** 2   **47.** −3

49. −6   **51.** −2.1   **53.** −4.9   **55.** 1   **57.** 9   **59.** 5   **61.** 2   **63.** 5

65. 7   **67.** 1   **69.** 0   **71.** 4   **73.** $\dfrac{1}{2}$ **75.** True   **77.** False

79. $|-3| + |7| = 10$ **81.** $|-6 + 7 + (-4)| = 3$ **83.** \$128   **85.** 23 yards

87. 70°   **a.** 1   **b.** $\dfrac{3}{2}$ **c.** $\dfrac{7}{6}$ **d.** $\dfrac{3}{4}$ **e.** $\dfrac{13}{3}$ **f.** $\dfrac{13}{20}$ **g.** $\dfrac{2}{35}$ **h.** $\dfrac{26}{15}$

2.3 Subtracting Signed Numbers; Finding the Range

2.3 OBJECTIVES

1. Find the difference of two signed numbers
2. Find the range for a set of numbers

To begin our discussion of subtraction when signed numbers are involved, we can look back at a problem using natural numbers. Of course, we know that

$$8 - 5 = 3 \tag{1}$$

From our work in adding signed numbers in the last section, we know that it is also true that

$$8 + (-5) = 3 \tag{2}$$

Comparing Equations (1) and (2), we see that the results are the same. This leads us to an important pattern. Any subtraction problem can be written as a problem in addition. Subtracting 5 is the same as adding the opposite of 5, or -5. We can write this fact as follows:

$$8 - 5 = 8 + (-5) = 3$$

This leads us to the following rule for subtracting signed numbers.

Subtracting Signed Numbers

STEP 1 Rewrite the subtraction problem as an addition problem by
a. Changing the minus sign to a plus sign.
b. Replacing the number being subtracted with its opposite.

STEP 2 Add the resulting signed numbers as before.
In symbols,

$$a - b = a + (-b)$$

This is the definition of subtraction.

Example 1 illustrates the use of this definition while subtracting.

● Example 1

Subtracting Signed Numbers

Subtraction   *Addition*

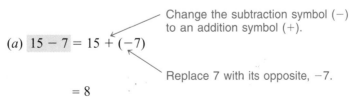

Change the subtraction symbol ($-$) to an addition symbol ($+$).

(*a*) $15 - 7 = 15 + (-7)$

Replace 7 with its opposite, -7.

$\qquad\qquad = 8$

(*b*) $9 - 12 = 9 + (-12) = -3$

(*c*) $-6 - 7 = -6 + (-7) = -13$

(d) $-\dfrac{3}{5} - \dfrac{7}{5} = -\dfrac{3}{5} + \left(-\dfrac{7}{5}\right) = \dfrac{-10}{5} = -2$

(e) $2.1 - 3.4 = 2.1 + (-3.4) = -1.3$

(f) Subtract 5 from -2. We write the statement as $-2 - 5$ and proceed as before:
$-2 - 5 = -2 + (-5) = -7$

● ● ●   **CHECK YOURSELF 1**

Subtract.

a. $18 - 7$ **b.** $5 - 13$ **c.** $-7 - 9$

d. $-\dfrac{5}{6} - \dfrac{7}{6}$ **e.** $-2 - 7$ **f.** $5.6 - 7.8$

The subtraction rule is used in the same way when the number being subtracted is negative. Change the subtraction to addition. Replace the negative number being subtracted with its opposite, which is positive. Example 2 will illustrate this principle.

● Example 2

Subtracting Signed Numbers

Subtraction   *Addition*

Change the subtraction to addition.

(a) $5 - (-2) = 5 + (+2) = 5 + 2 = 7$

Replace -2 with its opposite, $+2$ or 2.

(b) $7 - (-8) = 7 + (+8) = 7 + 8 = 15$

(c) $-9 - (-5) = -9 + 5 = -4$

(d) $-12.7 - (-3.7) = -12.7 + 3.7 = -9$

(e) $-\dfrac{3}{4} - \left(-\dfrac{7}{4}\right) = -\dfrac{3}{4} + \left(+\dfrac{7}{4}\right) = \dfrac{4}{4} = 1$

(f) Subtract -4 from -5. We write

$-5 - (-4) = -5 + 4 = -1$

● ● ● **CHECK YOURSELF 2**

Subtract.

a. $8 - (-2)$ **b.** $3 - (-10)$
c. $-7 - (-2)$ **d.** $-9.8 - (-5.8)$
e. $7 - (-7)$

As before, when parentheses are involved in an expression, you should do any operations inside parentheses as the first step. Example 3 illustrates this principle.

● Example 3

Subtracting Signed Numbers

Evaluate.   ⟍ Evaluate as the first step.

$-5 - 4 = -5 + (-4) = -9$

$$5 - \overbrace{(-5 - 4)}$$
$$= 5 - (-9) = 5 + 9 = 14$$

● ● ● **CHECK YOURSELF 3**

Evaluate.

$7 - (-9 + 6)$

Given a set of numbers, the **range** is the difference between the maximum and the minimum.

● Example 4

Finding the Range

Find the range for each set of numbers.

(*a*) $5, -2, -7, 9, 3$

Rewrite the set in ascending order. The maximum is 9, the minimum is -7. The range is the difference.

$$9 - (-7) = 9 + 7 = 16$$

The range is 16.

(*b*) $3, 8, -17, 12, -2$

Rewrite the set in ascending order. The maximum is 12. The minimum is -17. The range is $12 - (-17) = 29$.

● ● ● CHECK YOURSELF 4

Find the range for each set of numbers.

a. 2, −4, 7, −3, −1
b. −3, 4, −7, 5, 9, −4

Your scientific calculator can be used to do arithmetic with signed numbers. Before we look at an example, there are some keys on your calculator with which you should become familiar.

There are two similar keys you must find on the calculator. The first is used for subtraction ($\boxed{-}$) and is usually found in the right column of calculator keys. The second will "change the sign" of a number. It is usually a $\boxed{+/-}$ and is found on the bottom row.

We will now use these keys in our next example.

Some graphing calculators have a negative sign $\boxed{(-)}$ that goes in front of a negative number.

● Example 5

Subtracting Signed Numbers

Using your calculator, find the difference.

(*a*) −12.43 − 3.516

Enter the 12.43 and push the $\boxed{+/-}$ to make it negative. Then push $\boxed{-}$ 3.516 $\boxed{=}$. The result should be −15.946.

If you have a graphing calculator, the key sequence will be

$\boxed{(-)}$ 12.43 $\boxed{-}$ 3.516 $\boxed{=}$

(*b*) 23.56 − (−4.7)

The key sequence is

23.56 $\boxed{-}$ 4.7 $\boxed{+/-}$ $\boxed{=}$

The answer should be 28.26.

● ● ● CHECK YOURSELF 5

Use your calculator to find the difference.

a. −13.46 − 5.71   **b.** −3.575 − (−6.825)

● ● ● CHECK YOURSELF ANSWERS

1. **(a)** 11; **(b)** −8; **(c)** −16; **(d)** −2; **(e)** −9; **(f)** −2.2.   **2. (a)** 10; **(b)** 13; **(c)** −5;
(d) − 4; **(e)** 14.   **3.** 10.   **4. (a)** 7 − (−4) = 11; **(b)** 9 − (−7) = 16.
5. (a) −19.17; **(b)** 3.25.

Name

Section   Date

Subtract.

1. $21 - 13$

2. $36 - 22$

3. $82 - 45$

4. $103 - 56$

5. $\dfrac{15}{7} - \dfrac{8}{7}$

6. $\dfrac{17}{8} - \dfrac{9}{8}$

7. $7.9 - 5.4$

8. $11.7 - 4.5$

9. $8 - 10$

10. $14 - 19$

11. $24 - 45$

12. $136 - 352$

13. $\dfrac{7}{6} - \dfrac{19}{6}$

14. $\dfrac{5}{9} - \dfrac{32}{9}$

15. $7.8 - 11.6$

16. $14.3 - 25.5$

17. $-5 - 3$

18. $-15 - 8$

19. $-9 - 14$

20. $-8 - 12$

21. $-\dfrac{2}{5} - \dfrac{7}{10}$

22. $-\dfrac{5}{9} - \dfrac{7}{18}$

23. $-3.4 - 4.7$

24. $-8.1 - 7.6$

25. $3 - (-4)$

26. $6 - (-8)$

27. $5 - (-11)$

28. $7 - (-5)$

29. $7 - (-12)$

30. $3 - (-10)$

31. $\dfrac{3}{4} - \left(-\dfrac{3}{2}\right)$

32. $\dfrac{5}{6} - \left(-\dfrac{7}{6}\right)$

1. _____
2. _____
3. _____
4. _____
5. _____
6. _____
7. _____
8. _____
9. _____
10. _____
11. _____
12. _____
13. _____
14. _____
15. _____
16. _____
17. _____
18. _____
19. _____
20. _____
21. _____
22. _____
23. _____
24. _____
25. _____
26. _____
27. _____
28. _____
29. _____
30. _____
31. _____
32. _____

33. _____

34. _____

35. _____

36. _____

37. _____

38. _____

39. _____

40. _____

41. _____

42. _____

43. _____

44. _____

45. _____

46. _____

47. _____

48. _____

49. _____

50. _____

51. _____

52. _____

53. _____

54. _____

55. _____

56. _____

57. _____

58. _____

59. _____

60. _____

61. _____

62. _____

63. _____

64. _____

65. _____

66. _____

33. $\dfrac{6}{7} - \left(-\dfrac{5}{14}\right)$

34. $\dfrac{11}{16} - \left(-\dfrac{7}{8}\right)$

35. $8.3 - (-5.7)$

36. $6.5 - (-4.3)$

37. $8.9 - (-11.7)$

38. $14.5 - (-24.6)$

39. $-36 - (-24)$

40. $-28 - (-11)$

41. $-19 - (-27)$

42. $-11 - (-16)$

43. $\left(-\dfrac{3}{4}\right) - \left(-\dfrac{11}{4}\right)$

44. $-\dfrac{1}{2} - \left(-\dfrac{5}{8}\right)$

45. $-12.7 - (-5.7)$

46. $-5.6 - (-2.6)$

47. $-6.9 - (-10.1)$

48. $-3.4 - (-7.6)$

49. $-11 - (-11)$

50. $-15 - (-15)$

51. $0 - (-8)$

52. $0 - (-11)$

Do the indicated operations.

53. $4 - 9 - 5$

54. $7 - 10 - 6$

55. $8 + 9 - 15$

56. $8 + 12 - 7$

57. $-9 + 6 - 12$

58. $-11 + 7 - 6$

59. $-7 - (-5) - 2$

60. $-8 - (-2) - 3$

61. $-8 - (-3) + 7$

62. $-7 - (-5) + 9$

63. $-3 - 8 + 4$

64. $-12 - 6 + 14$

65. $-2 - (6 + 3)$

66. $-11 - (5 + 13)$

67. $-3 - 8 - 10$

68. $-2 - 9 - 7$

69. $10 - 6 - 3$

70. $15 - 6 - 4$

71. $-9 - (3 - 11)$

72. $-7 - (4 - 10)$

73. $15 - (12 - 7)$

74. $17 - (13 - 8)$

75. $7 - (3 - 5) + 2$

76. $4 - (5 - 7) + 3$

77. $8 - (6 - 2) - (-3)$

78. $12 - (8 - 3) - (-2)$

79. $-3 - (-2 - 5) - 8$

80. $-6 - (-1 - 4) - 9$

81. Subtract -8 from 5.

82. Subtract -7 from 3.

83. Subtract -7 from -2.

84. Subtract -9 from -2.

85. Subtract 12 from the sum of -6 and 3.

86. Subtract the sum of -9 and -3 from -2.

Evaluate using your calculator. Round your answer to the nearest tenth.

87. $-4.1623 - (-2.16897)$

88. $6.9786 - 2.3687 - (-3.1468)$

89. $-(-7.1689) - 2.5634 + (-4.1796) - 3.2876$

90. $8.6914 - (-3.7967) - 2.8678$

Evaluate each expression.

91. $|8 - (-7)|$

92. $|13 + (-6)|$

93. $|-35 - (-15)|$

94. $|18 - (-11)|$

95. $|18| - |-2|$

96. $|23| - |-6|$

97. $|-28 - (-34)|$

98. $|-64 - (-81)|$

67.

68.

69.

70.

71.

72.

73.

74.

75.

76.

77.

78.

79.

80.

81.

82.

83.

84.

85.

86.

87.

88.

89.

90.

91.

92.

93.

94.

95.

96.

97.

98.

99. $|-28| - |-34|$

100. $|-64| - |-81|$

Determine the range for each of the following sets.

101. 2, 7, 9, 15, 24

102. 4, 8, 11, 15, 27

103. $-4, -3, 2, 7, 9$

104. $-7, -2, 1, 8, 11$

105. $-8, -\frac{1}{2}, 2, \frac{3}{4}, \frac{7}{8}$

106. $-7, -\frac{1}{3}, 3, \frac{2}{3}, \frac{5}{6}$

107. $-3, -5, 6, 3, 2$

108. $-2, 7, -9, 3, 1$

109. $8, 9, -\frac{1}{2}, -\frac{3}{4}, 2$

110. $3, 11, -\frac{2}{3}, -\frac{1}{6}, 4$

Label the following as true or false.

111. $8 - 5 = 5 - 8$

112. $-16 - (-12) = -12 - (-16)$

113. $|-9| - |-10| = 9 - 10$

114. $|-12| - |-5| = 12 - 5$

Insert parentheses in the following expressions so that the statement is true.

115. $-9 - 5 - 6 = -8$

116. $-9 - 5 - 6 = -20$

117. Checking account. Omar's checking account was overdrawn by $72. He wrote another check for $23.50. How much was his checking account overdrawn after writing the check?

118. Personal finance. Angelo owed his sister $15. He later borrowed another $10. What positive or negative number represents his current financial condition?

119. Education. A local community college had a decrease in enrollment of 750 students in the fall of 1995. In the spring of 1996, there was another decrease of 425 students. What was the total decrease in enrollment for both semesters?

120. Temperature. At 7 AM, the temperature was $-15°$F. By 1 PM, the temperature had increased by $18°$ F. What was the temperature at 1 PM?

121. Education. Ezra's scores on five tests taken in a mathematics class were 87, 71, 95, 81, and 90. What was the range of his scores?

122. Science. The daily average temperatures in degrees Fahrenheit for a week in February were -1, 3, 5, -2, 4, 12, and 10. What was the range of temperatures for that week?

123. How long ago was the year—1250 BC? What year was 3,300 years ago? Make a number line and locate the following events, cultures, and objects on it. How long ago was each item in the list? Which two events are the closest to each other? You may want to learn more about some of the cultures in the list and the mathematics and science developed by that culture.

Inca culture in Peru—1400 AD
The *Ahmes Papyrus*, a mathematical text from Egypt—1650 BC
Babylonian arithmetic develops the use of a zero symbol—300 BC
First Olympic Games—776 BC
Pythagoras of Greece dies—580 BC
Mayans in Central America independently develop use of zero—500 AD
The *Chou Pei*, a mathematicas classic from China—1000 BC
The *Aryabhatiya*, a mathematics work from India—499 AD
Trigonometry arrives in Europe via the Arabs and India—1464 AD
Arabs receive algebra from Greek, Hindu and Babylonian sources and develop it into a new systematic form—850 AD
Development of calculus in Europe—1670 AD
Rise of abstract algebra—1860 AD
Growing importance of probability and development of statistics—1902 AD

124. What year does the third millennium AD begin? This is a concern of those party-goers who wish to have a grander-than-ever New Year's Eve celebration to celebrate the new millennium but are confused about what year is the beginning. Use your understanding of numbers and algebra to state your ideas about this and present a convincing argument.

125. Complete the following statement: "$3 - (-7)$ is the same as _____ because. . . ." Write a problem that might be answered by doing this subtraction.

126. Explain the difference between the two phrases: "a number subtracted from 5" and "a number less". Use algebra and English to explain the meaning of these phrases. Write other ways to express subtraction in English. Which ones are confusing?

Getting Ready for Section 2.4
[Section 2.2]

Add.

a. $(-1) + (-1) + (-1) + (-1)$ **b.** $3 + 3 + 3 + 3 + 3$

c. $9 + 9 + 9$ **d.** $(-10) + (-10) + (-10)$

e. $(-5) + (-5) + (-5) + (-5) + (-5)$ **f.** $(-8) + (-8) + (-8) + (-8)$

Answers

1. 8 **3.** 37 **5.** 1 **7.** 2.5 **9.** -2 **11.** -21 **13.** -2 **15.** -3.8

17. -8 **19.** -23 **21.** $-\dfrac{11}{10}$ **23.** -8.1 **25.** 7 **27.** 16 **29.** 19

31. $\dfrac{9}{4}$ **33.** $\dfrac{17}{14}$ **35.** 14 **37.** 20.6 **39.** -12 **41.** 8 **43.** 2 **45.** -7

47. 3.2 **49.** 0 **51.** 8 **53.** -10 **55.** 2 **57.** -15 **59.** -4

61. 2 **63.** -7 **65.** -11 **67.** -21 **69.** 1 **71.** -1 **73.** 10 **75.** 11

77. 7 **79.** -4 **81.** 13 **83.** 5 **85.** -15 **87.** -2.0 **89.** -2.9

91. 15 **93.** 20 **95.** 16 **97.** 6 **99.** -6 **101.** 22 **103.** 13 **105.** 10

107. 11 **109.** $\dfrac{39}{4}$ **111.** False **113.** True **115.** $-9 - (5 - 6) = -8$

117. \$95.50 **119.** 1175 **121.** 24 **a.** -4 **b.** 15 **c.** 27 **d.** -30

e. -25 **f.** -32

2.4 Multiplying Signed Numbers

2.4 OBJECTIVE

Find the product of two or more signed numbers

When you first considered multiplication in arithmetic, it was thought of as repeated addition. Let's see what our work with the addition of signed numbers can tell us about multiplication when signed numbers are involved. For example,

$$3 \cdot 4 = \underbrace{4 + 4 + 4} = 12$$

We interpret multiplication as repeated addition to find the product, 12.

Now, consider the product $(3)(-4)$:

$$(3)(-4) = (-4) + (-4) + (-4) = -12$$

Looking at this product suggests the first portion of our rule for multiplying signed numbers. The product of a positive number and a negative number is negative.

Multiplying Signed Numbers Case 1: Different Signs

The product of two numbers with different signs is negative.

To use this rule in multiplying two numbers with different signs, multiply their absolute values and attach a negative sign.

• Example 1

Multiplying Signed Numbers

Multiply.

(a) $(5)(-6) = -30$

The product is negative.

(b) $(-10)(10) = -100$

(c) $(8)(-12) = -96$

Multiply together numerators and then denominators and reduce.

(d) $\left(-\dfrac{3}{4}\right)\left(\dfrac{2}{5}\right) = -\dfrac{3}{10}$

● ● ● CHECK YOURSELF 1

Multiply.

a. $(-7)(5)$ **b.** $(-12)(9)$ **c.** $(-15)(8)$ **d.** $\left(-\dfrac{4}{7}\right)\left(\dfrac{14}{5}\right)$

The product of two negative numbers is harder to visualize. The following pattern may help you see how we can determine the sign of the product.

This number is decreasing by 1.

$$(3)(-2) = -6$$
$$(2)(-2) = -4$$
$$(1)(-2) = -2$$
$$(0)(-2) = 0$$
$$(-1)(-2) = 2$$
$$(-2)(-2) = 4$$

Do you see that the product is *increasing* by 2 each time?

What should the product $(-3)(-2)$ be? Continuing the pattern shown, we see that

$$(-3)(-2) = 6$$

This suggests that the product of two negative numbers is positive. That is the case. We can extend our multiplication rule.

If you would like a more detailed explanation, see the discussion at the end of this section.

Multiplying Signed Numbers Case 2: Same Sign

The product of two numbers with the same sign is positive.

● Example 2

Multiplying Signed Numbers

Multiply.

(a) $9 \cdot 7 = 63$ The product of two positive numbers (same sign, $+$) is positive.

(b) $(-8)(-5) = 40$ The product of two negative numbers (same sign, $-$) is positive.

(c) $\left(-\dfrac{1}{2}\right)\left(-\dfrac{1}{3}\right) = \dfrac{1}{6}$

● ● ● **CHECK YOURSELF 2**

Multiply.

a. $10 \cdot 12$ **b.** $(-8)(-9)$ **c.** $\left(-\dfrac{2}{3}\right)\left(-\dfrac{6}{7}\right)$

Two numbers, 0 and 1, have special properties in multiplication.

Multiplicative Identity Property

The product of 1 and any number is that number. In symbols,

$$a \cdot 1 = 1 \cdot a = a$$

The number 1 is called the **multiplicative identity** for this reason.

Multiplicative Property of Zero

The product of 0 and any number is 0. In symbols,

$$a \cdot 0 = 0 \cdot a = 0$$

• Example 3

Multiplying Signed Numbers

Find each product.

(a) $(1)(-7) = -7$

(b) $(15)(1) = 15$

(c) $(-7)(0) = 0$

(d) $0 \cdot 12 = 0$

(e) $\left(-\dfrac{4}{5}\right)(0) = 0$

● ● ● **CHECK YOURSELF 3**

Multiply.

a. $(-10)(1)$ **b.** $(0)(-17)$ **c.** $\left(\dfrac{5}{7}\right)(1)$ **d.** $(0)\left(\dfrac{3}{4}\right)$

To complete our discussion of the properties of multiplication, we state the following.

$\dfrac{1}{a}$ is called the **multiplicative inverse,** or the **reciprocal,** of a. The product of any nonzero number and its reciprocal is 1.

Multiplicative Inverse Property

For any number a, where $a \neq 0$, there is a number $\dfrac{1}{a}$ such that

$$a \cdot \dfrac{1}{a} = 1$$

Example 4 illustrates this property.

• Example 4

Multiplying Signed Numbers

(*a*) $3 \cdot \dfrac{1}{3} = 1$ The reciprocal of 3 is $\dfrac{1}{3}$.

(*b*) $-5\left(-\dfrac{1}{5}\right) = 1$ The reciprocal of -5 is $\dfrac{1}{-5}$ or $-\dfrac{1}{5}$.

(*c*) $\dfrac{2}{3} \cdot \dfrac{3}{2} = 1$ The reciprocal of $\dfrac{2}{3}$ is $\dfrac{1}{\frac{2}{3}}$, or $\dfrac{3}{2}$.

● ● ●   **CHECK YOURSELF 4**

Find the multiplicative inverse (or the reciprocal) of each of the following numbers.

a. 6   **b.** -4 **c.** $\dfrac{1}{4}$ **d.** $-\dfrac{3}{5}$

In addition to the properties just mentioned, we can extend the commutative and associative properties for multiplication to signed numbers. Our next example is an application of the associative property of multiplication.

• Example 5

Multiplying Signed Numbers

Find the following product.

$(-3)(2)(-7)$

Applying the associative property, we can group the first two factors to write

Once again, this "grouping" can be done mentally.

$[(-3)(2)](-7)$ Evaluate first.

$= (-6)(-7)$

$= 42$

● ● ●   **CHECK YOURSELF 5**

Find the product.

$(-5)(-8)(-2)$

When symbols of grouping, or more than one operator, are involved in an expression, we must again follow our rules for the order of operations. Consider the following example.

• Example 6

Multiplying Signed Numbers

Evaluate each expression.

(a) $7(-9 + 12)$ Evaluate inside the parentheses first.

$= 7(3) = 21$

(b) $(-8)(-7) - 40$ Multiply first, then subtract.

$= 56 - 40$

$= 16$

(c) $(-5)^2 - 3$ Evaluate the power first.

$= (-5)(-5) - 3$ Note that $(-5)^2 = (-5)(-5)$

$= 25 - 3$ $= 25$

$= 22$

(d) $-5^2 - 3$ Note that $-5^2 = -25$. The power applies *only* to the 5.

$= -25 - 3$

$= -28$

● ● ● **CHECK YOURSELF 6**

Evaluate each expression.

a. $8(-9 + 7)$ 　　　　　　　　　 **b.** $(-3)(-5) + 7$
c. $(-4)^2 - (-4)$ 　　　　　　　　 **d.** $-4^2 - (-4)$

Here is a more detailed explanation of why the product of two negative numbers is positive.

The Product of Two Negative Numbers

From our earlier work, we know that the sum of a number and its opposite is 0:

$5 + (-5) = 0$

Multiply both sides of the equation by -3:

$(-3)[5 + (-5)] = (-3)(0)$

Since the product of 0 and any number is 0, on the right we have 0.

$(-3)[5 + (-5)] = 0$

We use the distributive law on the left.

$(-3)(5) + (-3)(-5) = 0$

We know that $(-3)(5) = -15$, so the equation becomes

$$-15 + (-3)(-5) = 0$$

We now have a statement of the form

$$-15 + \square = 0$$

where $\square$ is the value of $(-3)(-5)$. We also know that $\square$ is the number that must be added to -15 to get 0, so $\square$ is the opposite of -15, or 15. This means that

$(-3)(-5) = 15$ The product is positive!

It doesn't matter what numbers we use in this argument. The resulting product of two negative numbers will always be positive.

● ● ●   **CHECK YOURSELF ANSWERS**

1. (a) -35; **(b)** -108; **(c)** -120; **(d)** $-\dfrac{8}{5}$.   **2. (a)** 120; **(b)** 72; **(c)** $\dfrac{4}{7}$.

3. (a) -10; **(b)** 0; **(c)** $\dfrac{5}{7}$; **(d)** 0.   **4. (a)** $\dfrac{1}{6}$; **(b)** $-\dfrac{1}{4}$; **(c)** 4; **(d)** $-\dfrac{5}{3}$.

5. -80.   **6. (a)** -16; **(b)** 22; **(c)** 20; **(d)** -12.

2.4 Exercises

Name

Section   Date

Multiply.

1. $4 \cdot 10$

2. $3 \cdot 14$

3. $(5)(-12)$

4. $(10)(-2)$

5. $(-8)(9)$

6. $(-12)(3)$

7. $(4)\left(-\dfrac{3}{2}\right)$

8. $(9)\left(-\dfrac{2}{3}\right)$

9. $\left(-\dfrac{1}{4}\right)(8)$

10. $\left(-\dfrac{3}{2}\right)(4)$

11. $(3.25)(-4)$

12. $(5.4)(-5)$

13. $(-8)(-7)$

14. $(-9)(-8)$

15. $(-5)(-12)$

16. $(-7)(-3)$

17. $(-9)\left(-\dfrac{2}{3}\right)$

18. $(-6)\left(-\dfrac{3}{2}\right)$

19. $(-1.25)(-12)$

20. $(-1.5)(-20)$

21. $(0)(-18)$

22. $(-17)(0)$

23. $(15)(0)$

24. $(0)(25)$

25. $\left(-\dfrac{11}{12}\right)(0)$

26. $\left(-\dfrac{8}{9}\right)(0)$

27. $(-3.57)(0)$

28. $(-2.37)(0)$

29. $\left(-\dfrac{3}{2}\right)\left(-\dfrac{2}{3}\right)$

30. $\left(-\dfrac{4}{5}\right)\left(-\dfrac{5}{4}\right)$

31. $\left(\dfrac{4}{7}\right)\left(-\dfrac{7}{4}\right)$

32. $\left(\dfrac{8}{9}\right)\left(-\dfrac{9}{8}\right)$

1.	
2.	
3.	
4.	
5.	
6.	
7.	
8.	
9.	
10.	
11.	
12.	
13.	
14.	
15.	
16.	
17.	
18.	
19.	
20.	
21.	
22.	
23.	
24.	
25.	
26.	
27.	
28.	
29.	
30.	
31.	
32.	

33. $(-5)(3)(-2)$

34. $(-4)(2)(-3)$

35. $(8)(-3)(7)$

36. $(13)(-2)(6)$

37. $(-3)(-5)(-2)$

38. $(-6)(4)(-3)$

39. $(-5)(-4)(2)$

40. $(-5)(2)(-6)$

41. $\left(-\dfrac{1}{3}\right)\left(\dfrac{6}{5}\right)(-10)$

42. $\left(-\dfrac{1}{2}\right)\left(\dfrac{4}{3}\right)(-6)$

43. $(-9)(-12)(0)$

44. $(-13)(0)(-7)$

Do the indicated operations. Remember the rules for the order of operations.

45. $5(7-2)$

46. $7(8-5)$

47. $2(5-8)$

48. $6(14-16)$

49. $-3(9-7)$

50. $-6(12-9)$

51. $-3(-2-5)$

52. $-2(-7-3)$

53. $(-2)(3)-5$

54. $(-6)(8)-27$

55. $4(-7)-5$

56. $(-3)(-9)-11$

57. $(-5)(-2)-12$

58. $(-7)(-3)-25$

59. $(3)(-7)+20$

60. $(2)(-6)+8$

61. $-4+(-3)(6)$

62. $-5+(-2)(3)$

63. $7-(-4)(-2)$

64. $9-(-2)(-7)$

65. $-6-(-4)(-3)$

66. $-5-(-5)(-2)$

67. $-12-(-6)(5)$

68. $-10-(-2)(7)$

69. $(-2)(-7) + (2)(-3)$

70. $(-3)(-6) + (4)(-2)$

71. $(-7)(3) - (-2)(-8)$

72. $(-5)(2) - (-3)(-4)$

73. $(-7)^2 - 17$

74. $(-6)^2 - 20$

75. $(-5)^2 + 18$

76. $(-2)^2 + 10$

77. $-6^2 - 4$

78. $-5^2 - 3$

79. $(-4)^2 - (-2)(-5)$

80. $(-3)^3 - (-8)(-2)$

81. $(-8)^2 - 5^2$

82. $(-6)^2 - 4^2$

83. $(-6)^2 - (-3)^2$

84. $(-8)^2 - (-4)^2$

85. $-8^2 - 5^2$

86. $-6^2 - 3^2$

87. $-8^2 - (-5)^2$

88. $-9^2 - (-6)^2$

89. $-11^2 - (-11)^2$

90. $-5^2 - (-5)^2$

91. $(-8)^2 - 8^2$

92. $(-11)^2 - 11^2$

In each of the following, place parentheses in the proper location so that the statement is true.

93. $-8 - 4 = -4$

94. $-6 - 3 \cdot 2 = -18$

Evaluate using your calculator. Round your answers to the nearest tenth.

95. $(-3.126)(4.159) - (-2.893)$

96. $(-5.23)(-3.689) - (-2.168)(3.145)$

97. $-(-3.1415)(4.263) - (-2.8976)^2(6.15)$

98. $(-5.7963)(-3.89) - (1.769)(2.534)$

99. Basketball. You score 23 points a game for 11 straight games. What is the total number of points that you scored?

#	
69.	
70.	
71.	
72.	
73.	
74.	
75.	
76.	
77.	
78.	
79.	
80.	
81.	
82.	
83.	
84.	
85.	
86.	
87.	
88.	
89.	
90.	
91.	
92.	
93.	
94.	
95.	
96.	
97.	
98.	
99.	

100. _____

101. _____

102. _____

103. _____

104. _____

105. _____

106. _____

a. _____

b. _____

c. _____

d. _____

e. _____

f. _____

g. _____

h. _____

100. Gambling. In Atlantic City, Nick played the slot machines for 12 hours. He lost $45 an hour. Use signed numbers to represent the change in Nick's financial status at the end of the 12 hours.

101. Stocks. Suppose you own 35 shares of stock. If the price increases $1.25 per share, how much money have you made?

102. Checking account. Your bank charges a flat service charge of $3.50 per month on your checking account. You have had the account for 3 years. How much have you paid in service charges?

103. Temperature. The temperature is −6°F at 5:00 in the evening. If the temperature drops 2°F every hour, what is the temperature at 1:00 a.m.?

104. Savings account. Kim's bank charges $2 per month if her savings account has no activity. If Kim's balance is $35 on Jan. 1 and she deposits $10 on Feb. 15, $15 on June 15, and $20 on Dec. 20, what is her balance on Dec. 31?

105. College expenses. A student has saved $12,000 to attend an 18-month accelerated bachelor's degree program. If his estimated expenses are $824.50 per month, how much additional money must he save?

106. There is a saying that "Two wrongs don't make a right," but in algebra we say "Two negatives make a positive." Is this always true? Investigate what happens with "two negatives" in addition, subtraction, multiplication, and division. Write a description of when the statement "Two negatives make a positive" is true and when it isn't.

● Getting Ready for Section 2.5

Simplify each of the following.

a. $\dfrac{25}{5}$ **b.** $\dfrac{49}{7}$ **c.** $\dfrac{66}{11}$ **d.** $\dfrac{84}{12}$

e. $\dfrac{90}{15}$ **f.** $\dfrac{144}{24}$ **g.** $\dfrac{81}{18}$ **h.** $\dfrac{80}{15}$

Answers

1. 40   **3.** −60   **5.** −72   **7.** −6   **9.** −2   **11.** −13   **13.** 56   **15.** 60

17. 6   **19.** 15   **21.** 0   **23.** 0   **25.** 0   **27.** 0   **29.** 1   **31.** −1   **33.** 30

35. −168   **37.** −30   **39.** 40   **41.** 4   **43.** 0   **45.** 25   **47.** −6

49. −6   **51.** 21   **53.** −11   **55.** −33   **57.** −2   **59.** −1   **61.** −22

63. −1   **65.** −18   **67.** 18   **69.** 8   **71.** −37   **73.** 32   **75.** 43

77. −40   **79.** 6   **81.** 39   **83.** 27   **85.** −89   **87.** −89   **89.** −242

91. 0   **93.** −(8 − 4) = −4   **95.** −10.1   **97.** −38.2   **99.** 253 points

101. $43.75   **103.** −22°F   **105.** $2841   **a.** 5   **b.** 7   **c.** 6   **d.** 7

e. 6   **f.** 6   **g.** $\dfrac{9}{2}$ **h.** $\dfrac{16}{3}$

Dividing Signed Numbers

2.5 OBJECTIVE

1. Find the quotient of two signed numbers

You know from your work in arithmetic that multiplication and division are related operations. We can use that fact, and our work of the last section, to determine rules for the division of signed numbers. Every division problem can be stated as an equivalent multiplication problem. For instance,

$$\frac{15}{5} = 3 \qquad \text{since} \qquad 15 = 5 \cdot 3$$

$$\frac{-24}{6} = -4 \qquad \text{since} \qquad -24 = (6)(-4)$$

$$\frac{-30}{-5} = 6 \qquad \text{since} \qquad -30 = (-5)(6)$$

The examples above illustrate that because the two operations are related, the rule of signs that we stated in the last section for multiplication is also true for division.

Dividing Signed Numbers

1. The quotient of two numbers with different signs is negative.
2. The quotient of two numbers with the same sign is positive.

Again, the rule is easy to use. To divide two signed numbers, divide their absolute values. Then attach the proper sign according to the rule above.

• Example 1

Dividing Signed Numbers

Divide.

(a)   Positive $\longrightarrow$ $\dfrac{28}{7} = 4$ $\longleftarrow$ Positive
      Positive $\longrightarrow$

(b)   Negative $\longrightarrow$ $\dfrac{-36}{-4} = 9$ $\longleftarrow$ Positive
      Negative $\longrightarrow$

(c)   Negative $\longrightarrow$ $\dfrac{-42}{7} = -6$ $\longleftarrow$ Negative
      Positive $\longrightarrow$

(d)   Positive $\longrightarrow$ $\dfrac{75}{-3} = -25$ $\longleftarrow$ Negative
      Negative $\longrightarrow$

(e)   Positive $\longrightarrow$ $\dfrac{15.2}{-3.8} = -4$ $\longleftarrow$ Negative
      Negative $\longrightarrow$

● ● ● **CHECK YOURSELF 1**

Divide.

a. $\dfrac{-55}{11}$ **b.** $\dfrac{80}{20}$ **c.** $\dfrac{-48}{-8}$ **d.** $\dfrac{144}{-12}$ **e.** $\dfrac{-13.5}{-2.7}$

You should be very careful when 0 is involved in a division problem. Remember that 0 divided by any nonzero number is just 0. Recall that

$$\frac{0}{-7} = 0 \quad \text{because} \quad 0 = (-7)(0)$$

However, if zero is the *divisor,* we have a special problem. Consider

$$\frac{9}{0} = ?$$

This means that $9 = 0 \cdot ?$.

Can 0 times a number ever be 9? No, so there is no solution.

Since $\dfrac{9}{0}$ cannot be replaced by any number, we agree that *division by 0 is not allowed.* We say that

Division by 0 is undefined.

● **Example 2**

Dividing Signed Numbers

Divide, if possible.

(*a*) $\dfrac{7}{0}$ is undefined.

(*b*) $\dfrac{-9}{0}$ is undefined.

(*c*) $\dfrac{0}{5} = 0$

(*d*) $\dfrac{0}{-8} = 0$

Note: The expression $\dfrac{0}{0}$ is called an **indeterminate form.** You will learn more about this in later mathematics classes.

● ● ● CHECK YOURSELF 2

Divide if possible.

a. $\dfrac{0}{3}$ **b.** $\dfrac{5}{0}$ **c.** $\dfrac{-7}{0}$ **d.** $\dfrac{0}{-9}$

Recall that the fraction bar serves as a grouping symbol. This means that all operations in the numerator and denominator should be performed separately. Then the division is done as the last step. Example 3 illustrates this property.

● Example 3

Dividing Signed Numbers

Evaluate each expression.

(a) $\dfrac{(-6)(-7)}{3} = \dfrac{42}{3} = 14$ Multiply in the numerator, then divide.

(b) $\dfrac{3 + (-12)}{3} = \dfrac{-9}{3} = -3$ Add in the numerator, then divide.

(c) $\dfrac{-4 + (2)(-6)}{-6 - 2} = \dfrac{-4 + (-12)}{-6 - 2}$ Multiply in the numerator. Then add in the numerator and subtract in the denominator.

$\qquad\qquad = \dfrac{-16}{-8} = 2$ Divide as the last step.

● ● ● CHECK YOURSELF 3

Evaluate each expression.

a. $\dfrac{-4 + (-8)}{6}$ **b.** $\dfrac{3 - (2)(-6)}{-5}$ **c.** $\dfrac{(-2)(-4) - (-6)(-5)}{(-4)(11)}$

Evaluating fractions with a calculator poses a special problem. Example 4 illustrates this problem.

● Example 4

Using a Calculator to Divide

Use your scientific calculator to evaluate each fraction.

(a) $\dfrac{4}{2 - 3}$

As you can see, the correct answer should be -4. To get this answer with your calculator, you must place the denominator in parentheses. The key stroke sequence will be

$$4 \boxed{\div} \boxed{(} \boxed{2} \boxed{-} \boxed{3} \boxed{)} \boxed{=}$$

(b) $\dfrac{-7 - 7}{3 - 10}$

In this problem, the correct answer is 2. This can be found on your calculator by placing the numerator in parentheses and then placing the denominator in parentheses. The key stroke sequence will be

$$\boxed{(} \boxed{7} \boxed{+/-} \boxed{-} \boxed{7} \boxed{)} \boxed{\div} \boxed{(} \boxed{3} \boxed{-} \boxed{10} \boxed{)} \boxed{=}$$

When evaluating a fraction with a calculator, it is safest to use parentheses in both the numerator and the denominator.

● ● ● **CHECK YOURSELF 4**

Evaluate using your calculator.

a. $\dfrac{-8}{5 - 7}$ **b.** $\dfrac{-3 - 2}{-13 + 23}$

● ● ● **CHECK YOURSELF ANSWERS**

1. **(a)** -5; **(b)** 4; **(c)** 6; **(d)** -12; **(e)** 5.
2. **(a)** 0; **(b)** undefined; **(c)** undefined; **(d)** 0.
3. **(a)** -2; **(b)** -3; **(c)** $\dfrac{1}{2}$. 4. **(a)** 4; **(b)** -0.5.

A N S W E R S

1. _____

2. _____

3. _____

4. _____

5. _____

6. _____

7. _____

8. _____

9. _____

10. _____

11. _____

12. _____

13. _____

14. _____

15. _____

16. _____

17. _____

18. _____

19. _____

20. _____

21. _____

22. _____

23. _____

24. _____

Divide.

1. $\dfrac{-20}{-4}$

2. $\dfrac{70}{14}$

3. $\dfrac{48}{6}$

4. $\dfrac{-24}{8}$

5. $\dfrac{50}{-5}$

6. $\dfrac{-32}{-8}$

7. $\dfrac{-52}{4}$

8. $\dfrac{56}{-7}$

9. $\dfrac{-75}{-3}$

10. $\dfrac{-60}{15}$

11. $\dfrac{0}{-8}$

12. $\dfrac{-125}{-25}$

13. $\dfrac{-9}{-1}$

14. $\dfrac{-10}{0}$

15. $\dfrac{-96}{-8}$

16. $\dfrac{-20}{2}$

17. $\dfrac{18}{0}$

18. $\dfrac{0}{8}$

19. $\dfrac{-17}{1}$

20. $\dfrac{-27}{-1}$

21. $\dfrac{-144}{-16}$

22. $\dfrac{-150}{6}$

23. $\dfrac{-29.4}{4.9}$

24. $\dfrac{-25.9}{-3.7}$

25. _____

26. _____

27. _____

28. _____

29. _____

30. _____

31. _____

32. _____

33. _____

34. _____

35. _____

36. _____

37. _____

38. _____

39. _____

40. _____

41. _____

42. _____

43. _____

44. _____

45. _____

46. _____

47. _____

48. _____

49. _____

50. _____

25. $\dfrac{-8}{32}$ **26.** $\dfrac{-6}{-30}$

27. $\dfrac{24}{-16}$ **28.** $\dfrac{-25}{10}$

29. $\dfrac{-28}{-42}$ **30.** $\dfrac{-125}{-75}$

Perform the indicated operations.

31. $\dfrac{(-6)(-3)}{2}$ **32.** $\dfrac{(-9)(5)}{-3}$

33. $\dfrac{(-8)(2)}{-4}$ **34.** $\dfrac{(7)(-8)}{-14}$

35. $\dfrac{24}{-4-8}$ **36.** $\dfrac{36}{-7+3}$

37. $\dfrac{-12-12}{-3}$ **38.** $\dfrac{-14-4}{-6}$

39. $\dfrac{55-19}{-12-6}$ **40.** $\dfrac{-11-7}{-14+8}$

41. $\dfrac{7-5}{2-2}$ **42.** $\dfrac{10-6}{4-4}$

43. $\dfrac{-15-(-3)}{3-(-1)}$ **44.** $\dfrac{21-(-4)}{-3-2}$

45. $\dfrac{(-9)(-6)-10}{18-(-4)}$ **46.** $\dfrac{4-2(-6)}{-14-(-6)}$

47. $\dfrac{(-3)(-6)-(-4)(8)}{6-(-4)}$ **48.** $\dfrac{(5)(-2)-(-4)(-5)}{-4-2}$

49. $\dfrac{2(-5)+4(6-8)}{3(-4+2)}$ **50.** $\dfrac{(-3)(-5)-3(5-8)}{4(-8+6)}$

51. $\dfrac{(-5)^2 - (-4)(5)}{3(5 - 8)}$

52. $\dfrac{(-3)^2 - (-9)(-5)}{4 - (-2)}$

Insert parentheses in each of the following so that the statement is true.

53. $8 \div 4 \cdot 2 = 1$

54. $6^2 \cdot \dfrac{1}{6} - 5 \cdot 3 = 3$

55. $|-8| - (-8) \div (-4) = -4$

56. $-5^2 \cdot (-2) \div (-10) = 5$

Label each of the following as true or false.

57. $12 \div 3^2 = 12 \div 3 \cdot 3$

58. $64 \div 4^3 = 64 \div 4^2 \cdot 4$

59. $8 \div 4 \cdot 2 = 8 \div 2 \cdot 4$

60. $(-18) \div (-3) \cdot (-2) = (-18) \cdot (-3) \div (-2)$

61. Dieting. A woman lost 42 pounds (lb). If she lost 3 lb each week, how long has she been dieting?

62. Mowing lawns. Patrick worked all day mowing lawns and was paid $9 per hour. If he had $125 at the end of a 9-hour day, how much did he have before he started working?

63. Unit pricing. A 4.5-lb can of food costs $8.91. What is the cost per pound?

64. Investment. Suppose that you and your two brothers bought equal shares of an investment for a total of $20,000 and sold it later for $16,232. How much did each person lose?

65. Temperature. Suppose that the temperature outside is dropping at a constant rate. At noon, the temperature is 70°F and it drops to 58°F at 5:00 p.m. How much did the temperature change each hour?

66. Test tube count. A chemist has 84 ounces (oz) of a solution. He pours the solution into test tubes. Each test tube holds $\dfrac{2}{3}$ oz. How many test tubes can he fill?

67. Some animal ecologists in Minnesota are planning to reintroduce a group of animals into a wilderness area. The animals, a mammal on the endangered species list, will be released into an area where they once prospered and where there is an abundant food supply. But, the animals will face predators. The ecologists expect the number of mammals to grow about 25 percent each year but that 30 of the animals will die from attacks by predators and hunters.

ANSWERS

51. _____

52. _____

53. _____

54. _____

55. _____

56 _____

57. _____

58. _____

59. _____

60. _____

61. _____

62. _____

63. _____

64. _____

65. _____

66. _____

67. _____

The ecologists need to decide how many animals they should release in order to establish a stable population. Work with other students to try several beginning populations and follow the numbers through 8 years. Is there a number of animals that will lead to a stable population? Write a letter to the editor of your local newspaper explaining how to decide what number of animals to release. Include a formula for the number of animals next year based on the number this year. Begin by filling out this table to track the number of animals living each year after the release:

No. Initially Released	Year							
	1	2	3	4	5	6	7	8
20	+ ___ – ___							
	= _____							
100	+ ___ – ___							
	= _____							
200	+ ___ – ___							
	= _____							

Evaluate using your calculator. Round your answer to the nearest tenth. (*Hint:* Be careful that the entire numerator is in one set of parentheses and the entire denominator is another set of parentheses.)

68. $\dfrac{3.16 + (-2.15)}{1.25}$

69. $\dfrac{(-4.95) + (-5.63)}{5.29 \cdot .78125}$

70. $\dfrac{(3.685) \cdot (-2.169) - (-4.258) \cdot (1.639)}{1.725 \cdot (3.168 - 4.751)}$

71. $\dfrac{(-4.125) \cdot (-3.615) - (-2.158) \cdot (-1.639)}{2.84 \cdot 5.76 - 3.98}$

● Getting Ready for Section 2.6

Evaluate each expression if $x = 2$, $y = 3$, and $z = 5$.

a. $5x + 3z$ **b.** $y^2 - 4x$ **c.** $3x^2 - 2z$ **d.** $x^3 + 2z^2$

e. $\dfrac{2x + 4z}{2y}$ **f.** $\dfrac{x(z - y)}{y + z}$ **g.** $\dfrac{2(x + y + 2z)}{y^2 - 2x}$ **h.** $\dfrac{3x - 2y + 5z}{3y - 2x}$

Answers

1. 5 **3.** 8 **5.** −10 **7.** −13 **9.** 25 **11.** 0 **13.** 9 **15.** 12

17. Undefined **19.** −17 **21.** 9 **23.** −6 **25.** $-\dfrac{1}{4}$ **27.** $-\dfrac{3}{2}$ **29.** $\dfrac{2}{3}$

31. 9 **33.** 4 **35.** −2 **37.** 8 **39.** −2 **41.** Undefined **43.** −3

45. 2 **47.** 5 **49.** 3 **51.** −5 **53.** $8 \div (4 \cdot 2) = 1$

55. $(|-8| - (-8)) \div (-4) = -4$ **57.** False **59.** False **61.** 14 weeks

63. $1.98 **65.** 2.4°F **69.** −2.6 **71.** 0.9 **a.** 25 **b.** 1 **c.** 2 **d.** 58

e. 4 **f.** $\dfrac{1}{2}$ **g.** 6 **h.** 5

Evaluating Algebraic Expressions; Summing a Set of Numbers

2.6 OBJECTIVES

1. Evaluate algebraic expressions given any signed-number values for the variables
2. Find the sum of a set of signed numbers

In applying algebra to problem solving, you will often want to find the value of an algebraic expression when you know certain values for the letters (or variables) in the expression. As we pointed out earlier, finding the value of an expression is called *evaluating the expression* and uses the following steps.

To Evaluate an Algebraic Expression

STEP 1 Replace each variable by the given number value.

STEP 2 Do the necessary arithmetic operations, following the rules for order of operation.

● Example 1

Evaluating Algebraic Expressions

Suppose that $a = 5$ and $b = 7$.

(a) To evaluate $a + b$, we replace a with 5 and b with 7.

$a + b = 5 + 7 = 12$

(b) To evaluate $3ab$, we again replace a with 5 and b with 7.

$3ab = 3 \cdot 5 \cdot 7 = 105$

● ● ● CHECK YOURSELF 1

If $x = 6$ and $y = 7$, evaluate.

a. $y - x$ **b.** $5xy$

We are now ready to evaluate algebraic expressions that require following the rules for the order of operations.

● Example 2

Evaluating Algebraic Expressions

CAUTION

This is different from
$(3c)^2 = (3 \cdot 4)^2$
$= 12^2 = 144$

Evaluate the following expressions if $a = 2$, $b = 3$, $c = 4$, and $d = 5$.

(a) $5a + 7b = 5 \cdot 2 + 7 \cdot 3$ Multiply first.

$\qquad\qquad = 10 + 21 = 31$ Then add.

(b) $3c^2 = 3 \cdot 4^2$ Evaluate the power.

$\qquad\quad = 3 \cdot 16 = 48$ Then multiply.

(c) $7(c + d) = 7(4 + 5)$ Add inside the parentheses.

$\quad\quad\quad\ = 7 \cdot 9 = 63$

(d) $5a^4 - 2d^2 = 5 \cdot 2^4 - 2 \cdot 5^2$ Evaluate the powers.

$\quad\quad\quad\quad = 5 \cdot 16 - 2 \cdot 25$ Multiply.

$\quad\quad\quad\quad = 80 - 50 = 30$ Subtract.

● ● ● **CHECK YOURSELF 2**

If $x = 3$, $y = 2$, $z = 4$, and $w = 5$, evaluate the following expressions.

a. $4x^2 + 2$ **b.** $5(z + w)$ **c.** $7(z^2 - y^2)$

To evaluate algebraic expressions when a fraction bar is used, do the following: Start by doing all the work in the numerator, then do the work in the denominator. Divide the numerator by the denominator as the last step.

● Example 3

Evaluating Algebraic Expressions

If $p = 2$, $q = 3$, and $r = 4$, evaluate:

(a) $\dfrac{8p}{r}$

Replace p with 2 and r with 4.

As we mentioned in Section 1.2, the fraction bar is a grouping symbol, like parenthesis. Work first in the numerator and then in the denominator.

$\dfrac{8p}{r} = \dfrac{8 \cdot 2}{4} = \dfrac{16}{4} = 4$ Divide as the last step.

(b) $\dfrac{7q + r}{p + q} = \dfrac{7 \cdot 3 + 4}{2 + 3}$ Now evaluate the top and bottom separately.

$\quad\quad\quad = \dfrac{21 + 4}{2 + 3} = \dfrac{25}{5} = 5$

● ● ● **CHECK YOURSELF 3**

Evaluate the following if $c = 5$, $d = 8$, and $e = 3$.

a. $\dfrac{6c}{e}$ **b.** $\dfrac{4d + e}{c}$ **c.** $\dfrac{10d - e}{d + e}$

Example 4 shows how a scientific calculator can be used to evaluate algebraic expressions.

● Example 4

Using a Calculator to Evaluate Expressions

Use a scientific calculator to evaluate the following expressions.

(a) $\dfrac{4x + y}{z}$ if $x = 2$, $y = 1$, and $z = 3$

Replace x with 2, y with 1, and z with 3:

$$\frac{4x + y}{z} = \frac{4 \cdot 2 + 1}{3}$$

Now, use the following keystrokes:

(4 × 2 + 1) ÷ 3 =

The display will read 3.

(b) $\dfrac{7x - y}{3z - x}$ if $x = 2$, $y = 6$, and $z = 2$

$$\frac{7x - y}{3z - x} = \frac{7 \cdot 2 - 6}{3 \cdot 2 - 2}$$

Use the following keystrokes:

(7 × 2 − 6) ÷ (3 × 2 − 2) =

The display will read 2.

● ● ● CHECK YOURSELF 4

Use a scientific calculator to evaluate the following if $x = 2$, $y = 6$, and $z = 5$.

a. $\dfrac{2x + y}{z}$

b. $\dfrac{4y - 2z}{x}$

● Example 5

Evaluating Expressions

Evaluate $5a + 4b$ if $a = -2$ and $b = 3$.

Remember the rules for the order of operations. Multiply first, then add.

Replace a with -2 and b with 3.

$$5a + 4b = 5(-2) + 4(3)$$
$$= -10 + 12$$
$$= 2$$

● ● ● CHECK YOURSELF 5

Evaluate $3x + 5y$ if $x = -2$ and $y = -5$.

We follow the same rules no matter how many variables are in the expression.

• Example 6

Evaluating Expressions

Evaluate the following expressions if $a = -4$, $b = 2$, $c = -5$, and $d = 6$.

This becomes $-(-20)$, or $+20$.

(a) $7a - 4c = 7(-4) - 4(-5)$

$= -28 + 20$

$= -8$

CAUTION

When a squared variable is replaced by a negative number, square the negative.

$(-5)^2 = (-5)(-5) = 25$

The exponent applies to -5!

$-5^2 = -(5 \cdot 5) = -25$

The exponent applies only to 5!

Evaluate the power first, then multiply by 7.

(b) $7c^2 = 7(-5)^2 = 7 \cdot 25$

$= 175$

(c) $b^2 - 4ac = 2^2 - 4(-4)(-5)$

$= 4 - 4(-4)(-5)$

$= 4 - 80$

$= -76$

Add inside the parentheses first.

(d) $b(a + d) = 2(-4 + 6)$

$= 2(2)$

$= 4$

● ● ● CHECK YOURSELF 6

Evaluate if $p = -4$, $q = 3$, and $r = -2$.

a. $5p - 3r$ **b.** $2p^2 + q$ **c.** $p(q + r)$

d. $-q^2$ **e.** $(-q)^2$

If an expression involves a fraction, remember that the fraction bar is a grouping symbol. This means that you should do the required operations first in the numerator and then the denominator. Divide as the last step.

• Example 7

Evaluating Expressions

Evaluate the following expressions if $x = 4$, $y = -5$, $z = 2$, and $w = -3$.

(a) $\dfrac{z - 2y}{x} = \dfrac{2 - 2(-5)}{4} = \dfrac{2 + 10}{4}$

$= \dfrac{12}{4} = 3$

(b) $\dfrac{3x - w}{2x + w} = \dfrac{3(4) - (-3)}{2(4) + (-3)} = \dfrac{12 + 3}{8 + (-3)}$

$\quad\quad\quad = \dfrac{15}{5} = 3$

● ● ● **CHECK YOURSELF 7**

Evaluate if $m = -6$, $n = 4$, and $p = -3$.

a. $\dfrac{m + 3n}{p}$ **b.** $\dfrac{4m + n}{m + 4n}$

When an expression is evaluated by a calculator, the same order-of-operations that we introduced in Section 1.2 is followed.

	Algebraic Notation	Calculator Notation
Addition	$6 + 2$	$6 + 2$
Subtraction	$4 - 8$	$4 - 8$
Multiplication	$(3)(-5)$	$3 \times (-5)$
Division	$\dfrac{8}{6}$	$8/6$
Exponential	3^4	$3{\wedge}4$ or $3y^x4$

The use of this notation is illustrated in Example 8.

● Example 8

Evaluating Expressions

Evaluate each of the following computer expressions if $A = 2.3$, $B = 8.4$, and $C = 4.5$. Round your answer to the nearest tenth.

(a) $A + B * (-C)$

Letting A, B, and C take on the given values, we have

$2.3 + 8.4 \times (-4.5) = -35.5$

(b) $-B + (-A) \times C{\wedge}2$

Substituting the given values, we have

$-8.4 + (-2.3) \times (4.5)^2 = -38.175$

Rounded to the nearest tenth gives us -38.2

● ● ●   CHECK YOURSELF 8

Evaluate each of the following expressions where, A = -2, B = 3, and C = 5.

a. $A + B \times (-C)$ **b.** $C + B \times A^3$ **c.** $4 \times (B - C)/(2 \times A)$

In many applications, you will need to find the sum of a set of numbers that you are working with. In mathematics, the shorthand symbol for "sum of" is the Greek letter Σ (capital sigma, the "S" of the Greek alphabet). The expression Σx, where x refers to all the numbers in a given set, means the sum of all the numbers in that set.

● Example 9

Summing a Set

Find Σx for the following set of numbers:

$-2, -6, 3, 5, -4$

$$\begin{aligned} \Sigma x &= -2 + (-6) + 3 + 5 + (-4) \\ &= (-8) + 3 + 5 + (-4) \\ &= (-8) + (8) + (-4) \\ &= -4 \end{aligned}$$

● ● ●   CHECK YOURSELF 9

Find Σx for each set of numbers.
a. $-3, 4, -7, -9, 8$ **b.** $-2, 6, -5, -3, 4, 7$

● ● ●   CHECK YOURSELF ANSWERS

1. (a) 1; **(b)** 210.   **2. (a)** 38; **(b)** 45; **(c)** 84.   **3. (a)** 10; **(b)** 7; **(c)** 7.
4. (a) 2; **(b)** 7.   **5.** -31.   **6. (a)** -14; **(b)** 35; **(c)** -4; **(d)** -9; **(e)** 9.
7. (a) -2; **(b)** -2.   **8. (a)** -17; **(b)** -19; **(c)** 2.   **9. (a)** -7; **(b)** 7.

2.6 Exercises

Name

Section   Date

Evaluate each of the expressions if $a = -2$, $b = 5$, $c = -4$, and $d = 6$.

1. $3c - 2b$ **2.** $4c - 2b$

3. $8b + 2c$ **4.** $7a - 2c$

5. $-b^2 + b$ **6.** $(-b)^2 + b$

7. $3a^2$ **8.** $6c^2$

9. $c^2 - 2d$ **10.** $3a^2 + 4c$

11. $2a^2 + 3b^2$ **12.** $4b^2 - 2c^2$

13. $2(a + b)$ **14.** $5(b - c)$

15. $4(2a - d)$ **16.** $6(3c - d)$

17. $a(b + 3c)$ **18.** $c(3a - d)$

19. $\dfrac{6d}{c}$ **20.** $\dfrac{8b}{5c}$

21. $\dfrac{3d + 2c}{b}$ **22.** $\dfrac{2b + 3d}{2a}$

23. $\dfrac{2b - 3a}{c + 2d}$ **24.** $\dfrac{3d - 2b}{5a + d}$

25. $d^2 - b^2$ **26.** $c^2 - a^2$

27. $(d - b)^2$ **28.** $(c - a)^2$

29. $(d - b)(d + b)$ **30.** $(c - a)(c + a)$

31. $d^3 - b^3$ **32.** $c^3 + a^3$

99

ANSWERS
1.
2.
3.
4.
5.
6.
7.
8.
9.
10.
11.
12.
13.
14.
15.
16.
17.
18.
19.
20.
21.
22.
23.
24.
25.
26.
27.
28.
29.
30.
31.
32.

33. $(d - b)^3$

34. $(c + a)^3$

35. $(d - b)(d^2 + db + b^2)$

36. $(c + a)(c^2 - ac + a^2)$

37. $b^2 + a^2$

38. $d^2 - a^2$

39. $(b + a)^2$

40. $(d - a)^2$

41. $a^2 + 2ad + d^2$

42. $b^2 - 2bc + c^2$

Use your calculator to evaluate each expression if $x = -2.34$, $y = -3.14$, and $z = 4.12$. Round your answer to the nearest tenth.

43. $x + yz$

44. $y - 2z$

45. $x^2 - z^2$

46. $x^2 + y^2$

47. $\dfrac{xy}{z - x}$

48. $\dfrac{y^2}{zy}$

49. $\dfrac{2x + y}{2x + z}$

50. $\dfrac{x^2 y^2}{xz}$

For the following data sets, evaluate Σx.

51. 1, 2, 3, 7, 8, 9, 11

52. 2, 4, 5, 6, 10, 11, 12

53. -5, -3, -1, 2, 3, 4, 8

54. -4, -2, -1, 5, 7, 8, 10

55. 3, 2, -1, -4, -3, 8, 6

56. 3, -4, 2, -1, 2, -7, 9

57. $-\dfrac{1}{2}$, $-\dfrac{3}{4}$, 2, 3, $\dfrac{1}{4}$, $\dfrac{3}{2}$, -1

58. $-\dfrac{1}{3}$, $-\dfrac{5}{3}$, -1, 1, 3, $\dfrac{2}{3}$, $\dfrac{5}{3}$

59. -2.5, -3.2, 2.6, -1, 2, 4, -3

60. -2.4, -3.1, -1.7, 3, 1, 2, 5

In each of the following problems, decide if the given number makes the statement true or false.

61. $x - 7 = 2y + 5$; $x = 22$, $y = 5$

62. $3(x - y) = 6$; $x = 5$, $y = -3$

63. $2(x + y) = 2x + y$; $x = -4$, $y = -2$

64. $x^2 - y^2 = x - y$; $x = 4$, $y = -3$

65. **Electrical resistance.** The formula for the total resistance in a parallel circuit is given by the formula $R_T = R_1R_2/(R_1 + R_2)$. Find the total resistance if $R_1 = 6$ ohms (Ω) and $R_2 = 10\ \Omega$.

66. **Area.** The formula for the area of a triangle is given by $A = \dfrac{1}{2}ab$. Find the area of a triangle if $a = 4$ centimeters (cm) and $b = 8$ cm.

67. **Perimeter.** The perimeter of a rectangle of length L and width W is given by the formula $P = 2L + 2W$. Find the perimeter when $L = 10$ inches (in.) and $W = 5$ in.

68. **Simple interest.** The simple interest I on a principal of P dollars at interest rate r for time t, in years, is given by $I = Prt$. Find the simple interest on a principal of \$6000 at 8 percent for 3 years. (**Note:** 8% = 0.08)

69. **Simple interest.** Use the simple interest formula to find the interest if the principal was \$150 and the rate of interest was 4% for 2 years.

70. **Simple interest.** Use the simple interest formula to find the interest if \$10,000 earns 3% interest for 3 years.

71. **Temperature conversion.** The formula that relates Celsius and Fahrenheit temperature is $F = \dfrac{9}{5}C + 32$. If the temperature of the day is $-10°$ C, what is the Fahrenheit temperature?

72. **Geometry.** If the area of a circle whose radius is r is given by $A = \pi r^2$, where $\pi = 3.14$, find the area when $r = 3$ meters (m).

73. Write an English interpretation of the following algebraic expression.

   (a) $(2x^2 - y)^3$ **(b)** $3n - \dfrac{n - 1}{2}$ **(c)** $(2n + 3)(n - 4)$

74. Is $a^n + b^n = (a + b)^n$? Try a few numbers and decide if you think this is true for all numbers, for some numbers, or never true. Write an explanation of your findings and give examples.

75. In Section 1.4 you investigated the numbers obtained by evaluating the following expressions for odd positive integer values of n: $\dfrac{n^2 - 1}{2}$, n, $\dfrac{n^2 + 1}{2}$. Work with other students to investigate what three numbers you get when you evaluate for a *negative* odd value? Does the pattern you observed before still hold? Try several negative numbers to test the pattern.

   Have no fear of fractions—does the pattern work with fractions? Try even integers. Is there a pattern for the three numbers obtained when you begin with even integers?

76. Enjoyment of patterns in art, music, and language are common to all cultures, and many cultures also delight in and draw spiritual significance from patterns in numbers. One such set of patterns is that of the "magic" square. One of these squares appears in a famous etching by Albrecht Dürer, who lived from 1471 to 1528 in Europe. He was one of the first artists in Europe to use geometry to give perspective, a feeling of three dimensions, in his work. The magic square in his work is this one:

16	3	2	13
5	10	11	8
9	6	7	12
4	15	14	1

Why is this square "magic?" It is magic because every row, every column, and both diagonals add to the same number. In this square there are sixteen spaces for the numbers 1 through 16.

Part 1: What number does each row and column add to?

Write the square that you obtain by adding -17 to each number. Is this still a magic square? If so, what number does each column and row add to? If you add 5 to each number in the original magic square, do you still have a magic square? You have been studying the operations of addition, multiplication, subtraction, and division with integers and with rational numbers. What operations can you perform on this magic square and still have a magic square? Try to find something that will not work. Use algebra to help you decide what will work and what won't. Write a description of your work and explain your conclusions.

Part 2: Here is the oldest published magic square. It is from China, about 250 BC. Legend has it that it was brought from the River Lo by a turtle to the Emperor Yii, who was a hydraulic engineer.

4	9	2
3	5	7
8	1	6

Check to make sure that this is a magic square. Work together to decide what operation might be done to every number in the magic square to make the sum of each row, column, and diagonal the *opposite* of what it is now. What would you do to every number to cause the sum of each row, column, and diagonal to equal zero?

Answers

1. -22 **3.** 32 **5.** -20 **7.** 12 **9.** 4 **11.** 83 **13.** 6 **15.** -40

17. 14 **19.** -9 **21.** 2 **23.** 2 **25.** 11 **27.** 1 **29.** 11 **31.** 91

33. 1 **35.** 91 **37.** 29 **39.** 9 **41.** 16 **43.** -15.3 **45.** -11.5

47. 1.1 **49.** 14.0 **51.** 41 **53.** 41 **53.** 8, 41 **55.** 11 **57.** $\frac{9}{2}$ **59.** -1.1

61. True **63.** False **65.** 3.75 Ω **67.** 30 in. **69.** $12 **71.** 14°F

Summary

Signed Numbers and Order [2.1]

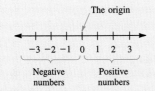

Positive Numbers Numbers used to name points to the right of the origin on the number line.

Negative Numbers Numbers used to name points to the left of the origin on the number line.

Signed Numbers The positive and negative numbers.

Integers The natural (or counting) numbers, their negatives, and zero. The intergers are

$$\{ \ldots, -3, -2, -1, 0, 1, 2, 3, \ldots \}$$

$|7| = 7$
$|-10| = 10$

Absolute Value The distance (on the number line) between the point named by a signed number and the origin.
The absolute value of x is written $|x|$.

Adding Signed Numbers [2.2]

$9 + 7 = 16$
$(-9) + (-7) = -16$

$15 + (-10) = 5$
$(-12) + 9 = -3$

1. If two numbers have the same sign, add their absolute values. Give the sum the sign of the original numbers.

2. If two numbers have different signs, subtract their absolute values, the smaller from the larger. Give the sum the sign of the number with the larger absolute value.

The Median [2.2]

$3, -4, 7, 2, -1$
in ascending order is
$-4, -1, 2, 3, 7$
The median is 2.

1. Rewrite the set in ascending order.

2. **a.** If there are an odd number of elements in the set, the median is the number in the middle.
   b. If there are an even number of elements in the set, find the median by adding the middle two numbers and dividing that sum by 2.

Subtracting Signed Numbers [2.3]

$16 - 8 = 16 + (-8)$
$\quad\quad = 8$
$8 - 15 = 8 + (-15)$
$\quad\quad = -7$
$-9 - (-7) = -9 + 7$
$\quad\quad\quad = -2$

1. Rewrite the subtraction problem as an addition problem by
   a. Changing the subtraction symbol to an addition symbol
   b. Replacing the number being subtracted with its opposite

2. Add the resulting signed numbers as before.

Range [2.3]

1. Rewrite the set in ascending order.

2. Subtract the smallest element from the largest to find the range.

Multiplying Signed Numbers [2.4]

$5(-7) = -35$
$(-10)(9) = -90$
$8 \cdot 7 = 56$
$(-9)(-8) = 72$

Multiply the absolute values of the two numbers.

1. If the numbers have different signs, the product is negative.

2. If the numbers have the same sign, the product is positive.

Dividing Signed Numbers [2.5]

$\dfrac{-32}{4} = -8$

$\dfrac{75}{-5} = -15$

$\dfrac{20}{5} = 4$

$\dfrac{-18}{-9} = 2$

Divide the absolute values of the two numbers.

1. If the numbers have different signs, the quotient is negative.

2. If the numbers have the same sign, the quotient is positive.

Evaluating Algebraic Expressions [2.6]

Evaluate

$\dfrac{4a - b}{2c}$

if $a = -6$, $b = 8$, and $c = -4$.

$\dfrac{4a - b}{2c} = \dfrac{4(-6) - 8}{2(-4)}$

$= \dfrac{-24 - 8}{-8}$

$= \dfrac{-32}{-8} = 4$

1. Replace each variable by the given number value.

2. Do the necessary arithmetic operations. (Be sure to follow the rules for the order of operations.)

Summing a Set of Numbers [2.6]

If x represents any of the numbers 3, -4, 7, 11, -8,

$\Sigma x = 3 + (-4) + 7 + 11\,(-8)$

$= 9$

The notation Σx indicates that all numbers in the set are to be summed.

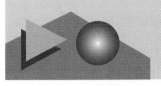

Summary Exercises

This supplementary exercise set will give you practice with each of the objectives of the chapter. Each exercise is keyed to the appropriate chapter section. The answers are provided in the *Instructor's Manual.* Your instructor will give you guidelines on how to best use these exercises in your instructional setting.

[2.1] Represent the integers on the number line shown.

1. $6, -18, -3, 2, 15, -9$

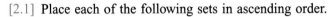

[2.1] Place each of the following sets in ascending order.

2. $4, -3, 6, -7, 0, 1, -2$

3. $-\dfrac{1}{2}, -\dfrac{2}{3}, \dfrac{3}{5}, -\dfrac{4}{5}, \dfrac{5}{6}, \dfrac{7}{10}$

[2.1] For each data set, determine the maximum and minimum.

4. $4, -2, 5, 1, -6, 3, -4$

5. $-4, 2, 5, -9, 8, 1, -6$

[2.1] Evaluate.

6. $|9|$

7. $|-9|$

8. $-|9|$

9. $-|-9|$

10. $|12 - 8|$

11. $|8| - |12|$

12. $-|8 - 12|$

13. $|-8| - |-12|$

[2.2] Add.

14. $-3 + (-8)$

15. $10 + (-4)$

16. $6 + (-6)$

17. $-16 + (-16)$

18. $-18 + 0$

19. $\dfrac{3}{8} + \left(-\dfrac{11}{8}\right)$

20. $5.7 + (-9.7)$

21. $-18 + 7 + (-3)$

[2.3] Subtract.

22. $8 - 13$

23. $-7 - 10$

24. $10 - (-7)$

25. $-5 - (-1)$

26. $-9 - (-9)$

27. $0 - (-2)$

28. $-\dfrac{5}{4} - \left(-\dfrac{17}{4}\right)$

29. $7.9 - (-8.1)$

[2.2] Find the median for each of the following sets.

30. $2, 4, 9, 10, 15$

31. $-7, -3, 2, 4, 5$

32. $-3, -8, 4, 1, 6$

33. $6, -3, 2, -5, 1$

34. $2, 4, 1, 8, 6, 7$

35. $-3, -1, -5, 3, 4, 1$

[2.3] Perform the indicated operations.

36. $|4 - 8|$ **37.** $|4| - |8|$ **38.** $|-4 - 8|$ **39.** $|-4| - |-8|$

40. $-6 - (-2) + 3$ **41.** $-5 - (5 - 8)$ **42.** $7 - (3 - 7) + 4$

43. Subtract -7 from -8.   **44.** Subtract -9 from the sum of 6 and -2.

[2.3] Determine the range for each of the following sets.

45. 3, 5, 1, 8, 9   **46.** $-4, -5, 6, 4, 2, 1$ **47.** $-5, 2, -1, 3, 8$ **48.** 7, 3, 5, 3, -4

[2.4] Multiply.

49. $(10)(-7)$ **50.** $(-8)(-5)$ **51.** $(-3)(-15)$ **52.** $(1)(-15)$

53. $(0)(-8)$ **54.** $\left(\dfrac{2}{3}\right)\left(-\dfrac{3}{2}\right)$ **55.** $(-4)\left(\dfrac{3}{8}\right)$ **56.** $\left(-\dfrac{5}{4}\right)(-1)$

57. $(-8)(-2)(5)$ **58.** $(-4)(-3)(2)$ **59.** $\left(\dfrac{2}{5}\right)(-10)\left(-\dfrac{5}{2}\right)$ **60.** $\left(\dfrac{4}{3}\right)(-6)\left(-\dfrac{3}{4}\right)$

[2.4] Perform the indicated operations.

61. $2(-4 + 3)$ **62.** $(2)(-3) - (-5)(-3)$ **63.** $(2 - 8)(2 + 8)$

[2.5] Divide.

64. $\dfrac{80}{16}$ **65.** $\dfrac{-63}{7}$ **66.** $\dfrac{-81}{-9}$

67. $\dfrac{0}{-5}$ **68.** $\dfrac{32}{-8}$ **69.** $\dfrac{-7}{0}$

[2.5] Perform the indicated operations.

70. $\dfrac{-8 + 6}{-8 - (-10)}$ **71.** $\dfrac{2(-3) - 1}{5 - (-2)}$ **72.** $\dfrac{(-5)^2 - (-2)^2}{-5 - (-2)}$

[2.6] Evaluate the expressions if $x = -3$, $y = 6$, $z = -4$, and $w = 2$.

73. $3x + w$ **74.** $5y - 4z$ **75.** $x + y - 3z$ **76.** $5z^2$

77. $3x^2 - 2w^2$ **78.** $3x^3$ **79.** $5(x^2 - w^2)$ **80.** $\dfrac{6z}{2w}$

81. $\dfrac{2x - 4z}{y - z}$ **82.** $\dfrac{x(y^2 - z^2)}{(y + z)(y - z)}$

Find the $\Sigma\, x$ for each set of numbers.

83. $-3, 5, 7, -15, 29$ **84.** $-12, -8, -3, 5, 17, 21$

Self-Test
for Chapter 2

Name

Section   Date

A N S W E R S

1. _____

2. _____

3. _____

4. _____

5. _____

6. _____

7. _____

8. _____

9. _____

10. _____

11. _____

12. _____

13. _____

14. _____

15. _____

16. _____

17. _____

The purpose of this self-test is to help you check your progress and to review for a chapter test in class. Allow yourself about an hour to take the test. When you are done, check your answers in the back of the book. If you missed any problems, go back and review the appropriate sections in the chapter and the exercises provided.

Represent the integers on the number line shown.

1. $5, -12, 4, -7, 18, -17$

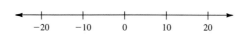

2. Place the following data set in ascending order: $4, -3, -6, 5, 0, \dfrac{3}{4}, \dfrac{1}{2}, 2, -2$

3. Determine the maximum and minimum of the following data set: $3, 2, -5, 6, 1, -2$

Evaluate.

4. $|7|$

5. $|-7|$

6. $|18 - 7|$

7. $|18| - |-7|$

Add.

8. $-8 + (-5)$

9. $6 + (-9)$

10. $(-9) + (-12)$

11. $-\dfrac{5}{3} + \dfrac{8}{3}$

Subtract.

12. $9 - 15$

13. $-9 - 15$

14. $5 - (-4)$

15. $-7 - (-7)$

Find the median of each of the following sets.

16. $2, -4, 5, -7, 8, 3, 10$

17. $-4, 6, -1, -9, 3, 7, -6, 11$

18. _____

19. _____

20. _____

21. _____

22. _____

23. _____

24. _____

25. _____

26. _____

27. _____

28. _____

29. _____

30. _____

Multiply.

18. $(-8)(5)$

19. $(-9)(-7)$

20. $(4.5)(-6)$

21. $(-2)(-3)(-4)$

22. Determine the range for the following set: 4, -1, 6, 3, -6, 2, 8, 5

Divide.

23. $\dfrac{75}{-3}$

24. $\dfrac{-27}{-9}$

25. $\dfrac{-45}{9}$

26. $\dfrac{9}{0}$

Evaluate if $a = -2$, $b = 6$, and $c = -4$.

27. $4a - c$

28. $5c^2$

29. $6(2b - 3c)$

30. $\dfrac{3a - 4b}{a + c}$

CHAPTER 3

EQUATIONS AND INEQUALITIES

INTRODUCTION

Many engineers, economists, and environmental scientists are working on the problem of meeting the increasing energy demands of a growing global population. One promising solution to this problem is power generated by wind-driven turbines.

The cost of wind-generated power has fallen from $0.25 per kilowatt hour (kwh) in the early 1980s to about $0.043 per kwh in 1996; thus, using this form of power production is becoming economically feasible. And compared to the cost of pollution from burning coal and oil, wind-generated power may be less expensive.

An economist for a city might use this equation to try to compute the cost for electricity for his city:

$C = P(0.043)(1000)$
where C = cost in dollars
$\quad\quad P$ = power in megawatts

The city engineer who is investigating the possibility of building turbines to supply the city with electricity knows that each turbine can produce 1.1 million kwh of power, so she uses the equation

$P = n(1.1)$
where P = power in megawatts
$\quad\quad n$ = number of turbines required to produce power

The equation is an ancient tool for solving problems and writing numerical relationships clearly and accurately. In this chapter you will learn methods to solve linear equations and practice writing equations that accurately describe problem situations. ■

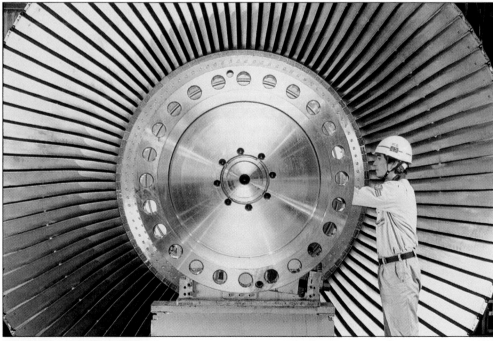

© Alan Levenson / Tony Stone Images

Solving Equations by Adding and Subtracting

3.1 OBJECTIVES

1. Determine whether a given number is a solution for an equation
2. Use the addition property to solve equations
3. Determine whether a given number is a solution for an application
4. Translate words to equation symbols
5. Solve application problems

An equation such as

$x + 3 = 5$

is called a **conditional equation** because it can be either true or false depending on the value given to the variable.

In this chapter you will begin working with one of the most important tools of mathematics, the equation. The ability to recognize and solve various types of equations is probably the most useful algebraic skill you will learn. We will continue to build upon the methods of this chapter throughout the remainder of the text. To start, let's describe what we mean by an *equation*.

> An **equation** is a mathematical statement that two expressions are equal.

Some examples are $3 + 4 = 7$, $x + 3 = 5$, $P = 2L + 2W$.

As you can see, an equals sign ($=$) separates the two equal expressions. These expressions are usually called the *left side* and the *right side* of the equation.

$x + 3 = 5$

Left side   Equals   Right side

An equation may be either true or false. For instance, $3 + 4 = 7$ is true because both sides name the same number. What about an equation such as $x + 3 = 5$ that has a letter or variable on one side? Any numbers can replace x in the equation. However, only one number will make this equation a true statement.

$$\text{If } x = \begin{cases} 1 & 1 + 3 = 5 \text{ is false} \\ 2 & 2 + 3 = 5 \text{ is true} \\ 3 & 3 + 3 = 5 \text{ is false} \end{cases}$$

The number 2 is called the **solution** (or *root*) of the equation $x + 3 = 5$ because substituting 2 for x gives a true statement.

> A **solution** for an equation is any value for the variable that makes the equation a true statement.

• Example 1

Verifying a Solution

(*a*) Is 3 a solution for the equation $2x + 4 = 10$?

To find out, replace x with 3 and evaluate $2x + 4$ on the left.

Left side		Right side
$2 \cdot 3 + 4$	$\stackrel{?}{=}$	10
$6 + 4$	$\stackrel{?}{=}$	10
10	$=$	10

Since $10 = 10$ is a true statement, 3 is a solution of the equation.

(*b*) Is 5 a solution of the equation $3x - 2 = 2x + 1$?

To find out, replace x with 5 and evaluate each side separately.

Remember the rules for the order of operation. Multiply first; then add or subtract.

Left side		*Right side*
$3 \cdot 5 - 2$	$\stackrel{?}{=}$	$2 \cdot 5 + 1$
$15 - 2$	$\stackrel{?}{=}$	$10 + 1$
13	$\neq$	11

Since the two sides do not name the same number, we do not have a true statement, and 5 is not a solution.

● ● ● **CHECK YOURSELF 1**

For the equation

$$2x - 1 = x + 5$$

a. Is 4 a solution? **b.** Is 6 a solution?

You may be wondering whether an equation can have more than one solution. It certainly can. For instance,

$$x^2 = 9$$

This is an example of a **quadratic equation.** We will consider methods of solution in Chapter 5 and then again in Chapter 10.

has two solutions. They are 3 and -3 because

$$3^2 = 9 \quad \text{and} \quad (-3)^2 = 9$$

In this chapter, however, we will always work with *linear equations in one variable.* These are equations that can be put into the form

$$ax + b = 0$$

where the variable is x, where a and b are any numbers, and a is not equal to 0. In a linear equation, the variable can appear only to the first power. No other power (x^2, x^3, etc.) can appear. Linear equations are also called **first-degree equations.** The degree of an equation in one variable is the highest degree to which the variable appears.

> Linear equations in one variable that can be written in the form
>
> $$ax + b = 0 \qquad a \neq 0$$
>
> will have exactly one solution.

• Example 2

Identifying Expressions and Equations

Label each of the following as an expression, a linear equation, or an equation that is not linear.

(*a*) $4x + 5$ is an expression

(*b*) $2x + 8 = 0$ is a linear equation

(*c*) $3x^2 - 9 = 0$ is not a linear equation

(*d*) $5x = 15$ is a linear equation

● ● ● **CHECK YOURSELF 2**

Label each as an expression, a linear equation, or an equation that is not linear.

a. $2x^2 = 8$ **b.** $2x - 3 = 0$ **c.** $5x - 10$ **d.** $2x + 1 = 7$

It is not difficult to find the solution for an equation such as $x + 3 = 8$ by guessing the answer to the question "What plus 3 is 8?" Here the answer to the question is 5, and that is also the solution for the equation. But for more complicated equations you are going to need something more than guesswork. A better method is to transform the given equation to an *equivalent equation* whose solution can be found by inspection. Let's make a definition.

> Equations that have the same solution are called **equivalent equations.**

The following are all equivalent equations:

$2x + 3 = 5$ $2x = 2$ and $x = 1$

They all have the same solution, 1. We say that a linear equation is *solved* when it is transformed to an equivalent equation of the form

Note: In some cases we'll write the equation in the form

$\Box = x$

The number will be our solution when the equation has the variable isolated on the left or on the right.

$x = \Box$

The variable is alone on the left side.   The right side is some number, the solution.

The addition property of equality is the first property you will need to transform an equation to an equivalent form.

> ### The Addition Property of Equality
>
> If $a = b$
>
> then $a + c = b + c$
>
> In words, adding the same quantity to both sides of an equation gives an equivalent equation.

Remember: An equation is a statement that the two sides are equal. Adding the same quantity to both sides does not change the equality or "balance."

Let's look at an example of applying this property to solve an equation.

● Example 3

Using the Addition Property to Solve an Equation

Solve

$$x - 3 = 9$$

Remember that our goal is to isolate x on one side of the equation. Since 3 is being subtracted from x, we can add 3 to remove it. We must use the addition property to add 3 to both sides of the equation.

To check, replace x with 12 in the original equation:

$$x - 3 = 9$$
$$12 - 3 = 9$$
$$9 = 9$$

Since we have a true statement, 12 is the solution.

$$
\begin{aligned}
x - 3 &= 9 \\
+\,3 &\quad +3 \\
\hline
x &= 12
\end{aligned}
$$

{ Adding 3 "undoes" the subtraction and leaves x alone on the left.

Since 12 is the solution for the equivalent equation $x = 12$, it is the solution for our original equation.

● ● ● **CHECK YOURSELF 3**

Solve and check.

$$x - 5 = 4$$

The addition property also allows us to add a negative number to both sides of an equation. This is really the same as subtracting the same quantity from both sides.

● Example 4

Using the Addition Property to Solve an Equation

Solve

$$x + 5 = 9$$

In this case, 5 is *added* to x on the left. We can use the addition property to subtract 5 from both sides. This will "undo" the addition and leave the variable x alone on one side of the equation.

Recall our comment that we could write an equation in the equivalent forms $x = \square$ or $\square = x$, where $\square$ represents some number. Suppose we have an equation like

$$12 = x + 7$$

Subtracting 7 will isolate x *on the right*:

$$
\begin{aligned}
12 &= x + 7 \\
-7 &\quad\;\; -7 \\
\hline
5 &= x
\end{aligned}
$$

and the solution is 5.

$$
\begin{aligned}
x + 5 &= 9 \\
-5 &\quad -5 \\
\hline
x &= 4
\end{aligned}
$$

The solution is 4. To check, replace x with 4:

$$4 + 5 = 9 \quad \text{(True)}$$

● ● ● **CHECK YOURSELF 4**

Solve and check.

$x + 6 = 13$

What if the equation has a variable term on both sides? You will have to use the addition property to add or subtract a term involving the variable to get the desired result.

• Example 5

Using the Addition Property to Solve an Equation

Solve

$5x = 4x + 7$

We will start by subtracting $4x$ from both sides of the equation. Do you see why? Remember that an equation is solved when we have an equivalent equation of the form $x = \square$.

$$\begin{array}{rl} 5x = & 4x + 7 \\ \underline{-4x \quad -4x} & \\ x = & 7 \end{array} \quad \left\{ \begin{array}{l} \text{Subtracting } 4x \text{ from} \\ \text{both sides } \textit{removes} \\ 4x \text{ from the right.} \end{array} \right.$$

To check: Since 7 is a solution for the equivalent equation $x = 7$, it should be a solution for the original equation. To find out, replace x with 7:

$5 \cdot 7 \overset{?}{=} 4 \cdot 7 + 7$

$35 \overset{?}{=} 28 + 7$

$35 = 35 \qquad \text{(True)}$

● ● ● **CHECK YOURSELF 5**

Solve and check.

$7x = 6x + 3$

You may have to apply the addition property more than once to solve an equation. Look at Example 6.

• Example 6

Using the Addition Property to Solve an Equation

Solve

$$7x - 8 = 6x$$

We want all variables on *one* side of the equation. If we choose the left, we subtract $6x$ from both sides of the equation. This will remove $6x$ from the right:

$$
\begin{array}{rcl}
7x - 8 = & & 6x \\
\underline{-6x} & & \underline{-6x} \\
x - 8 = & & 0
\end{array}
$$

We want the variable alone, so we add 8 to both sides. This isolates x on the left.

$$
\begin{array}{rcl}
x - 8 = & & 0 \\
\underline{+8} & & \underline{+8} \\
x \quad = & & 8
\end{array}
$$

The solution is 8. We'll leave it to you to check this result.

● ● ●   **CHECK YOURSELF 6**

Solve and check.

$$9x + 3 = 8x$$

   Often an equation will have more than one variable term *and* more than one number. You will have to apply the addition property twice in solving these equations.

• Example 7

Using the Addition Property to Solve an Equation

Solve

$$5x - 7 = 4x + 3$$

We would like the variable terms on the left, so we start by subtracting $4x$ to remove that term from the right side of the equation:

$$
\begin{array}{rcl}
5x - 7 = & & 4x + 3 \\
\underline{-4x} & & \underline{-4x} \\
x - 7 = & & 3
\end{array}
$$

Now, to isolate the variable, we add 7 to both sides to undo the subtraction on the left:

$$
\begin{array}{rcl}
x - 7 &=& 3 \\
+\,7 && +7 \\
\hline
x &=& 10
\end{array}
$$

The solution is 10. To check, replace x with 10 in the original equation:

$$5 \cdot 10 - 7 = 4 \cdot 10 + 3$$

$$43 = 43 \qquad \text{(True)}$$

You could just as easily have added 7 to both sides and *then* subtracted 4x. The result would be the same. In fact, some students prefer to combine the two steps.

● ● ● **CHECK YOURSELF 7**

Solve and check.

a. $4x - 5 = 3x + 2$

b. $6x + 2 = 5x - 4$

Remember, by *simplify* we mean to combine all like terms.

In solving an equation, you should always simplify each side as much as possible before using the addition property.

•Example 8

Combining Like Terms and Solving the Equation

Solve

Like terms   Like terms

$$5 + 8x - 2 = 2x - 3 + 5x$$

Since like terms appear on each side of the equation, we start by combining the numbers on the left (5 and -2). Then we combine the like terms ($2x$ and $5x$) on the right. We have

$$3 + 8x = 7x - 3$$

Now we can apply the addition property, as before:

$$
\begin{array}{rcll}
3 + 8x &=& 7x - 3 & \\
-\,7x &=& -7x & \text{Subtract } 7x. \\
\hline
3 + x &=& -3 & \\
-3 && -3 & \text{Subtract } 3. \\
\hline
x &=& -6 & \text{Isolate } x.
\end{array}
$$

The solution is -6. To check, always return to the original equation. That will catch any possible errors in simplifying. Replacing x with -6 gives

$$5 + 8(-6) - 2 \overset{?}{=} 2(-6) - 3 + 5(-6)$$
$$5 - 48 - 2 \overset{?}{=} -12 - 3 - 30$$
$$-45 = -45 \qquad \text{(True)}$$

● ● ● **CHECK YOURSELF 8**

Solve and check.

a. $3 + 6x + 4 = 8x - 3 - 3x$ **b.** $5x + 21 + 3x = 20 + 7x - 2$

We may have to apply some of the properties discussed in Section 1.3 in solving equations. Example 9 illustrates the use of the distributive property to clear an equation of parentheses.

● Example 9

Using the Distributive Property and Solving Equations

Solve

$$2(3x + 4) = 5x - 6$$

Applying the distributive property on the left, we have

$$6x + 8 = 5x - 6$$

We can then proceed as before:

Note: $2(3x + 4)$
$= 2(3x) + 2(4)$
$= 6x + 8$

$$
\begin{array}{rcl}
6x + 8 = & 5x & - 6 \\
-5x & -5x & \qquad \text{Subtract } 5x. \\
\hline
x + 8 = & & - 6 \\
- 8 & & - 8 \qquad \text{Subtract } 8. \\
\hline
x \quad = & & -14
\end{array}
$$

Remember that
$x = -14$ and $-14 = x$
are equivalent equations.

The solution is -14. We will leave the checking of this result to the reader. **Remember:** Always return to the original equation to check.

● ● ● **CHECK YOURSELF 9**

Solve and check each of the following equations.

a. $4(5x - 2) = 19x + 4$ **b.** $3(5x + 1) = 2(7x - 3) - 4$

The main reason for learning how to set up and solve algebraic equations is so that we can use them to solve word problems. In fact, algebraic equations were *invented* to make solving word problems much easier. The first word problems that we know about are over 4000 years old. They were literally "written in stone," on Babylonian tablets, about 500 years before the first algebraic equation made its appearance.

Before algebra, people solved word problems primarily by **substitution,** which is a method of finding unknown integers by using trial and error in a logical way. Example 10 shows how to solve a word problem using substitution.

•Example 10

Solving a Word Problem by Substitution

The sum of two consecutive integers is 37. Find the two integers.

If the two integers were 20 and 21, their sum would be 41. Since that's more than 37, the integers must be smaller. If the integers were 15 and 16, the sum would be 31. More trials yield that the sum of 18 and 19 is 37.

● ● ● **CHECK YOURSELF 10**

The sum of two consecutive integers is 91. Find the two integers.

Most word problems are not so easily solved by substitution. For more complicated word problems, a five-step procedure is used. Using this step-by-step approach will, with practice, allow you to organize your work. Organization is the key to solving word problems. Here are the five steps.

To Solve Word Problems

STEP 1 Read the problem carefully. Then reread it to decide what you are asked to find.

STEP 2 Choose a letter to represent one of the unknowns in the problem. Then represent all other unknowns of the problem with expressions that use the same letter.

STEP 3 Translate the problem to the language of algebra to form an equation.

STEP 4 Solve the equation and answer the question of the original problem.

STEP 5 Check your solution by returning to the original problem.

We discussed these translations in Section 1.1. You might find it helpful to review that section before going on.

The third step is usually the hardest part. We must translate words to the language of algebra. Before we look at a complete example, the following table may help you review that translation step.

Translating Words to Algebra

Words	Algebra
The sum of x and y	$x + y$
3 plus a	$3 + a$ or $a + 3$
5 more than m	$m + 5$
b increased by 7	$b + 7$
The difference of x and y	$x - y$
4 less than a	$a - 4$
s decreased by 8	$s - 8$
The product of x and y	$x \cdot y$ or xy
5 times a	$5 \cdot a$ or $5a$
Twice m	$2m$
The quotient of x and y	$\dfrac{x}{y}$
a divided by 6	$\dfrac{a}{6}$
One-half of b	$\dfrac{b}{2}$ or $\dfrac{1}{2}b$

Now let's look at some typical examples of translating phrases to algebra.

•Example 11

Translating Statements

Translate each statement to an algebraic expression.

(a) The sum of a and 2 times b $a + 2b$

         Sum   2 times b

(b) 5 times m increased by 1 $5m + 1$

         5 times m Increased by 1

(c) 5 less than 3 times x $3x - 5$

         3 times x 5 less than

(d) The product of x and y, divided by 3 $\dfrac{xy}{3}$ — The product of x and y

         Divided by 3

● ● ●   **CHECK YOURSELF 11**

Translate to algebra.

a. 2 more than twice x **b.** 4 less than 5 times n

c. The product of twice a and b **d.** The sum of s and t, divided by 5

Now let's work through a complete example. Although this problem could be solved by substitution, it is presented here to help you practice the five-step approach.

• Example 12

Solving an Application

The sum of a number and 5 is 17. What is the number?

Step 1 *Read carefully.* You must find the unknown number.

Step 2 *Choose letters or variables.* Let x represent the unknown number. There are no other unknowns.

Step 3 *Translate.*

The sum of

$x + 5 = 17$

is

Step 4 *Solve.*

$$x + 5 = 17$$
$$x + 5 - 5 = 17 - 5 \qquad \text{Subtract 5.}$$
$$x = 12$$

So the number is 12.

Always return to the *original problem* to check your result and *not* to the equation of step 3. This will prevent possible errors!

Step 5 *Check.* Is the sum of 12 and 5 equal to 17? Yes ($12 + 5 = 17$). We have checked our solution.

● ● ● CHECK YOURSELF 12

The sum of a number and 8 is 35. What is the number?

● ● ● CHECK YOURSELF ANSWERS

1. (a) 4 is not a solution; **(b)** 6 is a solution.   **2. (a)** Nonlinear equation; **(b)** linear equation; **(c)** expression; **(d)** linear equation.   **3.** 9.   **4.** 7.
5. 3.   **6.** -3.   **7. (a)** 7; **(b)** -6.   **8. (a)** -10; **(2)** -3.   **9. (a)** 12; **(b)** -13.
10. 45 and 46.   **11. (a)** $2x + 2$; **(b)** $5n - 4$; **(c)** $2ab$; **(d)** $\dfrac{s + t}{5}$.

12. The equation is $x + 8 = 35$. The number is 27.

Name

Section   Date

Is the number shown in parentheses a solution for the given equation?

1. $x + 4 = 9$ (5)

2. $x + 2 = 11$ (8)

3. $x - 15 = 6$ (-21)

4. $x - 11 = 5$ (16)

5. $5 - x = 2$ (4)

6. $10 - x = 7$ (3)

7. $4 - x = 6$ (-2)

8. $5 - x = 6$ (-3)

9. $3x + 4 = 13$ (8)

10. $5x + 6 = 31$ (5)

11. $4x - 5 = 7$ (2)

12. $2x - 5 = 1$ (3)

13. $5 - 2x = 7$ (-1)

14. $4 - 5x = 9$ (-2)

15. $4x - 5 = 2x + 3$ (4)

16. $5x + 4 = 2x + 10$ (4)

17. $x + 3 + 2x = 5 + x + 8$ (5)

18. $5x - 3 + 2x = 3 + x - 12$ (-2)

19. $\dfrac{3}{4}x = 18$ (20)

20. $\dfrac{3}{5}x = 24$ (40)

21. $\dfrac{3}{5}x + 5 = 11$ (10)

22. $\dfrac{2}{3}x + 8 = -12$ (-6)

Label each of the following as an expression or a linear equation.

23. $2x + 1 = 9$

24. $7x + 14$

	ANSWERS
1.	
2.	
3.	
4.	
5.	
6.	
7.	
8.	
9.	
10.	
11.	
12.	
13.	
14.	
15.	
16.	
17.	
18.	
19.	
20.	
21.	
22.	
23.	
24.	

25. _____

26. _____

27. _____

28. _____

29. _____

30. _____

31. _____

32. _____

33. _____

34. _____

35. _____

36. _____

37. _____

38. _____

39. _____

40. _____

41. _____

42. _____

43. _____

44. _____

45. _____

46. _____

47. _____

48. _____

49. _____

50. _____

51. _____

52. _____

25. $2x - 8$

26. $5x - 3 = 12$

27. $7x + 2x + 8 - 3$

28. $x + 5 = 13$

29. $2x - 8 = 3$

30. $12x - 5x + 2 + 5$

Solve and check the following equations.

31. $x + 9 = 11$

32. $x - 4 = 6$

33. $x - 8 = 3$

34. $x + 11 = 15$

35. $x - 8 = -10$

36. $x + 5 = 2$

37. $x + 4 = -3$

38. $x - 5 = -4$

39. $11 = x + 5$

40. $x + 7 = 0$

41. $4x = 3x + 4$

42. $7x = 6x - 8$

43. $11x = 10x - 10$

44. $9x = 8x + 5$

45. $6x + 3 = 5x$

46. $12x - 6 = 11x$

47. $8x - 4 = 7x$

48. $9x - 7 = 8x$

49. $2x + 3 = x + 5$

50. $3x - 2 = 2x + 1$

51. $5x - 7 = 4x - 3$

52. $8x + 5 = 7x - 2$

53. $7x - 2 = 6x + 4$

54. $10x - 3 = 9x - 6$

55. $3 + 6x + 2 = 3x + 11 + 2x$

56. $6x - 3 + 2x = 7x + 8$

57. $4x + 7 + 3x = 5x + 13 + x$

58. $5x + 9 + 4x = 9 + 8x - 7$

59. $3x - 5 + 2x - 7 + x = 5x + 2$

60. $5x + 8 + 3x - x + 5 = 6x - 3$

61. $4(3x + 4) = 11x - 2$

62. $2(5x - 3) = 9x + 7$

63. $3(7x + 2) = 5(4x + 1) + 17$

64. $5(5x + 3) = 3(8x - 2) + 4$

65. $\dfrac{5}{4}x - 1 = \dfrac{1}{4}x + 7$

66. $\dfrac{7}{5}x + 3 = \dfrac{2}{5}x - 8$

67. $\dfrac{9}{2}x - \dfrac{3}{4} = \dfrac{7}{2}x + \dfrac{5}{4}$

68. $\dfrac{11}{3}x + \dfrac{1}{6} = \dfrac{8}{3}x + \dfrac{19}{6}$

Translate each statement to an algebraic equation. Let x represent the number in each case.

69. 3 more than a number is 7.

70. 5 less than a number is 12.

71. 7 less than 3 times a number is twice that same number.

72. 4 more than 5 times a number is 6 times that same number.

73. 2 times the sum of a number and 5 is 18 more than that same number.

74. 3 times the sum of a number and 7 is 4 times that same number.

75. Which of the following is equivalent to the equation $8x + 5 = 9x - 4$?
    a. $17x = -9$ **b.** $x = -9$ **c.** $8x + 9 = 9x$ **d.** $9 = 17x$

53. _____

54. _____

55. _____

56. _____

57. _____

58. _____

59. _____

60. _____

61. _____

62. _____

63. _____

64. _____

65. _____

66. _____

67. _____

68. _____

69. _____

70. _____

71. _____

72. _____

73. _____

74. _____

75. _____

76. _____

77. _____

78. _____

79. _____

80. _____

81. _____

82. _____

83. _____

84. _____

85. _____

86. _____

76. Which of the following is equivalent to the equation $5x - 7 = 4x - 12$?
 a. $9x = 19$ **b.** $9x - 7 = -12$ **c.** $x = -18$ **d.** $x - 7 = -12$

77. Which of the following is equivalent to the equation $12x - 6 = 8x + 14$?
 a. $4x - 6 = 14$ **b.** $x = 20$ **c.** $20x = 20$ **d.** $4x = 8$

78. Which of the following is equivalent to the equation $7x + 5 = 12x - 10$?
 a. $5x = -15$ **b.** $7x - 5 = 12x$ **c.** $-5 = 5x$ **d.** $7x + 15 = 12x$

True or false?

79. Every linear equation with one variable has exactly one solution.

80. Isolating the variable on the right side of the equation will result in a negative solution.

Solve the following word problems. Be sure to label the unknowns and to show the equation you use for the solution.

81. Number problem. The sum of a number and 7 is 33. What is the number?

82. Number problem. The sum of a number and 15 is 22. What is the number?

83. Number problem. The sum of a number and -15 is 7. What is the number?

84. Number problem. The sum of a number and -8 is 17. What is the number?

85. Number of votes cast. In an election, the winning candidate has 1840 votes. If the total number of votes cast was 3260, how many votes did the losing candidate receive?

86. Monthly earnings. Mike and Stefanie work at the same company and make a total of $2760 per month. If Stefanie makes $1400 per month, how much does Mike earn every month?

87. Appliance costs. A washer-dryer combination costs $650. If the washer costs $360, what does the dryer cost?

88. Computer costs. You have $2350 saved for the purchase of a new computer that costs $3675. How much more must you save?

89. Price increases. The price of an item has increased by $225 over last year. If the item is now selling for $965, what was the price last year?

90. An algebraic equation is a complete sentence. It has a subject, a verb, and a predicate. For example, $x + 2 = 5$ can be written in English as "Two more than a number is five." Or, "A number added to two is five." Write an English version of the following equations. Be sure you write complete sentences and that the sentences express the same idea as the equations. Exchange sentences with another student, and see if your interpretation of each other's sentences result in the same equation.

(a) $2x - 5 = x + 1$

(b) $2(x + 2) = 14$

(c) $n + 5 = \dfrac{n}{2} - 6$

(d) $7 - 3a = 5 + a$

91. Complete the following explanation in your own words: "The difference between $3(x - 1) + 4 - 2x$ and $3(x - 1) + 4 = 2x$ is . . . ."

92. "I make $2.50 an hour more in my new job." If x = the amount I used to make per hour and y = the amount I now make, which equation(s) below say the same thing as the statement above? Explain your choice(s) by translating the equation into English and comparing with the original statement.

(a) $x + y = 2.50$

(b) $x - y = 2.50$

(c) $x + 2.50 = y$

(d) $2.50 + y = x$

(e) $y - x = 2.50$

(f) $2.50 - x = y$

93. "The river rose 4 feet above flood stage last night." If a = the river's height at flood stage, b = the river's height now (the morning after), which equations below say the same thing as the statement? Explain your choices by reanslating the equations into English and comparing the meaning with the original statement.

(a) $a + b = 4$

(b) $b - 4 = a$

(c) $a - 4 = b$

(d) $a + 4 = b$

(e) $b + 4 = b$

(f) $b - a = 4$

87.

88.

89.

90.

91.

92.

93.

94. "Surprising Results!" Work with other students to try this experiment. Each person should do the following six steps mentally, not telling anyone else what their calculations are:

(a) Think of a number.

(b) Add 7.

(c) Multiply by 3.

(d) Add 3 more than the original number.

(e) Divide by 4.

(f) Subtract the original number.

What number do you end up with? Compare your answer with everyone else's. Does everyone have the same answer? Make sure that everyone followed the directions accurately. How do you explain the results? Algebra makes the explanation clear. Work together to do the problem again, using a variable for the number. Make up another series of computations that give "surprising results."

Getting Ready for Section 3.2 [Section 2.4]

Multiply.

a. $\left(\dfrac{1}{3}\right)(3)$

b. $(-6)\left(-\dfrac{1}{6}\right)$

c. $(7)\left(\dfrac{1}{7}\right)$

d. $\left(-\dfrac{1}{4}\right)(-4)$

e. $\left(\dfrac{3}{5}\right)\left(\dfrac{5}{3}\right)$

f. $\left(\dfrac{7}{8}\right)\left(\dfrac{8}{7}\right)$

g. $\left(-\dfrac{4}{7}\right)\left(-\dfrac{7}{4}\right)$

h. $\left(-\dfrac{6}{11}\right)\left(-\dfrac{11}{6}\right)$

Answers

1. Yes **3.** No **5.** No **7.** Yes **9.** No **11.** No **13.** Yes
15. Yes **17.** Yes **19.** No **21.** Yes **23.** Linear equation
25. Expression **27.** Expression **29.** Linear equation **31.** 2 **33.** 11
35. -2 **37.** -7 **39.** 6 **41.** 4 **43.** -10 **45.** -3 **47.** 4
49. 2 **51.** 4 **53.** 6 **55.** 6 **57.** 6 **59.** 14 **61.** -18
63. 16 **65.** 8 **67.** 2 **69.** $x + 3 = 7$ **71.** $3x - 7 = 2x$
73. $2(x + 5) = x + 18$ **75.** c **77.** a **79.** True **81.** 26 **83.** 22
85. 1420 **87.** $290 **89.** $740 **a.** 1 **b.** 1 **c.** 1 **d.** 1 **e.** 1
f. 1 **g.** 1 **h.** 1

3.2 Solving Equations by Multiplying or Dividing; The Mean

3.2 OBJECTIVES

1. Determine whether a given number is a solution for an equation
2. Use the multiplication property to solve equations
3. Find the mean for a given set

Again, as long as you do the *same* thing to *both* sides of the equation, the "balance" is maintained.

Do you see why the number cannot be 0? Multiplying by 0 gives $0 = 0$. We have lost the variable!

Let's look at a different type of equation. For instance, what if we want to solve an equation like the following?

$$6x = 18$$

Using the addition property of the last section won't help. We will need a second property for solving equations.

> **The Multiplication Property of Equality**
>
> If $a = b$ then $ac = bc$ where $c \neq 0$
>
> In words, multiplying both sides of an equation by the same nonzero number gives an equivalent equation.

Let's work through some examples, using this second rule.

● Example 1

Solving Equations by Using the Multiplication Property

Solve

$$6x = 18$$

Here the variable x is multiplied by 6. So we apply the multiplication property and multiply both sides by $\frac{1}{6}$. Keep in mind that we want an equation of the form

$$x = \boxed{}$$

$$\frac{1}{6}(6x) = \left(\frac{1}{6}\cdot 6\right)x$$

$$= 1 \cdot x, \text{ or } x$$

We then have x alone on the left, which is what we want.

$$\frac{1}{6}(6x) = \left(\frac{1}{6}\right)18$$

We can now simplify.

$$1 \cdot x = 3 \qquad \text{or} \qquad x = 3$$

The solution is 3. To check, replace x with 3:

$$6 \cdot 3 \stackrel{?}{=} 18$$

$$18 = 18 \qquad \text{(True)}$$

CHECK YOURSELF 1

Solve and check.

$8x = 32$

In Example 1 we solved the equation by multiplying both sides by the reciprocal of the coefficient of the variable.

Example 2 illustrates a slightly different approach to solving an equation by using the multiplication property.

● Example 2

Solving Equations by Using the Multiplication Property

Solve

$5x = -35$

The variable x is multiplied by 5. We *divide* both sides by 5 to "undo" that multiplication:

Since division is defined in terms of multiplication, we can also divide both sides of an equation by the same nonzero number.

$$\frac{5x}{5} = \frac{-35}{5}$$
$$x = -7$$

{ Note that the right side reduces to −7. Be careful with the rules for signs.

We will leave it to you to check the solution.

● ● ● CHECK YOURSELF 2

Solve and check.

$7x = -42$

● Example 3

Solving Equations by Using the Multiplication Property

Solve

$-9x = 54$

In this case, x is multiplied by -9, so we divide both sides by -9 to isolate x on the left:

$$\frac{-9x}{-9} = \frac{54}{-9}$$

$$x = -6$$

The solution is -6. To check:

$$(-9)(-6) \stackrel{?}{=} 54$$

$$54 = 54 \qquad \text{(True)}$$

● ● ● **CHECK YOURSELF 3**

Solve and check.

$$-10x = -60$$

Example 4 illustrates the use of the multiplication property when fractions appear in an equation.

• Example 4

Solving Equations by Using the Multiplication Property

(*a*) Solve

$$\frac{x}{3} = 6$$

Here x is *divided* by 3. We will use multiplication to isolate x.

$$3\left(\frac{x}{3}\right) = 3 \cdot 6$$

$$x = 18$$

This leaves x alone on the left because

$$3\left(\frac{x}{3}\right) = \frac{3}{1} \cdot \frac{x}{3} = \frac{x}{1} = x$$

To check:

$$\frac{18}{3} \stackrel{?}{=} 6$$

$$6 = 6 \qquad \text{(True)}$$

(*b*) Solve

$$\frac{x}{5} = -9$$

$$5\left(\frac{x}{5}\right) = 5(-9)$$

$$x = -45$$

Since x is divided by 5, multiply both sides by 5

The solution is -45. To check, we replace x with -45:

$$\frac{-45}{5} \overset{?}{=} -9$$

$$-9 = -9 \qquad \text{(True)}$$

The solution is verified.

● ● ● **CHECK YOURSELF 4**

Solve and check.

a. $\dfrac{x}{7} = 3$ **b.** $\dfrac{x}{4} = -8$

When the variable is multiplied by a fraction that has a numerator other than 1, there are two approaches to finding the solution.

● Example 5

Solving Equations by Using Reciprocals

Solve

$$\frac{3}{5}x = 9$$

One approach is to multiply by 5 as the first step.

$$5\left(\frac{3}{5}x\right) = 5 \cdot 9$$

$$3x = 45$$

Now we divide by 3.

$$\frac{3x}{3} = \frac{45}{3}$$

$$x = 15$$

To check:

$$\frac{3}{5} \cdot 15 \overset{?}{=} 9$$

$$9 = 9 \qquad \text{(True)}$$

A second approach combines the multiplication and division steps and is generally a bit more efficient. We multiply by $\dfrac{5}{3}$.

Recall that $\frac{5}{3}$ is the *reciprocal* of $\frac{3}{5}$, and the product of a number and its reciprocal is just 1! So

$$\left(\frac{5}{3}\right)\left(\frac{3}{5}\right) = 1$$

$$\frac{5}{3}\left(\frac{3}{5}x\right) = \frac{5}{3} \cdot 9$$

$$x = \frac{5}{\cancel{3}} \cdot \frac{\cancel{9}^{3}}{1} = 15$$

So $x = 15$, as before.

● ● ● **CHECK YOURSELF 5**

Solve and check.

$$\frac{2}{3}x = 18$$

You may sometimes have to simplify an equation before applying the methods of this section. Example 6 illustrates this property.

● Example 6

Combining Like Terms and Solving Equations

Solve and check:

$$3x + 5x = 40$$

Using the distributive property, we can combine the like terms on the left to write

$$8x = 40$$

We can now proceed as before.

$$\frac{8x}{8} = \frac{40}{8} \qquad \text{Divide by 8.}$$
$$x = 5$$

The solution is 5. To check, we return to the original equation. Substituting 5 for x yields

$$3 \cdot 5 + 5 \cdot 5 \stackrel{?}{=} 40$$
$$15 + 25 \stackrel{?}{=} 40$$
$$40 = 40 \qquad \text{(True)}$$

The solution is verified.

● ● ● **CHECK YOURSELF 6**

Solve and check.

$$7x + 4x = -66$$

In Section 2.2 we introduced the median. We said that it was sometimes used to show a typical, or average, number from a set of numbers. Another kind of average is the *mean*. The mean of a set is the sum of the set divided by the number of elements in the set. The mean is written as $\bar{x}$ (sometimes called "x-bar"). In mathematical symbols, we say

$$\bar{x} = \frac{\Sigma x}{n} \qquad \begin{array}{l} \leftarrow \text{The sum of the set} \\ \leftarrow \text{The number of elements in the set} \end{array}$$

• Example 7

Finding the Mean

Find the mean for each set of numbers.

(*a*) 2, −3, 5, 4, 7

We begin by finding Σx.

$\Sigma x = 2 + (-3) + 5 + 4 + 7 = 15$

Next we find n.

$n = 5$ Remember that n is the number of elements in the set.

Finally, we substitute our numbers into the equation.

$$\bar{x} = \frac{\Sigma x}{n} = \frac{15}{5} = 3$$

The mean of the set is 3.

(*b*) −4, 7, 9, −3, 6, −2, −3, 8

First find Σx.

$\Sigma x = (-4) + 7 + 9 + (-3) + 6 + (-2) + (-3) + 8 = 18$

Next find n.

$n = 8$

Substitute these numbers into the equation

$$\bar{x} = \frac{\Sigma x}{n} = \frac{18}{8} = \frac{9}{4} \text{ (or 2.25)}$$

The mean of this set is $\frac{9}{4}$ or 2.25

● ● ● **CHECK YOURSELF 7**

Find the mean for each set of numbers.

a. 5, −2, 6, 3, −2

b. 6, −2, 3, 8, 5, −6, 1, −3

The mean and median usually produce different values for the average of a set of numbers. The mean is commonly used for averages in which each number in the set is equally important. When your instructor computes your average grade, the mean is almost definitely the method used.

On the other hand, if you were reading an article about average income in some area, the median would probably be used. One advantage of the median is that extreme values are not overly influential. What if Bill Gates lived in the area in which the "average income" was being computed? It is likely that his income (which could be in the hundred millions of dollars per year) would cause the mean to be so high that it would not be at all typical of the actual incomes of the people surveyed.

In Example 8 you will be asked to compute both the median and the mean for each set of numbers. You will be asked to consider which type of average seems more appropriate for the set.

● Example 8

Finding the Median and the Mean

During a week in February the low temperature in Fargo, North Dakota was recorded each day. The results are presented in the following table. Find both the median and the mean for the set of numbers.

M	T	W	Th	F	Sa	Su
−11	−17	−15	−18	−20	−2	20

To find the median we place the numbers in ascending order:

−20   −18   −17   −15   −11   −2   20

The median is the middle value, so the median is −15 degrees.

To find the mean, we first find Σx.

$$\Sigma x = (-11) + (-17) + (-15) + (-18) + (-20) + (-2) + 20 = -63$$

Then, given that $n = 7$, we use the equation for the mean.

$$\bar{x} = \frac{\Sigma x}{n} = \frac{-63}{7} = -9$$

The mean is −9.

Which average was more appropriate? There is really no "right" answer to that question. In this case, the median would probably be preferred by most statisticians. It yields a temperature that was actually the low temperature on Wednesday of that week, so it is more representative of the set of low temperatures.

● ● ● **CHECK YOURSELF 8**

The low temperatures in Anchorage, Alaska, for 1 week in January are given in the following table. Compute both the mean and the median low temperature for that week.

M	T	W	Th	F	Sa	Su
6	-10	-12	-22	-28	-26	-27

● ● ● **CHECK YOURSELF ANSWERS**

1. 4. **2.** -6. **3.** 6. **4. a.** 21; **b.** -32. **5.** 27. **6.** -6. **7. a.** 2; **b.** 1.5.
8. median $= -22$, mean $= -17$.

3.2 Exercises

Solve for x and check your result.

1. $5x = 20$

2. $6x = 30$

3. $9x = 54$

4. $6x = -42$

5. $63 = 9x$

6. $66 = 6x$

7. $4x = -16$

8. $-3x = 27$

9. $-9x = 72$

10. $10x = -100$

11. $6x = -54$

12. $-7x = 49$

13. $-4x = -12$

14. $52 = -4x$

15. $-42 = 6x$

16. $-7x = -35$

17. $-6x = -54$

18. $-4x = -24$

19. $\dfrac{x}{2} = 4$

20. $\dfrac{x}{3} = 2$

21. $\dfrac{x}{5} = 3$

22. $\dfrac{x}{8} = 5$

23. $6 = \dfrac{x}{7}$

24. $6 = \dfrac{x}{3}$

25. $\dfrac{x}{5} = -4$

26. $\dfrac{x}{7} = -5$

1. _____
2. _____
3. _____
4. _____
5. _____
6. _____
7. _____
8. _____
9. _____
10. _____
11. _____
12. _____
13. _____
14. _____
15. _____
16. _____
17. _____
18. _____
19. _____
20. _____
21. _____
22. _____
23. _____
24. _____
25. _____
26. _____

27. $-\dfrac{x}{3} = 8$ **28.** $-\dfrac{x}{4} = -3$

29. $\dfrac{2}{3}x = 6$ **30.** $\dfrac{4}{5}x = 8$

31. $\dfrac{3}{4}x = -15$ **32.** $\dfrac{7}{8}x = -21$

33. $-\dfrac{2}{5}x = 10$ **34.** $-\dfrac{5}{6}x = -15$

35. $5x + 4x = 36$ **36.** $8x - 3x = -50$

37. $16x - 9x = -42$ **38.** $5x + 7x = 60$

39. $4x - 2x + 7x = 36$ **40.** $6x + 7x - 5x = -48$

Once again, certain equations involving decimal fractions can be solved by the methods of this section. For instance, to solve $2.3x = 6.9$ we simply use our multiplication property to divide both sides of the equation by 2.3. This will isolate x on the left as desired. Use this idea to solve each of the following equations for x.

41. $3.2x = 12.8$ **42.** $5.1x = -15.3$

43. $-4.5x = 13.5$ **44.** $-8.2x = -32.8$

45. $1.3x + 2.8x = 12.3$ **46.** $2.7x + 5.4x = -16.2$

47. $9.3x - 6.2x = 12.4$ **48.** $12.5x - 7.2x = -21.2$

Translate each of the following statements to an equation. Let x represent the number in each case.

49. 5 times a number is 40.   **50.** Twice a number is 36.

51. A number divided by 7 is equal to 6.   **52.** A number divided by 5 is equal to -4.

53. $\dfrac{1}{3}$ of a number is 8.   **54.** $\dfrac{1}{5}$ of a number is 10.

55. $\dfrac{3}{4}$ of a number is 18.

56. $\dfrac{2}{7}$ of a number is 8.

57. Twice a number, divided by 5, is 12.

58. 3 times a number, divided by 4, is 36.

Find the mean of each data set.

59. 2, 3, 4, 5, 6

60. 1, 3, 8, 10, 18

61. $-3, -1, 2, 4, 6, 10$

62. $-5, -2, 1, 4, 6, 8$

63. $-\dfrac{3}{2}, -1, 2, \dfrac{5}{2}, 3, 7$

64. $-\dfrac{4}{3}, -\dfrac{1}{3}, \dfrac{2}{3}, 5, 6$

65. $-3.4, -1.5, -.8, 2.3, 3, 6.4$

66. $-4.3, -2.1, -1.6, 2, 6, 8$

67. Plant density. Assume that tropical forests contain 457 metric tons (t) of plants per hectare and that the equation $0.45x = 457$ describes the amount of plant material in the average Pacific northwest forest. About how many metric tons of plant material per hectare does a typical Pacific northwest forest contain?

68. Plant density. A typical forest contains only one-tenth of the plant material of some redwood forests of the northern California coast. Use an equation similar to that of Exercise 67 to determine the amount of plant material per hectare in some redwood forests.

69. Forestland. In the mid-1980s, Canada had 1.5 times as much forestland as the United States. If Canada had 4.4 million square kilometers (km^2) of forestland in 1986, approximately how much forestland was in the United States?

70. Number problem. The sum of 4 times a number and 14 is 34. Find the number.

71. Number problem. If 6 times a number is subtracted from 42, the result is 24. Find the number.

72. Number problem. When a number is divided by -6, the result is 3. Find the number.

ANSWERS

55. _____

56. _____

57. _____

58. _____

59. _____

60. _____

61. _____

62. _____

63. _____

64. _____

65. _____

66. _____

67. _____

68. _____

69. _____

70. _____

71. _____

72. _____

73. _____

74. _____

75. _____

a. _____

b. _____

c. _____

d. _____

e. _____

f. _____

g. _____

h. _____

73. Average weight. Kareem bought four bags of candy. The weights of the bags were 16 ounces (oz), 21 oz, 18 oz, and 15 oz. Find the mean and median weight of the bags of candy.

74. Average savings. Jose has savings accounts for each of his five children. They contain $215, $156, $318, $75, and $25. Find the mean and median amount of money per account.

75. In your math class, your teacher says that there will be five tests and the grade for the course will be based on the *average* if these five tests. You study hard and try your best during the whole course, and at the end, you compute both the mean and the median of your scores.

   (a) After looking at your scores, you want to convince the teacher that she should use the mean to compute your *average*. Write a note to your teacher explaining why this is a better choice. Choose numbers for your test scores that make a convincing argument.

   (b) After looking at the scores, you hope the teacher will use the median as the average. Write a note to the teacher explaining why you would like her to use the median. Be sure to include your test scores in your explanation.

Getting Ready for Section 3.3 [Section 1.3]

Use the distributive property to remove the parentheses in the following expressions.

a. $2(x - 3)$ **b.** $3(a + 4)$ **c.** $5(2b + 1)$ **d.** $3(3p - 4)$

e. $7(3x - 4)$ **f.** $-4(5x + 4)$ **g.** $-3(4x - 3)$ **h.** $-5(3y - 2)$

Answers

1. 4   **3.** 6   **5.** 7   **7.** -4 **9.** -8 **11.** -9 **13.** 3   **15.** -7

17. 9   **19.** 8   **21.** 15   **23.** 42   **25.** -20 **27.** -24 **29.** 9

31. -20 **33.** -25 **35.** 4   **37.** -6 **39.** 4   **41.** 4   **43.** -3

45. 3   **47.** 4   **49.** $5x = 40$ **51.** $\frac{x}{7} = 6$ **53.** $\frac{x}{3} = 8$ **55.** $\frac{3}{4}x = 18$

57. $\frac{2x}{5} = 12$ **59.** 4   **61.** 3   **63.** 2   **65.** 1   **67.** 1016 t

69. 2.9 million km^2 **71.** 3   **73.** 17.5 oz; 17 oz   **a.** $2x - 6$

b. $3a + 12$ **c.** $10b + 5$ **d.** $9p - 12$ **e.** $21x - 28$ **f.** $-20x - 16$

g. $-12x + 9$ **h.** $-15y + 10$

3.3 Combining the Rules to Solve Equations

3.3 OBJECTIVE

Use both the addition and multiplication properties to solve equations

In all our examples thus far, either the addition property or the multiplication property was used in solving an equation. Often, finding a solution will require the use of both properties.

• Example 1

Solving Equations

(a) Solve

$$4x - 5 = 7$$

Here x is *multiplied* by 4. The result, $4x$, then has 5 subtracted from it on the left side of the equation. These two operations mean that both properties must be applied in solving the equation.

Since the variable term is already on the left, we start by adding 5 to both sides:

Note: We usually show the steps of the solution in a *horizontal form*, which is what you will probably want to use in practice.

$$4x - 5 + 5 = 7 + 5 \qquad \text{or} \qquad 4x = 12$$

We now divide both sides by 4:

$$\frac{4x}{4} = \frac{12}{4}$$
$$x = 3$$

The solution is 3. To check, replace x with 3 in the original equation. Be careful to follow the rules for the order of operations.

$$4 \cdot 3 - 5 \stackrel{?}{=} 7$$
$$12 - 5 \stackrel{?}{=} 7$$
$$7 = 7 \qquad \text{(True)}$$

(b) Solve

$$3x + 8 = -4$$
$$3x + 8 - 8 = -4 - 8 \qquad \text{Subtract 8 from both sides.}$$
$$3x = -12$$

Now divide both sides by 3 to isolate x on the left.

$$\frac{3x}{3} = \frac{-12}{3}$$
$$x = -4$$

The solution is -4. We'll leave the check of this result to you.

● ● ● **CHECK YOURSELF 1**

Solve and check.

a. $6x + 9 = -15$ **b.** $5x - 8 = 7$

The variable may appear in any position in an equation. Just apply the rules carefully as you try to write an equivalent equation, and you will find the solution. Example 2 illustrates this property.

● Example 2

Solving Equations

Solve

$$3 - 2x = 9$$
$$3 - 3 - 2x = 9 - 3 \qquad \text{First subtract 3 from both sides.}$$
$$-2x = 6$$

Note: $\dfrac{-2}{-2} = 1$, so we divide by -2 to isolate x on the left.

Now divide both sides by -2. This will leave x alone on the left.

$$\frac{-2x}{-2} = \frac{6}{-2}$$
$$x = -3$$

The solution is -3. We'll leave it to you to check this result.

● ● ● **CHECK YOURSELF 2**

Solve and check.

$$10 - 3x = 1$$

You may also have to combine multiplication with addition or subtraction to solve an equation. Consider Example 3.

● Example 3

Solving Equations

(*a*) Solve

$$\frac{x}{5} - 3 = 4$$

To get the x term alone, we first add 3 to both sides.

$$\frac{x}{5} - 3 + 3 = 4 + 3$$
$$\frac{x}{5} = 7$$

Now, to undo the division multiply both sides of the equation by 5.

$$5\left(\frac{x}{5}\right) = 5 \cdot 7$$
$$x = 35$$

The solution is 35. Just return to the original equation to check the result.

$$\frac{35}{5} - 3 = 4$$
$$7 - 3 = 4$$
$$4 = 4 \qquad \text{(True)}$$

(b) Solve

$$\frac{2}{3}x + 5 = 13$$
$$\frac{2}{3}x + 5 - 5 = 13 - 5 \qquad \text{First subtract 5 from both sides.}$$
$$\frac{2}{3}x = 8$$

Now multiply both sides by $\frac{3}{2}$, the reciprocal of $\frac{2}{3}$.

$$\left(\frac{3}{2}\right)\left(\frac{2}{3}x\right) = \left(\frac{3}{2}\right)8$$

or

$$x = 12$$

The solution is 12. We'll leave it to you to check this result.

● ● ● **CHECK YOURSELF 3**

Solve and check.

a. $\dfrac{x}{6} + 5 = 3$ **b.** $\dfrac{3}{4}x - 8 = 10$

In Section 3.1, you learned how to solve certain equations when the variable appeared on both sides. Example 4 will show you how to extend that work by using the multiplication property of equality.

• Example 4

Combining Terms to Solve an Equation

Solve

$$6x - 4 = 3x - 2$$

First add 4 to both sides. This will undo the subtraction on the left.

$$6x - 4 = 3x - 2$$
$$6x - 4 + 4 = 3x - 2 + 4$$
$$6x = 3x + 2$$

Now subtract $3x$ so that the terms in x will be on the left only.

$$6x = 3x \qquad + 2$$
$$6x - 3x = 3x - 3x + 2$$
$$3x = \qquad 2$$

Finally divide by 3.

$$\frac{3x}{3} = \frac{2}{3}$$
$$x = \frac{2}{3}$$

Check:

$$6\left(\frac{2}{3}\right) - 4 \stackrel{?}{=} 3\left(\frac{2}{3}\right) - 2$$
$$4 - 4 \stackrel{?}{=} 2 - 2$$
$$0 = 0 \qquad \text{(True)}$$

As you know, the basic idea is to use our two properties to form an equivalent equation with the x isolated. Here we added 4 and then subtracted $3x$. You can do these steps in either order. Try it for yourself the other way. In either case, the multiplication property is then used as the *last step* in finding the solution.

● ● ●   **CHECK YOURSELF 4**

Solve and check.

$$7x - 5 = 3x + 5$$

Let's look at two approaches to solving equations in which the coefficient on the right side is greater than the coefficient on the left side.

• Example 5

Combining Terms to Solve an Equation (Two Methods)

Solve $4x - 8 = 7x + 7$.

Method 1

$4x - 8 = 7x + 7$

$4x - 8 + 8 = 7x + 7 + 8$ Adding 8 will leave the *x* term alone on the left.

$4x = 7x + 15$

$4x - 7x = 7x - 7x + 15$ Subtracting 7*x* will get the variable terms on the left.

$-3x = 15$

$\dfrac{-3x}{-3} = \dfrac{15}{-3}$ Dividing by -3 will isolate *x* on the left.

$x = -5$

We'll let you check this result.

To avoid a negative coefficient (in Example 5, -3), some students prefer a different approach.

This time we'll work toward having the number on the *left* and the *x* term on the *right,* or

$\boxed{} = x$

It is usually easier to isolate the variable term on the side that will result in a positive coefficient.

Method 2

$4x - 8 = 7x + 7$

$4x - 8 - 7 = 7x + 7 - 7$ Subtract 7.

$4x - 15 = 7x$

$4x - 4x - 15 = 7x - 4x$ Subtract 4*x* to get the variables on the right.

$-15 = 3x$

$\dfrac{-15}{3} = \dfrac{3x}{3}$ Divide by 3 to isolate *x* on the right.

$-5 = x$

Since $-5 = x$ and $x = -5$ are equivalent equations, it really makes no difference; the solution is still -5! You can use whichever approach you prefer.

● ● ● **CHECK YOURSELF 5**

Solve $5x + 3 = 9x - 21$ by finding equivalent equations of the form $x = \boxed{}$ and $\boxed{} = x$ to compare the two methods of finding the solution.

Where possible, we start by combining like terms on each side of the equation.

• Example 6

Combining Terms to Solve an Equation

Solve.

$$7x - 3 + 5x + 4 = 6x + 25$$
$$12x + 1 = 6x + 25$$
$$12x + 1 - 1 = 6x + 25 - 1 \qquad \text{Subtract 1.}$$
$$12x = 6x + 24$$
$$12x - 6x = 6x - 6x + 24 \qquad \text{Subtract } 6x.$$
$$6x = 24$$
$$\frac{6x}{6} = \frac{24}{6} \qquad \text{Divide by 6.}$$

or $\qquad x = 4$

The solution is 4. We leave the checking of this result to you.

● ● ● **CHECK YOURSELF 6**

Solve and check.

$$9x - 6 - 3x + 1 = 2x + 15$$

It may also be necessary to remove grouping symbols in solving an equation. Example 7 illustrates this property.

• Example 7

Solving Equations That Contain Parentheses

Solve and check.

$$5(x - 3) - 2x = x + 7 \qquad \text{First, apply the distributive property.}$$
$$5x - 15 - 2x = x + 7 \qquad \text{Combine like terms.}$$
$$3x - 15 = x + 7$$
$$3x - 15 + 15 = x + 7 + 15 \qquad \text{Add 15.}$$
$$3x = x + 22$$
$$3x - x = x - x + 22 \qquad \text{Subtract } x.$$
$$2x = 22 \qquad \text{Divide by 2.}$$
$$x = 11$$

Note: $5(x - 3)$
$= 5(x) - 5(3)$
$= 5x - 15$

The solution is 11. To check, substitute 11 for x in the original equation. Again note the use of our rules for the order of operations.

$5(11 - 3) - 2 \cdot 11 \stackrel{?}{=} 11 + 7$ Simplify terms in parentheses.

$5 \cdot 8 - 2 \cdot 11 \stackrel{?}{=} 11 + 7$ Multiply.

$40 - 22 \stackrel{?}{=} 11 + 7$ Add and subtract.

$18 = 18$ A true statement.

● ● ●   **CHECK YOURSELF 7**

Solve and check.

$7(x + 5) - 3x = x - 7$

---

*Such an outline of steps is sometimes called an **algorithm** for the process.*

    Let's summarize our work with an outline of the steps involved in solving linear equations.

Solving Linear Equations

Step 1   Use the distributive property to remove any grouping symbols. Then simplify by combining like terms on each side of the equation.

Step 2   Add or subtract the same term on each side of the equation until the term involving the variable is on one side and a number is on the other.

Step 3   Multiply or divide both sides of the equation by the same nonzero number so that the variable is alone on one side of the equation.

Step 4   Check the solution in the original equation.

Consecutive Integers

Consecutive integers are integers that follow one another, like 10, 11, and 12. To represent them in algebra:

If x is an integer, then $x + 1$ is the next consecutive integer, $x + 2$ is the next, and so on.

We'll need this idea in Example 8.

•Example 8

Solving an Application

The sum of two consecutive integers is 41. What are the two integers?

Step 1   We want to find the two consecutive integers.

Step 2   Let x be the first integer. Then $x + 1$ must be the next.

Step 3

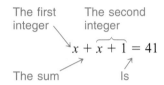

The first integer   The second integer

$$x + x + 1 = 41$$

The sum   Is

Step 4

$$x + x + 1 = 41$$
$$2x + 1 = 41$$
$$2x = 40$$
$$x = 20$$

The first integer (x) is 20, and the next integer ($x + 1$) is 21.

Step 5   The sum of the two integers 20 and 21 is 41.

● ● ●   **CHECK YOURSELF 8**

The sum of three consecutive integers is 51. What are the three integers?

Sometimes algebra is used to reconstruct missing information. Example 9 does just that with some election information.

•Example 9

Solving an Application

There were 55 more yes votes than no votes on an election measure. If 735 votes were cast in all, how many yes votes were there? How many no votes?

Step 1   We want to find the number of yes votes and the number of no votes.

Step 2   Let x be the number of no votes. Then

$$\underbrace{x + 55}$$

55 more than x

is the number of yes votes.

Write an equation.

Step 3

$$x + x + 55 = 735$$

No votes   Yes votes

Solve the equation.

Step 4

$$x + x + 55 = 735$$
$$2x + 55 = 735$$
$$2x = 680$$
$$x = 340$$
$$\text{No votes } (x) = 340$$
$$\text{Yes votes } (x + 55) = 395$$

Check.

Step 5 Thus 340 no votes plus 395 yes votes equals 735 total votes. The solution checks.

● ● ●   **CHECK YOURSELF 9**

Francine earns $120 per month more than Rob. If they earn a total of $2680 per month, what are their monthly salaries?

    Similar methods will allow you to solve a variety of word problems. Example 10 includes three unknown quantities but uses the same basic solution steps.

•Example 10

Solving an Application

There are other choices for x, but choosing the smallest quantity will usually give the easiest equation to write and solve.

Juan worked twice as many hours as Jerry. Marcia worked 3 more hours than Jerry. If they worked a total of 31 hours, find out how many hours each worked.

Step 1   We want to find the hours each worked, so there are three unknowns.

Step 2   Let x be the hours that Jerry worked.

Twice Jerry's hours

Then $2x$ is Juan's hours worked

3 more hours than Jerry worked

and $x + 3$ is Marcia's hours.

Step 3

Jerry   Juan   Marcia

$$x + 2x + x + 3 = 31$$

Sum of their hours

Step 4

$$x + 2x + x + 3 = 31$$
$$4x + 3 = 31$$
$$4x = 28$$
$$x = 7$$

Jerry's hours (x) = 7

Juan's hours ($2x$) = 14

Marcia's hours ($x + 3$) = 10

Step 5   The sum of their hours (7 + 14 + 10) is 31, and the solution is verified.

● ● ●   **CHECK YOURSELF 10**

Lucy jogged twice as many miles (mi) as Paul but 3 less than Isaac. If the three ran a total of 23 mi, how far did each person run?

───

● ● ●   **CHECK YOURSELF ANSWERS**

1. (a) −4; **(b)** 3.   **2.** 3.   **3. (a)** −12; **(b)** 24.   **4.** $\dfrac{5}{2}$.   **5.** 6.   **6.** 5.   **7.** −14.
8. The equation is $x + x + 1 + x + 2 = 51$. The integers are 16, 17, and 18.
9. The equation is $x + x + 120 = 2680$. Rob's salary is $1280, and Francine's is
$1400.   **10.** Paul: 4 mi; Lucy: 8 mi; Isaac: 11 mi.

───

3.3 Exercises

Name

Section   Date

Solve for x and check your result.

1. $2x + 1 = 9$

2. $3x - 1 = 17$

3. $3x - 2 = 7$

4. $5x + 3 = 23$

5. $4x + 7 = 35$

6. $7x - 8 = 13$

7. $2x + 9 = 5$

8. $6x + 25 = -5$

9. $4 - 7x = 18$

10. $8 - 5x = -7$

11. $3 - 4x = -9$

12. $5 - 4x = 25$

13. $\dfrac{x}{2} + 1 = 5$

14. $\dfrac{x}{3} - 2 = 3$

15. $\dfrac{x}{4} - 5 = 3$

16. $\dfrac{x}{5} + 3 = 8$

17. $\dfrac{2}{3}x + 5 = 17$

18. $\dfrac{3}{4}x - 5 = 4$

19. $\dfrac{4}{5}x - 3 = 13$

20. $\dfrac{5}{7}x + 4 = 14$

21. $5x = 2x + 9$

22. $7x = 18 - 2x$

23. $3x = 10 - 2x$

24. $11x = 7x + 20$

25. $9x + 2 = 3x + 38$

26. $8x - 3 = 4x + 17$

1. _____

2. _____

3. _____

4. _____

5. _____

6. _____

7. _____

8. _____

9. _____

10. _____

11. _____

12. _____

13. _____

14. _____

15. _____

16. _____

17. _____

18. _____

19. _____

20. _____

21. _____

22. _____

23. _____

24. _____

25. _____

26. _____

27. $4x - 8 = x - 14$

28. $6x - 5 = 3x - 29$

29. $5x + 7 = 2x - 3$

30. $9x + 7 = 5x - 3$

31. $7x - 3 = 9x + 5$

32. $5x - 2 = 8x - 11$

33. $5x + 4 = 7x - 8$

34. $2x + 23 = 6x - 5$

35. $2x - 3 + 5x = 7 + 4x + 2$

36. $8x - 7 - 2x = 2 + 4x - 5$

37. $6x + 7 - 4x = 8 + 7x - 26$

38. $7x - 2 - 3x = 5 + 8x + 13$

39. $9x - 2 + 7x + 13 = 10x - 13$

40. $5x + 3 + 6x - 11 = 8x + 25$

41. $8x - 7 + 5x - 10 = 10x - 12$

42. $10x - 9 + 2x - 3 = 8x - 18$

43. $7(2x - 1) - 5x = x + 25$

44. $9(3x + 2) - 10x = 12x - 7$

45. $3x + 2(4x - 3) = 6x - 9$

46. $7x + 3(2x + 5) = 10x + 17$

47. $\dfrac{8}{3}x - 3 = \dfrac{2}{3}x + 15$

48. $\dfrac{12}{5}x + 7 = 31 - \dfrac{3}{5}x$

49. $\dfrac{2}{5}x - 5 = \dfrac{12}{5}x + 8$

50. $\dfrac{3}{7}x - 5 = \dfrac{24}{7}x + 7$

51. $5.3x - 7 = 2.3x + 5$

52. $9.8x + 2 = 3.8x + 20$

Translate each of the following statements to an equation. Let x represent the number in each case.

53. 3 more than twice a number is 7.

54. 5 less than 3 times a number is 25.

55. 7 less than 4 times a number is 41.

56. 10 more than twice a number is 44.

57. 5 more than two-thirds of a number is 21.

58. 3 less than three-fourths of a number is 24.

59. 3 times a number is 12 more than that number.

60. 5 times a number is 8 less than that number.

61. Number addition. The sum of twice a number and 7 is 33. What is the number?

62. Number addition. 3 times a number, increased by 8, is 50. Find the number.

63. Number subtraction. 5 times a number, minus 12, is 78. Find the number.

64. Number subtraction. 4 times a number, decreased by 20, is 44. What is the number?

65. Consecutive integers. The sum of two consecutive integers is 71. Find the two integers.

66. Consecutive integers. The sum of two consecutive integers is 145. Find the two integers.

67. Consecutive integers. The sum of three consecutive integers is 63. What are the three integers?

68. Consecutive integers. If the sum of three consecutive integers is 93, find the three integers.

69. Even integers. The sum of two consecutive even integers is 66. What are the two integers? (*Hint:* Consecutive even integers such as 10, 12, and 14 can be represented by x, $x + 2$, $x + 4$, and so on.)

70. Even integers. If the sum of two consecutive even integers is 86, find the two integers.

ANSWERS

55. _____
56. _____
57. _____
58. _____
59. _____
60. _____
61. _____
62. _____
63. _____
64. _____
65. _____
66. _____
67. _____
68. _____
69. _____
70. _____

71. _____

72. _____

73. _____

74. _____

75. _____

76. _____

77. _____

78. _____

79. _____

80. _____

81. _____

82. _____

83. _____

71. Odd integers. If the sum of two consecutive odd integers is 52, what are the two integers? (*Hint:* Consecutive odd integers such as 21, 23, and 25 can be represented by $x, x + 2, x + 4$, and so on.)

72. Odd integers. The sum of two consecutive odd integers is 88. Find the two integers.

73. Odd integers. The sum of three consecutive odd integers is 105. What are the three integers?

74. Even integers. The sum of three consecutive even integers is 126. What are the three integers?

75. Consecutive integers. The sum of four consecutive integers is 86. What are the four integers?

76. Consecutive integers. The sum of four consecutive integers is 62. What are the four integers?

77. Consecutive integers. 4 times an integer is 9 more than 3 times the next consecutive integer. What are the two integers?

78. Consecutive integers. 4 times an integer is 30 less than 5 times the next consecutive even integer. Find the two integers.

79. Election votes. In an election, the winning candidate had 160 more votes than the loser. If the total number of votes cast was 3260, how many votes did each candidate receive?

80. Monthly salaries. Jody earns $140 more per month than Frank. If their monthly salaries total $2760, what amount does each earn?

81. Appliance costs. A washer-dryer combination costs $650. If the washer costs $70 more than the dryer, what does each appliance cost?

82. Length of materials. Yuri has a board that is 98 inches (in.) long. He wishes to cut the board into two pieces so that one piece will be 10 in. longer than the other. What should be the length of each piece?

83. Age. Yan Ling is 1 year less than twice as old as his sister. If the sum of their ages is 14 years, how old is Yan Ling?

A N S W E R S

84. _____

85. _____

86. _____

87. _____

88. _____

89. _____

90. _____

91. _____

92. _____

84. Age. Diane is twice as old as her brother Dan. If the sum of their ages is 27 years, how old are Diane and her brother?

85. Age. Maritza is 3 years less than 4 times as old as her daughter. If the sum of their ages is 37, how old is Maritza?

86. Age. Mrs. Jackson is 2 years more than 3 times as old as her son. If the difference between their ages is 22 years, how old is Mrs. Jackson?

87. Airfare costs. On her vacation in Europe, Jovita's expenses for food and lodging were $60 less than twice as much as her airfare. If she spent $2400 in all, what was her airfare?

88. Earnings. Rachel earns $6000 less than twice as much as Tom. If their two incomes total $48,000, how much does each earn?

89. Number of students. There are 99 students registered in three sections of algebra. There are twice as many students in the 10 AM section as the 8 AM section and 7 more students at 12 PM than at 8 AM. How many students are in each section?

90. Gallons of fuel. The Randolphs used 12 more gallons (gal) of fuel oil in October than in September and twice as much oil in November as in September. If they used 132 gal for the 3 months, how much was used during each month?

91. Complete this statement in your own words: "You can tell that an equation is a linear equation when . . . ."

92. Maxine lives in Pittsburgh, Pennsylvania, and pays 8.33 cents per kilowatt hour (kwh) for electricity. During the 6 months of cold winter weather, her household uses about 1500 kwh of electric power per month. During the two hottest summer months, the usage is also high because the family uses electricity to run an air conditioner. During these summer months, the usage is 1200 kwh per month; the rest of the year, usage averages 900 kwn per month.

(a) Write an expression for the total yearly electric bill.

(b) Maxine is considering spending $2000 for more insulation for her home so that it is less expensive to heat and to cool. The insulation company claims that "with proper installation the insulation will reduce your heating and cooling bills by 25 percent." If Maxine invests the money in insulation, how long will it take her to get her money back in saving on her electric bill? Write to her about what information she needs to answer this question. Give her your opinion about how long it will take to save $2000 on heating bills, and explain your reasoning. What is your advice to Maxine?

Getting Ready for Section 3.4 [Section 1.4]

Evaluate the following where $a = 3$, $b = 4$, and $c = 5$.

a. $\dfrac{3b}{3}$

b. $\dfrac{5a}{5}$

c. $\dfrac{4ab}{4a}$

d. $\dfrac{6a^2 b}{6a^2}$

e. $\dfrac{7ab^2}{7b^2}$

f. $\dfrac{\pi ab}{\pi a}$

g. $\dfrac{abc}{ab}$

h. $\dfrac{a^2 bc}{a^2 c}$

Answers

1. 4   **3.** 3   **5.** 7   **7.** -2 **9.** -2 **11.** 3   **13.** 8   **15.** 32

17. 18   **19.** 20   **21.** 3   **23.** 2   **25.** 6   **27.** -2 **29.** $-\dfrac{10}{3}$

31. -4 **33.** 6   **35.** 4   **37.** 5   **39.** -4 **41.** $\dfrac{5}{3}$ **43.** 4

45. $-\dfrac{3}{5}$ **47.** 9   **49.** $-\dfrac{13}{2}$ **51.** 4   **53.** $2x + 3 = 7$

55. $4x - 7 = 41$ **57.** $\dfrac{2}{3}x + 5 = 21$ **59.** $3x = x + 12$ **61.** 13

63. 18   **65.** 35, 36   **67.** 20, 21, 22   **69.** 32, 34   **71.** 25, 27

73. 33, 35, 37   **75.** 20, 21, 22, 23   **77.** 12, 13   **79.** 1710, 1550

81. Washer $360; dryer, $290   **83.** 9 years old   **85.** 29 years old

87. $820   **89.** 8 AM: 23, 10 AM: 46, 12 PM: 30   **a.** -4

b. 3   **c.** 5   **d.** -4 **e.** 3   **f.** -4 **g.** 5   **h.** -4

Solving Literal Equations

3.4 OBJECTIVES

1. Solve a literal equation for any one of its variables
2. Solve applications involving geometric figures

Formulas are extremely useful tools in any field in which mathematics is applied. Formulas are simply equations that express a relationship between more than one letter or variable. You are no doubt familiar with all kinds of formulas, such as

$$A = \frac{1}{2}bh \qquad \text{The area of a triangle.}$$

$$I = Prt \qquad \text{Interest.}$$

$$V = \pi r^2 h \qquad \text{The volume of a cylinder.}$$

Actually a formula is also called a **literal equation** because it involves several letters or variables. For instance, our first formula or literal equation, $A = \frac{1}{2}bh$, involves the three letters A (for area), b (for base), and h (for height).

Unfortunately, formulas are not always given in the form needed to solve a particular problem. Then algebra is needed to change the formula to a more useful equivalent equation, which is solved for a particular letter or variable. The steps used in the process are very similar to those you used in solving linear equations. Let's consider an example.

• Example 1

Solving a Literal Equation Involving a Triangle

Suppose that we know the area A and the base b of a triangle and want to find its height h.

We are given

$$A = \frac{1}{2}bh$$

Our job is to find an equivalent equation with h, the unknown, by itself on one side. We call $\frac{1}{2}b$ the **coefficient** of h. We can remove the two *factors* of that coefficient, $\frac{1}{2}$ and b, separately.

Note:
$$2\left(\frac{1}{2}bh\right) = \left(2 \cdot \frac{1}{2}\right)(bh)$$
$$= 1 \cdot bh$$
$$= bh$$

$$2A = 2\left(\frac{1}{2}bh\right) \qquad \text{Multiply both sides by 2 to clear the equation of fractions.}$$

or

$$2A = bh$$

$$\frac{2A}{b} = \frac{bh}{b} \qquad \text{Divide by } b \text{ to isolate } h.$$

$$\frac{2A}{b} = h$$

or

$$h = \frac{2A}{b}$$ Reverse the sides to write h on the left.

We now have the height h in terms of the area A and the base b. This is called **solving the equation for h** and means that we are rewriting the formula as an equivalent equation of the form

Here $\square$ means an expression containing all the numbers or letters *other than* h.

$$h = \square$$

● ● ● **CHECK YOURSELF 1**

Solve $V = \frac{1}{3}Bh$ for h.

You have already learned the methods needed to solve most literal equations or formulas for some specified variable. As Example 1 illustrates, the rules of Sections 3.2 and 3.3 are applied in exactly the same way as they were applied to equations with one variable.

You may have to apply both the addition and the multiplication properties when solving a formula for a specified variable. Example 2 illustrates this property.

● Example 2

Solving a Literal Equation

This is a linear equation in two variables. You will see this again in Chapter 7.

Solve $y = mx + b$ for x.

Remember that we want to end up with x alone on one side of the equation. Let's start by subtracting b from both sides to undo the addition on the right.

$$y = mx + b$$
$$y - b = mx + b - b$$
$$y - b = mx$$

If we now divide both sides by m, then x will be alone on the right-hand side.

$$\frac{y - b}{m} = \frac{mx}{m}$$

$$\frac{y - b}{m} = x$$

or

$$x = \frac{y - b}{m}$$

● ● ● **CHECK YOURSELF 2**

Solve $v = v_0 + gt$ for t.

Let's summarize the steps illustrated by our examples.

Solving a Formula or Literal Equation

STEP 1 If necessary, multiply both sides of the equation by the same term to clear of fractions.

STEP 2 Add or subtract the same term on both sides of the equation so that all terms involving the variable that you are solving for are on one side of the equation and all other terms are on the other side.

STEP 3 Divide both sides of the equation by the coefficient of the variable that you are solving for.

Let's look at one more example, using the above steps.

•Example 3

Solving a Literal Equation Involving Money

This is a formula for the *amount* of money in an account after interest has been earned.

Solve $A = P + Prt$ for r.

$$A = P + Prt$$

$$A - P = P - P + Prt$$ Subtracting P from both sides will leave the term involving r alone on the right.

$$A - P = Prt$$

$$\frac{A - P}{Pt} = \frac{Prt}{Pt}$$ Dividing both sides by Pt will isolate r on the right.

$$\frac{A - P}{Pt} = r$$

or

$$r = \frac{A - P}{Pt}$$

● ● ● **CHECK YOURSELF 3**

Solve $2x + 3y = 6$ for y.

Now let's look at an application of solving a literal equation.

• Example 4

Solving a Literal Equation Involving Money

Suppose that the amount in an account, 3 years after a principal of $5000 was invested, is $6050. What was the interest rate?

From our previous example,

$$A = P + Prt \tag{1}$$

where A is the amount in the account, P is the principal, r is the interest rate, and t is the time that the money has been invested. By the result of Example 3 we have

$$r = \frac{A - P}{Pt} \tag{2}$$

Do you see the advantage of having our equation solved for the desired variable?

and we can substitute the known values in equation (2):

$$r = \frac{6050 - 5000}{(5000)(3)}$$

$$= \frac{1050}{15,000} = 0.07 = 7\%$$

The interest rate is 7 percent.

● ● ● **CHECK YOURSELF 4**

Suppose that the amount in an account, 4 years after a principal of $3000 was invested, is $3720. What was the interest rate?

● ● ● **CHECK YOURSELF ANSWERS**

1. $h = \dfrac{3V}{B}$.

2. $t = \dfrac{v - v_0}{g}$.

3. $y = \dfrac{6 - 2x}{3}$ or $y = -\dfrac{2}{3}x + 2$.

4. 6 percent.

3.4 Exercises

Solve each literal equation for the indicated variable.

1. $p = 4s$ (for s)   Perimeter of a square

2. $V = Bh$ (for B)   Volume of a prism

3. $E = IR$ (for R)   Voltage in an electric circuit

4. $I = Prt$ (for r)   Simple interest

5. $V = LWH$ (for H)   Volume of a rectangular solid

6. $V = \pi r^2 h$ (for h)   Volume of a cylinder

7. $A + B + C = 180$ (for B)   Measure of angles in a triangle

8. $P = I^2 R$ (for R)   Power in an electric circuit

9. $ax + b = 0$ (for x)   Linear equation in one variable

10. $y = mx + b$ (for m)   Point-slope form for a line

11. $s = \dfrac{1}{2} gt^2$ (for g)   Distance

12. $K = \dfrac{1}{2} mv^2$ (for m)   Energy

1. _____
2. _____
3. _____
4. _____
5. _____
6. _____
7. _____
8. _____
9. _____
10. _____
11. _____
12. _____

13. _____

14. _____

15. _____

16. _____

17. _____

18. _____

19. _____

20. _____

21. _____

22. _____

23. _____

24. _____

25. _____

26. _____

13. $x + 5y = 15$ (for y)   Linear equation

14. $2x + 3y = 6$ (for x)   Linear equation

15. $P = 2L + 2W$ (for L)   Perimeter of a rectangle

16. $ax + by = c$ (for y)   Linear equation in two variables

17. $V = \dfrac{KT}{P}$ (for T)   Volume of a gas

18. $V = \dfrac{1}{3}\pi r^2 h$ (for h)   Volume of a cone

19. $x = \dfrac{a + b}{2}$ (for b)   Average of two numbers

20. $D = \dfrac{C - s}{n}$ (for s)   Depreciation

21. $F = \dfrac{9}{5}C + 32$ (for C)   Celsius/Fahrenheit

22. $A = P + Prt$ (for t)   Amount at simple interest

23. $S = 2\pi r^2 + 2\pi rh$ (for h)   Total surface area of a cylinder

24. $A = \dfrac{1}{2}h (B + b)$ (for b)   Area of a trapezoid

25. Height of a solid. A rectangular solid has a base with length 8 centimeters (cm) and width 5 cm. If the volume of the solid is 120 cm^3, find the height of the solid. (See Exercise 5.)

26. Height of a cylinder. A cylinder has a radius of 4 inches (in.). If the volume of the cylinder is 144 π/in.^{3}, what is the height of the cylinder? (See Exercise 6.)

27. **Interest rate.** A principal of $3000 was invested in a savings account for 3 years. If the interest earned for the period was $450, what was the interest rate? (See Exercise 4.)

28. **Length of a rectangle.** If the perimeter of a rectangle is 60 feet (ft) and the width is 12 ft, find its length.

29. **Temperature conversion.** The high temperature in New York for a particular day was reported at 77°F. How would the same temperature have been given in degrees Celsius? (See Exercise 21.)

30. **Garden length.** Rose's garden is in the shape of a trapezoid. If the height of the trapezoid is 16 meters (m), one base is 20 m, and the area is 224 m^2, find the length of the other base. (See Exercise 24.)

We considered the notation for the four arithmetic operations on a calculator in Section 2.6. To review, those operations are indicated by the following:

Algebraic Expression	Calculator Expression
$a + b$	A + B
$a - b$	A − B
ab	A * B
$\dfrac{a}{b}$	A ÷ B

Using the above information, write a calculator expression for the given formula solved for the specified letter. (*Hint:* The operations of multiplication and division are done *in order* from left to right. Then the operations of addition and subtraction are performed in the same manner. You may have to insert parentheses in the following answers to achieve your desired result.)

31. $V = Bh$ (for h)

32. $I = Prt$ (for t)

33. $A = P + Prt$ (for t)

34. $A = \dfrac{1}{2}h(B + b)$ (for b)

27. _____

28. _____

29. _____

30. _____

31. _____

32. _____

33. _____

34. _____

⬤ Getting Ready for Section 3.5 [Section 2.1]

Perform the indicated operations.

a. $4 \cdot (8 \cdot 6) + 7$

b. $3 \cdot (8 - 5) + 10 \div 2$

c. $4(6 - 8) \div 4 + 5$

d. $8(7 - 3 \cdot 4) + 12(5 - 3)$

e. $-2(16 \div 4 \cdot 2) - 5(3 - 5)$

f. $8 \cdot (4 \cdot 5 - 2)(10 \div 2 \cdot 5)$

g. $-7(13 - 4 \cdot 2) \div (25 - 10 \cdot 2)$

h. $2(-25 + 5 \cdot 3) \cdot (4 - 3 \cdot 2)$

Answers

1. $\dfrac{p}{4}$ **3.** $\dfrac{E}{I}$ **5.** $\dfrac{V}{LW}$ **7.** $180 - A - C$ **9.** $-\dfrac{b}{a}$ **11.** $\dfrac{2s}{t^2}$

13. $\dfrac{15 - x}{5}$ or $-\dfrac{1}{5}x + 3$ **15.** $\dfrac{P - 2W}{2}$ **17.** $\dfrac{PV}{K}$ **19.** $2x - a$

21. $\dfrac{5}{9}(F - 32)$ or $\dfrac{5(F - 32)}{9}$ **23.** $\dfrac{S - 2\pi r^2}{2\pi r}$ or $\dfrac{S}{2\pi r} - r$

25. 3 cm **27.** 6% **29.** 25°C **31.** $h = V/B$ **33.** $t = (A - P)/(P * r)$

3.5 More on Linear Equations

© 1998 McGraw-Hill Companies

3.5 OBJECTIVES

1. Solve linear equations when signs of grouping are present
2. Solve applications involving numbers
3. Solve mixture problems
4. Solve motion problems

In Section 1.2, we looked at the distributive property. That property is used when solving equations where parentheses are involved.

Let's start by reviewing an example similar to those we considered earlier. We will then solve other equations involving grouping symbols.

• Example 1

Solving Equations with Parentheses

Solve for x:

$$5(2x - 1) = 25$$

First, multiply on the left to remove the parentheses, then solve as before.

$$10x - 5 = 25$$

$$10x - 5 + 5 = 25 + 5 \qquad \text{Add 5.}$$
$$10x = 30$$
$$\frac{10x}{10} = \frac{30}{10} \qquad \text{Divide by 10.}$$
$$x = 3$$

Again, returning to the *original equation* will catch any possible errors in the removal of the parentheses.

Left side	Right side
$5(2 \cdot 3 - 1) \stackrel{?}{=} 25$	
$5(6 - 1) \stackrel{?}{=} 25$	
$5 \cdot 5 \stackrel{?}{=} 25$	
$25 = 25$ (True)	

The answer is 3. To check, return to the *original equation*. Substitute 3 for x. Then evaluate the left and right sides separately.

● ● ● CHECK YOURSELF 1

Solve for x.

$$8(3x + 5) = 16$$

Be especially careful if a minus sign precedes a grouping symbol. The sign of each term inside the grouping symbol must be changed.

• Example 2

Solving Equations with Parentheses

Remember,

$-(3x + 1) = -3x - 1$

Change *both* signs.

Solve $8 - (3x + 1) = -8$.

First, remove the parentheses. The original equation then becomes

$8 - 3x - 1 = -8$

$-3x + 7 = -8$ Combine like terms.

$-3x + 7 - 7 = -8 - 7$ Subtract 7.

$-3x = -15$

$x = 5$ Divide by -3.

The solution is 5. You should verify this result.

● ● ●   **CHECK YOURSELF 2**

Solve for x.

$7 - (4x - 3) = 22$

Example 3 illustrates the solution process when more than one grouping symbol is involved in an equation.

● Example 3

Solving Equations with Parentheses

Solve $2(3x - 1) - 3(x + 5) = 4$.

$2(3x - 1) - 3(x + 5) = 4$ Use the distributive property to remove the parentheses.

$6x - 2 - 3x - 15 = 4$

$3x - 17 = 4$ Combine like terms on the left.

$3x = 21$ Add 17.

$x = 7$ Divide by 3.

The solution is 7.

To check, return to the original equation to replace x with 7.

Note how the rules for the order of operations are applied.

$2(3 \cdot 7 - 1) - 3(7 + 5) \overset{?}{=} 4$

$2(21 - 1) - 3(7 + 5) \overset{?}{=} 4$

$2 \cdot 20 - 3 \cdot 12 \overset{?}{=} 4$

$40 - 36 \overset{?}{=} 4$

$4 = 4$ (True)

The solution is verified.

● ● ●   **CHECK YOURSELF 3**

Solve for x.

$5(2x + 4) = 7 - 3(1 - 2x)$

Many applications lead to equations involving parentheses. That means the methods of Examples 2 and 3 will have to be applied during the solution process. Before we look at examples, you should review the five-step process for solving word problems found in Section 3.1.

These steps are illustrated in Example 4.

● Example 4

Solving Applications Using Parentheses

One number is 5 more than a second number. If 3 times the smaller number plus 4 times the larger is 104, find the two numbers.

Step 1 What are you asked to find? You must find the two numbers.

Step 2 Represent the unknowns. Let x be the smaller number. Then

"5 more than" x

$$x + 5$$

is the larger number.

Step 3 Write an equation.

Note that the parentheses are *essential* in writing the correct equation.

$$3x + 4(x + 5) = 104$$

3 times the smaller   Plus   4 times the larger

Step 4 Solve the equation.

$$3x + 4(x + 5) = 104$$
$$3x + 4x + 20 = 104$$
$$7x + 20 = 104$$
$$7x = 84$$
$$x = 12$$

The smaller number (x) is 12, and the larger number $(x + 5)$ is 17.

Step 5 Check the solution: 12 is the smaller number, and 17 is the larger number.

$$3 \cdot 12 + 4 \cdot 17 = 104 \qquad \text{(True)}$$

● ● ● CHECK YOURSELF 4

One number is 4 more than another. If 6 times the smaller minus 4 times the larger is 4, what are the two numbers?

The solutions for many problems from geometry will also yield equations involving parentheses. Consider Example 5.

• Example 5

Solving a Geometry Application

The length of a rectangle is 1 centimeter (cm) less than 3 times the width. If the perimeter is 54 cm, find the dimensions of the rectangle.

Step 1   You want to find the dimensions (the width and length).

Step 2   Let x be the width.

Then $3x - 1$ is the length.

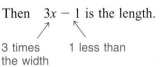

3 times   1 less than
the width

Step 3   To write an equation, we'll use this formula for the perimeter of a rectangle:

$$P = 2W + 2L$$

So

$$2x + 2(3x - 1) = 54$$

Twice the   Twice the   Perimeter
width   length

Step 4   Solve the equation.

$$2x + 2(3x - 1) = 54$$
$$2x + 6x - 2 = 54$$
$$8x = 56$$
$$x = 7$$

The width x is 7 cm, and the length, $3x - 1$, is 20 cm. We leave step 5, the check, to you.

Whenever you are working on an application involving geometric figures, you should draw a sketch of the problem, including the labels assigned in Step 2.

Length $3x - 1$

Width
x

Be sure to return to the original statement of the problem when checking your result.

● ● ●   **CHECK YOURSELF 5**

The length of a rectangle is 5 inches (in.) more than twice the width. If the perimeter of the rectangle is 76 in., what are the dimensions of the rectangle?

You will also often use parentheses in solving *mixture problems*. Mixture problems involve combining things that have a different value, rate, or strength. Look at Example 6.

•Example 6

Solving a Mixture Problem

Four hundred tickets were sold for a school play. General admission tickets were $4, while student tickets were $3. If the total ticket sales were $1350, how many of each type of ticket were sold?

Step 1   You want to find the number of each type of ticket sold.

Step 2   Let x be the number of general admission tickets.

Then $\underbrace{400 - x}$ student tickets were sold.

400 tickets were
sold in all.

We subtract x, the number of general admission tickets, from 400, the total number of tickets, to find the number of student tickets.

Step 3   The sales value for each kind of ticket is found by multiplying the price of the ticket by the number sold.

General admission tickets:	$4x$	$4 for each of the x tickets
Student tickets:	$3(400 - x)$	$3 for each of the $400 - x$ tickets

So to form an equation, we have

$$4x + \underbrace{3(400 - x)} = 1350$$

Value of general admission tickets   Value of student tickets   Total value

Step 4   Solve the equation.

$$4x + 3(400 - x) = 1350$$
$$4x + 1200 - 3x = 1350$$
$$x + 1200 = 1350$$
$$x = 150$$

So 150 general admission and 250 student tickets were sold. We leave the check to you.

●●●   **CHECK YOURSELF 6**

Beth bought 35¢ stamps and 15¢ stamps at the post office. If she purchased 60 stamps at a cost of $17, how many of each kind did she buy?

The next group of applications we will look at in this section involves *motion problems*. They involve a distance traveled, a rate or speed, and time. To solve motion problems, we need a relationship among these three quantities.

Suppose you travel at a rate of 50 miles per hour (mi/h) on a highway for 6 hours (h). How far (what distance) will you have gone? To find the distance, you multiply:

Be careful to make your units consistent. If a rate is given in *miles per hour*, then the time must be given in *hours* and the distance in *miles*.

$$(50 \text{ mi/h})(6 \text{ h}) = 300 \text{ mi}$$

Speed   Time   Distance
or rate

In general, if r is a rate, t is the time, and d is the distance traveled,

$$d = r \cdot t$$

This is the key relationship, and it will be used in all motion problems. Let's see how it is applied in Example 7.

• Example 7

Solving a Motion Problem

On Friday morning Ricardo drove from his house to the beach in 4 h. In coming back on Sunday afternoon, heavy traffic slowed his speed by 10 mi/h, and the trip took 5 h. What was his average speed (rate) in each direction?

Step 1   We want the speed or rate in each direction.

Step 2   Let x be Ricardo's speed to the beach. Then $x - 10$ is his return speed.
    It is always a good idea to sketch the given information in a motion problem. Here we would have

Going x mi/h for 4 h
    →

Returning   ← $x - 10$ mi/h for 5 h

Step 3   Since we know that the distance is the same each way, we can write an equation, using the fact that the product of the rate and the time each way must be the same.
    So

Distance (going)
= distance (returning)

or

Time · rate (going) = time · rate (returning)

$$4x = 5(x - 10)$$

Time · rate   Time · rate
(going)   (returning)

A chart can help summarize the given information. We begin by filling in the information given in the problem.

	Distance	Rate	Time
Going		x	4
Returning		$x - 10$	5

Now we fill in the missing information. Here we use the fact that $d = rt$ to complete the chart.

	Distance	Rate	Time
Going	$4x$	x	4
Returning	$5(x - 10)$	$x - 10$	5

From here we set the two distances equal to each other and solve as before.

Step 4 Solve.

$$4x = 5(x - 10)$$
$$4x = 5x - 50$$
$$-x = -50$$
$$x = 50 \text{ mi/h}$$

x was his rate going, x − 10 his rate returning.

So Ricardo's rate going to the beach was 50 mi/h, and his rate returning was 40 mi/h.

Step 5 To check, you should verify that the product of the time and the rate is the same in each direction.

● ● ● **CHECK YOURSELF 7**

A plane made a flight (with the wind) between two towns in 2 h. Returning against the wind, the plane's speed was 60 mi/h slower, and the flight took 3 h. What was the plane's speed in each direction?

Example 8 illustrates another way of using the distance relationship.

● Example 8

Solving a Motion Problem

Katy leaves Las Vegas for Los Angeles at 10 AM, driving at 50 mi/h. At 11 AM Jensen leaves Los Angeles for Las Vegas, driving at 55 mi/h along the same route. If the cities are 260 mi apart, at what time will they meet?

Step 1 Let's find the time that Katy travels until they meet.

Step 2 Let x be Katy's time.

Then $x - 1$ is Jensen's time.

Jensen left 1 h later!

Again, you should draw a sketch of the given information.

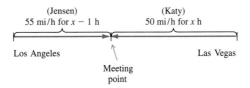

(Jensen)
55 mi/h for $x - 1$ h

(Katy)
50 mi/h for x h

Los Angeles

Las Vegas

Meeting
point

Step 3   To write an equation, we will again need the relationship $d = rt$. From this equation, we can write

Katy's distance = $50x$

Jensen's distance = $55(x - 1)$

As before, we can use a table to solve.

	Distance	Rate	Time
Katy	$50x$	50	x
Jensen	$55(x - 1)$	55	$x - 1$

From the original problem, the sum of those distances is 260 mi, so

$$50x + 55(x - 1) = 260$$

Step 4

$$50x + 55(x - 1) = 260$$
$$50x + 55x - 55 = 260$$
$$105x - 55 = 260$$
$$105x = 315$$
$$x = 3 \text{ h}$$

Be sure to answer the question asked in the problem.

Finally, since Katy left at 10 AM, the two will meet at 1 PM. We leave the check of this result to you.

● ● ●   **CHECK YOURSELF 8**

At noon a jogger leaves one point, running at 8 mi/h. One hour later a bicyclist leaves the same point, traveling at 20 mi/h in the opposite direction. At what time will they be 36 mi apart?

● ● ●   **CHECK YOURSELF ANSWERS**

1. -1.   **2.** -3.   **3.** -4.   **4.** The numbers are 10 and 14.   **5.** The width is 11 in.; the length is 27 in.   **6.** 40 at 35¢, and 20 at 15¢.   **7.** 180 mi/h with the wind and 120 mi/h against the wind.   **8.** At 2 PM

A N S W E R S

Solve each of the following equations for x, and check your results.

1. $3(x - 5) = 6$

2. $2(x + 3) = -6$

3. $5(2x + 3) = 35$

4. $4(3x - 5) = 88$

5. $7(5x + 8) = -84$

6. $6(3x + 2) = -60$

7. $10 - (x - 2) = 15$

8. $12 - (x + 3) = 3$

9. $5 - (2x + 1) = 12$

10. $9 - (3x - 2) = 2$

11. $7 - (3x - 5) = 13$

12. $5 - (4x + 3) = 4$

13. $5x = 3(x - 6)$

14. $5x = 2(x + 12)$

15. $7(2x - 3) = 20x$

16. $4(3x + 5) = 18x$

17. $6(6 - x) = 3x$

18. $5(8 - x) = 3x$

19. $2(2x - 1) = 3(x + 1)$

20. $3(3x - 1) = 4(2x + 1)$

21. $5(4x + 2) = 6(3x + 4)$

22. $4(6x - 1) = 7(3x + 2)$

23. $9(8x - 1) = 5(4x + 6)$

24. $7(3x + 11) = 9(3 - 6x)$

25. $-4(2x - 1) + 3(3x + 1) = 9$

26. $7(3x + 4) = 8(2x + 5) + 13$

1. _____

2. _____

3. _____

4. _____

5. _____

6. _____

7. _____

8. _____

9. _____

10. _____

11. _____

12. _____

13. _____

14. _____

15. _____

16. _____

17. _____

18. _____

19. _____

20. _____

21. _____

22. _____

23. _____

24. _____

25. _____

26. _____

A N S W E R S

27. _____

28. _____

29. _____

30. _____

31. _____

32. _____

33. _____

34. _____

35. _____

36. _____

37. _____

38. _____

39. _____

40. _____

27. $5(2x - 1) - 3(x - 4) = 4(x + 4)$ **28.** $2(x - 3) - 3(x + 5) = 3(x - 2) - 7$

29. $3(3 - 4x) + 30 = 5x - 2(6x - 7)$ **30.** $3x - 5(3x - 7) = 2(x + 9) + 45$

Translate each of the following statements to equations. Let x represent the number in each case.

31. Twice the sum of a number and 4 is 20.

32. The sum of twice a number and 4 is 20.

33. 3 times the difference of a number and 5 is 21.

34. The difference of 3 times a number and 5 is 21.

35. The sum of twice an integer and 3 times the next consecutive integer is 48.

36. The sum of 4 times an odd integer and twice the next consecutive odd integer is 46.

Solve each of the following equations.

37. $-2x + [3x - (-2x + 5)] = -(15 + 2x)$

38. $-3x + [5x - (-x + 4)] = -2(x - 3)$

39. $3x^2 - 2(x^2 + 2) = x^2 - 4$

40. $5x^2 - [2(2x^2 + 3)] - 3 = x^2 - 9$

Solve the following word problems. Be sure to show the equation you use for the solution.

41. **Number problem.** One number is 8 more than another. If the sum of the smaller number and twice the larger number is 46, find the two numbers.

42. **Number problem.** One number is 3 less than another. If 4 times the smaller number minus 3 times the larger number is 4, find the two numbers.

43. **Number problem.** One number is 7 less than another. If 4 times the smaller number plus 2 times the larger number is 62, find the two numbers.

44. **Number problem.** One number is 10 more than another. If the sum of twice the smaller number and 3 times the larger number is 55, find the two numbers.

45. **Consecutive integers.** Find two consecutive integers such that the sum of twice the first integer and 3 times the second integer is 28. (*Hint:* If x represents the first integer, $x + 1$ represents the next consecutive integer.)

46. **Consecutive integers.** Find two consecutive odd integers such that 3 times the first integer is 5 more than twice the second. (*Hint:* If x represents the first integer, $x + 2$ represents the next consecutive odd integer.)

47. **Dimensions of a rectangle.** The length of a rectangle is 1 inch (in.) more than twice its width. If the perimeter of the rectangle is 74 in., find the dimensions of the rectangle.

48. **Dimensions of a rectangle.** The length of a rectangle is 5 centimeters (cm) less than 3 times its width. If the perimeter of the rectangle is 46 cm, find the dimensions of the rectangle.

49. **Garden size.** The length of a rectangular garden is 4 meters (m) more than 3 times its width. The perimeter of the garden is 56 m. What are the dimensions of the garden?

50. **Size of a playing field.** The length of a rectangular playing field is 5 feet (ft) less than twice its width. If the perimeter of the playing field is 230 ft, find the length and width of the field.

ANSWERS

41. _____

42. _____

43. _____

44. _____

45. _____

46. _____

47. _____

48. _____

49. _____

50. _____

51. **Isosceles triangle.** The base of an isosceles triangle is 3 cm less than the length of the equal sides. If the perimeter of the triangle is 36 cm, find the length of each of the sides.

52. **Isosceles triangle.** The length of one of the equal legs of an isosceles triangle is 3 in. less than twice the length of the base. If the perimeter is 29 in., find the length of each of the sides.

53. **Ticket sales.** Tickets for a play cost $8 for the main floor and $6 in the balcony. If the total receipts from 500 tickets were $3600, how many of each type of ticket were sold?

54. **Ticket sales.** Tickets for a basketball tournament were $6 for students and $9 for nonstudents. Total sales were $10,500, and 250 more student tickets were sold than nonstudent tickets. How many of each type of ticket were sold?

55. **Number of stamps.** Maria bought 80 stamps at the post office in 32¢ and 20¢ denominations. If she paid $22 for the stamps, how many of each denomination did she buy?

56. **Money denominations.** A bank teller had a total of 125 $10 bills and $20 bills to start the day. If the value of the bills was $1650, how many of each denomination did he have?

57. **Ticket sales.** Tickets for a train excursion were $120 for a sleeping room, $80 for a berth, and $50 for a coach seat. The total ticket sales were $8600. If there were 20 more berth tickets sold than sleeping room tickets and 3 times as many coach tickets as sleeping room tickets, how many of each type of ticket were sold?

58. **Baseball tickets.** Admission for a college baseball game is $6 for box seats, $5 for the grandstand, and $3 for the bleachers. The total receipts for one evening were $9000. There were 100 more grandstand tickets sold than box seat tickets. Twice as many bleacher tickets were sold as box seat tickets. How many tickets of each type were sold?

59. **Driving speed.** Patrick drove 3 hours (h) to attend a meeting. On the return trip, his speed was 10 miles per hour (mi/h) less and the trip took 4 h. What was his speed each way?

60. **Bicycle speed.** A bicyclist rode into the country for 5 h. In returning, her speed was 5 mi/h faster and the trip took 4 h. What was her speed each way?

61. Driving speed. A car leaves a city and goes north at a rate of 50 mi/h at 2 PM One hour later a second car leaves, traveling south at a rate of 40 mi/h. At what time will the two cars be 320 mi apart?

62. Bus distance. A bus leaves a station at 1 PM, traveling west at an average rate of 44 mi/h. One hour later a second bus leaves the same station, traveling east at a rate of 48 mi/h. At what time will the two buses be 274 mi apart?

63. Traveling time. At 8:00 AM, Catherine leaves on a trip at 45 mi/h. One hour later, Max decides to join her and leaves along the same route, traveling at 54 mi/h. When will Max catch up with Catherine?

64. Bicycling time. Martina leaves home at 9 AM, bicycling at a rate of 24 mi/h. Two hours later, John leaves, driving at the rate of 48 mi/h. At what time will John catch up with Martina?

65. Traveling time. Mika leaves Boston for Baltimore at 10:00 AM, traveling at 45 mi/h. One hour later, Hiroko leaves Baltimore for Boston on the same route, traveling at 50 mi/h. If the two cities are 425 mi apart, when will Mika and Hiroko meet?

66. Traveling time. A train leaves town A for town B, traveling at 35 mi/h. At the same time, a second train leaves town B for town A at 45 mi/h. If the two towns are 320 mi apart, how long will it take for the two trains to meet?

67. Tree inventory. There are 500 Douglas fir and hemlock trees in a section of forest bought by Hoodoo Logging Co. The company paid an average of $250 for each Douglas fir and $300 for each hemlock. If the company paid $132,000 for the trees, how many of each kind did the company buy?

68. Tree inventory. There are 850 Douglas fir and ponderosa pine trees in a section of forest bought by Sawz Logging Co. The company paid an average of $300 for each Douglas fir and $225 for each ponderosa pine. If the company paid $217,500 for the trees, how many of each kind did the company buy?

69. There is an universally agreed on "order of operations" used to simplify expressions. Explain how the order of operations is used in solving equations. Be sure to use complete sentences.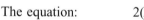

70. A common mistake when solving equations is the following:

The equation: $2(x - 2) = x + 3$
First step in solving: $2x - 2 = x + 3$
Write a clear explanation of what error has been made. What could be done to avoid this error?

71. Another very common mistake is in the equation below:

The equation: $6x - (x + 3) = 5 + 2x$
First step in solving: $6x - x + 3 = 5 + 2x$
Write a clear explanation of what error has been made and what could be done to avoid the mistake.

72. Write an algebraic equation for the English statement "Subtract 5 from the sum of x and 7 times 3 and the result is 20." Compare your equation with other students. Did you all write the same equation? Are all the equations correct even though they don't look alike? Do all the equations have the same solution? What is wrong? The English statement is *ambiguous*. Write another English statement that leads correctly to more than one algebraic equation. Exchange with another student and see if they think the statement is ambiguous. Notice that the algebra is *not* ambiguous!

ANSWERS

61.

62.

63.

64.

65.

66.

67.

68.

69.

70.

71.

72.

175

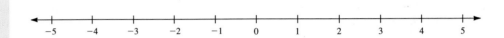

Getting Ready for Section 3.6
[Section 2.1]

Locate each of the following numbers on the number line.

a. 4   **b.** −5   **c.** −3   **d.** 2

e. $-\dfrac{7}{2}$ **f.** $\dfrac{2}{3}$ **g.** 2.5   **h.** −1.1

A N S W E R S

1. 7   **3.** 2   **5.** −4   **7.** −3   **9.** −4   **11.** $-\dfrac{1}{3}$ **13.** −9

15. $-\dfrac{7}{2}$ **17.** 4   **19.** 5   **21.** 7   **23.** $\dfrac{3}{4}$ **25.** 2   **27.** 3   **29.** 5

31. $2(x + 4) = 20$ **33.** $3(x − 5) = 21$ **35.** $2x + 3(x + 1) = 48$ **37.** −2

39. All numbers   **41.** 10, 18   **43.** 8, 15   **45.** 5, 6   **47.** 12 in., 25 in.

49. 6 m, 22 m   **51.** Legs, 13 cm; base, 10 cm

53. 200 $6 tickets, 300 $8 tickets   **55.** 30 20¢ stamps, 50 32¢ stamps

57. 60 coach, 40 berth, and 20 sleeping room   **59.** 40 mi/h, 30 mi/h

61. 6 PM   **63.** 2 PM   **65.** 3 PM   **67.** 360 Douglas fir, 140 hemlock

a.–h. (number line with points plotted)

3.6 Inequalities—An Introduction

3.6 OBJECTIVES

1. Use the notation of inequalities
2. Graph the solution set of an inequality
3. Solve and graph the solution set for an inequality in one variable

To help you remember, the "arrowhead" always points toward the smaller quantity.

As pointed out in the introduction to this chapter, an equation is just a statement that two expressions are equal. In algebra, an **inequality** is a statement that one expression is less than or greater than another. Four new symbols are used in writing inequalities. The use of two of them is illustrated in Example 1.

• Example 1

Reading the Inequality Symbol

$5 < 8$ is an inequality read "5 is less than 8."

$9 > 6$ is an inequality read "9 is greater than 6."

● ● ● **CHECK YOURSELF 1**

Fill in the blanks, using the symbols $<$ and $>$.

a. 12 _____ 8

b. 20 _____ 25

Just as was the case with equations, inequalities that involve variables may be either true or false depending on the value that we give to the variable. For instance, consider the inequality

$x < 6$

If $x = \begin{cases} 3 & 3 < 6 \text{ is true} \\ 5 & 5 < 6 \text{ is true} \\ -10 & -10 < 6 \text{ is true} \\ 8 & 8 < 6 \text{ is false} \end{cases}$

Therefore 3, 5, and -10 are some *solutions* for the inequality $x < 6$; they make the inequality a true statement. You should see that 8 is *not* a solution. We call the set of all solutions the **solution set** for the inequality. Of course, there are many possible solutions.

Since there are so many solutions (an infinite number, in fact), we certainly do not want to try to list them all! A convenient way to show the solution set of an inequality is with the use of a number line.

• Example 2

Graphing Inequalities

To graph the solution set for the inequality $x < 6$, we want to include all real numbers that are "less than" 6. This means all numbers *to the left* of 6 on the number line.

We then start at 6 and draw an arrow extending left, as shown:

The colored arrow indicates the direction of the solution.

Note: The **open circle** at 6 means that we do not include 6 in the solution set (6 is not less than itself). The colored arrow shows all the numbers in the solution set, with the arrowhead indicating that the solution set continues indefinitely to the left.

● ● ●   **CHECK YOURSELF 2**

Graph the solution set of $x < -2$.

_____

Two other symbols are used in writing inequalities. They are used with inequalities such as

$$x \geq 5 \qquad \text{and} \qquad x \leq 2$$

Here $x \geq 5$ is really a combination of the two statements $x > 5$ and $x = 5$. It is read "x is greater than or equal to 5." The solution set includes 5 in this case.

The inequality $x \leq 2$ combines the statements $x < 2$ and $x = 2$. It is read "x is less than or equal to 2."

● Example 3

Graphing Inequalities

*Here the filled-in circle means that we want to include 5 in the solution set. This is often called a **closed** circle.*

The solution set for $x \geq 5$ is graphed as follows.

● ● ●   **CHECK YOURSELF 3**

Graph the solution sets.

a. $x \leq -4$ **b.** $x \geq 3$

_____

You learned how to graph the solution sets of some simple inequalities, such as $x < 8$ or $x \geq 10$, in the last section. Now we will look at more complicated inequalities, such as

$$2x - 3 < x + 4$$

This is called a **linear inequality in one variable.** Only one variable is involved in the inequality, and it appears only to the first power. Fortunately, the methods used to solve this type of inequality are very similar to those we used earlier in this chapter to solve linear equations in one variable. Here is our first property for inequalities.

> ### The Addition Property of Inequality
>
> If $a < b$ then $a + c < b + c$
>
> In words, adding the same quantity to both sides of an inequality gives an **equivalent inequality.**

Equivalent inequalities have exactly the same solution sets.

● Example 4

Solving Inequalities

Solve and graph the solution set for $x - 8 < 7$.

    To solve $x - 8 < 7$, add 8 to both sides of the inequality by the addition property.

The inequality is solved when an equivalent inequality has the form

$x < \square$ or $x > \square$

$$x - 8 < 7$$
$$x - 8 + 8 < 7 + 8$$
$$x < 15 \qquad \text{(The solution)}$$

The graph of the solution set is

● ● ●   **CHECK YOURSELF 4**

Solve and graph the solution set for

$x - 9 > -3$

● Example 5

Solving Inequalities

Solve and graph the solution set for $4x - 2 \geq 3x + 5$.

    First, we subtract $3x$ from both sides of the inequality.

As with equations, the addition property allows us to *subtract* the same quantity from both sides of an inequality.

$$4x - 2 \geq 3x + 5$$
$$4x - 3x - 2 \geq 3x - 3x + 5$$
$$x - 2 \geq 5 \qquad \text{Now we add 2 to both sides.}$$
$$x - 2 + 2 \geq 5 + 2$$
$$x \geq 7$$

We subtracted $3x$ and then added 2 to both sides. If these steps are done in the other order, the resulting inequality will be the same.

The graph of the solution set is

● ● ● CHECK YOURSELF 5

Solve and graph the solution set.

$7x - 8 \leq 6x + 2$

You will also need a rule for multiplying on both sides of an inequality. Here you'll have to be a bit careful. There is a difference between the multiplication property for inequalities and that for equations. Look at the following:

$2 < 7$ (A true inequality)

Let's multiply both sides by 3.

$2 < 7$

$3 \cdot 2 < 3 \cdot 7$

$6 < 21$ (A true inequality)

Now we multiply both sides by -3.

$2 < 7$

$(-3)(2) < (-3)(7)$

$-6 < -21$ (*Not* a true inequality)

Let's try something different.

$2 < 7$ Change the "sense" of the inequality: $<$ becomes $>$.

$(-3)(2) > (-3)(7)$ (This is now a true inequality.)

$-6 > -21$

This suggests that multiplying both sides of an inequality by a negative number changes the "sense" of the inequality.

We can state the following general property.

The Multiplication Property of Inequality

If $a < b$ then $ac < bc$ where $c > 0$

         and $ac > bc$ where $c < 0$

In words, multiplying both sides of an inequality by the same *positive* number gives an equivalent inequality.

When both sides of an inequality are multiplied by the same *negative* number, it is necessary to *reverse the sense* of the inequality to give an equivalent inequality.

• Example 6

Solving and Graphing Inequalities

(*a*) Solve and graph the solution set for $5x < 30$.

Multiplying both sides of the inequality by $\dfrac{1}{5}$ gives

$$\frac{1}{5}(5x) < \frac{1}{5}(30)$$

Simplifying, we have

$$x < 6$$

The graph of the solution set is

(*b*) Solve and graph the solution set for $-4x \geq 28$.

In this case we want to multiply both sides of the inequality by $-\dfrac{1}{4}$ to leave x alone on the left.

$$\left(-\frac{1}{4}\right)(-4x) \leq \left(-\frac{1}{4}\right)(28)$$

Reverse the sense of the inequality because you are multiplying by a negative number!

or $\qquad x \leq -7$

The graph of the solution set is

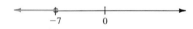

● ● ● **CHECK YOURSELF 6**

Solve and graph the solution sets:

a. $7x > 35$ **b.** $-8x \leq 48$

    Example 7 illustrates the use of the multiplication property when fractions are involved in an inequality.

• Example 7

Solving and Graphing Inequalities

(*a*) Solve and graph the solution set for

$$\frac{x}{4} > 3$$

Here we multiply both sides of the inequality by 4. This will isolate x on the left.

$$4\left(\frac{x}{4}\right) > 4(3)$$

$$x > 12$$

The graph of the solution set is

(b) Solve and graph the solution set for

$$-\frac{x}{6} \geq -3$$

In this case, we multiply both sides of the inequality by -6:

Note that we reverse the sense of the inequality since we are multiplying by a negative number.

$$(-6)\left(-\frac{x}{6}\right) \leq (-6)(-3)$$

$$x \leq 18$$

The graph of the solution set is

● ● ● **CHECK YOURSELF 7**

Solve and graph the solution sets for the following inequalities.

a. $\dfrac{x}{5} \leq 4$ **b.** $-\dfrac{x}{3} < -7$

● **Example 8**

Solving and Graphing Inequalities

(a) Solve and graph the solution set for $5x - 3 < 2x$.

First, add 3 to both sides to undo the subtraction on the left.

$$5x - 3 < 2x$$

$$5x - 3 \boxed{+ 3} < 2x \boxed{+ 3} \qquad \text{Add 3 to both sides to undo the subtraction.}$$

$$5x < 2x + 3$$

Now subtract $2x$, so that only the number remains on the right.

$$5x < 2x + 3$$

$$5x \boxed{- 2x} < 2x \boxed{- 2x} + 3 \qquad \text{Subtract } 2x \text{ to isolate the number on the right.}$$

$$3x < 3$$

Note that the multiplication property also allows us to divide both sides by a nonzero number.

Next *divide* both sides by 3.

$$\frac{3x}{3} < \frac{3}{3}$$

$$x < 1$$

The graph of the solution set is

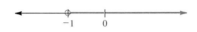

(*b*) Solve and graph the solution set for $2 - 5x < 7$.

$$2 - 5x < 7$$

$$2 - 2 - 5x < 7 - 2 \qquad \text{Subtract 2.}$$

$$-5x < 5$$

$$\frac{-5x}{-5} > \frac{5}{-5} \qquad \text{Divide by } -5. \text{ Be sure to reverse the sense of the inequality.}$$

or $\qquad x > -1$

The graph is

● ● ● CHECK YOURSELF 8

Solve and graph the solution sets.

a. $4x + 9 \geq x$ **b.** $5 - 6x < 41$

As with equations, we will collect all variable terms on one side and all constant terms on the other.

● Example 9

Solving and Graphing Inequalities

Solve and graph the solution set for $5x - 5 \geq 3x + 4$.

$$5x - 5 \geq 3x + 4$$

$$5x - 5 + 5 \geq 3x + 4 + 5 \qquad \text{Add 5.}$$

$$5x \geq 3x + 9$$

$$5x - 3x \geq 3x - 3x + 9 \qquad \text{Subtract } 3x.$$

$$2x \geq 9$$

$$\frac{2x}{2} \geq \frac{9}{2} \qquad \text{Divide by 2.}$$

$$x \geq \frac{9}{2}$$

The graph of the solution set is

● ● ● CHECK YOURSELF 9

Solve and graph the solution set for

$8x + 3 < 4x - 13$

Be especially careful when negative coefficients occur in the solution process.

● Example 10

Solving and Graphing Inequalities

Solve and graph the solution set for $2x + 4 < 5x - 2$.

$$2x + 4 < 5x - 2$$

$$2x + 4 - 4 < 5x - 2 - 4 \qquad \text{Subtract 4.}$$

$$2x < 5x - 6$$

$$2x - 5x < 5x - 5x - 6 \qquad \text{Subtract } 5x.$$

$$-3x < -6$$

$$\frac{-3x}{-3} > \frac{-6}{-3} \qquad \begin{array}{l}\text{Divide by } -3\text{, and reverse the sense of}\\ \text{the inequality.}\end{array}$$

$$x > 2$$

The graph of the solution set is

● ● ● CHECK YOURSELF 10

Solve and graph the solution set.

$5x + 12 \geq 10x - 8$

The solution of inequalities may also require the use of the distributive property.

● Example 11

Solving and Graphing Inequalities

Solve and graph the solution set for

$5(x - 2) \geq -8$

Applying the distributive property on the left yields

$5x - 10 \geq -8$

Solving as before yields

$$5x - 10 + 10 \geq -8 + 10 \qquad \text{Add 10.}$$

$$5x \geq 2$$

or $\qquad x \geq \dfrac{2}{5} \qquad \text{Divide by 5.}$

The graph of the solution set is

● ● ● **CHECK YOURSELF 11**

Solve and graph the solution set.

$4(x + 3) < 9$

Some applications are solved by using an inequality instead of an equation. Example 1 illustrates such an application.

● Example 12

Solving an Application with Inequalities

Mohammed needs a mean score of 92 or higher on four tests to get an A. So far his scores are 94, 89, and 88. What score on the fourth test will get him an A?

What do you need to find? **Step 1** We are looking for the score that will, when combined with the other scores, give Mohammed an A.

Assign a letter to the unknown. **Step 2** Let x represent a fourth-test score that will get him an A.

Write an inequality. **Step 3** The inequality will have the average mean on the left side which must be greater than or equal to the 92 on the right.

$$\frac{94 + 89 + 88 + x}{4} \geq 92$$

Solve the question. **Step 4** First, multiply both sides by 4:

$$94 + 89 + 88 + x \geq 368$$

Then add the test scores:

$$183 + 88 + x \geq 368$$

$$271 + x \geq 368$$

Subtracting 271 from both sides,

$$x \geq 97$$

Step 5 To check the solution, we find the mean of the four test scores, 94, 89, 88, and 97.

$$\frac{94 + 89 + 88 + 97}{4} = \frac{368}{4} = 92$$

● ● ● **CHECK YOURSELF 12**

Felicia needs a mean score of at least 75 on five tests to get a passing grade in her health class. On her first four tests she has scores of 68, 79, 71, and 70. What score on the fifth test will give her a passing grade?

The following outline (or algorithm) summarizes our work in this section.

Solving Linear Inequalities

STEP 1 Remove any grouping symbols and combine any like terms appearing on either side of the inequality.

STEP 2 Apply the addition property to write an equivalent inequality with the variable term on one side of the inequality and the number on the other.

STEP 3 Apply the multiplication property to write an equivalent inequality with the variable isolated on one side of the inequality. Be sure to reverse the sense of the inequality if you multiply or divide by a negative number. The solution derived in step 3 can then be graphed on a number line.

● ● ● **CHECK YOURSELF ANSWERS**

1. **a.** $>$;   **b.** $<$

2.

3. **a.**   **b.**

4. $x > 6$ 5. $x \le 10$

6. **a.** $x > 5$ **b.** $x \ge -6$

7. **a.** $x \le 20$ **b.** $x > 21$

8. **a.** $x \ge -3$ **b.** $x > -6$

9. $x < -4$ 10. $x \le 4$

11. $x < -\dfrac{3}{4}$ 12. 87 or greater.

Complete the statements, using the symbol $<$ or $>$.

1. 5 _____ 10

2. 9 _____ 8

3. 7 _____ -2

4. 0 _____ -5

5. 0 _____ 4

6. -10 _____ -5

7. -2 _____ -5

8. -4 _____ -11

Write each inequality in words.

9. $x < 3$

10. $x \leq -5$

11. $x \geq -4$

12. $x < -2$

13. $-5 \leq x$

14. $2 < x$

Graph the solution set of each of the following inequalities.

15. $x > 2$

16. $x < -3$

17. $x < 9$

18. $x > 4$

19. $x > 1$

20. $x < -2$

21. $x < 8$

22. $x > 3$

23. $x > -5$

24. $x < -4$

1. _____

2. _____

3. _____

4. _____

5. _____

6. _____

7. _____

8. _____

9. _____

10. _____

11. _____

12. _____

13. _____

14. _____

15. _____

16. _____

17. _____

18. _____

19. _____

20. _____

21. _____

22. _____

23. _____

24. _____

25. _____

26. _____

27. _____

28. _____

29. _____

30. _____

31. _____

32. _____

33. _____

34. _____

35. _____

36. _____

37. _____

38. _____

39. _____

40. _____

41. _____

42. _____

43. _____

44. _____

45. _____

46. _____

47. _____

48. _____

49. _____

50. _____

25. $x \geq 9$

26. $x \geq 0$

27. $x < 0$

28. $x \leq -3$

Solve and graph the solution set of each of the following inequalities.

29. $x - 7 < 6$

30. $x + 5 \leq 4$

31. $x + 8 \geq 10$

32. $x - 11 > -14$

33. $5x < 4x + 7$

34. $3x \geq 2x - 4$

35. $6x - 8 \leq 5x$

36. $3x + 2 > 2x$

37. $4x - 3 \geq 3x + 5$

38. $5x + 2 \leq 4x - 6$

39. $7x + 5 < 6x - 4$

40. $8x - 7 > 7x + 3$

41. $3x \leq 9$

42. $5x > 20$

43. $5x > -35$

44. $7x \leq -21$

45. $-6x \geq 18$

46. $-9x < 45$

47. $-10x < -60$

48. $-12x \geq -48$

49. $\dfrac{x}{4} > 5$

50. $\dfrac{x}{3} \leq -3$

188

51. $-\dfrac{x}{2} \geq -3$

←——————————————→

52. $-\dfrac{x}{5} < 4$

←——————————————→

53. $\dfrac{2x}{3} < 6$

←——————————————→

54. $\dfrac{3x}{4} \geq -9$

←——————————————→

55. $5x > 3x + 8$

←——————————————→

56. $4x \leq x - 9$

←——————————————→

57. $5x - 2 > 3x$

←——————————————→

58. $7x + 3 \geq 2x$

←——————————————→

59. $3 - 2x > 5$

←——————————————→

60. $5 - 3x \leq 17$

←——————————————→

61. $2x \geq 5x + 18$

←——————————————→

62. $3x < 7x - 28$

←——————————————→

63. $5x - 3 \leq 3x + 15$

←——————————————→

64. $8x + 7 > 5x + 34$

←——————————————→

65. $9x + 7 > 2x - 28$

←——————————————→

66. $10x - 5 \leq 8x - 25$

←——————————————→

67. $7x - 5 < 3x + 2$

←——————————————→

68. $5x - 2 \geq 2x - 7$

←——————————————→

69. $5x + 7 > 8x - 17$

←——————————————→

70. $4x - 3 \leq 9x + 27$

←——————————————→

71. $3x - 2 \leq 5x + 3$

←——————————————→

72. $2x + 3 > 8x - 2$

←——————————————→

73. $4(x + 7) \leq 2x + 31$

←——————————————→

74. $6(x - 5) > 3x - 26$

←——————————————→

75. $2(x - 7) > 5x - 12$

←——————————————→

76. $3(x + 4) \leq 7x + 7$

←——————————————→

A N S W E R S

51. _____

52. _____

53. _____

54. _____

55. _____

56. _____

57. _____

58. _____

59. _____

60. _____

61. _____

62. _____

63. _____

64. _____

65. _____

66. _____

67. _____

68. _____

69. _____

70. _____

71. _____

72. _____

73. _____

74. _____

75. _____

76. _____

77. _____

78. _____

79. _____

80. _____

81. _____

82. _____

83. _____

84. _____

85. _____

86. _____

87. _____

88. _____

89. _____

90. _____

91. _____

Translate the following statements into inequalities. Let x represent the number in each case.

77. 5 more than a number is greater than 3.

78. 3 less than a number is less than or equal to 5.

79. 4 less than twice a number is less than or equal to 7.

80. 10 more than a number is greater than negative 2.

81. 4 times a number, decreased by 15, is greater than that number.

82. 2 times a number, increased by 28, is less than or equal to 6 times that number.

Match each inequality on the right with a statement on the left.

83. x is nonnegative   **a.** $x \geq 0$

84. x is negative   **b.** $x \geq 5$

85. x is no more than 5   **c.** $x \leq 5$

86. x is positive   **d.** $x > 0$

87. x is at least 5   **e.** $x < 5$

88. x is less than 5   **f.** $x < 0$

89. Panda population. There are fewer than 1000 wild giant pandas left in the bamboo forests of China. Write an inequality expressing this relationship.

90. Forestry. Let C represent the amount of Canadian forest and M represent the amount of Mexican forest. Write an inequality showing the relationship of the forests of Mexico and Canada if Canada contains at least 9 times as much forest as Mexico.

91. Test scores. To pass a course with a grade of B or better, Liza must have an average of 80 or more. Her grades on three tests are 72, 81, and 79. Write an inequality representing the score that Liza must get on the fourth test to obtain a B average or better for the course.

92. Test scores. Sam must have an average of 70 or more in his summer course in order to obtain a grade of C. His first three test grades were 75, 63, and 68. Write an inequality representing the score that Sam must get in the last test in order to get a C grade.

92.

93.

94.

95.

96.

97.

93. Commission. Juanita is a salesperson for a manufacturing company. She may choose to receive $500 or 5 percent commission on her sales as payment for her work. How much does she need to sell to make the 5 percent offer a better deal?

94. Telephone costs. The cost for a long distance telephone call is $0.36 for the first minute and $0.21 for each additional minute or portion thereof. The total cost of the call cannot exceed $3. Write an inequality representing the number of minutes a person could talk without exceeding $3.

95. You are the office manager for a small company. You need to acquire a new copier for the office. You find a suitable one that leases for $250 a month from the copy machine company. It costs 2.5¢ per copy to run the machine. You purchase paper for $3.50 a ream (500 sheets). If your copying budget is no more than $950 per month, is this machine a good choice? Write a brief recommendation to the Purchasing Department. Use equations and inequalities to explain your recommendation.

96. Nutritionists recommend that, for good health, no more than 30 percent of our daily intake of calories should come from fat. Algebraically, we can write this as $f \leq 0.30(c)$, where f = calories from fat and c = total calories for the day. But this does not mean that everything we eat must meet this requirement. For example, if you eat 1/2 cup of Ben and Jerry's vanilla ice cream for dessert after lunch, you are eating a total of 250 calories, of which 150 are from fat. This amount is considerably more than 30 percent from fat, but if you are careful about what you eat the rest of the day, you can stay within the guidelines.

Set up an inequality based on your normal caloric intake. Solve the inequality to find how many calories in fat you could eat over the day and still have no more than 30 percent of your daily calories from fat. The American Heart Association says that to maintain your weight, your daily caloric intake should be 15 calories for every pound. You can compute this number to estimate the number of calories a day you normally eat. Do some research in your grocery store or library to determine what foods satisfy the requirements for your diet for the rest of the day. There are 9 calories in every gram of fat; many food labels give the amount of fat only in grams.

97. Your aunt calls to ask your help in making a decision about buying a new refrigerator. She says that she found two that seem to fit her needs, and both are supposed to last at least 14 years, according to *Consumer's Reports*. The initial cost for one refrigerator is $712, but it only uses 88 kilowatts an hour (kwh) per month. The other refrigerator costs $519 and uses an estimated 100 kwh/per month. You do not know the price of electricity per kilowatt hour where your aunt lives, so you will have to decide what in cents per kilowatt hour will make the first refrigerator cheaper to run for its 14 years of expected usefulness. Write your aunt a letter explaining what you did to calculate this cost, and tell her to make her decision based on how the kilowatt hour rate she has to pay in her area compares with your estimation.

ANSWERS

1. $5 < 10$ **3.** $7 > -2$ **5.** $0 < 4$ **7.** $-2 > -5$

9. x is less than 3 **11.** x is greater than or equal to -4

13. -5 is less than or equal to x

15. **17.**

19. **21.**

23. **25.**

27. **29.** $x < 13$

31. $x \geq 2$ **33.** $x < 7$

35. $x \leq 8$ **37.** $x \geq 8$

39. $x < -9$ **41.** $x \leq 3$

43. $x > -7$ **45.** $x \leq -3$

47. $x > 6$ **49.** $x > 20$

51. $x \leq 6$ **53.** $x < 9$

55. $x > 4$ **57.** $x > 1$

59. $x < -1$ **61.** $x \leq -6$

63. $x \leq 9$ **65.** $x > -5$

67. $x < \dfrac{7}{4}$ **69.** $x < 8$

71. $x \geq -\dfrac{5}{2}$ **73.** $x \leq \dfrac{3}{2}$

75. $x < -\dfrac{2}{3}$ **77.** $x + 5 > 3$ **79.** $2x - 4 \leq 7$

81. $4x - 15 > x$ **83.** a **85.** c **87.** b **89.** $P < 1000$ **91.** $x \geq 88$

93. $10,000

 # Summary

Algebraic Equations [3.1–3.3]

3x − 5 = 7 is an equation

Equation A statement that two expressions are equal.

4 is a solution for the
equation because
$3 \cdot 4 − 5 = 7$
$12 − 5 = 7$
$7 = 7$ (True)

Solution A value for the variable that will make an equation a true statement.

Equivalent Equations Equations that have exactly the same solutions.

Writing Equivalent Equations There are two basic properties that will yield equivalent equations.

5x = 20 and x = 4 are
equivalent equations.

1. If $a = b$, then $a + c = b + c$.
Adding (or subtracting) the same quantity on each side of an equation gives an equivalent equation.

2. If $a = b$, then $ac = bc$, $c \neq 0$.
Multiplying (or dividing) both sides of an equation by the same number gives an equivalent equation.

Solve:

$3(x − 2) + 4x = 3x + 14$

$3x − 6 + 4x = 3x + 14$

$\begin{aligned} 7x − 6 &= 3x + 14 \\ + 6 &\quad\; + 6 \end{aligned}$

$\begin{aligned} 7x &= 3x + 20 \\ − 3x &\quad\; − 3x \end{aligned}$

$4x = 20$

$\dfrac{4x}{4} = \dfrac{20}{4}$

$x = 5$

Solving Linear Equations We say that an equation is "solved" when we have an equivalent equation of the form

$x = \boxed{}$ or $\boxed{} = x$ Where the $\boxed{}$ is some number

The steps of solving a linear equation are as follows:

1. Use the distributive property to remove any grouping symbols that appear. Then simplify by combining any like terms.

2. Add or subtract the same term on both sides of the equation until the term containing the variable is on one side and a number is on the other.

3. Multiply or divide both sides of the equation by the same nonzero number so that the variable is alone on one side of the equation.

4. Check the solution in the original equation.

Solving Literal Equations [3.4]

Solve for b:

$a = \dfrac{2b + c}{3}$

$3a = \left(\dfrac{2b + c}{3}\right)3$

$3a = 2b + c$

$\begin{aligned} &\quad\; − c \quad\; − c \end{aligned}$

$3a − c = 2b$

$\dfrac{3a − c}{2} = b$

Literal Equation An equation that involves more than one letter or variable.

Solving Literal Equations

1. Multiply both sides of the equation by the lowest common denominator (LCD) to clear of fractions.

2. Add or subtract the same term on both sides of the equation so that all terms containing the variable you are solving for are on one side.

3. Divide both sides by any numbers or letters multiplying the variable that you are solving for.

Inequalities—An Introduction [3.6]

Inequality A statement that one quantity is less than (or greater than) another. Four symbols are used:

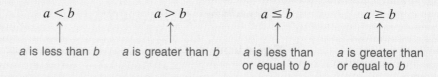

$a < b$	$a > b$	$a \leq b$	$a \geq b$
a is less than b	a is greater than b	a is less than or equal to b	a is greater than or equal to b

Graphing Inequalities To graph $x < a$, we use an open circle and an arrow pointing left.

The heavy arrow indicates all numbers less than (or to the left of) a.

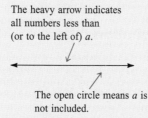

The open circle means a is not included.

To graph $x \geq b$, we use a closed circle and an arrow pointing right.

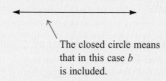

The closed circle means that in this case b is included.

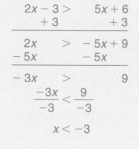

$$2x - 3 > 5x + 6$$
$$ + 3 + 3$$
$$\overline{2x > -5x + 9}$$
$$-5x -5x$$
$$\overline{-3x > 9}$$
$$\frac{-3x}{-3} < \frac{9}{-3}$$
$$x < -3$$

Solving Inequalities An inequality is "solved" when it is in the form $x < \square$ or $x > \square$.

Proceed as in solving equations by using the following properties.

1. If $a < b$, then $a + c < b + c$.

Adding (or subtracting) the same quantity to both sides of an inequality gives an equivalent inequality.

2. If $a < b$, then $ac < bc$ when $c > 0$ and $ac > bc$ when $c < 0$.

Multiplying both sides of an inequality by the same *positive number* gives an equivalent inequality. When both sides of an inequality are multiplied by the same *negative number, you must reverse the sense* of the inequality to give an equivalent inequality.

Applying Equations [All sections]

Using Equations to Solve Word Problems Follow these steps.

1. Read the problem carefully. Then reread it to decide what you are asked to find.

2. Choose a letter to represent one of the unknowns in the problem. Then represent each of the unknowns with an expression that uses the same letter.

3. Translate the problem to the language of algebra to form an equation.

4. Solve the equation and answer the question of the original problem.

5. Check your solution by returning to the original problem.

Summary Exercises

This summary exercise set is provided to give you practice with each of the objectives of the chapter. Each exercise is keyed to the appropriate chapter section. The answers are provided in the *Instructor's Manual*. Your instructor will give you guidelines on how to best use these exercises in your instructional setting.

[3.1]   Tell whether the number shown in parentheses is a solution for the given equation.

1. $7x + 2 = 16$ (2)

2. $5x - 8 = 3x + 2$ (4)

3. $7x - 2 = 2x + 8$ (2)

4. $4x + 3 = 2x - 11$ (−7)

5. $x + 5 + 3x = 2 + x + 23$ (6)

6. $\frac{2}{3}x - 2 = 10$ (21)

[3.1]   Solve the following equations and check your results.

7. $x + 5 = 7$

8. $x - 9 = 3$

9. $5x = 4x - 5$

10. $3x - 9 = 2x$

11. $5x - 3 = 4x + 2$

12. $9x + 2 = 8x - 7$

13. $7x - 5 = 6x - 4$

14. $3 + 4x - 1 = x - 7 + 2x$

15. $4(2x + 3) = 7x + 5$

16. $5(5x - 3) = 6(4x + 1)$

[3.2]   Solve the following equations and check your results.
[3.3]

17. $5x = 35$

18. $7x = -28$

19. $-6x = 24$

20. $-9x = -63$

21. $\frac{x}{4} = 8$

22. $-\frac{x}{5} = -3$

23. $\frac{2}{3}x = 18$

24. $\frac{3}{4}x = 24$

25. $5x - 3 = 12$

26. $4x + 3 = -13$

27. $7x + 8 = 3x$

28. $3 - 5x = -17$

29. $3x - 7 = x$

30. $2 - 4x = 5$

31. $\frac{x}{3} - 5 = 1$

32. $\frac{3}{4}x - 2 = 7$

33. $6x - 5 = 3x + 13$

34. $3x + 7 = x - 9$

35. $7x + 4 = 2x + 6$

36. $9x - 8 = 7x - 3$

37. $2x + 7 = 4x - 5$

38. $3x - 15 = 7x - 10$

39. $\frac{10}{3}x - 5 = \frac{4}{3}x + 7$

40. $\frac{11}{4}x - 15 = 5 - \frac{5}{4}x$

41. $3.7x + 8 = 1.7x + 16$

42. $5.4x - 3 = 8.4x + 9$

43. $3x - 2 + 5x = 7 + 2x + 21$

44. $8x + 3 - 2x + 5 = 3 - 4x$

45. $5(3x - 1) - 6x = 3x - 2$

46. $5x + 2(3x - 4) = 14x + 7$

[3.4]   Solve for the indicated variable.

47. $V = LWH$ (for L)

48. $P = 2L + 2W$ (for L)

49. $ax + by = c$ (for y)

50. $A = \frac{1}{2}bh$ (for h)

51. $A = P + Prt$ (for t)

52. $m = \dfrac{n - p}{q}$ (for n)

[3.6]   Graph the solution sets.

53. $x > 5$ ⟵―――――⟶

54. $x < -3$ ⟵―――――⟶

55. $x \leq -4$ ⟵―――――⟶

56. $x \geq 9$ ⟵―――――⟶

57. $x \geq -6$ ⟵―――――⟶

58. $x < 0$ ⟵―――――⟶

[3.6]   Solve and graph the solution sets for the following inequalities.

59. $x - 4 \leq 7$

60. $x + 3 > -2$

61. $5x > 4x - 3$

62. $4x \geq -12$

63. $-12x < 36$

64. $-\dfrac{x}{5} \geq 3$

65. $2x \leq 8x - 3$

66. $2x + 3 \geq 9$

67. $4 - 3x > 8$

68. $5x - 2 \leq 4x + 5$

69. $7x + 13 \geq 3x + 19$

70. $4x - 2 < 7x + 16$

71. $5(x - 3) < 2x + 12$

72. $4(x + 3) \geq x + 7$

[3.1–3.5]   Solve the following word problems. Be sure to label the unknowns and to show the equation you used for the solution.

73. The sum of 3 times a number and 7 is 25. What is the number?

74. 5 times a number, decreased by 8, is 32. Find the number.

75. If the sum of two consecutive integers is 85, find the two integers.

76. The sum of three consecutive odd integers is 57. What are the three integers?

77. Rafael earns $35 more per week than Andrew. If their weekly salaries total $715, what amount does each earn?

78. Larry is 2 years older than Susan, while Nathan is twice as old as Susan. If the sum of their ages is 30 years, find each of their ages.

A N S W E R S

1. _____

2. _____

3. _____

4. _____

5. _____

6. _____

7. _____

8. _____

9. _____

10. _____

11. _____

12. _____

13. _____

14. _____

15. _____

16. _____

17. _____

The purpose of this self-test is to help you check your progress and to review for a chapter test in class. Allow yourself about an hour to take the test. When you are done, check your answers in the back of the book. If you missed any answers, be sure to go back and review the appropriate sections in the chapter and the exercises that are provided.

Tell whether the number shown in parentheses is a solution for the given equation.

1. $7x - 3 = 25$ (5)

2. $8x - 3 = 5x + 9$ (4)

Solve the following equations and check your results.

3. $x - 7 = 4$

4. $7x - 12 = 6x$

5. $9x - 2 = 8x + 5$

Solve the following equations and check your results.

6. $7x = 49$

7. $\dfrac{1}{4}x = -3$

8. $\dfrac{4}{5}x = 20$

Solve the following equations and check your results.

9. $7x - 5 = 16$

10. $10 - 3x = -2$

11. $7x - 3 = 4x - 5$

12. $2x - 7 = 5x + 8$

Solve for the indicated variable.

13. $C = 2\pi r$ (for r)

14. $V = \dfrac{1}{3}Bh$ (for h)

15. $3x + 2y = 6$ (for y)

Graph the solution sets.

16. $x \geq 9$ ◄————————►

17. $x < -3$ ◄————————►

Solve and graph the solution sets for the following inequalities.

18. $x - 5 \leq 9$ **19.** $5 - 3x > 17$

20. $5x + 13 \geq 2x + 17$ **21.** $2x - 3 < 7x + 2$

Solve the following word problems. Be sure to show the equation you used for the solution.

22. 5 times a number, decreased by 7, is 28. What is the number?

23. The sum of three consecutive integers is 66. Find the three integers.

24. Jan is twice as old as Juwan, while Rick is 5 years older than Jan. If the sum of their ages is 35 years, find each of their ages.

25. The perimeter of a rectangle is 62 inches (in.). If the length of the rectangle is 1 in. more than twice its width, what are the dimensions of the rectangle?

A N S W E R S

1. _____

2. _____

3. _____

4. _____

5. _____

6. _____

7. _____

8. _____

9. _____

10. _____

11. _____

12. _____

13. _____

14. _____

15. _____

16. _____

17. _____

18. _____

19. _____

20. _____

21. _____

22. _____

This test is provided to help you in the process of reviewing the previous chapters. Answers are provided in the back of the book. If you missed any answers, be sure to go back and review the appropriate chapter sections.

Write, using symbols.

1. 3 times the sum of r and s

2. The quotient when 5 less than x is divided by 3

Write in exponential form.

3. $5 \cdot 5 \cdot 5 \cdot 5 \cdot 5$

4. $8 \cdot x \cdot x \cdot x \cdot y \cdot y$

Identify the property that is illustrated by each of the following statements.

5. $7 + (5 + 2) = (7 + 5) + 2$

6. $2(3 + 5) = 2 \cdot 3 + 2 \cdot 5$

Simplify each of the following expressions.

7. $7a^2b - 2a^2b$

8. $10a^2 + 5a + 2a^2 - 2a$

9. Arrange the following data in ascending order and determine the range: 4, −6, 9, 8, −9, 2.

10. Find the mean and median of the following set of numbers: 7, 2, −1, 4, 10, 1, −2.

Evaluate each of the following expressions.

11. $2 \cdot 3^2 - 8 \cdot 2$

12. $5(7 - 3)^2$

13. $|12 - 5|$

14. $|12| - |5|$

15. $(-7) + (-9)$

16. $\dfrac{17}{3} + \left(-\dfrac{5}{3}\right)$

17. $(-7)(-9)$

18. $(-3.2)(5)$

19. $\dfrac{0}{-13}$

Evaluate each of the following expressions if $x = -2$, $y = 3$, and $z = 5$.

20. $3x - y$

21. $4x^2 - y$

22. $\dfrac{5z - 4x}{2y + z}$

23. _____

24. _____

25. _____

26. _____

27. _____

28. _____

29. _____

30. _____

31. _____

32. _____

33. _____

34. _____

35. _____

36. _____

37. _____

38. _____

39. _____

40. _____

Solve the following equations and check your results.

23. $9x - 5 = 8x$　　　**24.** $-\dfrac{3}{4}x = 18$　　　**25.** $6x - 8 = 2x - 3$

26. $2x + 3 = 7x + 5$　　　**27.** $\dfrac{4}{3}x - 6 = 4 - \dfrac{2}{3}x$

Solve the following equations for the indicated variable.

28. $I = Prt$ (for r)　　　**29.** $A = \dfrac{1}{2}bh$ (for h)　　　**30.** $ax + by = c$ (for y)

Solve and graph the solution sets for the following inequalities.

31. $3x - 5 < 4$　　　　　　　　**32.** $7 - 2x \geq 10$

33. $7x - 2 > 4x + 10$　　　　　　**34.** $2x + 5 \leq 8x - 3$

Solve the following word problems. Be sure to show the equation used for the solution.

35. If 4 times a number decreased by 7 is 45, find that number.

36. The sum of two consecutive integers is 85. What are those two integers?

37. If 3 times an integer is 12 more than the next consecutive odd integer, what is that integer?

38. Michelle earns $120 more per week than Dmitri. If their weekly salaries total $720, how much does Michelle earn?

39. The length of a rectangle is 2 centimeters (cm) more than 3 times its width. If the perimeter of the rectangle is 44 cm, what are the dimensions of the rectangle?

40. One side of a triangle is 5 inches (in.) longer than the shortest side. The third side is twice the length of the shortest side. If the triangle perimeter is 37 in., find the length of each leg.

INTRODUCTION

The U.S. Post Office limits the size of rectangular boxes it will accept for mailing. The regulations state that "length plus girth cannot exceed 108 inches." "Girth" means the distance around a cross section; in this case, this measurement is $2h + 2w$. Using the polynomial $l + 2w + 2h$ to describe the measurement required by the Post Office, the regulations say that $l + 2w + 2h \leq 108$ inches.

The volume of a rectangular box is expressed by another polynomial:

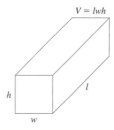

A company that wishes to produce boxes for use by postal patrons must use these formulas as well as do a statistical survey about the shapes that are useful to the most customers. The surface area, expressed by another polynomial expression, $2lw + 2wh + 2lh$, is also used so each box can be manufactured with the least amount of material, in order to help lower costs. _____

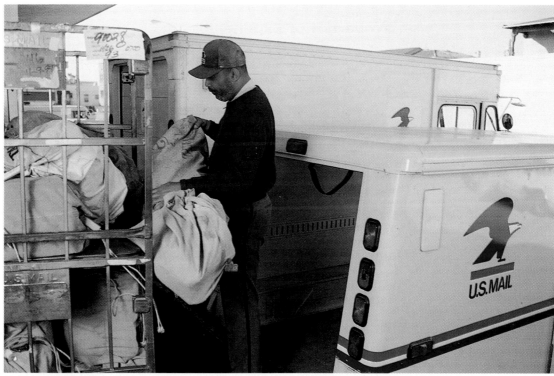

© Michael Newmant/PhotoEdit

Multiplying and Dividing Algebraic Expressions

4.1

4.1 OBJECTIVES

1. Find the product of two algebraic expressions
2. Find the quotient of two algebraic expressions

In general,

$$x^m = \underbrace{x \cdot x \cdot \cdots \cdot x}_{m \text{ factors}}$$

where *m* is a natural number. **Natural numbers** are the numbers we use for counting: 1, 2, 3, and so on.

Note that the exponent of x^5 is the *sum* of the exponents in x^2 and x^3.

In Section 1.2, we introduced exponential notation. Remember that the exponent tells us how many times the base is to be used as a factor.

Exponent
↓
$$2^5 = 2 \cdot 2 \cdot 2 \cdot 2 \cdot 2 = 32$$
↑   ↖
Base   The fifth power of 2

The notation can also be used when you are working with letters or variables.

$$x^4 = \underbrace{x \cdot x \cdot x \cdot x}_{4 \text{ factors}}$$

Now look at the product $x^2 \cdot x^3$.

$$x^2 \cdot x^3 = \underbrace{(x \cdot x)(x \cdot x \cdot x)}_{} = \underbrace{x \cdot x \cdot x \cdot x \cdot x}_{} = x^5$$

$$2 \text{ factors} + 3 \text{ factors} = 5 \text{ factors}$$

So

$$x^2 \cdot x^3 = x^{2+3} = x^5$$

This leads us to the following property of exponents.

Property 1 of Exponents

For any positive integers *m* and *n* and any real number *a*,

$$a^m \cdot a^n = a^{m+n}$$

In words, to multiply expressions with the same base, keep the base and add the exponents.

• Example 1

Using the First Property of Exponents

(a) $a^5 \cdot a^7 = a^{5+7} = a^{12}$

(b) $x \cdot x^8 = x^1 \cdot x^8 = x^{1+8} = x^9 \quad x = x^1$

(c) $3^2 \cdot 3^4 = 3^{2+4} = 3^6$

(d) $y^2 \cdot y^3 \cdot y^5 = y^{2+3+5} = y^{10}$

(e) $x^3 \cdot y^4$ *cannot* be simplified. The bases are not the same.

CAUTION

The product is *not* 9^6. The base does not change.

● ● ● **CHECK YOURSELF 1**

Multiply.

a. $b^6 \cdot b^8$ **b.** $y^7 \cdot y$ **c.** $2^3 \cdot 2^4$ **d.** $a^2 \cdot a^4 \cdot a^3$

Suppose that numerical coefficients (other than 1) are involved in a product. To find the product, multiply the numbers and then use the first property of exponents to combine the variables.

Note that although we have several factors, this is still a single term.

$$2x^3 \cdot 3x^5 = (2 \cdot 3)(x^3 \cdot x^5) \quad \text{Multiply the numbers.}$$
$$= 6x^{3+5} \quad \text{Add the exponents.}$$
$$= 6x^8$$

You may have noticed that we have again changed the order and grouping. This method uses the commutative and associative properties of Section 1.3.

● Example 2

Using the First Property of Exponents

Multiply.

Again we have written out all the steps. You can do the multiplication mentally with practice.

(a) $5a^4 \cdot 7a^6 = (5 \cdot 7)(a^4 \cdot a^6) = 35a^{10}$
(b) $y^2 \cdot 3y^3 \cdot 6y^4 = (1 \cdot 3 \cdot 6)(y^2 \cdot y^3 \cdot y^4) = 18y^9$
(c) $2x^2y^3 \cdot 3x^5y^2 = (2 \cdot 3)(x^2 \cdot x^5)(y^3 \cdot y^2) = 6x^7y^5$

● ● ● **CHECK YOURSELF 2**

Multiply.

a. $4x^3 \cdot 7x^5$ **b.** $3a^2 \cdot 2a^4 \cdot 2a^5$ **c.** $3m^2n^4 \cdot 5m^3n$

What about dividing expressions when exponents are involved? For instance, what if we want to divide x^5 by x^2? We can use the following approach to division:

$$\frac{x^5}{x^2} = \frac{\overbrace{x \cdot x \cdot x \cdot x \cdot x}^{5 \text{ factors}}}{\underbrace{x \cdot x}_{2 \text{ factors}}} = \frac{x \cdot x \cdot x \cdot x \cdot x}{x \cdot x}$$

We can divide by 2 factors of x.

$$= \overbrace{x \cdot x \cdot x}^{3 \text{ factors}} = x^3$$

So

Note that the exponent of x^3 is the difference of the exponents in x^5 and x^2.

$$\frac{x^5}{x^2} = x^{5-2} = x^3$$

This leads us to a second property of exponents.

Property 2 of Exponents

For any positive intergers m and n, where m is greater than n, and any real number a, where a, is not equal to zero,

$$\frac{a^m}{a^n} = a^{m-n}$$

In words, to divide expressions with the same base, keep the base and subtract the exponents.

• Example 3

Using the Second Property of Exponents

Divide the following.

(a) $\dfrac{y^7}{y^3} = y^{7-3} = y^4$

(b) $\dfrac{m^6}{m} = \dfrac{m^6}{m^1} = m^{6-1} = m^5$

Apply the second property to each variable separately.

(c) $\dfrac{a^3 b^5}{a^2 b^2} = a^{3-2} \cdot b^{5-2} = ab^3$

● ● ● CHECK YOURSELF 3

Divide.

a. $\dfrac{m^9}{m^6}$ **b.** $\dfrac{a^8}{a}$ **c.** $\dfrac{a^3 b^5}{a^2}$ **d.** $\dfrac{r^5 s^6}{r^3 s^2}$

If numerical coefficients are involved, just divide the numbers and then use the second law of exponents to divide the variables. Look at Example 4.

• Example 4

Using the Second Property of Exponents

Divide the following.

Subtract the exponents.

(a) $\dfrac{6x^5}{3x^2} = 2x^{5-2} = 2x^3$

6 divided by 3

20 divided by 5

$$(b) \ \frac{20a^7b^5}{5a^3b^4} = 4a^{7-3} \cdot b^{5-4}$$

Again apply the second property to each variable separately.

$$= 4a^4b$$

● ● ● ● **CHECK YOURSELF 4**

Divide.

a. $\dfrac{4x^3}{2x}$ 　　　　　　 **b.** $\dfrac{20a^6}{5a^2}$ 　　　　　　 **c.** $\dfrac{24x^5y^3}{4x^2y^2}$

In applying algebra to problem solving, you will often want to find the value of an algebraic expression when you know certain values for the letters (or variables) in the expression. As we pointed out earlier, finding the value of an expression is called **evaluating the expression** and uses the following steps.

To Evaluate an Algebraic Expression

STEP 1 Replace each variable by the given number value.

STEP 2 Do the indicated arithmetic, following the order of the operations.

Next, we will evaluate algebraic expressions that require following the rules for the order of operations.

● **Example 5**

Evaluating an Expression

Evaluate the following expressions if $x = 3$.

$(a) \ 3x - 5 = 3(3) - 5$ 　　Multiply first.
$\quad\quad\quad\quad = 9 - 5$ 　　　Then add or subtract.
$\quad\quad\quad\quad = 4$

$(b) \ 2x^2 - 4x + 1 = 2(3)^2 - 4(3) + 1$ 　　Evaluate the power first.
$\quad\quad\quad\quad\quad\quad = 2(9) - 4(3) + 1$ 　　Then multiply.
$\quad\quad\quad\quad\quad\quad = 18 - 12 + 1$ 　　Then add and subtract (left to right).
$\quad\quad\quad\quad\quad\quad = 6 + 1$
$\quad\quad\quad\quad\quad\quad = 7$

CAUTION

$2x^2 = 2(3)^2 = 2 \cdot 9 = 18$
is different from
$(2x)^2 = (2 \cdot 3)^2 = 6^2 = 36$

●●● **CHECK YOURSELF 5**

Evaluate the following expressions if $x = 2$.

a. $6x - 8$ **b.** $3x^2 - 5x + 1$

Rules for Negative Numbers

When substituting a negative value for a variable, you should remember these three rules.

1. A negative number multiplied by another negative number results in a positive product.

2. A negative number raised to an *even* power results in a positive product.

3. A negative number raised to an *odd* power results in a negative product.

●Example 6

Evaluating Expressions with Negatives

Evaluate the following expressions if $x = -3$.

(a) $-2x + 5 = -2(-3) + 5$

$= 6 + 5$ The product of two negatives is positive.

$= 11$

(b) $2x^2 + 5x - 3 = 2(-3)^2 + 5(-3) - 3$

$= 2(9) + 5(-3) - 3$ Two is an *even* power.

$= 18 - 15 - 3$

$= 3 - 3$

$= 0$

●●● **CHECK YOURSELF 6**

Evaluate the following expressions if $x = -2$.

a. $-3x + 4$ **b.** $3x^2 + 2x - 5$ **c.** $x^3 + 3x^2 - 4x + 1$

●●● **CHECK YOURSELF ANSWERS**

1. (a) b^{14}; **(b)** y^8; **(c)** 2^7; **(d)** a^9.   **2. (a)** $28x^8$; **(b)** $12a^{11}$; **(c)** $15m^5n^5$.

3. (a) m^3; **(b)** a^7; **(c)** ab^5; **(d)** r^2s^4.   **4. (a)** $2x^2$; **(b)** $4a^4$; **(c)** $6x^3y$.

5. (a) 4; **(b)** 3.   **6. (a)** 10; **(b)** 3; **(c)** 13.

4.1 Exercises

Multiply.

1. $x^5 \cdot x^7$

2. $b^2 \cdot b^4$

3. $5 \cdot 5^5$

4. $y^6 \cdot y^4$

5. $a^9 \cdot a$

6. $3^4 \cdot 3^5$

7. $z^{10} \cdot z^3$

8. $x^7 \cdot x$

9. $p^5 \cdot p^7$

10. $s^6 \cdot s^9$

11. $x^3y \cdot x^2y^4$

12. $m^2n^3 \cdot mn^4$

13. $w^5 \cdot w^2 \cdot w$

14. $x^5 \cdot x^4 \cdot x^6$

15. $m^3 \cdot m^2 \cdot m^4$

16. $r^3 \cdot r \cdot r^5$

17. $a^3b \cdot a^2b^2 \cdot ab^3$

18. $w^2z^3 \cdot wz \cdot w^3z^4$

19. $p^2q \cdot p^3q^5 \cdot pq^4$

20. $c^3d \cdot c^4d^2 \cdot cd^5$

21. $3a^6 \cdot 2a^3$

22. $5s^6 \cdot s^4$

23. $x^2 \cdot 3x^5$

24. $2m^4 \cdot 6m^7$

25. $5m^3n^2 \cdot 4mn^3$

26. $7x^2y^5 \cdot 6xy^4$

1.	
2.	
3.	
4.	
5.	
6.	
7.	
8.	
9.	
10.	
11.	
12.	
13.	
14.	
15.	
16.	
17.	
18.	
19.	
20.	
21.	
22.	
23.	
24.	
25.	
26.	

27.	
28.	
29.	
30.	
31.	
32.	
33.	
34.	
35.	
36.	
37.	
38.	
39.	
40.	
41.	
42.	
43.	
44.	
45.	
46.	
47.	
48.	
49.	
50.	
51.	
52.	
53.	
54.	

27. $6x^3y \cdot 9xy^5$

28. $5a^3b \cdot 10ab^4$

29. $2a^2 \cdot a^3 \cdot 3a^7$

30. $4x^5 \cdot 2x^3 \cdot 3x^2$

31. $3c^2d \cdot 4cd^3 \cdot 2c^5d$

32. $5p^2q \cdot p^3q^2 \cdot 3pq^3$

33. $5m^2 \cdot m^3 \cdot 2m \cdot 3m^4$

34. $3a^3 \cdot 2a \cdot a^4 \cdot 2a^5$

35. $2r^3s \cdot rs^2 \cdot 3r^2s \cdot 5rs$

36. $6a^2b \cdot ab \cdot 3ab^3 \cdot 2a^2b$

Divide.

37. $\dfrac{a^9}{a^6}$

38. $\dfrac{m^8}{m^2}$

39. $\dfrac{y^{10}}{y^4}$

40. $\dfrac{b^9}{b^4}$

41. $\dfrac{p^{15}}{p^{10}}$

42. $\dfrac{s^{18}}{s^{12}}$

43. $\dfrac{x^5y^3}{x^2y^2}$

44. $\dfrac{s^5t^4}{s^3t^2}$

45. $\dfrac{6m^3}{3m}$

46. $\dfrac{8x^5}{4x}$

47. $\dfrac{24a^7}{6a^4}$

48. $\dfrac{25x^9}{5x^8}$

49. $\dfrac{26m^8n}{13m^6}$

50. $\dfrac{30a^4b^5}{6b^4}$

51. $\dfrac{28w^3z^5}{7wz}$

52. $\dfrac{48p^6q^7}{8p^4q}$

53. $\dfrac{18x^3y^4z^5}{9xy^2z^2}$

54. $\dfrac{25a^5b^4c^3}{5a^4bc^2}$

Simplify each of the following expressions where possible.

55. $2a^3b \cdot 3a^2b$

56. $2xy^3 \cdot 3xy^2$

57. $2a^3b + 3a^2b$

58. $2xy^3 + 3xy^2$

59. $2x^2y^3 \cdot 3x^2y^3$

60. $5a^3b^2 \cdot 10a^3b^2$

61. $2x^2y^3 + 3x^2y^3$

62. $5a^3b^2 + 10a^3b^2$

63. $\dfrac{8a^2b \cdot 6a^2b}{2ab}$

64. $\dfrac{6x^2y^3 \cdot 9x^2y^3}{3x^2y^2}$

65. $\dfrac{8a^2b + 6a^2b}{2ab}$

66. $\dfrac{6x^2y^3 + 9x^2y^3}{3x^2y^2}$

Evaluate each of the following expressions if $a = 2$, $b = -3$, $c = 5$, and $d = 6$.

67. $2ab$

68. $3cd$

69. $2b^2c$

70. $3d^2c$

71. a^3b^2c

72. b^2c^2d

73. $2b^2c + 3c^2b$

74. $4c^2d - 2d^2c$

75. $-3ac^2 - 2c$

76. $-3b^2d - 2dc^2$

77. $-3d^2c + 7ab^2$

78. $4b^2a^2 - cd$

79. $-2abc + 3d^2$

80. $-3bcd + 2a^2$

81. $2c^2b^2 - 2a^3b$

82. $-c^2d + 3a^3c^2$

55. _____

56. _____

57. _____

58. _____

59. _____

60. _____

61. _____

62. _____

63. _____

64. _____

65. _____

66. _____

67. _____

68. _____

69. _____

70. _____

71. _____

72. _____

73. _____

74. _____

75. _____

76. _____

77. _____

78. _____

79. _____

80. _____

81. _____

82. _____

83. _____

84. _____

85. _____

86. _____

87. _____

88. _____

89. _____

90. _____

91. _____

92. _____

93. _____

94. _____

Evaluate each of the following expressions if $a = 2$, $b = -3$, $c = 5$, and $d = 6$.

83. $\dfrac{10a^2b^2}{cd}$

84. $\dfrac{2c^2d}{5a^2b}$

85. $\dfrac{4cd^2}{3ab}$

86. $\dfrac{-2cd^2}{3a^3b}$

87. $\dfrac{18a^5b}{9a^3}$

88. $\dfrac{50c^4b^3}{10c^2b^2}$

89. $\dfrac{28a^3c^5}{7ac^3}$

90. $\dfrac{48b^6d^7}{8b^4d^5}$

Solve the following problems.

91. Volume of a prism. The volume of a square prism is given by $V = LW^2$. Find the volume in cubic centimeters (cm^3) of a prism with $L = 5$ cm and $W = 3$ cm.

92. Surface area. The surface area of a square prism is given by $S = 2W^2 + 4LW$. Find the surface area in square inches (in.^{2}) of a prism with $L = 8$ in. and $W = 3$ in.

93. Kinetic energy. The kinetic energy (KE) of a moving body is given by $\text{KE} = \dfrac{wv^2}{2g}$. Find the kinetic energy, in foot-pounds (ft-lb), of a moving body where $w = 20$ pounds (lb), $v = 60$ feet per second (ft/s), and $g = 32$ ft/s^2.

94. Area. The area of a triangle is given by the formula $A = \dfrac{1}{2}bh$. Find the area in square feet (ft^2) of a triangle with $b = 4$ ft and $h = 6$ ft.

95. Temperature. The conversion of Fahrenheit temperature to Celsius temperature is given by the formula $C = \dfrac{5}{9}(F - 32)$. Find the Celsius temperature if the Fahrenheit temperature is 50°.

96. Area of a trapezoid. The area of a trapezoid is given by the formula $A = \dfrac{1}{2}(b_1 + b_2)h$. Find the area of a trapezoid if $b_1 = 5$ ft, $b_2 = 7$ ft, and $h = 8$ ft.

97. Electric circuits. The resistance R, of a circuit varies with time, t, according to the equation: $R = \dfrac{t + 2}{t^2}$. Find the resistance in a circuit if $t = 2$.

98. Distance. If an object is dropped from a bridge, the height above the water is given by the formula $s = \dfrac{1}{2}gt^2$. Find the height above the water if $g = 32$ and $t = 4$.

99. Complete the following statements:

(a) a^n is negative when _____ because _____.

(b) a^n is positive when _____ because _____.
           (give all possiblities)

100. "Earn Big Bucks!" reads an ad for a job. "You will be paid 1 cent for the first day and 2 cents for the second day, 4 cents for the third day, 8 cents for the fourth day, and so on, doubling each day. Apply now!" What kind of deal is this—where is the big money offered in the headline? In the fine print at the bottom of the ad following: "Highly qualified people may be paid $1,000,000 for the first 28 working days if they choose." Well, *that* does sound like big bucks! Work with other students to decide which method of payment is better and how much better. You may want to make a table and try to find a formula for the first offer.

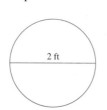

101. An oil spill from a tanker in pristine Prince Williams Sound in Alaska begins in a circular shape only 2 ft across. The area of the circle is $A = \pi r^2$. Make a table to decide what happens to the area if the diameter is doubling each hour. How large will the spill be in 24 h?

2 ft

a. _____

b. _____

c. _____

d. _____

e. _____

f. _____

 Getting Ready for Section 4.2
[Section 1.2]

Evaluate the following;

a. $\left(\dfrac{1}{2}\right)^2$ **b.** $\left(\dfrac{1}{3}\right)^3$ **c.** $(2^2)^2$ **d.** $(3^2)^2$ **e.** $\left(\dfrac{2}{3}\right)^2$ **f.** $\left(\dfrac{3}{4}\right)^3$

Answers

1. x^{12} **3.** 5^6 **5.** a^{10} **7.** z^{13} **9.** p^{12} **11.** $x^5 y^5$ **13.** w^8 **15.** m^9

17. $a^6 b^6$ **19.** $p^6 q^{10}$ **21.** $6a^9$ **23.** $3x^7$ **25.** $20m^4 n^5$ **27.** $54x^4 y^6$

29. $6a^{12}$ **31.** $24c^8 d^5$ **33.** $30m^{10}$ **35.** $30r^7 s^5$ **37.** a^3 **39.** y^6 **41.** p^5

43. $x^3 y$ **45.** $2m^2$ **47.** $4a^3$ **49.** $2m^2 n$ **51.** $4w^2 z^4$ **53.** $2x^2 y^2 z^3$

55. $6a^5 b^2$ **57.** Cannot simplify **59.** $6x^4 y^6$ **61.** $5x^2 y^3$ **63.** $24a^3 b$

65. $7a$ **67.** -12 **69.** 90 **71.** 360 **73.** -135 **75.** -160 **77.** -414

79. 168 **81.** 498 **83.** 12 **85.** -40 **87.** -24 **89.** 400 **91.** 45 cm^3

93. 1125 ft-lb **95.** $10°C$ **97.** 1 **a.** $\dfrac{1}{4}$ **b.** $\dfrac{1}{27}$ **c.** 16 **d.** 81

e. $\dfrac{4}{9}$ **f.** $\dfrac{27}{64}$

Extending the Properties of Exponents

4.2 OBJECTIVES

1. Recognize the five properties of exponents
2. Use the properties of exponents to simplify expressions

In the previous section we introduced the first two properties of exponents. Recall that the exponent notation indicates repeated multiplication and that the exponent tells us how many times the base is to be used as a factor.

Exponent

$$3^5 = \underbrace{3 \cdot 3 \cdot 3 \cdot 3 \cdot 3}_{5 \text{ factors}} = 243$$

Base

Our first property of exponents allowed us to multiply expressions that have the same base. For example,

$$x^6 \cdot x^7 = x^{6+7} = x^{13}$$

Our second property allowed us to divide expressions with the same base. For example,

$$\frac{x^8}{x^4} = x^{8-4} = x^4$$

In this section we want to expand our work with exponents to introduce three further properties. Consider the following:

Note that this means that the base, x^2, is used as a factor 4 times.

$$(x^2)^4 = x^2 \cdot x^2 \cdot x^2 \cdot x^2 = x^8$$

This leads us to our third property for exponents.

Property 3 of Exponents

For any real number a and positive integers m and n,

$$(a^m)^n = a^{m \cdot n}$$

In words, to raise a factor with an exponent to a power, keep the base and multiply the exponents.

The use of this new property is illustrated in Example 1.

● Example 1

C A U T I O N

Be careful! Be sure to distinguish between the correct use of Property 1 and Property 3.

$(x^4)^5 = x^{4 \cdot 5} = x^{20}$

but

$x^4 \cdot x^5 = x^{4+5} = x^9$

Using the Third Property of Exponents

Simplify each expression.

(a) $(x^4)^5 = x^{4 \cdot 5} = x^{20}$ Multiply the exponents.

(b) $(2^3)^4 = 2^{3 \cdot 4} = 2^{12}$

213

Simplify each expression.

a. $(m^5)^6$ **b.** $(m^5)(m^6)$ **c.** $(3^2)^4$ **d.** $(3^2)(3^4)$

Suppose we now have a product raised to a power. Consider an expression such as

Here the base is $3x$.

$$(3x)^4$$

We know that

Here we have applied the commutative and associative properties.

$$(3x)^4 = (3x)(3x)(3x)(3x)$$
$$= (3 \cdot 3 \cdot 3 \cdot 3)(x \cdot x \cdot x \cdot x)$$
$$= 3^4 \cdot x^4 = 81x^4$$

Note that the power, here 4, has been applied to each factor, 3 and x. In general, we have

---

Property 4 of Exponents

For any real numbers a and b and positive integer m,

$$(ab)^m = a^m b^m$$

In words, to raise a product to a power, raise each factor to that same power.

The use of this property is shown in Example 2.

● Example 2

Using the Fourth Property of Exponents

Note that $(2x)^5$ and $2x^5$ are entirely different expressions. For $(2x)^5$, the base is $2x$, so we raise each factor to the fifth power. For $2x^5$, the base is x, and so the exponent applies only to x.

Simplify each expression.

(a) $(2x)^5 = 2^5 \cdot x^5 = 32x^5$

(b) $(3ab)^4 = 3^4 \cdot a^4 \cdot b^4 = 81a^4 b^4$

(c) $5(2r)^3 = 5 \cdot 2^3 \cdot r^3 = 40r^3$

Simplify each expression.

a. $(3y)^4$ **b.** $(2mn)^6$ **c.** $3(4x)^2$ **d.** $5x^3$

We may have to use more than one of our properties in simplifying an expression involving exponents. Consider Example 3.

● Example 3

Using the Properties of Exponents

Simplify each expression.

To help you understand each step of the simplification, we refer to the property being applied. Make a list of the properties now to help you as you work through the remainder of this and the next section.

(a) $(r^4s^3)^3 = (r^4)^3 \cdot (s^3)^3$ Property 4

$\qquad = r^{12}s^9$ Property 3

(b) $(3x^2)^2 \cdot (2x^3)^3$

$\qquad = 3^2(x^2)^2 \cdot 2^3 \cdot (x^3)^3$ Property 4

$\qquad\qquad\qquad\qquad\qquad$ Property 3

$\qquad = 9x^4 \cdot 8x^9$ Multiply the coefficients and apply Property 1.

$\qquad = 72x^{13}$

(c) $\dfrac{(a^3)^5}{a^4} = \dfrac{a^{15}}{a^4}$ Property 3

$\qquad\qquad\qquad\qquad$ Property 2

$\qquad = a^{11}$

● ● ●   **CHECK YOURSELF 3**

Simplify each expression.

a. $(m^5n^2)^3$ $\qquad\qquad$ **b.** $(2p)^4(4p^2)^2$ $\qquad\qquad$ **c.** $\dfrac{(s^4)^3}{s^5}$

We have one final exponent property to develop. Suppose we have a quotient raised to a power. Consider the following:

$$\left(\frac{x}{3}\right)^3 = \frac{x}{3} \cdot \frac{x}{3} \cdot \frac{x}{3} = \frac{x \cdot x \cdot x}{3 \cdot 3 \cdot 3} = \frac{x^3}{3^3}$$

Note that the power, here 3, has been applied to the numerator x and to the denominator 3. This gives us our fifth property of exponents.

Property 5 of Exponents

For any real numbers a and b, where b is not equal to 0, and positive integer m,

$$\left(\frac{a}{b}\right)^m = \frac{a^m}{b^m}$$

In words, to raise a quotient to a power, raise the numerator and denominator to that same power.

Example 4 illustrates the use of this property. Again note that the other properties may also have to be applied in simplifying an expression.

• Example 4

Using the Fifth Property of Exponents

Simplify each expression.

(a) $\left(\dfrac{3}{4}\right)^3 = \dfrac{3^3}{4^3} = \dfrac{27}{64}$ Property 5

(b) $\left(\dfrac{x^3}{y^2}\right)^4 = \dfrac{(x^3)^4}{(y^2)^4}$ Property 5

$= \dfrac{x^{12}}{y^8}$ Property 3

(c) $\left(\dfrac{r^2 s^3}{t^4}\right)^2 = \dfrac{(r^2 s^3)^2}{(t^4)^2}$ Property 5

$= \dfrac{(r^2)^2(s^3)^2}{(t^4)^2}$ Property 4

$= \dfrac{r^4 s^6}{t^8}$ Property 3

● ● ● **CHECK YOURSELF 4**

Simplify each expression.

a. $\left(\dfrac{2}{3}\right)^4$ **b.** $\left(\dfrac{m^3}{n^4}\right)^5$ **c.** $\left(\dfrac{a^2 b^3}{c^5}\right)^2$

The following table summarizes the five properties of exponents that were discussed in this section:

General Form	Example
1. $a^m a^n = a^{m+n}$	$x^2 \cdot x^3 = x^5$
2. $\dfrac{a^m}{a^n} = a^{m-n}$ $(m > n)$	$\dfrac{5^7}{5^3} = 5^4$
3. $(a^m)^n = a^{mn}$	$(z^5)^4 = z^{20}$
4. $(ab)^m = a^m b^m$	$(4x)^3 = 4^3 x^3 = 64x^3$
5. $\left(\dfrac{a}{b}\right)^m = \dfrac{a^m}{b^m}$	$\left(\dfrac{2}{3}\right)^6 = \dfrac{2^6}{3^6} = \dfrac{64}{729}$

● ● ● **CHECK YOURSELF ANSWERS**

1. (a) m^{30}; **(b)** m^{11}; **(c)** 3^8; **(d)** 3^6.   **2. (a)** $81y^4$; **(b)** $64m^6 n^6$; **(c)** $48x^2$; **(d)** $5x^3$.

3. (a) $m^{15} n^6$; **(b)** $256p^8$; **(c)** s^7.   **4. (a)** $\dfrac{16}{81}$; **(b)** $\dfrac{m^{15}}{n^{20}}$; **(c)** $\dfrac{a^4 b^6}{c^{10}}$.

Use Property 3 of exponents to simplify each of the following expressions.

1. $(x^2)^3$ **2.** $(a^5)^3$

3. $(m^4)^4$ **4.** $(p^7)^2$

5. $(2^4)^2$ **6.** $(3^3)^2$

7. $(5^3)^5$ **8.** $(7^2)^4$

Use Properties 4 and 5 of exponents to simplify each of the following expressions.

9. $(3x)^3$ **10.** $(4m)^2$

11. $(2xy)^4$ **12.** $(5pq)^3$

13. $5(3ab)^3$ **14.** $4(2rs)^4$

15. $\left(\dfrac{3}{4}\right)^2$ **16.** $\left(\dfrac{2}{3}\right)^3$

17. $\left(\dfrac{x}{5}\right)^3$ **18.** $\left(\dfrac{a}{2}\right)^5$

19. $(2x^2)^4$ **20.** $(3y^2)^5$

21. $(a^8b^6)^2$ **22.** $(p^3q^4)^2$

23. $(4x^2y)^3$ **24.** $(4m^4n^4)^2$

1. _____
2. _____
3. _____
4. _____
5. _____
6. _____
7. _____
8. _____
9. _____
10. _____
11. _____
12. _____
13. _____
14. _____
15. _____
16. _____
17. _____
18. _____
19. _____
20. _____
21. _____
22. _____
23. _____
24. _____

ANSWERS

25. _____

26. _____

27. _____

28. _____

29. _____

30. _____

31. _____

32. _____

33. _____

34. _____

35. _____

36. _____

37. _____

38. _____

39. _____

40. _____

41. _____

42. _____

25. $(3m^2)^4(m^3)^2$

26. $(y^4)^3(4y^3)^2$

27. $\dfrac{(x^4)^3}{x^2}$

28. $\dfrac{(m^5)^3}{m^6}$

29. $\dfrac{(s^3)^2(s^2)^3}{(s^5)^2}$

30. $\dfrac{(y^5)^3(y^3)^2}{(y^4)^4}$

31. $\left(\dfrac{m^3}{n^2}\right)^3$

32. $\left(\dfrac{a^4}{b^3}\right)^4$

33. $\left(\dfrac{a^3b^2}{c^4}\right)^2$

34. $\left(\dfrac{x^5y^2}{z^4}\right)^3$

Solve the following problems.

35. Write x^{12} as a power of x^2.

36. Write y^{15} as a power of y^3.

37. Write a^{16} as a power of a^2.

38. Write m^{20} as a power of m^5.

39. Write each of the following as powers of 8. (Remember that $8 = 2^3$.)

2^{12}, 2^{18}, $(2^5)^3$, $(2^7)^6$

40. Write each of the following as powers of 9.

3^8, 3^{14}, $(3^5)^8$, $(3^4)^7$

41. What expression raised to the third power is $-8x^6y^9z^{15}$?

42. What expression raised to the fourth power is $81x^{12}y^8z^{16}$?

The formula $(1 + R)^Y = G$ gives us useful information about the growth of a population. Here R is the rate of growth expressed as a decimal, y is the time in years, and G is the growth factor. If a country has a 2 percent growth rate for 35 years, then it will double its population:

$(1.02)^{35} \approx 2$

43. a. With this growth rate, how many doublings will occur in 105 years? How much larger will the country's population be?

b. The less developed countries of the world had an average growth rate of 2 percent in 1986. If their total population was 3.8 billion, what will their population be in 105 years if this rate remains unchanged?

44. The United States has a growth rate of 0.7 percent. What will be its growth factor after 35 years?

45. Write an explanation of why $(x^3)(x^4)$ is *not* x^{12}.

46. Your algebra study partners are confused. "Why isn't $x^2 \cdot x^3 = 2x^5$?", they ask you. Write an explanation that will convince them.

47. Suppose that when you were born, a rich uncle put $1000 in the bank for you. He never deposited money again, but the bank paid 5 percent interest on the money every year on your birthday. How much money was in the bank after 1 year? After 2 years? After 1 year (as you know), the amount is $500 + 500(0.05)$, which can be written as $500(1 + 0.05)$ because of the distributive property. (You will learn more about this property in Chapter 5.) $1 + 0.05 = 1.05$, so after 1 year the amount in the bank was $500(1.05)$. After 2 years, this amount was again multiplied by 1.05. How much is in the bank today? Complete the following chart.

Birthday	Computation	Amount
0 **(Day of Birth)**		$500
1	$500(1.05)	
2	$500(1.05)(1.05)	
3	$500(1.05)(1.05)(1.05)	
4	$500(1.05)	
5	$500(1.05)	
6		
7		
8		

Write a formula for the amount in the bank on your *n*th birthday. About how many years does it take for the money to double? How many years for it to double again? Can you see any connection between this and the rules for exponents? Explain why you think there may or may not be a connection.

219

48. Work with another student to correctly complete the statements:

(a) $\dfrac{m^3}{n^3} < 1$ when . . .   **(b)** $\dfrac{a^x}{a^y} > 1$ when . . .

$\dfrac{m^3}{n^3} > 1$ when . . . $\dfrac{a^x}{a^y} = 1$ when . . .

$\dfrac{m^3}{n^3} = 1$ when . . . $\dfrac{a^x}{a^y} < 1$ when . . .

$\dfrac{m^3}{n^3} < 0$ (is negative) when . . . $\dfrac{a^x}{a^y} = 0$ when . . .

$\dfrac{m^3}{n^3} = 0$ when . . . $\dfrac{a^x}{a^y} < 0$ when . . .

Getting Ready for Section 4.3 [Section 4.1]

Reduce each of the following fractions to simplest form.

a. $\dfrac{m^3}{m^5}$ **b.** $\dfrac{x^7}{x^{10}}$ **c.** $\dfrac{a^3}{a^9}$ **d.** $\dfrac{y^4}{y^8}$

e. $\dfrac{x^3}{x^3}$ **f.** $\dfrac{b^5}{b^5}$ **g.** $\dfrac{s^7}{s^7}$ **h.** $\dfrac{r^{10}}{r^{10}}$

Answers

1. x^6 **3.** m^{16} **5.** 2^8 **7.** 5^{15} **9.** $27x^3$ **11.** $16x^4y^4$ **13.** $135a^3b^3$

15. $\dfrac{9}{16}$ **17.** $\dfrac{x^3}{125}$ **19.** $16x^8$ **21.** $a^{16}b^{12}$ **23.** $64x^6y^3$ **25.** $81m^{14}$

27. x^{10} **29.** s^2 **31.** $\dfrac{m^9}{n^6}$ **33.** $\dfrac{a^6b^4}{c^8}$ **35.** $(x^2)^6$ **37.** $(a^2)^8$

39. $8^4, 8^6, 8^5, 8^{14}$ **41.** $-2x^2y^3z^5$

43. (a) Three doublings, 8 times as large; **(b)** 30.4 billion

a. $\dfrac{1}{m^2}$ **b.** $\dfrac{1}{x^3}$ **c.** $\dfrac{1}{a^6}$ **d.** $\dfrac{1}{y^4}$ **e.** 1   **f.** 1   **g.** 1   **h.** 1

4.3 Zero and Negative Exponents

4.3 OBJECTIVES

1. Evaluate expressions involving zero or a negative exponent
2. Simplify expressions involving zero or a negative exponent

By Property 2,

$$\frac{a^m}{a^n} = a^{m-n}$$

where $m > n$. Here m and n are *both* 5 so $m = n$.

As was the case with $\frac{0}{0}$, 0^0 will not be discussed until you study calculus.

In the last section, we continued our discussion of the properties of exponents with the introduction of rules for raising expressions involving powers, products, and quotients to a power. We now want to extend our exponent notation to include 0 and negative integers as exponents.

First, what do we do with x^0? It will help to look at a problem that gives us x^0 as a result. What if the numerator and denominator of a fraction have the same base raised to the same power and we extend our divison rule? For example,

$$\frac{a^5}{a^5} = a^{5-5} = a^0 \tag{1}$$

But from our experience with fractions we know that

$$\frac{a^5}{a^5} = 1 \tag{2}$$

By comparing equations (1) and (2), it seems reasonable to make the following definition:

> For any number a, $a \neq 0$,
>
> $a^0 = 1$
>
> In words, any expression, except 0, raised to the 0 power is 1.

Example 1 illustrates the use of this definition.

● Example 1

Raising Expressions to the Zero Power

CAUTION

In part (*d*) the 0 exponent applies only to the x and *not* to the factor 6, since the base is x.

Evaluate. Assume all variables are nonzero.

(*a*) $5^0 = 1$
(*b*) $27^0 = 1$
(*c*) $(x^2y)^0 = 1$ if $x \neq 0$ and $y \neq 0$
(*d*) $6x^0 = 6 \cdot 1 = 6$ if $x \neq 0$

● ● ● CHECK YOURSELF 1

Evaluate. Assume all variables are nonzero.

a. 7^0 **b.** $(-8)^0$ **c.** $(xy^3)^0$ **d.** $3x^0$

The second property of exponents allows us to define a negative exponent. Suppose that the exponent in the denominator is *greater than* the exponent in the numerator. Consider the expression $\dfrac{x^2}{x^5}$.

Our previous work with fractions tells us that

Divide the numerator and denominator by the two common factors of *x*.

$$\frac{x^2}{x^5} = \frac{x \cdot x}{x \cdot x \cdot x \cdot x \cdot x} = \frac{1}{x^3} \tag{1}$$

However, if we extend the second property to let *n* be greater than *m*, we have

Remember: $\dfrac{a^m}{a^n} = a^{m-n}$

$$\frac{x^2}{x^5} = x^{2-5} = x^{-3} \tag{2}$$

Now, by comparing equations (1) and (2), it seems reasonable to define x^{-3} as $\dfrac{1}{x^3}$. In general, we have this result:

John Wallis (1616–1703), an English mathematician, was the first to fully discuss the meaning of 0 and negative exponents.

> For any number *a*, $a \neq 0$, and any positive integer *n*,
> $$a^{-n} = \frac{1}{a^n}$$

• Example 2

Rewriting Expressions That Contain Negative Exponents

Rewrite each expression, using only positive exponents.

Negative exponent in numerator

(*a*) $x^{-4} = \dfrac{1}{x^4}$

Positive exponent in denominator

(*b*) $m^{-7} = \dfrac{1}{m^7}$

(*c*) $3^{-2} = \dfrac{1}{3^2}$ or $\dfrac{1}{9}$

(*d*) $10^{-3} = \dfrac{1}{10^3}$ or $\dfrac{1}{1000}$

CAUTION

(*e*) $2x^{-3} = 2 \cdot \dfrac{1}{x^3} = \dfrac{2}{x^3}$

The -3 exponent applies only to *x*, since *x* is the base.

(*f*) $\dfrac{a^5}{a^9} = a^{5-9} = a^{-4} = \dfrac{1}{a^4}$

(*g*) $-4x^{-5} = -4 \cdot \dfrac{1}{x^5} = \dfrac{-4}{x^5}$

● ● ● CHECK YOURSELF 2

Write, using only positive exponents.

a. a^{-10} **b.** 4^{-3} **c.** $3x^{-2}$ **d.** $\dfrac{x^5}{x^8}$

We will now allow negative integers as exponents in our first property for exponents. Consider Example 3.

● Example 3

Simplifying Expressions Containing Exponents

Simplify each expression.

$a^m \cdot a^n = a^{m+n}$ for *any* integers *m* and *n*. So add the exponents.

(a) $x^5 x^{-2} = x^{5+(-2)} = x^3$

Note: An alternative approach would be

By definition
$x^{-2} = \dfrac{1}{x^2}$

$$x^5 x^{-2} = x^5 \cdot \frac{1}{x^2} = \frac{x^5}{x^2} = x^3$$

(b) $a^7 a^{-5} = a^{7+(-5)} = a^2$

(c) $y^5 y^{-9} = y^{5+(-9)} = y^{-4} = \dfrac{1}{y^4}$

● ● ● CHECK YOURSELF 3

Simplify.

a. $x^7 x^{-2}$ **b.** $b^3 b^{-8}$

Example 4 shows that all the properties of exponents introduced in the last section can be extended to expressions with negative exponents.

● Example 4

Simplifying Expressions Containing Exponents

Simplify each expression.

(a) $\dfrac{m^{-3}}{m^4} = m^{-3-4}$ Property 2

$$= m^{-7} = \frac{1}{m^7}$$

(b) $\dfrac{a^{-2}b^6}{a^5b^{-4}} = a^{-2-5}b^{6-(-4)}$ Apply Property 2 to each variable.

$$= a^{-7}b^{10} = \dfrac{b^{10}}{a^7}$$

This could also be done by using Property 4 first, so

$(2x^4)^{-3} = 2^{-3}x^{-12}$

$= \dfrac{1}{2^3x^{12}}$

$= \dfrac{1}{8x^{12}}$

(c) $(2x^4)^{-3} = \dfrac{1}{(2x^4)^3}$ Definition of the negative exponent

$$= \dfrac{1}{2^3(x^4)^3}$$ Property 4

$$= \dfrac{1}{8x^{12}}$$ Property 3

(d) $\dfrac{(y^{-2})^4}{(y^3)^{-2}} = \dfrac{y^{-8}}{y^{-6}}$ Property 3

$$= y^{-8-(-6)}$$ Property 2

$$= y^{-2} = \dfrac{1}{y^2}$$

●●● **CHECK YOURSELF 4**

Simplify each expression.

a. $\dfrac{x^5}{x^{-3}}$ **b.** $\dfrac{m^3n^{-5}}{m^{-2}n^3}$ **c.** $(3a^3)^{-4}$ **d.** $\dfrac{(r^3)^{-2}}{(r^{-4})^2}$

●●● **CHECK YOURSELF ANSWERS**

1. (a) 1; (b) 1; (c) 1; (d) 3.   **2.** (a) $\dfrac{1}{a^{10}}$; (b) $\dfrac{1}{4^3}$ or $\dfrac{1}{64}$; (c) $\dfrac{3}{x^2}$; (d) $\dfrac{1}{x^3}$.   **3.** (a) x^5;

(b) $\dfrac{1}{b^5}$.   **4.** (a) x^8; (b) $\dfrac{m^5}{n^8}$; (c) $\dfrac{1}{81a^{12}}$; (d) r^2.

Evaluate (assume the variables are nonzero).

1. 4^0

2. $(-7)^0$

3. $(-29)^0$

4. 75^0

5. $(x^3y^2)^0$

6. $7m^0$

7. $11x^0$

8. $(2a^3b^7)^0$

9. $(-3p^6q^8)^0$

10. $-7x^0$

Write each of the following expressions using positive exponents; simplify where possible.

11. b^{-8}

12. p^{-12}

13. 3^{-4}

14. 2^{-5}

15. 5^{-2}

16. 4^{-3}

17. 10^{-4}

18. 10^{-5}

19. $5x^{-1}$

20. $3a^{-2}$

21. $(5x)^{-1}$

22. $(3a)^{-2}$

23. $-2x^{-5}$

24. $3x^{-4}$

25. $(-2x)^{-5}$

26. $(3x)^{-4}$

1.

2.

3.

4.

5.

6.

7.

8.

9.

10.

11.

12.

13.

14.

15.

16.

17.

18.

19.

20.

21.

22.

23.

24.

25.

26.

225

27. _____

28. _____

29. _____

30. _____

31. _____

32. _____

33. _____

34. _____

35. _____

36. _____

37. _____

38. _____

39. _____

40. _____

41. _____

42. _____

43. _____

44. _____

45. _____

46. _____

47. _____

48. _____

49. _____

50. _____

Use Properties 1 and 2 to simplify each of the following expressions. Write your answers with positive exponents only.

27. $a^5 a^3$

28. $m^5 m^7$

29. $x^8 x^{-2}$

30. $a^{12} a^{-8}$

31. $b^7 b^{-11}$

32. $y^5 y^{-12}$

33. $x^0 x^5$

34. $r^{-3} r^0$

35. $\dfrac{a^8}{a^5}$

36. $\dfrac{m^9}{m^4}$

37. $\dfrac{x^7}{x^9}$

38. $\dfrac{a^3}{a^{10}}$

39. $\dfrac{r^{-3}}{r^5}$

40. $\dfrac{x^3}{x^{-5}}$

41. $\dfrac{x^{-4}}{x^{-5}}$

42. $\dfrac{p^{-6}}{p^{-3}}$

Simplify each of the following expressions. Write your answers with positive exponents only.

43. $\dfrac{m^5 n^{-3}}{m^{-4} n^5}$

44. $\dfrac{p^{-3} q^{-2}}{p^4 q^{-3}}$

45. $(2a^{-3})^4$

46. $(3x^2)^{-3}$

47. $(x^{-2} y^3)^{-2}$

48. $(a^5 b^{-3})^{-3}$

49. $\dfrac{(r^{-2})^3}{r^{-4}}$

50. $\dfrac{(y^3)^{-4}}{y^{-6}}$

51. $\dfrac{(x^{-3})^3}{(x^4)^{-2}}$

52. $\dfrac{(m^4)^{-3}}{(m^{-2})^4}$

53. $\dfrac{(a^{-3})^2(a^4)}{(a^{-3})^{-3}}$

54. $\dfrac{(x^2)^{-3}(x^{-2})}{(x^2)^{-4}}$

Decide which variables cannot be equal to zero.

55. $a^{-4}b^3$

56. $x^{-4}y^3$

57. $x^{-3}y^3z^2$

58. $a^3b^{-3}c^{-2}$

59. $\dfrac{a^4b^{-3}}{c^3}$

60. $\dfrac{m^{-2}n^3}{r^2s^3}$

In 1975 the population of Earth was approximately 4 billion and doubling every 35 years. The formula for the population P in year Y for this doubling rate is

$$P \text{ (in billions)} = 4 \times 2^{2(Y-1975)/35}$$

61. What was the approximate population of earth in 1960?

62. What will the Earth's population be in 2025?

The United States population in 1990 was approximately 250 million, and the average growth rate for the past 30 years gives a doubling time of 66 years. The above formula for the United States then becomes

$$P \text{ (in millions)} = 250 \times 2^{(Y-1990)/66}$$

63. What was the approximate population of the United States in 1960?

64. What will be the population of the United States in 2025 if this growth rate continues?

ANSWERS

51. _____
52. _____ _____
53. _____
54. _____
55. _____
56. _____
57. _____
58. _____
59. _____
60. _____
61. _____
62. _____
63. _____
64. _____

Getting Ready for Section 4.4
[Section 2.4]

Evaluate each expression.

a. 3^2 **b.** $(-3)^2$ **c.** 5^3 **d.** $(-5)^3$

e. 2^4 **f.** $(-2)^4$ **g.** 3^5 **h.** $(-3)^5$

Answers

1. 1   **3.** 1   **5.** 1   **7.** 11   **9.** 1   **11.** $\dfrac{1}{b^8}$ **13.** $\dfrac{1}{3^4}$ or $\dfrac{1}{81}$

15. $\dfrac{1}{5^2}$ or $\dfrac{1}{25}$ **17.** $\dfrac{1}{10^4}$ or $\dfrac{1}{10,000}$ **19.** $\dfrac{5}{x}$ **21.** $\dfrac{1}{5x}$ **23.** $-\dfrac{2}{x^5}$

25. $-\dfrac{1}{32x^5}$ **27.** a^8 **29.** x^6 **31.** $\dfrac{1}{b^4}$ **33.** x^5 **35.** a^3 **37.** $\dfrac{1}{x^2}$

39. $\dfrac{1}{r^8}$ **41.** x **43.** $\dfrac{m^9}{n^8}$ **45.** $\dfrac{16}{a^{12}}$ **47.** $\dfrac{x^4}{y^6}$ **49.** $\dfrac{1}{r^2}$ **51.** $\dfrac{1}{x}$

53. $\dfrac{1}{a^{11}}$ **55.** a **57.** x **59.** b, c **61.** 2.2 billion   **63.** 182 million

a. 9   **b.** 9   **c.** 125   **d.** -125 **e.** 16   **f.** 16   **g.** 243

h. -243

An Introduction to Polynomials

4.4 OBJECTIVES

1. Identify types of polynomials
2. Find the degree of a polynomial
3. Write polynomials in descending-exponent form

Our work in this chapter deals with the most common kind of algebraic expression, a *polynomial.* To define a polynomial, let's recall our earlier definition of the word "term."

> A **term** is a number or the product of a number and one or more variables.

For example, x^5, $3x$, $-4xy^2$, 8, $\dfrac{5}{x}$, and $-14\sqrt{x}$ are terms. A **polynomial** consists of one or more terms in which the only allowable exponents are the whole numbers, 0, 1, 2, 3, . . . and so on. These terms are connected by addition or subtraction signs.

In a polynomial, terms are separated by $+$ and $-$ signs.

> In each term of a polynomial, the number is called the **numerical coefficient,** or more simply the **coefficient,** of that term.

●Example 1

Identifying Polynomials

Note: Each sign ($+$ or $-$) is attached to the term that *follows* that sign.

(*a*) $x + 3$ is a polynomial. The terms are x and 3. The coefficients are 1 and 3.

(*b*) $3x^2 - 2x + 5$ is also a polynomial. Its terms are $3x^2$, $-2x$, and 5. The coefficients are 3, -2, and 5.

(*c*) $5x^3 + 2 - \dfrac{3}{x}$ is *not* a polynomial because of the division by x in the third term.

● ● ● **CHECK YOURSELF 1**

Which of the following are polynomials?

a. $5x^2$ **b.** $3y^3 - 2y + \dfrac{5}{y}$ **c.** $4x^2 - 2x + 3$

Certain polynomials are given special names because of the number of terms that they have.

The prefix "mono" means 1. The prefix "bi" means 2. The prefix "tri" means 3. There are no special names for polynomials with more than four terms.

> A polynomial with one term is called a **monomial**.
>
> A polynomial with two terms is called a **binomial**.
>
> A polynomial with three terms is called a **trinomial**.

• Example 2

Identifying Types of Polynomials

(a) $3x^2y$ is a monomial. It has one term.
(b) $2x^3 + 5x$ is a binomial. It has two terms, $2x^3$ and $5x$.
(c) $5x^2 - 4x + 3$ is a trinomial. Its three terms are $5x^2$, $-4x$, and 3.

● ● ● **CHECK YOURSELF 2**

Classify each of these as a monomial, binomial, or trinomial.

a. $5x^4 - 2x^3$ **b.** $4x^7$ **c.** $2x^2 + 5x - 3$

Remember, in a polynomial the allowable exponents are the whole numbers 0, 1, 2, 3, and so on. The degree will be a whole number.

We also classify polynomials by their *degree*. The **degree** of a polynomial that has only one variable is the highest power appearing in any one term.

• Example 3

Classifying Polynomials by Their Degree

The highest power

(a) $5x^3 - 3x^2 + 4x$ has degree 3.

The highest power

(b) $4x - 5x^4 + 3x^3 + 2$ has degree 4.
(c) $8x$ has degree 1.

(Because $8x = 8x^1$)

Remember that $x^0 = 1$.

(d) 7 has degree 0.

(Because $7 = 7 \cdot 1 = 7x^0$)

Note: Polynomials can have more than one variable, such as $4x^2y^3 + 5xy^2$. The degree is then the sum of the highest powers in any single term (here $2 + 3$, or 5). In general, we will be working with polynomials in a single variable, such as x.

● ● ● **CHECK YOURSELF 3**

Find the degree of each polynomial.

a. $6x^5 - 3x^3 - 2$ **b.** $5x$ **c.** $3x^3 + 2x^6 - 1$ **d.** 9

Working with polynomials is much easier if you get used to writing them in **descending-exponent form** (sometimes called *descending-power form*). This simply means that the term with the highest exponent is written first, then the term with the next highest exponent, and so on.

• Example 4

Writing Polynomials in Descending Order

The exponents get smaller from left to right.

(*a*) $5x^7 - 3x^4 + 2x^2$ is in descending-exponent form.
(*b*) $4x^4 + 5x^6 - 3x^5$ is *not* in descending-exponent form. The polynomial should be written as

$$5x^6 - 3x^5 + 4x^4$$

Notice that the degree of the polynomial is the power of the *first,* or *leading,* term once the polynomial is arranged in descending-exponent form.

● ● ● **CHECK YOURSELF 4**

Write the following polynomials in descending-exponent form.

a. $5x^4 - 4x^5 + 7$ **b.** $4x^3 + 9x^4 + 6x^8$

A polynomial can represent any number. Its value depends on the value given to the variable.

• Example 5

Evaluating Polynomials

Given the polynomial

$$3x^3 - 2x^2 - 4x + 1$$

(*a*) Find the value of the polynomial when $x = 2$.

Substituting 2 for x, we have

Again note how the rules for the order of operations are applied. See Section 2.6 for a review.

$$3(2)^3 - 2(2)^2 - 4(2) + 1$$
$$= 3(8) - 2(4) - 4(2) + 1$$
$$= 24 - 8 - 8 + 1$$
$$= 9$$

CAUTION

Be particularly careful when dealing with powers of negative numbers!

(*b*) Find the value of the polynomial when $x = -2$.

Now we substitute -2 for x.

$$3(-2)^3 - 2(-2)^2 - 4(-2) + 1$$
$$= 3(-8) - 2(4) - 4(-2) + 1$$
$$= -24 - 8 + 8 + 1$$
$$= -23$$

● ● ● **CHECK YOURSELF 5**

Find the value of the polynomial

$$4x^3 - 3x^2 + 2x - 1$$

when

a. $x = 3$ **b.** $x = -3$

● ● ● **CHECK YOURSELF ANSWERS**

1. **(a)** and **(c)** are polynomials.   **2.** **(a)** Binomial; **(b)** monomial; **(c)** trinomial.

3. **(a)** 5; **(b)** 1; **(c)** 6; **(d)** 0.   **4.** **(a)** $-4x^5 + 5x^4 + 7$; **(b)** $6x^8 + 9x^4 + 4x^3$.

5. **(a)** 86; **(b)** -142.

Name

Section   Date

Which of the following expressions are polynomials?

1. $7x^3$

2. $5x^3 - \dfrac{3}{x}$

3. $4x^4y^2 - 3x^3y$

4. 7

5. -7

6. $4x^3 + x$

7. $\dfrac{3 + x}{x^2}$

8. $5a^2 - 2a + 7$

For each of the following polynomials, list the terms and the coefficients.

9. $2x^2 - 3x$

10. $5x^3 + x$

11. $4x^3 - 3x + 2$

12. $7x^2$

Classify each of the following as a monomial, binomial, or trinomial where possible.

13. $7x^3 - 3x^2$

14. $4x^7$

15. $7y^2 + 4y + 5$

16. $2x^2 + 3xy + y^2$

17. $2x^4 - 3x^2 + 5x - 2$

18. $x^4 + \dfrac{5}{x} + 7$

19. $6y^8$

20. $4x^4 - 2x^2 + 5x - 7$

21. $x^5 - \dfrac{3}{x^2}$

22. $4x^2 - 9$

Arrange in descending-exponent form if necessary, and give the degree of each polynomial.

23. $4x^5 - 3x^2$

24. $5x^2 + 3x^3 + 4$

25. $7x^7 - 5x^9 + 4x^3$

26. $2 + x$

ANSWERS
1.
2.
3.
4.
5.
6.
7.
8.
9.
10.
11.
12.
13.
14.
15.
16.
17.
18.
19.
20.
21.
22.
23.
24.
25.
26.

A N S W E R S

27.

28.

29.

30.

31.

32.

33.

34.

35.

36.

37.

38.

39.

40.

41.

42.

43.

44.

45.

46.

27. $4x$

28. $x^{17} - 3x^4$

29. $5x^2 - 3x^5 + x^6 - 7$

30. 5

Find the values of each of the following polynomials for the given values of the variable.

31. $6x + 1$, $x = 1$ and $x = -1$

32. $5x - 5$, $x = 2$ and $x = -2$

33. $x^3 - 2x$, $x = 2$ and $x = -2$

34. $3x^2 + 7$, $x = 3$ and $x = -3$

35. $3x^2 + 4x - 2$, $x = 4$ and $x = -4$

36. $2x^2 - 5x + 1$, $x = 2$ and $x = -2$

37. $-x^2 - 2x + 3$, $x = 1$ and $x = -3$

38. $-x^2 - 5x - 6$, $x = -3$ and $x = -2$

Indicate whether each of the following statements is always true, sometimes true, or never true.

39. A monomial is a polynomial.

40. A binomial is a trinomial.

41. The degree of a trinomial is 3.

42. A trinomial has three terms.

43. A polynomial has four or more terms.

44. A binomial must have two coefficients.

45. If x equals 0, the value of a polynomial in x equals 0.

46. The coefficient of the leading term in a polynomial is the largest coefficient of the polynomial.

Capital italic letters such as P or Q are often used to name polynomials. For example, we might write $P(x) = 3x^3 - 5x^2 + 2$ where $P(x)$ is read "P of x." The notation permits a convenient shorthand. We write $P(2)$, read "P of 2," to indicate the value of the polynomial when $x = 2$. Here

$$P(2) = 3(2)^3 - 5(2)^2 + 2$$
$$= 3 \cdot 8 - 5 \cdot 4 + 2$$
$$= 6$$

Use the information above in the following problems.

If $P(x) = x^3 - 2x^2 + 5$ and $Q(x) = 2x^2 + 3$, find:

47. $P(1)$ **48.** $P(-1)$

49. $Q(2)$ **50.** $Q(-2)$

51. $P(3)$ **52.** $Q(-3)$

53. $P(0)$ **54.** $Q(0)$

55. $P(2) + Q(-1)$ **56.** $P(-2) + Q(3)$

57. $P(3) - Q(-3) \div Q(0)$ **58.** $Q(-2) \div Q(2) \cdot P(0)$

59. $|Q(4)| - |P(4)|$ **60.** $\dfrac{P(-1) + Q(0)}{P(0)}$

61. Cost of typing. The cost, in dollars, of typing a term paper is given as 3 times the number of pages plus 20. Use y as the number of pages to be typed and write a polynomial to describe this cost. Find the cost of typing a 50-page paper.

62. Manufacturing. The cost, in dollars, of making suits is described as 20 times the number of suits plus 150. Use s as the number of suits and write a polynomial to describe this cost. Find the cost of making seven suits.

63. Revenue. The revenue, in dollars, when x pairs of shoes are solid is given by $3x^2 - 95$. Find the revenue when 12 pairs of shoes are sold. What is the average revenue per pair of shoes?

64. Manufacturing. The cost in dollars of manufacturing w wing nuts is given by the expression $0.07x + 13.3$. Find the cost when 375 wing nuts are made. What is the average cost to manufacture one wing nut?

ANSWERS

47.

48.

49.

50.

51.

52.

53.

54.

55.

56.

57.

58.

59.

60.

61.

62.

63.

64.

Getting Ready for Section 4.5
[Section 1.4]

Combine like terms where possible.

a. $8m + 7m$

b. $9x - 5x$

c. $9m^2 - 8m$

d. $8x^2 - 7x^2$

e. $5c^3 + 15c^3$

f. $9s^3 + 8s^3$

g. $8c^2 - 6c + 2c^2$

h. $8r^3 - 7r^2 + 5r^3$

Answers

1. Polynomial   **3.** Polynomial   **5.** Polynomial   **7.** Not a polynomial
9. $2x^2, -3x; 2, -3$ **11.** $4x^3, -3x, 2; 4, -3, 2$ **13.** Binomial
15. Trinomial   **17.** Not classified   **19.** Monomial   **21.** Not a polynomial
23. $4x^5 - 3x^2; 5$ **25.** $-5x^9 + 7x^7 + 4x^3; 9$ **27.** $4x; 1$
29. $x^6 - 3x^5 + 5x^2 - 7; 6$ **31.** $7, -5$ **33.** $4, -4$ **35.** 62, 30
37. 0, 0   **39.** Always   **41.** Sometimes   **43.** Sometimes
45. Sometimes   **47.** 4   **49.** 11   **51.** 14   **53.** 5   **55.** 10   **57.** 7
59. -2 **61.** $3y + 20$, \$170   **63.** \$337, \$28.08
a. $15m$ **b.** $4x$ **c.** $9m^2 - 8m$ **d.** x^2 **e.** $20c^3$ **f.** $17s^3$
g. $10c^2 - 6c$ **h.** $13r^3 - 7r^2$

4.5 Adding and Subtracting Polynomials

Addition is always a matter of combining like quantities (two apples plus three apples, four books plus five books, and so on). If you keep that basic idea in mind, adding polynomials will be easy. It is just a matter of combining like terms. Suppose that you want to add

$$5x^2 + 3x + 4 \qquad \text{and} \qquad 4x^2 + 5x - 6$$

Parentheses are sometimes used in adding, so for the sum of these polynomials, we can write

The plus sign between the parentheses indicates the addition.

$$(5x^2 + 3x + 4) + (4x^2 + 5x - 6)$$

Now what about the parentheses? You can use the following rule.

Removing Signs of Grouping Case 1

If a plus sign (+) or nothing at all appears in front of parentheses, just remove the parentheses. No other changes are necessary.

Now let's return to the addition.

Just remove the parentheses. No other changes are necessary.

$$(5x^2 + 3x + 4) + (4x^2 + 5x - 6)$$
$$= 5x^2 + 3x + 4 + 4x^2 + 5x - 6$$

Like terms — Like terms

Like terms

Note the use of the associative and commutative properties in reordering and regrouping.

Collect like terms. (*Remember:* Like terms have the same variables raised to the same power.)

$$= (5x^2 + 4x^2) + (3x + 5x) + (4 - 6)$$

Combine like terms for the result:

Here we use the distributive property. For example,
$5x^2 + 4x^2 = 9x^2$

$$= 9x^2 + 8x - 2$$

As should be clear, much of this work can be done mentally. You can then write the sum directly by locating like terms and combining. Example 1 illustrates this property.

● Example 1

Combining Like Terms

Add $3x - 5$ and $2x + 3$.

Write the sum.

$(3x - 5) + (2x + 3)$

$= 3x - 5 + 2x + 3 = 5x - 2$

Like terms Like terms

● ● ● **CHECK YOURSELF 1**

Add $6x^2 + 2x$ and $4x^2 - 7x$.

The same technique is used to find the sum of two trinomials.

● Example 2

Adding Polynomials

Add $4a^2 - 7a + 5$ and $3a^2 + 3a - 4$.

Write the sum.

Remember: Only the like terms are combined in the sum.

$(4a^2 - 7a + 5) + (3a^2 + 3a - 4)$

$= 4a^2 - 7a + 5 + 3a^2 + 3a - 4 = 7a^2 - 4a + 1$

Like terms
Like terms
Like terms

● ● ● **CHECK YOURSELF 2**

Add $5y^2 - 3y + 7$ and $3y^2 - 5y - 7$.

● Example 3

Adding Polynomials

Add $2x^2 + 7x$ and $4x - 6$.

Write the sum.

$(2x^2 + 7x) + (4x - 6)$

$= 2x^2 + \underline{7x + 4x} - 6$

These are the only like terms; $2x^2$ and -6 cannot be combined.

$= 2x^2 + 11x - 6$

● ● ● **CHECK YOURSELF 3**

Add $5m^2 + 8$ and $8m^2 - 3m$.

As we mentioned in Section 4.4, writing polynomials in descending-exponent form usually makes the work easier. Look at Example 4.

●**Example 4**

Adding Polynomials

Add $3x - 2x^2 + 7$ and $5 + 4x^2 - 3x$.

Write the polynomials in descending-exponent form, then add.

$(-2x^2 + 3x + 7) + (4x^2 - 3x + 5)$

$= 2x^2 + 12$

● ● ● **CHECK YOURSELF 4**

Add $8 - 5x^2 + 4x$ and $7x - 8 + 8x^2$.

Subtracting polynomials requires another rule for removing signs of grouping.

Removing Signs of Grouping Case 2

If a minus sign $(-)$ appears in front of a set of parentheses, the parentheses can be removed by changing the sign of each term inside the parentheses.

The use of this rule is illustrated in Example 5.

●**Example 5**

Removing Parentheses

In each of the following, remove the parentheses.

Note: This uses the distributive property, since

$-(2x + 3y) = (-1)(2x + 3y)$

$\qquad = -2x - 3y$

(*a*) $-(2x + 3y) = -2x - 3y$ Change each sign to remove the parentheses.

(*b*) $m - (5n - 3p) = m \underbrace{- 5n + 3p}$

                Sign changes.

(*c*) $2x - (-3y + z) = 2x \underbrace{+ 3y - z}$

             Sign changes.

● ● ● **CHECK YOURSELF 5**

Remove the parentheses.

a. $-(3m + 5n)$ **b.** $-(5w - 7z)$ **c.** $3r - (2s - 5t)$ **d.** $5a - (-3b - 2c)$

Subtracting polynomials is now a matter of using the previous rule to remove the parentheses and then combining the like terms. Consider Example 6.

• Example 6

Subtracting Polynomials

(a) Subtract $5x - 3$ from $8x + 2$.

Write

Note: The expression following "from" is written first in the problem.

$(8x + 2) - (5x - 3)$

$= 8x + 2 \underbrace{- 5x + 3}_{\text{Sign changes.}}$

$= 3x + 5$

(b) Subtract $4x^2 - 8x + 3$ from $8x^2 + 5x - 3$.

Write

$(8x^2 + 5x - 3) - (4x^2 - 8x + 3)$

$= 8x^2 + 5x - 3 \underbrace{- 4x^2 + 8x - 3}_{\text{Sign changes.}}$

$= 4x^2 + 13x - 6$

● ● ● **CHECK YOURSELF 6**

a. Subtract $7x + 3$ from $10x - 7$.
b. Subtract $5x^2 - 3x + 2$ from $8x^2 - 3x - 6$.

Again, writing all polynomials in descending-exponent form will make locating and combining like terms much easier. Look at Example 7.

• Example 7

Subtracting Polynomials

(a) Subtract $4x^2 - 3x^3 + 5x$ from $8x^3 - 7x + 2x^2$.

Write

$$(8x^3 + 2x^2 - 7x) - (-3x^3 + 4x^2 + 5x)$$

$$= 8x^3 + 2x^2 - 7x \underbrace{+ 3x^3 - 4x^2 - 5x}_{\text{Sign changes.}}$$

$$= 11x^3 - 2x^2 - 12x$$

(b) Subtract $8x - 5$ from $-5x + 3x^2$.

Write

$$(3x^2 - 5x) - (8x - 5)$$

$$= 3x^2 \underbrace{- 5x - 8x}_{} + 5$$

Only the like terms can be combined.

$$= 3x^2 - 13x + 5$$

●●● **CHECK YOURSELF 7**

a. Subtract $7x - 3x^2 + 5$ from $5 - 3x + 4x^2$.
b. Subtract $3a - 2$ from $5a + 4a^2$.

If you think back to addition and subtraction in arithmetic, you'll remember that the work was arranged vertically. That is, the numbers being added or subtracted were placed under one another so that each column represented the same place value. This meant that in adding or subtracting columns you were always dealing with "like quantities."

It is also possible to use a vertical method for adding or subtracting polynomials. First rewrite the polynomials in descending-exponent form, then arrange them one under another, so that each column contains like terms. Then add or subtract in each column.

• Example 8

Adding Using the Vertical Method

Add $2x^2 - 5x$, $3x^2 + 2$, and $6x - 3$.

Like terms

$$
\begin{array}{r}
2x^2 - 5x \\
3x^2 \quad\quad + 2 \\
6x - 3 \\
\hline
5x^2 + \; x - 1
\end{array}
$$

●●● **CHECK YOURSELF 8**

Add $3x^2 + 5$, $x^2 - 4x$, and $6x + 7$.

The following example illustrates subtraction by the vertical method.

• Example 9

Subtracting Using the Vertical Method

(*a*) Subtract $5x - 3$ from $8x - 7$.

Write

$$
\begin{array}{r}
8x - 7 \\
(-)\ \underline{5x - 3} \\
3x - 4
\end{array}
$$

To subtract, change each sign of $5x - 3$ to get $-5x + 3$, then add.

$$
=
\begin{array}{r}
8x - 7 \\
\underline{-5x + 3} \\
3x - 4
\end{array}
$$

(*b*) Subtract $5x^2 - 3x + 4$ from $8x^2 + 5x - 3$.

Write

$$
\begin{array}{r}
8x^2 + 5x - 3 \\
(-)\ \underline{5x^2 - 3x + 4} \\
3x^2 + 8x - 7
\end{array}
$$

To subtract, change each sign of $5x^2 - 3x + 4$ to get $-5x^2 + 3x - 4$, then add.

$$
=
\begin{array}{r}
8x^2 + 5x - 3 \\
\underline{-5x^2 + 3x - 4} \\
3x^2 + 8x - 7
\end{array}
$$

Subtracting using the vertical method takes some practice. Take time to study the method carefully. You'll be using it in long division in Section 4.7.

● ● ● ● **CHECK YOURSELF 9**

Subtract, using the vertical method.

a. $4x^2 - 3x$ from $8x^2 + 2x$ **b.** $8x^2 + 4x - 3$ from $9x^2 - 5x + 7$

● ● ● **CHECK YOURSELF ANSWERS**

1. $10x^2 - 5x.$ **2.** $8y^2 - 8y.$ **3.** $13m^2 - 3m + 8.$ **4.** $3x^2 + 11x.$
5. (a) $-3m - 5n;$ **(b)** $-5w + 7z;$ **(c)** $3r - 2s + 5t;$ **(d)** $5a + 3b + 2c.$
6. (a) $3x - 10;$ **(b)** $3x^2 - 8.$ **7. (a)** $7x^2 - 10x;$ **(b)** $4a^2 + 2a + 2.$
8. $4x^2 + 2x + 12.$ **9. (a)** $4x^2 + 5x;$ **(b)** $x^2 - 9x + 10.$

4.5 **Exercises**

Name

Section   Date

Add.

1. $6a - 5$ and $3a + 9$

2. $9x + 3$ and $3x - 4$

3. $8b^2 - 11b$ and $5b^2 - 7b$

4. $2m^2 + 3m$ and $6m^2 - 8m$

5. $3x^2 - 2x$ and $-5x^2 + 2x$

6. $3p^2 + 5p$ and $-7p^2 - 5p$

7. $2x^2 + 5x - 3$ and $3x^2 - 7x + 4$

8. $4d^2 - 8d + 7$ and $5d^2 - 6d - 9$

9. $2b^2 + 8$ and $5b + 8$

10. $4x - 3$ and $3x^2 - 9x$

11. $8y^3 - 5y^2$ and $5y^2 - 2y$

12. $9x^4 - 2x^2$ and $2x^2 + 3$

13. $2a^2 - 4a^3$ and $3a^3 + 2a^2$

14. $9m^3 - 2m$ and $-6m - 4m^3$

15. $4x^2 - 2 + 7x$ and $5 - 8x - 6x^2$

16. $5b^3 - 8b + 2b^2$ and $3b^2 - 7b^3 + 5b$

Remove the parentheses in each of the following expressions, and simplify where possible.

17. $-(2a + 3b)$

18. $-(7x - 4y)$

19. $5a - (2b - 3c)$

20. $7x - (4y + 3z)$

21. $9r - (3r + 5s)$

22. $10m - (3m - 2n)$

23. $5p - (-3p + 2q)$

24. $8d - (-7c - 2d)$

Subtract.

25. $x + 4$ from $2x - 3$

26. $x - 2$ from $3x + 5$

1.
2.
3.
4.
5.
6.
7.
8.
9.
10.
11.
12.
13.
14.
15.
16.
17.
18.
19.
20.
21.
22.
23.
24.
25.
26.

243

27. $3m^2 - 2m$ from $4m^2 - 5m$

28. $9a^2 - 5a$ from $11a^2 - 10a$

29. $6y^2 + 5y$ from $4y^2 + 5y$

30. $9n^2 - 4n$ from $7n^2 - 4n$

31. $x^2 - 4x - 3$ from $3x^2 - 5x - 2$

32. $3x^2 - 2x + 4$ from $5x^2 - 8x - 3$

33. $3a + 7$ from $8a^2 - 9a$

34. $3x^3 + x^2$ from $4x^3 - 5x$

35. $4b^2 - 3b$ from $5b - 2b^2$

36. $7y - 3y^2$ from $3y^2 - 2y$

37. $x^2 - 5 - 8x$ from $3x^2 - 8x + 7$

38. $4x - 2x^2 + 4x^3$ from $4x^3 + x - 3x^2$

Perform the indicated operations.

39. Subtract $3b + 2$ from the sum of $4b - 2$ and $5b + 3$.

40. Subtract $5m - 7$ from the sum of $2m - 8$ and $9m - 2$.

41. Subtract $3x^2 + 2x - 1$ from the sum of $x^2 + 5x - 2$ and $2x^2 + 7x - 8$.

42. Subtract $4x^2 - 5x - 3$ from the sum of $x^2 - 3x - 7$ and $2x^2 - 2x + 9$.

43. Subtract $2x^2 - 3x$ from the sum of $4x^2 - 5$ and $2x - 7$.

44. Subtract $5a^2 - 3a$ from the sum of $3a - 3$ and $5a^2 + 5$.

45. Subtract the sum of $3y^2 - 3y$ and $5y^2 + 3y$ from $2y^2 - 8y$.

46. Subtract the sum of $7r^3 - 4r^2$ and $-3r^3 + 4r^2$ from $2r^3 + 3r^2$.

Add, using the vertical method.

47. $2w^2 + 7$, $3w - 5$, and $4w^2 - 5w$

48. $3x^2 - 4x - 2$, $6x - 3$, and $2x^2 + 8$

49. $3x^2 + 3x - 4$, $4x^2 - 3x - 3$, and $2x^2 - x + 7$

50. $5x^2 + 2x - 4$, $x^2 - 2x - 3$, and $2x^2 - 4x - 3$

Subtract, using the vertical method.

51. $3a^2 - 2a$ from $5a^2 + 3a$ **52.** $6r^3 + 4r^2$ from $4r^3 - 2r^2$

53. $5x^2 - 6x + 7$ from $8x^2 - 5x + 7$ **54.** $8x^2 - 4x + 2$ from $9x^2 - 8x + 6$

55. $5x^2 - 3x$ from $8x^2 - 9$ **56.** $7x^2 + 6x$ from $9x^2 - 3$

Perform the indicated operations.

57. $[(9x^2 - 3x + 5) - (3x^2 + 2x - 1)] - (x^2 - 2x - 3)$

58. $[(5x^2 + 2x - 3) - (-2x^2 + x - 2)] - (2x^2 + 3x - 5)$

ANSWERS
43.
44.
45.
46.
47.
48.
49.
50.
51.
52.
53.
54.
55.
56.
57.
58.

Find values for a, b, c, and d so that the following equations are true.

59. $3ax^4 - 5x^3 + x^2 - cx + 2 = 9x^4 - bx^3 + x^2 - 2d$

60. $(4ax^3 - 3bx^2 - 10) - 3(x^3 + 4x^2 - cx - d) = x^2 - 6x + 8$

61. Geometry. A rectangle has sides of $8x + 9$ and $6x - 7$. Find the polynomial that represents its perimeter.

62. Geometry. A triangle has sides $3x + 7$, $4x - 9$, and $5x + 6$. Find the polynomial that represents its perimeter.

63. Business. The cost of producing x units of an item is $C = 150 + 25x$. The revenue for selling x units is $R = 90x - x^2$. The profit is given by the revenue minus the cost. Find the polynomial that represents profit.

64. Business. The revenue for selling y units is $R = 3y^2 - 2y + 5$ and the cost of producing y units is $y^2 + y - 3$. Find the polynomial that represents profit.

● Getting Ready for Section 4.6

Multiply.

a. $x^5 \cdot x^7$ **b.** $y^8 \cdot y^{12}$

c. $2a^3 \cdot a^4$ **d.** $3m^5 \cdot m^2$

e. $4r^5 \cdot 3r$ **f.** $6w^2 \cdot 5w^3$

g. $(-2x^2)(8x^7)$ **h.** $(-10a)(-3a^5)$

Answers

1. $9a + 4$ **3.** $13b^2 - 18b$ **5.** $-2x^2$ **7.** $5x^2 - 2x + 1$ **9.** $2b^2 + 5b + 16$
11. $8y^3 - 2y$ **13.** $-a^3 + 4a^2$ **15.** $-2x^2 - x + 3$ **17.** $-2a - 3b$
19. $5a - 2b + 3c$ **21.** $6r - 5s$ **23.** $8p - 2q$ **25.** $x - 7$
27. $m^2 - 3m$ **29.** $-2y^2$ **31.** $2x^2 - x + 1$ **33.** $8a^2 - 12a - 7$
35. $-6b^2 + 8b$ **37.** $2x^2 + 12$ **39.** $6b - 1$ **41.** $10x - 9$
43. $2x^2 + 5x - 12$ **45.** $-6y^2 - 8y$ **47.** $6w^2 - 2w + 2$ **49.** $9x^2 - x$
51. $2a^2 + 5a$ **53.** $3x^2 + x$ **55.** $3x^2 + 3x - 9$ **57.** $5x^2 - 3x + 9$
59. $a = 3$, $b = 5$, $c = 0$, $d = -1$ **61.** $28x + 4$ **63.** $-x^2 + 65x - 150$
a. x^{12} **b.** y^{20} **c.** $2a^7$ **d.** $3m^7$ **e.** $12r^6$ **f.** $30w^5$ **g.** $-16x^9$
h. $30a^6$

Multiplying Polynomials

4.6 OBJECTIVES

1. Find the product of a monomial and a polynomial
2. Find the product of two polynomials

The first property of exponents:

$x^m \cdot x^n = x^{m+n}$

You have already had some experience in multiplying polynomials. In Section 4.1 we stated the first property of exponents and used that property to find the product of two monomials. Let's review briefly.

To Find the Product of Monomials

STEP 1 Multiply the coefficients.

STEP 2 Use the first property of exponents to combine the variables.

● Example 1

Multiplying Monomials

Multiply $3x^2y$ and $2x^3y^5$.

Write

Once again we have used the commutative and associative properties to rewrite the problems.

$(3x^2y)(2x^3y^5)$

$= (3 \cdot 2)(x^2 \cdot x^3)(y \cdot y^5)$

Multiply the coefficients. Add the exponents.

$= 6x^5y^6$

● ● ● **CHECK YOURSELF 1**

Multiply.

a. $(5a^2b)(3a^2b^4)$ **b.** $(-3xy)(4x^3y^5)$

You might want to review Section 1.3 before going on.

Our next task is to find the product of a monomial and a polynomial. Here we use the distributive property, which we introduced in Section 1.3. That property leads us to the following rule for multiplication.

To Multiply a Polynomial by a Monomial

Use the distributive property to multiply each term of the polynomial by the monomial.

Distributive property:

$a(b + c) = ab + ac$

● Example 2

Multiplying a Monomial and a Binomial

(*a*) Multiply $2x + 3$ by x.

Write

Note: With practice you will do this step mentally.

$x(2x + 3)$

$= x \cdot 2x + x \cdot 3$

$= 2x^2 + 3x$

Multiply x by $2x$ and then by 3, the terms of the polynomial. That is, "distribute" the multiplication over the sum.

(*b*) Multiply $2a^3 + 4a$ by $3a^2$.

Write

$3a^2(2a^3 + 4a)$

$= 3a^2 \cdot 2a^3 + 3a^2 \cdot 4a = 6a^5 + 12a^3$

● ● ● **CHECK YOURSELF 2**

Multiply.

a. $2y(y^2 + 3y)$ **b.** $3w^2(2w^3 + 5w)$

The patterns of Example 2 extend to *any* number of terms.

● Example 3

Multiplying a Monomial and a Polynomial

Multiply the following.

(*a*) $3x(4x^3 + 5x^2 + 2)$

$= 3x \cdot 4x^3 + 3x \cdot 5x^2 + 3x \cdot 2 = 12x^4 + 15x^3 + 6x$

Again we have shown all the steps of the process. With practice you can write the product directly, and you should try to do so.

(*b*) $5y^2(2y^3 - 4)$

$= 5y^2 \cdot 2y^3 - (5y^2)(4) = 10y^5 - 20y^2$

(*c*) $-5c(4c^2 - 8c)$

$= (-5c)(4c^2) - (-5c)(8c) = -20c^3 + 40c^2$

(*d*) $3c^2d^2(7cd^2 - 5c^2d^3)$

$= 3c^2d^2 \cdot 7cd^2 - (3c^2d^2)(5c^2d^3) = 21c^3d^4 - 15c^4d^5$

● ● ● **CHECK YOURSELF 3**

Multiply.

a. $3(5a^2 + 2a + 7)$
c. $-5m(8m^2 - 5m)$

b. $4x^2(8x^3 - 6)$
d. $9a^2b(3a^3b - 6a^2b^4)$

● Example 4

Multiplying Binomials

(*a*) Multiply $x + 2$ by $x + 3$.

We can think of $x + 2$ as a single quantity and apply the distributive property.

Note that this ensures that each term, x and 2, of the first binomial is multiplied by each term, x and 3, of the second binomial.

$(x + 2)(x + 3)$ Multiply $x + 2$ by x and then by 3.

$= (x + 2)x + (x + 2)\, 3$

$= x \cdot x + 2 \cdot x + x \cdot 3 + 2 \cdot 3$

$= x^2 + 2x + 3x + 6$

$= x^2 + 5x + 6$

(*b*) Multiply $a - 3$ by $a - 4$. (Think of $a - 3$ as a single quantity and distribute.)

$(a - 3)(a - 4)$

$= (a - 3)a - (a - 3)(4)$

$= a \cdot a - 3 \cdot a - [(a \cdot 4) - (3 \cdot 4)]$

$= a^2 - 3a - (4a - 12)$ Note that the parentheses are needed here because a *minus sign* precedes the binomial.

$= a^2 - 3a - 4a + 12$

$= a^2 - 7a + 12$

● ● ● CHECK YOURSELF 4

Multiply.

a. $(x + 4)(x + 5)$ **b.** $(y + 5)(y - 6)$

Fortunately, there is a pattern to this kind of multiplication that allows you to write the product of the two binomials directly without going through all these steps. We call it the **FOIL method** of multiplying. The reason for this name will be clear as we look at the process in more detail.

To multiply $(x + 2)(x + 3)$:

1. $(x + 2)(x + 3)$

Remember this by F!

$x \cdot x$ Find the product of the *first* terms of the factors.

2. $(x + 2)(x + 3)$

Remember this by O!

$x \cdot 3$ Find the product of the *outer* terms.

3. $(x + 2)(x + 3)$

Remember this by I!

$2 \cdot x$ Find the product of the *inner* terms.

4. $(x + 2)(x + 3)$

Remember this by L!

$2 \cdot 3$ Find the product of the *last* terms.

Combining the four steps, we have

Of course these are the same four terms found in Example 4a.

$(x + 2)(x + 3)$

$= x^2 + 3x + 2x + 6$

$= x^2 + 5x + 6$

It's called FOIL to give you an easy way of remembering the steps: *First, Outer, Inner,* and *Last.*

With practice, the FOIL method will let you write the products quickly and easily. Consider Example 5, which illustrates this approach.

• Example 5

Using the FOIL Method

Find the following products, using the FOIL method.

(a) $(x + 4)(x + 5)$

$= x^2 + 5x + 4x + 20$

$= x^2 + 9x + 20$

When possible, you should combine the outer and inner products mentally and write just the final product.

(b) $(x - 7)(x + 3)$

Combine the outer and inner products as $-4x$.

$= x^2 - 4x - 21$

● ● ● CHECK YOURSELF 5

Multiply.

a. $(x + 6)(x + 7)$ **b.** $(x + 3)(x - 5)$ **c.** $(x - 2)(x - 8)$

Using the FOIL method, you can also find the product of binomials with coefficients other than 1 or with more than one variable.

•Example 6

Using the FOIL Method

Find the following products, using the FOIL method.

(a) $(4x - 3)(3x + 2)$

$\qquad$ Combine: $-9x + 8x = -x$

$$= 12x^2 - x - 6$$

(b) $(3x - 5y)(2x - 7y)$

$\qquad$ Combine: $-10xy - 21xy = -31xy$

$$= 6x^2 - 31xy + 35y^2$$

The following rule summarizes our work in multiplying binomials.

To Multiply Two Binomials

Step 1 Find the first term of the product of the binomials by multiplying the first terms of the binomials (F).

Step 2 Find the middle term of the product as the sum of the outer and inner products (O + I).

Step 3 Find the last term of the product by multiplying the last terms of the binomials (L).

● ● ● CHECK YOURSELF 6

Multiply.

a. $(5x + 2)(3x - 7)$ **b.** $(4a - 3b)(5a - 4b)$ **c.** $(3m + 5n)(2m + 3n)$

The FOIL method works well when multiplying any two binomials. But what if one of the factors has three or more terms? The vertical format, shown in Example 7, works for factors with any number of terms.

● Example 7

Using the Vertical Method

Multiply $x^2 - 5x + 8$ by $x + 3$.

Step 1
$$\begin{array}{r} x^2 - 5x + 8 \\ x + 3 \\ \hline 3x^2 - 15x + 24 \end{array}$$
Multiply each term of $x^2 - 5x + 8$ by 3.

Step 2
$$\begin{array}{r} x^2 - 5x + 8 \\ x + 3 \\ \hline 3x^2 - 15x + 24 \\ x^3 - 5x^2 + 8x \end{array}$$
Now multiply each term by x.

Note that this line is shifted over so that like terms are in the same columns.

Note: Using this vertical method ensures that each term of one factor multiplies each term of the other. That's why it works!

Step 3
$$\begin{array}{r} x^2 - 5x + 8 \\ x + 3 \\ \hline 3x^2 - 15x + 24 \\ x^3 - 5x^2 + 8x \\ \hline x^3 - 2x^2 - 7x + 24 \end{array}$$
Now add to combine like terms to write the product.

● ● ● ● **CHECK YOURSELF 7**

Multiply $2x^2 - 5x + 3$ by $3x + 4$.

● ● ● **CHECK YOURSELF ANSWERS**

1. **(a)** $15a^4b^5$; **(b)** $-12x^4y^6$. **2.** **(a)** $2y^3 + 6y^2$; **(b)** $6w^5 + 15w^3$.
3. **(a)** $15a^2 + 6a + 21$; **(b)** $32x^5 - 24x^2$; **(c)** $-40m^3 + 25m^2$; **(d)** $27a^5b^2 - 54a^4b^5$.
4. **(a)** $x^2 + 9x + 20$; **(b)** $y^2 - y - 30$. **5.** **(a)** $x^2 + 13x + 42$; **(b)** $x^2 - 2x - 15$;
(c) $x^2 - 10x + 16$. **6.** **(a)** $15x^2 - 29x - 14$; **(b)** $20a^2 - 31ab + 12b^2$;
(c) $6m^2 + 19mn + 15n^2$. **7.** $6x^3 - 7x^2 - 11x + 12$.

A N S W E R S

Multiply.

1. $(5x^2)(3x^3)$

2. $(7a^5)(4a^6)$

3. $(-2b^2)(14b^8)$

4. $(14y^4)(-4y^6)$

5. $(-10p^6)(-4p^7)$

6. $(-6m^8)(9m^7)$

7. $(4m^5)(-3m)$

8. $(-5r^7)(-3r)$

9. $(4x^3y^2)(8x^2y)$

10. $(-3r^4s^2)(-7r^2s^5)$

11. $(-3m^5n^2)(2m^4n)$

12. $(7a^3b^5)(-6a^4b)$

13. $5(2x + 6)$

14. $4(7b - 5)$

15. $3a(4a + 5)$

16. $5x(2x - 7)$

17. $3s^2(4s^2 - 7s)$

18. $9a^2(3a^3 + 5a)$

19. $2x(4x^2 - 2x + 1)$

20. $5m(4m^3 - 3m^2 + 2)$

ANSWERS
1.
2.
3.
4.
5.
6.
7.
8.
9.
10.
11.
12.
13.
14.
15.
16.
17.
18.
19.
20.

A N S W E R S

21.

22.

23.

24.

25.

26.

27.

28.

29.

30.

31.

32.

33.

34.

35.

36.

37.

38.

39.

40.

21. $3xy(2x^2y + xy^2 + 5xy)$

22. $5ab^2(ab - 3a + 5b)$

23. $6m^2n(3m^2n - 2mn + mn^2)$

24. $8pq^2(2pq - 3p + 5q)$

Multiply.

25. $(x + 3)(x + 2)$

26. $(a - 3)(a - 7)$

27. $(m - 5)(m - 9)$

28. $(b + 7)(b + 5)$

29. $(p - 8)(p + 7)$

30. $(x - 10)(x + 9)$

31. $(w + 10)(w + 20)$

32. $(s - 12)(s - 8)$

33. $(3x - 5)(x - 8)$

34. $(w + 5)(4w - 7)$

35. $(2x - 3)(3x + 4)$

36. $(5a + 1)(3a + 7)$

37. $(3a - b)(4a - 9b)$

38. $(7s - 3t)(3s + 8t)$

39. $(3p - 4q)(7p + 5q)$

40. $(5x - 4y)(2x - y)$

41. $(2x + 5y)(3x + 4y)$

42. $(4x - 5y)(4x + 3y)$

43. $(x + 5)^2$

44. $(y + 8)^2$

45. $(y - 9)^2$

46. $(2a + 3)^2$

47. $(6m + n)^2$

48. $(7b - c)^2$

49. $(a - 5)(a + 5)$

50. $(x - 7)(x + 7)$

51. $(x - 2y)(x + 2y)$

52. $(7x + y)(7x - y)$

53. $(5s + 3t)(5s - 3t)$

54. $(9c - 4d)(9c + 4d)$

Multiply, using the vertical method.

55. $(x + 2)(x^2 + 2x - 3)$

56. $(a - 3)(a^2 + 4a + 1)$

57. $(2m - 5)(2m^2 + 3m - 2)$

58. $(5p + 3)(p^2 + 4p + 1)$

59. $(3x + 4y)(x^2 + xy + 5y^2)$

60. $(7a - 2b)(2a^2 - ab + 4b^2)$

ANSWERS

41. _____

42. _____

43. _____

44. _____

45. _____

46. _____

47. _____

48. _____

49. _____

50. _____

51. _____

52. _____

53. _____

54. _____

55. _____

56. _____

57. _____

58. _____

59. _____

60. _____

61. _____

62. _____

63. _____

64 _____

65. _____

66. _____

67. _____

68. _____

69. _____

70. _____

71. _____

72. _____

73. _____

74. _____

75. _____

76. _____

77. _____

78. _____

79. _____

80. _____

61. $(a^2 + 3ab - b^2)(a^2 - 5ab + b^2)$

62. $(m^2 - 5mn + 3n^2)(m^2 + 4mn - 2n^2)$

63. $(x - 2y)(x^2 + 2xy + 4y^2)$

64. $(m + 3n)(m^2 - 3mn + 9n^2)$

65. $(3a + 4b)(9a^2 - 12ab + 16b^2)$

66. $(2r - 3s)(4r^2 + 6rs + 9s^2)$

Multiply.

67. $2x(3x - 2)(4x + 1)$

68. $3x(2x + 1)(2x - 1)$

69. $5a(4a - 3)(4a + 3)$

70. $6m(3m - 2)(3m - 7)$

71. $3s(5s - 2)(4s - 1)$

72. $7w(2w - 3)(2w + 3)$

73. $(x - 2)(x + 1)(x - 3)$

74. $(y + 3)(y - 2)(y - 4)$

75. $(a - 1)^3$

76. $(x + 1)^3$

Multiply the following.

77. $\left(\dfrac{x}{2} + \dfrac{2}{3}\right)\left(\dfrac{2x}{3} - \dfrac{2}{5}\right)$

78. $\left(\dfrac{x}{3} + \dfrac{3}{4}\right)\left(\dfrac{3x}{4} - \dfrac{3}{5}\right)$

79. $[x + (y - 2)][x - (y - 2)]$

80. $[x + (3 - y)][x - (3 - y)]$

Label the following as true or false.

85. Length. The length of a rectangle is given by $3x + 5$ centimeters (cm) and the width is given by $2x - 7$ cm. Express the area of the rectangle in terms of x.

86. Area. The base of a triangle measures $3y + 7$ inches (in.) and the height is $2y - 3$ in. Express the area of the triangle in terms of y.

87. Revenue. The price of an item is given by $p = 10 - 3x$. If the revenue generated is found by multiplying the number of items (x) sold by the price of an item, find the polynomial which represents the revenue.

88. Revenue. The price of an item is given by $p = 100 - 2x^2$. Find the polynomial that represents the revenue generated from the sale of x items.

89. Work with another student to complete this table and write the polynomial. A paper box is to be made from a piece of cardboard 20 inches (in.) wide and 30 in. long. The box will be formed by cutting squares out of each of the four corners and folding up the sides to make a box.

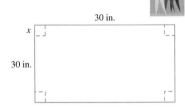

30 in.

x

30 in.

If x is the dimension of the side of the square cut out of the corner, when the sides are folded up, the box will be x inches tall. You should use a piece of paper to try this to see how the box will be made. Complete the following chart.

Length of side of corner square	Length of box	Width of box	Depth of box	Volume of box
1 in.				
2 in.				
3 in.				
n in.				

Write a general formula for the width, length, and height of the box and a general formula for the *volume* of the box, and simplify it by multiplying. The variable will be the height, the side of the square cut out of the corners. What is the highest power of the variable in the polynomial you have written for the volume _____? Extend the table from Section 4.5 in order to decide what the dimensions are for a box with maximum volume. Draw a sketch of this box and write in the dimensions.

A N S W E R S

81. _____

82. _____

83. _____

84. _____

85. _____

86. _____

87. _____

88. _____

89. _____

Getting Ready for Section 4.7

Simplify.

a. $(3a)(3a)$ **b.** $(3a)^2$

c. $(5x)(5x)$ **d.** $(5x)^2$

e. $(-2w)(-2w)$ **f.** $(-2w)^2$

g. $(-4r)(-4r)$ **h.** $(-4r)^2$

Answers

1. $15x^5$ **3.** $-28b^{10}$ **5.** $40p^{13}$ **7.** $-12m^6$ **9.** $32x^5y^3$ **11.** $-6m^9n^3$

13. $10x + 30$ **15.** $12a^2 + 15a$ **17.** $12s^4 - 21s^3$ **19.** $8x^3 - 4x^2 + 2x$

21. $6x^3y^2 + 3x^2y^3 + 15x^2y^2$ **23.** $18m^4n^2 - 12m^3n^2 + 6m^3n^3$ **25.** $x^2 + 5x + 6$

27. $m^2 - 14m + 45$ **29.** $p^2 - p - 56$ **31.** $w^2 + 30w + 200$

33. $3x^2 - 29x + 40$ **35.** $6x^2 - x - 12$ **37.** $12a^2 - 31ab + 9b^2$

39. $21p^2 - 13pq - 20q^2$ **41.** $6x^2 + 23xy + 20y^2$ **43.** $x^2 + 10x + 25$

45. $y^2 - 18y + 81$ **47.** $36m^2 + 12mn + n^2$ **49.** $a^2 - 25$ **51.** $x^2 - 4y^2$

53. $25s^2 - 9t^2$ **55.** $x^3 + 4x^2 + x - 6$ **57.** $4m^3 - 4m^2 - 19m + 10$

59. $3x^3 + 7x^2y + 19xy^2 + 20y^3$ **61.** $a^4 - 2a^3b - 15a^2b^2 + 8ab^3 - b^4$

63. $x^3 - 8y^3$ **65.** $27a^3 + 64b^3$ **67.** $24x^3 - 10x^2 - 4x$ **69.** $80a^3 - 45a$

71. $60s^3 - 39s^2 + 6s$ **73.** $x^3 - 4x^2 + x + 6$ **75.** $a^3 - 3a^2 + 3a - 1$

77. $\dfrac{x^2}{3} + \dfrac{11x}{45} - \dfrac{4}{15}$ **79.** $x^2 - y^2 + 4y - 4$ **81.** False   **83.** True

85. $6x^2 - 11x - 35$ cm^2 **87.** $10x - 3x^2$ **a.** $9a^2$ **b.** $9a^2$ **c.** $25x^2$

d. $25x^2$ **e.** $4w^2$ **f.** $4w^2$ **g.** $16r^2$ **h.** $16r^2$

4.7 Special Products

4.7 OBJECTIVES

1. Square a polynomial
2. Find the product of two binomials that differ only in sign

Certain products occur frequently enough in algebra that it is worth learning special formulas for dealing with them. First, let's look at the **square of a binomial,** which is the product of two equal binomial factors.

$$(x + y)^2 = (x + y)(x + y)$$
$$= x^2 + 2xy + y^2$$

$$(x - y)^2 = (x - y)(x - y)$$
$$= x^2 - 2xy + y^2$$

The patterns above lead us to the following rule.

To Square a Binomial

STEP 1 Find the first term of the square by squaring the first term of the binomial.

STEP 2 Find the middle term of the square as twice the product of the two terms of the binomial.

STEP 3 Find the last term of the square by squaring the last term of the binomial.

• Example 1

CAUTION

A very common mistake in squaring binomials is to forget the middle term.

Squaring a Binomial

(a) $(x + 3)^2 = x^2 + 2 \cdot x \cdot 3 + 3^2$

Square of first term — Twice the product of the two terms — Square of the last term

$$= x^2 + 6x + 9$$

(b) $(3a + 4b)^2 = (3a)^2 + 2(3a)(4b) + (4b)^2$
$$= 9a^2 + 24ab + 16b^2$$

(c) $(y - 5)^2 = y^2 + 2 \cdot y \cdot (-5) + (-5)^2$
$$= y^2 - 10y + 25$$

(d) $(5c - 3d)^2 = (5c)^2 + 2(5c)(-3d) + (-3d)^2$
$$= 25c^2 - 30cd + 9d^2$$

Again we have shown all the steps. With practice you can write just the square.

© 1998 McGraw-Hill Companies

259

● ● ● **CHECK YOURSELF 1**

Multiply.

a. $(2x + 1)^2$ **b.** $(4x - 3y)^2$

● **Example 2**

Squaring a Binomial

Find $(y + 4)^2$.

$(y + 4)^2$ is *not* equal to $y^2 + 4^2$ or $y^2 + 16$

The correct square is

You should see that
$(2 + 3)^2 \neq 2^2 + 3^2$ because
$5^2 \neq 4 + 9$

$(y + 4)^2 = y^2 + 8y + 16$

The middle term is twice the product of y and 4.

● ● ● **CHECK YOURSELF 2**

Multiply.

a. $(x + 5)^2$ **b.** $(3a + 2)^2$ **c.** $(y - 7)^2$ **d.** $(5x - 2y)^2$

A second special product will be very important in the next chapter, which deals with factoring. Suppose the form of a product is

$(x + y)(x - y)$

The two terms differ
only in sign.

Let's see what happens when we multiply.

$(x + y)(x - y)$
$= x^2 - xy + xy - y^2$
                $= 0$
$= x^2 - y^2$

Since the middle term becomes 0, we have the following rule.

Special Product

The product of two binomials that differ only in the sign between the terms is the square of the first term minus the square of the second term.

Let's look at the application of this rule in Example 3.

● Example 3

Multiplying Polynomials

Multiply each pair of factors.

(a) $(x + 5)(x - 5) = x^2 - 5^2$

Square of the first term   Square of the second term

$= x^2 - 25$

Note: $(2y)^2 = (2y)(2y)$
$= 4y^2$

(b) $(x + 2y)(x - 2y) = x^2 - (2y)^2$

Square of the first term   Square of the second term

$= x^2 - 4y^2$

(c) $(3m + n)(3m - n) = 9m^2 - n^2$

(d) $(4a - 3b)(4a + 3b) = 16a^2 - 9b^2$

● ● ●   CHECK YOURSELF 3

Find the products.

a. $(a - 6)(a + 6)$ **b.** $(x - 3y)(x + 3y)$
c. $(5n + 2p)(5n - 2p)$ **d.** $(7b - 3c)(7b + 3c)$

When finding the product of three or more factors, it is useful to first look for the pattern in which two binomials differ only in their sign. Finding this product first will make it easier to find the product of all the factors.

• Example 4

Multiplying Polynomials

(*a*) $x(x - 3)(x + 3)$ These binomials differ only in the sign.

$= x(x^2 - 9)$

$= x^3 - 9x$

(*b*) $(x + 1)(x - 5)(x + 5)$ These binomials differ only in the sign.

$= (x + 1)(x^2 - 25)$ With two binomials, use the FOIL method.

$= x^3 + x^2 - 25x - 25$

(*c*) $(2x - 1)(x + 3)(2x + 1)$ These two binomials differ only in the sign of the second term. We can use the commutative property to rearrange the terms.

$= (x + 3)(2x - 1)(2x + 1)$

$= (x + 3)(4x^2 - 1)$

$= 4x^3 + 12x^2 - x - 3$

● ● ● **CHECK YOURSELF 4**

Multiply.

a. $3x(x - 5)(x + 5)$ **b.** $(x - 4)(2x + 3)(2x - 3)$

c. $(x - 7)(3x - 1)(x + 7)$

● ● ● **CHECK YOURSELF ANSWERS**

1. **(a)** $4x^2 + 4x + 1$; **(b)** $16x^2 - 24xy + 9y^2$.

2. **(a)** $x^2 + 10x + 25$; **(b)** $9a^2 + 12a + 4$; **(c)** $y^2 - 14y + 49$; **(d)** $25x^2 - 20xy + 4y^2$.

3. **(a)** $a^2 - 36$; **(b)** $x^2 - 9y^2$; **(c)** $25n^2 - 4p^2$; **(d)** $49b^2 - 9c^2$.

4. **(a)** $3x^3 - 75x$; **(b)** $4x^3 - 16x^2 - 9x + 36$; **(c)** $3x^3 - x^2 - 147x + 49$.

Find each of the following squares.

1. $(x + 5)^2$ **2.** $(y + 9)^2$

3. $(w - 6)^2$ **4.** $(a - 8)^2$

5. $(z + 12)^2$ **6.** $(p - 20)^2$

7. $(2a - 1)^2$ **8.** $(3x - 2)^2$

9. $(6m + 1)^2$ **10.** $(7b - 2)^2$

11. $(3x - y)^2$ **12.** $(5m + n)^2$

13. $(2r + 5s)^2$ **14.** $(3a - 4b)^2$

15. $(8a - 9b)^2$ **16.** $(7p + 6q)^2$

17. $\left(x + \dfrac{1}{2}\right)^2$ **18.** $\left(w - \dfrac{1}{4}\right)^2$

Find each of the following products.

19. $(x - 6)(x + 6)$ **20.** $(y + 8)(y - 8)$

21. $(m + 12)(m - 12)$ **22.** $(w - 10)(w + 10)$

23. $\left(x - \dfrac{1}{2}\right)\left(x + \dfrac{1}{2}\right)$ **24.** $\left(x + \dfrac{2}{3}\right)\left(x - \dfrac{2}{3}\right)$

ANSWERS

1. _____

2. _____

3. _____

4. _____

5. _____

6. _____

7. _____

8. _____

9. _____

10. _____

11. _____

12. _____

13. _____

14. _____

15. _____

16. _____

17. _____

18. _____

19. _____

20. _____

21. _____

22. _____

23. _____

24. _____

25. $(p - 0.4)(p + 0.4)$ **26.** $(m - 0.6)(m + 0.6)$

27. $(a - 3b)(a + 3b)$ **28.** $(p + 4q)(p - 4q)$

29. $(4r - s)(4r + s)$ **30.** $(7x - y)(7x + y)$

31. $(8w + 5z)(8w - 5z)$ **32.** $(7c + 2d)(7c - 2d)$

33. $(5x - 9y)(5x + 9y)$ **34.** $(6s - 5t)(6s + 5t)$

35. $x(x - 2)(x + 2)$ **36.** $a(a + 5)(a - 5)$

37. $2s(s - 3r)(s + 3r)$ **38.** $5w(2w - z)(2w + z)$

39. $5r(r + 3)^2$ **40.** $3x(x - 2)^2$

For each of the following problems, let x represent the number, then write an expression for the product.

41. The product of 6 more than a number and 6 less than that number

42. The square of 5 more than a number

43. The square of 4 less than a number

44. The product of 5 less than a number and 5 more than that number

Note that $(28)(32) = (30 - 2)(30 + 2) = 900 - 4 = 896$. Use this pattern to find each of the following products.

45. $(49)(51)$

46. $(27)(33)$

47. $(34)(26)$

48. $(98)(102)$

49. $(55)(65)$

50. $(64)(56)$

51. Tree planting. Suppose an orchard is planted with trees in straight rows. If there are $5x - 4$ rows with $5x - 4$ trees in each row, how many trees are there in the orchard?

52. Area of a square. A square has sides of length $3x - 2$ centimeters (cm). Express the area of the square as a polynomial.

53. Area of a rectangle. The length and width of a rectangle are given by two consecutive odd integers. Write an expression for the area of the rectangle.

54. Area of a rectangle. The width of a rectangle is 6 less than three times the width. Write an expression for the area of the rectangle.

55. Complete the following statement: $(a + b)^2$ is not equal to $a^2 + b^2$ because .... But, wait! Isn't $(a + b)^2$ *sometimes* equal to a^2+b^2? What do you think?

56. Is $(a + b)^3$ ever equal to a^3+b^3? Explain.

57. In the following figures, identify the length and the width of the square:

	a	b
a		
b		

Length = _____

Width = _____

Area = _____

	a	3
a		
3		

Length = _____

Width = _____

Area = _____

	x	
x	x^2	$2x$
	$2x$	

Length = _____

Width = _____

Area = _____

ANSWERS

45. _____

46. _____

47. _____

48. _____

49. _____

50. _____

51. _____

52. _____

53. _____

54. _____

55. _____

56. _____

57. _____

58. The square below is x units on a side. The area is _____.

Draw a picture of what happens when the sides are doubled. The area is _____.

Continue the picture to show what happens when the sides are tripled. The area is _____.

If the sides are quadrupled, the area is _____.

In general, if the sides are multiplied by n, the area is _____.

If each side is increased by 3, the area is increased by _____.

If each side is decreased by 2, the area is decreased by _____.

In general, if each side is increased by n, the area is increased by _____, and if each side is decreased by n, the area is decreased by _____.

Getting Ready for Section 4.8 [Section 4.1]

Divide.

a. $\dfrac{2x^2}{2x}$

b. $\dfrac{3a^3}{3a}$

c. $\dfrac{6p^3}{2p^2}$

d. $\dfrac{10m^4}{5m^2}$

e. $\dfrac{20a^3}{5a^3}$

f. $\dfrac{6x^2y}{3xy}$

g. $\dfrac{12r^3s^2}{4rs}$

h. $\dfrac{49c^4d^6}{7cd^3}$

Answers

1. $x^2 + 10x + 25$ **3.** $w^2 - 12w + 36$ **5.** $z^2 + 24z + 144$
7. $4a^2 - 4a + 1$ **9.** $36m^2 + 12m + 1$ **11.** $9x^2 - 6xy + y^2$
13. $4r^2 + 20rs + 25s^2$ **15.** $64a^2 - 144ab + 81b^2$ **17.** $x^2 + x + \dfrac{1}{4}$
19. $x^2 - 36$ **21.** $m^2 - 144$ **23.** $x^2 - \dfrac{1}{4}$ **25.** $p^2 - 0.16$ **27.** $a^2 - 9b^2$
29. $16r^2 - s^2$ **31.** $64w^2 - 25z^2$ **33.** $25x^2 - 81y^2$ **35.** $x^3 - 4x$
37. $2s^3 - 18r^2s$ **39.** $5r^3 + 30r^2 + 45r$ **41.** $x^2 - 36$ **43.** $x^2 - 8x + 16$
45. 2499 **47.** 884 **49.** 3575 **51.** $25x^2 - 40x + 16$
53. $x(x + 2) = x^2 + 2x$ **a.** x **b.** a^2 **c.** $3p$ **d.** $2m^2$ **e.** 4 **f.** $2x$
g. $3r^2s$ **h.** $7c^3d^3$

 **4.8**

Dividing Polynomials

4.8 OBJECTIVES

1. Find the quotient when a polynomial is divided by a monomial
2. Find the quotient of two polynomials

In Section 4.1, we introduced the second property of exponents, which was used to divide one monomial by another monomial. Let's review that process.

> **To Divide a Monomial by a Monomial**
>
> **STEP 1** Divide the coefficients.
>
> **STEP 2** Use the second property of exponents to combine the variables.

The second property says: If x is not zero and $m > n$,

$$\frac{x^m}{x^n} = x^{m-n}$$

● Example 1

Dividing Monomials

Divide: $\dfrac{8}{2} = 4$

(a) $\dfrac{8x^4}{2x^2} = 4x^{4-2}$ ← Subtract the exponents.

$= 4x^2$

(b) $\dfrac{45a^5b^3}{9a^2b} = 5a^3b^2$

● ● ● CHECK YOURSELF 1

Divide.

a. $\dfrac{16a^5}{8a^3}$

b. $\dfrac{28m^4n^3}{7m^3n}$

Now let's look at how this can be extended to divide any polynomial by a monomial. For example, to divide $12a^3 + 8a^2$ by $4a$, proceed as follows:

Technically, this step depends on the distributive law and the definition of division.

$$\frac{12a^3 + 8a^2}{4a} = \frac{12a^3}{4a} + \frac{8a^2}{4a}$$

Divide each term in the numerator by the denominator, $4a$.

Now do each division.

$$= 3a^2 + 2a$$

The work above leads us to the following rule.

> **To Divide a Polynomial by a Monomial**
>
> Divide each term of the polynomial by the monomial. Then combine the results.

• Example 2

Dividing by Monomials

Divide each term by 2.

(a) $\dfrac{4a^2 + 8}{2} = \dfrac{4a^2}{2} + \dfrac{8}{2}$

$= 2a^2 + 4$

Divide each term by $6y$.

(b) $\dfrac{24y^3 - 18y^2}{6y} = \dfrac{24y^3}{6y} - \dfrac{18y^2}{6y}$

$= 4y^2 - 3y$

Remember the rules for signs in division.

(c) $\dfrac{15x^2 + 10x}{-5x} = \dfrac{15x^2}{-5x} + \dfrac{10x}{-5x}$

$= -3x - 2$

With practice you can write just the quotient.

(d) $\dfrac{14x^4 + 28x^3 - 21x^2}{7x^2} = \dfrac{14x^4}{7x^2} + \dfrac{28x^3}{7x^2} - \dfrac{21x^2}{7x^2}$

$= 2x^2 + 4x - 3$

(e) $\dfrac{9a^3b^4 - 6a^2b^3 + 12ab^4}{3ab} = \dfrac{9a^3b^4}{3ab} - \dfrac{6a^2b^3}{3ab} + \dfrac{12ab^4}{3ab}$

$= 3a^2b^3 - 2ab^2 + 4b^3$

● ● ● **CHECK YOURSELF 2**

Divide.

a. $\dfrac{20y^3 - 15y^2}{5y}$ **b.** $\dfrac{8a^3 - 12a^2 + 4a}{-4a}$

c. $\dfrac{16m^4n^3 - 12m^3n^2 + 8mn}{4mn}$

We are now ready to look at dividing one polynomial by another polynomial (with more than one term). The process is very much like long division in arithmetic, as Example 3 illustrates.

• Example 3

Dividing by Binomials

Divide $x^2 + 7x + 10$ by $x + 2$.

The first term in the dividend, x^2, is divided by the first term in the divisor, x.

Step 1 $x + 2 \overline{) x^2 + 7x + 10}$ quotient x Divide x^2 by x to get x.

Step 2 $x + 2 \overline{) x^2 + 7x + 10}$, $x^2 + 2x$ Multiply the divisor, $x + 2$, by x.

Remember: To subtract $x^2 + 2x$, mentally change each sign to $-x^2 - 2x$, and add. Take your time and be careful here. It's where most errors are made.

Step 3 quotient x; $x^2 + 2x$; $5x + 10$ Subtract and bring down 10.

Step 4 quotient $x + 5$; $x^2 + 2x$; $5x + 10$ Divide $5x$ by x to get 5.

Note that we repeat the process until the degree of the remainder is less than that of the divisor or until there is no remainder.

Step 5 quotient $x + 5$; $x^2 + 2x$; $5x + 10$; $5x + 10$; 0 Multiply $x + 2$ by 5 and then subtract.

The quotient is $x + 5$.

● ● ● CHECK YOURSELF 3

Divide $x^2 + 9x + 20$ by $x + 4$.

In Example 3, we showed all the steps separately to help you see the process. In practice, the work can be shortened.

• Example 4

Dividing by Binomials

Divide $x^2 + x - 12$ by $x - 3$.

You might want to write out a problem like $408 \div 17$, to compare the steps.

$$
\begin{array}{r}
x + 4 \\
x - 3\overline{)x^2 + x - 12} \\
\underline{x^2 - 3x} \\
4x - 12 \\
\underline{4x - 12} \\
0
\end{array}
$$

The Steps
1. Divide x^2 by x to get x, the first term of the quotient.
2. Multiply $x - 3$ by x.
3. Subtract and bring down -12. Remember to mentally change the signs to $-x^2 + 3x$ and add.
4. Divide $4x$ by x to get 4, the second term of the quotient.
5. Multiply $x - 3$ by 4 and subtract.

The quotient is $x + 4$.

● ● ● **CHECK YOURSELF 4**

Divide.

$(x^2 + 2x - 24) \div (x - 4)$

You may have a remainder in algebraic long division just as in arithmetic. Consider Example 5.

• Example 5

Dividing by Binomials

Divide $4x^2 - 8x + 11$ by $2x - 3$.

$$
\begin{array}{r}
2x - 1 \qquad \text{Quotient} \\
2x - 3\overline{)4x^2 - 8x + 11} \\
\underline{4x^2 - 6x} \\
-2x + 11 \\
\underline{-2x + 3} \\
8
\end{array}
$$

Divisor

Remainder

This result can be written as

$$
\frac{4x^2 - 8x + 11}{2x - 3}
$$

$$
= 2x - 1 + \frac{8}{2x - 3} \qquad \text{Remainder}
$$

Quotient   Divisor

● ● ● **CHECK YOURSELF 5**

Divide.

$(6x^2 - 7x + 15) \div (3x - 5)$

The division process shown in our previous examples can be extended to dividends of a higher degree. The steps involved in the division process are exactly the same, as Example 6 illustrates.

● Example 6

Dividing by Binomials

Divide $6x^3 + x^2 - 4x - 5$ by $3x - 1$.

$$
\begin{array}{r}
2x^2 + x - 1 \\
3x - 1 \overline{\smash{)}6x^3 + x^2 - 4x - 5} \\
\underline{6x^3 - 2x^2} \\
3x^2 - 4x \\
\underline{3x^2 - x} \\
-3x - 5 \\
\underline{-3x + 1} \\
-6
\end{array}
$$

This result can be written as

$$
\frac{6x^3 + x^2 - 4x - 5}{3x - 1} = 2x^2 + x - 1 + \frac{-6}{3x - 1}
$$

● ● ● **CHECK YOURSELF 6**

Divide $4x^3 - 2x^2 + 2x + 15$ by $2x + 3$.

Suppose that the dividend is "missing" a term in some power of the variable. You can use 0 as the coefficient for the missing term. Consider Example 7.

● Example 7

Dividing by Binomials

Divide $x^3 - 2x^2 + 5$ by $x + 3$.

$$
\begin{array}{r}
x^2 - 5x + 15 \\
x + 3 \overline{\smash{)}x^3 - 2x^2 + 0x + 5} \\
\underline{x^3 + 3x^2} \\
-5x^2 + 0x \\
\underline{-5x^2 - 15x} \\
15x + 5 \\
\underline{15x + 45} \\
-40
\end{array}
$$

Write $0x$ for the "missing" term in x.

This result can be written as

$$\frac{x^3 - 2x^2 + 5}{x + 3} = x^2 - 5x + 15 + \frac{-40}{x + 3}$$

●●● **CHECK YOURSELF 7**

Divide.

$(4x^3 + x + 10) \div (2x - 1)$

You should always arrange the terms of the divisor and dividend in descending-exponent form before starting the long division process, as illustrated in Example 8.

● Example 8

Dividing by Binomials

Divide $5x^2 - x + x^3 - 5$ by $-1 + x^2$.

Write the divisor as $x^2 - 1$ and the dividend as $x^3 + 5x^2 - x - 5$.

$$
\begin{array}{r}
x + 5 \\
x^2 - 1 \overline{)\, x^3 + 5x^2 - x - 5} \\
\underline{x3 \qquad\;\; - x} \\
5x^2 \qquad - 5 \\
\underline{5x^2 \qquad - 5} \\
0
\end{array}
$$

Write $x^3 - x$, the product of x and $x^2 - 1$, so that like terms fall in the same columns.

●●● **CHECK YOURSELF 8**

Divide:

$(5x^2 + 10 + 2x^3 + 4x) \div (2 + x^2)$

●●● **CHECK YOURSELF ANSWERS**

1. (a) $2a^2$; (b) $4mn^2$. **2.** (a) $4y^2 - 3y$; (b) $-2a^2 + 3a - 1$; (c) $4m^3n^2 - 3m^2n + 2$.

3. $x + 5$. **4.** $x + 6$. **5.** $2x + 1 + \dfrac{20}{3x - 5}$. **6.** $2x^2 - 4x + 7 + \dfrac{-6}{2x + 3}$.

7. $2x^2 + x + 1 + \dfrac{11}{2x - 1}$. **8.** $2x + 5$.

Divide.

1. $\dfrac{18x^6}{9x^2}$

2. $\dfrac{20a^7}{5a^5}$

3. $\dfrac{35m^3n^2}{7mn^2}$

4. $\dfrac{42x^5y^2}{6x^3y}$

5. $\dfrac{3a + 6}{3}$

6. $\dfrac{4x - 8}{4}$

7. $\dfrac{9b^2 - 12}{3}$

8. $\dfrac{10m^2 + 5m}{5}$

9. $\dfrac{16a^3 - 24a^2}{4a}$

10. $\dfrac{9x^3 + 12x^2}{3x}$

11. $\dfrac{12m^2 + 6m}{-3m}$

12. $\dfrac{20b^3 - 25b^2}{-5b}$

13. $\dfrac{18a^4 + 12a^3 - 6a^2}{6a}$

14. $\dfrac{21x^5 - 28x^4 + 14x^3}{7x}$

15. $\dfrac{20x^4y^2 - 15x^2y^3 + 10x^3y}{5x^2y}$

16. $\dfrac{16m^3n^3 + 24m^2n^2 - 40mn^3}{8mn^2}$

Perform the indicated divisions.

17. $\dfrac{x^2 + 5x + 6}{x + 2}$

18. $\dfrac{x^2 + 8x + 15}{x + 3}$

19. $\dfrac{x^2 - x - 20}{x + 4}$

20. $\dfrac{x^2 - 2x - 35}{x + 5}$

21. $\dfrac{2x^2 + 5x - 3}{2x - 1}$

22. $\dfrac{3x^2 + 20x - 32}{3x - 4}$

A N S W E R S

1. _____

2. _____

3. _____

4. _____

5. _____

6. _____

7. _____

8. _____

9. _____

10. _____

11. _____

12. _____

13. _____

14. _____

15. _____

16. _____

17. _____

18. _____

19. _____

20. _____

21. _____

22. _____

23. _____

24. _____

25. _____

26. _____

27. _____

28. _____

29. _____

30. _____

31. _____

32. _____

33. _____

34. _____

35. _____

36. _____

37. _____

38. _____

39. _____

40. _____

41. _____

42. _____

43. _____

44. _____

23. $\dfrac{2x^2 - 3x - 5}{x - 3}$

24. $\dfrac{3x^2 + 17x - 12}{x + 6}$

25. $\dfrac{4x^2 - 18x - 15}{x - 5}$

26. $\dfrac{3x^2 - 18x - 32}{x - 8}$

27. $\dfrac{6x^2 - x - 10}{3x - 5}$

28. $\dfrac{4x^2 + 6x - 25}{2x + 7}$

29. $\dfrac{x^3 + x^2 - 4x - 4}{x + 2}$

30. $\dfrac{x^3 - 2x^2 + 4x - 21}{x - 3}$

31. $\dfrac{4x^3 + 7x^2 + 10x + 5}{4x - 1}$

32. $\dfrac{2x^3 - 3x^2 + 4x + 4}{2x + 1}$

33. $\dfrac{x^3 - x^2 + 5}{x - 2}$

34. $\dfrac{x^3 + 4x - 3}{x + 3}$

35. $\dfrac{25x^3 + x}{5x - 2}$

36. $\dfrac{8x^3 - 6x^2 + 2x}{4x + 1}$

37. $\dfrac{2x^2 - 8 - 3x + x^3}{x - 2}$

38. $\dfrac{x^2 - 18x + 2x^3 + 32}{x + 4}$

39. $\dfrac{x^4 - 1}{x - 1}$

40. $\dfrac{x^4 + x^2 - 16}{x + 2}$

41. $\dfrac{x^3 - 3x^2 - x + 3}{x^2 - 1}$

42. $\dfrac{x^3 + 2x^2 + 3x + 6}{x^2 + 3}$

43. $\dfrac{x^4 + 2x^2 - 2}{x^2 + 3}$

44. $\dfrac{x^4 + x^2 - 5}{x^2 - 2}$

45. $\dfrac{y^3 + 1}{y + 1}$

46. $\dfrac{y^3 - 8}{y - 2}$

47. $\dfrac{x^4 - 1}{x^2 - 1}$

48. $\dfrac{x^6 - 1}{x^3 - 1}$

49. Find the value of c so that $\dfrac{y^2 - y + c}{y + 1} = y - 2$

50. Find the value of c so that $\dfrac{x^3 + x^2 + x + c}{x^2 + 1} = x + 1$

51. Write a summary of your work with polynomials. Explain how a polynomial is recognized, and explain the rules for the arithmetic of polynomials—how to add, subtract, multiply, and divide. What parts of this chapter do you feel you understand very well, and what part(s) do you still have questions about, or feel unsure of? Exchange papers with another student and compare your questions.

52. A funny (and useful) thing about division of polynomials: To find out about this funny thing, do this division. Compare your answer with another student.

$$(x - 2)\overline{)2x^2 + 3x - 5} \qquad \text{Is there a remainder?}$$

Now, evaluate the polynomial $2x^2 + 3x - 5$ when $x = 2$. Is this value the same as the remainder?

$$\text{Try } (x + 3)\overline{)5x^2 - 2x + 1} \qquad \text{Is there a remainder?}$$

Evaluate the polynomial $5x^2 - 2x + 1$ when $x = -3$. Is this value the same as the remainder?
What happens when there is no remainder?

$$\text{Try } (x - 6)\overline{)3x^3 + 14x^2 - 23x + 6} \qquad \text{Is the remainder zero?}$$

Evaluate the polynomial $3x^3 + 14x - 23x + 6$ when $x = 6$. Is this value zero? Write a description of the patterns you see. When does the pattern hold? Make up several more examples, and test your conjecture.

ANSWERS

45. _____

46. _____

47. _____

48. _____

49. _____

50. _____

51.

52.

Answers

1. $2x^4$　　**3.** $5m^2$　　**5.** $a + 2$　　**7.** $3b^2 - 4$　　**9.** $4a^2 - 6a$　　**11.** $-4m - 2$

13. $3a^3 + 2a^2 - a$　　**15.** $4x^2y - 3y^2 + 2x$　　**17.** $x + 3$　　**19.** $x - 5$

21. $x + 3$　　**23.** $2x + 3 + \dfrac{4}{x - 3}$　　**25.** $4x + 2 + \dfrac{-5}{x - 5}$

27. $2x + 3 + \dfrac{5}{3x - 5}$　　**29.** $x^2 - x - 2$　　**31.** $x^2 + 2x + 3 + \dfrac{8}{4x - 1}$

33. $x^2 + x + 2 + \dfrac{9}{x - 2}$　　**35.** $5x^2 + 2x + 1 + \dfrac{2}{5x - 2}$

37. $x^2 + 4x + 5 + \dfrac{2}{x - 2}$　　**39.** $x^3 + x^2 + x + 1$　　**41.** $x - 3$

43. $x^2 - 1 + \dfrac{1}{x^2 + 3}$　　**45.** $y^2 - y + 1$　　**47.** $x^2 + 1$　　**49.** $c = -2$

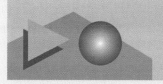

Summary

Algebraic Expressions [4.1–4.3]

Properties of Exponents

1. $a^m \cdot a^n = a^{m+n}$
2. $\dfrac{a^m}{a^n} = a^{m-n}$
3. $(a^m)^n = a^{mn}$
4. $(ab)^m = a^m b^m$
5. $\left(\dfrac{a}{b}\right)^m = \dfrac{a^m}{b^m}$

Properties of Negative Numbers

1. A negative number multiplied by another negative yields a positive product.
2. A negative number raised to an even power results in a positive product.
3. A negative number raised to an odd power results in a negative product.

Evaluating an Algebraic Expression

Step 1 Replace each variable by the given number value.

Step 2 Do the indicated arithmetic, following the order of operations.

Polynomials [4.4]

$4x^3 - 3x^2 + 5x$ is a polynomial. The terms of $4x^3 - 3x^2 + 5x$ are $4x^3$, $-3x^2$, and $5x$.

Polynomial An algebraic expression made up of terms in which the exponents are whole numbers. These terms are connected by plus or minus signs. Each sign (+ or −) is attached to the term following that sign.

Term A number, or the product of a number and variables, raised to a power.

The coefficients of $4x^3 - 3x^2$ are 4 and −3.

Coefficient In each term of a polynomial, the number is called the *numerical coefficient* or, more simply, the *coefficient* of that term.

Types of Polynomials A polynomial can be classified according to the number of terms it has.

$2x^3$ is a monomial.

A *mono*mial has one term.

$3x^2 - 7x$ is a binomial.

A *bi*nomial has two terms.

$5x^5 - 5x^3 + 2$ is a trinomial.

A *tri*nomial has three terms.

The degree of $4x^5 - 5x^3 + 3x$ is 5.

Degree The highest power of the variable appearing in any one term.

$4x^5 - 5x^3 + 3x$ is written in descending-exponent form.

Descending-Exponent Form The form of a polynomial when it is written with the highest-degree term first, the next highest-degree term second, and so on.

Adding and Subtracting Polynomials [4.5]

Removing Signs of Grouping

$(2x + 3) + (3x − 5)$
$= 2x + 3 + 3x − 5$

1. If a plus sign (+) or no sign at all appears in front of parentheses, just remove the parentheses. No other changes are necessary.

2. If a minus sign (−) appears in front of parentheses, the parentheses can be removed by changing the sign of each term inside the parentheses.

Adding Polynomials Remove the signs of grouping. Then collect and combine any like terms.

$(3x^2 + 2x) − (2x^2 + 3x − 1)$
$= 3x^2 + 2x \geq − 2x^2 − 3x + 1$

Sign changes

$3x^2 − 2x^2 + 2x − 3x + 1$
$x^2 − x + 1$

Subtracting Polynomials Remove the signs of grouping by changing the sign of each term in the polynomial being subtracted. Then combine any like terms.

Multiplying Polynomials [4.6]

To Multiply a Polynomial by a Monomial Multiply each term of the polynomial by the monomial, and add the results.

To Multiply a Binomial by a Binomial Use the FOIL method:

$$\overset{F \qquad O \qquad I \qquad L}{(a + b)(c + d) = a \cdot c + a \cdot d + b \cdot c + b \cdot d}$$

$(2x − 3)(3x + 5)$
$= 6x^2 + 10x − 9x − 15$
$\overset{F \quad O \quad I \quad L}{}$
$= 6x^2 + x − 15$

$$
\begin{array}{r}
x^2 − 3x + 5 \\
2x − 3 \\
\hline
− 3x^2 + 9x − 15 \\
2x^3 − 6x^2 + 10x \\
\hline
2x^3 − 9x^2 + 19x − 15
\end{array}
$$

To Multiply a Polynomial by a Polynomial Arrange the polynomials vertically. Multiply each term of the upper polynomial by each term of the lower polynomial, and add the results.

Special Products [4.7]

The Square of a Binomial

$(a + b)^2 = a^2 + 2ab + b^2$

$(2x − 5)^2$
$= 4x^2 + 2 \cdot 2x \cdot (−5) + 25$
$= 4x^2 − 20x + 25$

1. The first term of the square is the square of the first term of the binomial.
2. The middle term is twice the product of the two terms of the binomial.
3. The last term is the square of the last term of the binomial.

$(2x − 5y)(2x + 5y)$
$= (2x)^2 − (5y)^2$
$= 4x^2 − 25y^2$

The Product of Binomials That Differ Only in Sign Subtract the square of the second term from the square of the first term.

$(a + b)(a − b) = a^2 − b^2$

Dividing Polynomials [4.8]

$\dfrac{9x^4 + 6x^3 − 15x^2}{3x}$

$= 3x^3 + 2x^2 − 5x$

To Divide a Polynomial by a Monomial Divide each term of the polynomial by the monomial. Then combine the results.

$$
\begin{array}{r}
x + 5 \\
x − 3{\overline{\smash{\big)}\,x^2 + 2x − 7}} \\
\underline{x^2 − 3x} \\
5x − 7 \\
\underline{5x − 15} \\
8
\end{array}
$$

To Divide a Polynomial by a Polynomial Use the long division method.

Summary Exercises

This summary exercise set is provided to give you practice with each of the objectives of the chapter. Each exercise is keyed to the appropriate chapter section. The answers are provided in the *Instructor's Manual*.

[4.1] Divide.

1. $\dfrac{x^{10}}{x^3}$

2. $\dfrac{a^5}{a^4}$

3. $\dfrac{x^2 \cdot x^3}{x^4}$

4. $\dfrac{m^2 \cdot m^3 \cdot m^4}{m^5}$

5. $\dfrac{18p^7}{9p^5}$

6. $\dfrac{24x^{17}}{8x^{13}}$

7. $\dfrac{30m^7n^5}{6m^2n^3}$

8. $\dfrac{108x^9y^4}{9xy^4}$

9. $\dfrac{48p^5q^3}{6p^3q}$

[4.1] Evaluate each expression where $x = 2$, $y = 3$, $z = -4$, and $w = 5$.

10. $5(2z - w)$ $\quad -65$

11. $\dfrac{5yz}{2xw}$ $\quad -3$

12. $\dfrac{wx^3y}{10z}$ $\quad -3$

[4.2] Use the properties of exponents to simplify each expression.

13. $(2x^2)^3$ $\quad 8x^6$

14. $(5ab^2)^3$ $\quad 125a^3b^6$

15. $\left(\dfrac{2}{5}\right)^3$ $\quad \dfrac{8}{125}$

16. $(x^8y^2z^3)^2$ $\quad x^{16}y^4z^6$

17. $(p^4q^5)^3$ $\quad p^{12}q^{15}$

18. $\left(\dfrac{x}{3}\right)^4$ $\quad \dfrac{x^4}{81}$

19. $\dfrac{(x^4)^3}{x^2}$ $\quad x^{10}$

20. $\dfrac{(m^4)^3}{(m^3)^4}$ $\quad 1$

21. $(x^3)^2(x^2)^3$ $\quad x^{12}$

22. $(2x^3)^2(3x^5)^2$ $\quad 36x^{16}$

23. $\dfrac{(2x)^6}{(4x^2)^3}$ $\quad 1$

24. $\dfrac{(xy^2)^5}{xy^5}$ $\quad x^4y^5$

[4.3] Simplify each of the following. Use only positive exponents in your answers.

25. $\dfrac{a^5}{a^{12}}$ $\quad \dfrac{1}{a^7}$

26. $\dfrac{xy^3z}{x^3yz}$ $\quad \dfrac{y^2}{x^2}$

27. $\dfrac{x^{-5}}{x^{-3}}$ $\quad \dfrac{1}{x^2}$

28. $(a^{-2}b^{-3})^{-4}$ $\quad a^8b^{12}$

29. $(3x^3)^{-2}$ $\quad \dfrac{1}{9x^6}$

30. $(x^{-2}y^3z^{-1})^{-1}$ $\quad \dfrac{x^2z}{y^3}$

[4.4] Classify each of the following polynomials as a monomial, binomial, or trinomial, where possible.

31. $5x^3 - 2x^2$ **32.** $7x^5$ **33.** $4x^5 - 8x^3 + 5$

34. $x^3 + 2x^2 - 5x + 3$ **35.** $9a^2 - 18a^2$

[4.4] Arrange in descending-exponent form, if necessary, and give the degree of each polynomial.

36. $5x^5 + 3x^2$ **37.** $9x$ **38.** $6x^2 + 4x^4 + 6$

39. $5 + x$ **40.** -8 **41.** $9x^4 - 3x + 7x^6$

[4.5] Add.

42. $9a^2 - 5a$ and $12a^2 + 3a$ **43.** $5x^2 + 3x - 5$ and $4x^2 - 6x - 2$

44. $5y^3 - 3y^2$ and $4y + 3y^2$

[4.5] Subtract.

45. $4x^2 - 3x$ from $8x^2 + 5x$ **46.** $2x^2 - 5x - 7$ from $7x^2 - 2x + 3$

47. $5x^2 + 3$ from $9x^2 - 4x$

[4.5] Perform the indicated operations.

48. Subtract $5x - 3$ from the sum of $9x + 2$ and $-3x - 7$.

49. Subtract $5a^2 - 3a$ from the sum of $5a^2 + 2$ and $7a - 7$.

50. Subtract the sum of $16w^2 - 3w$ and $8w + 2$ from $7w^2 - 5w + 2$.

[4.5]   Add, using the vertical method.

51. $x^2 + 5x - 3$ and $2x^2 + 4x - 3$ **52.** $9b^2 - 7$ and $8b + 5$

53. $x^2 + 7$, $3x - 2$, and $4x^2 - 8x$

[4.5]   Subtract, using the vertical method.

54. $5x^2 - 3x + 2$ from $7x^2 - 5x - 7$ **55.** $8m - 7$ from $9m^2 - 7$

[4.6]   Multiply.

56. $(5a^3)(a^2)$ **57.** $(2x^2)(3x^5)$ **58.** $(-9p^3)(-6p^2)$

59. $(3a^2b^3)(-7a^3b^4)$ **60.** $5(3x - 8)$

61. $4a(3a + 7)$ **62.** $(-5rs)(2r^2s - 5rs)$

63. $7mn(3m^2n - 2mn^2 + 5mn)$

64. $(x + 5)(x + 4)$ **65.** $(w - 9)(w - 10)$

66. $(a - 7b)(a + 7b)$ **67.** $(p - 3q)^2$

68. $(a + 4b)(a + 3b)$ **69.** $(b - 8)(2b + 3)$

70. $(3x - 5y)(2x - 3y)$ **71.** $(5r + 7s)(3r - 9s)$

72. $(y + 2)(y^2 - 2y + 3)$ **73.** $(b + 3)(b^2 - 5b - 7)$

74. $(x - 2)(x^2 + 2x + 4)$ **75.** $(m^2 - 3)(m^2 + 7)$

76. $2x(x + 5)(x - 6)$ **77.** $a(2a - 5b)(2a - 7b)$

[4.7]   Find the following products.

78. $(x + 7)^2$ **79.** $(a - 8)^2$

80. $(2w - 5)^2$ **81.** $(3p + 4)^2$

82. $(a + 7b)^2$ **83.** $(8x - 3y)^2$

84. $(x - 5)(x + 5)$

85. $(y + 9)(y - 9)$

86. $(2m + 3)(2m - 3)$

87. $(3r - 7)(3r + 7)$

88. $(5r - 2s)(5r + 2s)$

89. $(7a + 3b)(7a - 3b)$

90. $2x(x - 5)^2$

91. $3c(c + 5d)(c - 5d)$

[4.8]   Divide.

92. $\dfrac{9a^5}{3a^2}$

93. $\dfrac{24m^4n^2}{6m^2n}$

94. $\dfrac{15a - 10}{5}$

95. $\dfrac{32a^3 + 24a}{8a}$

96. $\dfrac{9r^2s^3 - 18r^3s^2}{-3rs^2}$

97. $\dfrac{35x^3y^2 - 21x^2y^3 + 14x^3y}{7x^2y}$

[4.8]   Perform the indicated long division.

98. $\dfrac{x^2 - 2x - 15}{x + 3}$

99. $\dfrac{2x^2 + 9x - 35}{2x - 5}$

100. $\dfrac{x^2 - 8x + 17}{x - 5}$

101. $\dfrac{6x^2 - x - 10}{3x + 4}$

102. $\dfrac{6x^3 + 14x^2 - 2x - 6}{6x + 2}$

103. $\dfrac{4x^3 + x + 3}{2x - 1}$

104. $\dfrac{3x^2 + x^3 + 5 + 4x}{x + 2}$

105. $\dfrac{2x^4 - 2x^2 - 10}{x^2 - 3}$

A N S W E R S

The purpose of this self-test is to help you check your progress and to review for a chapter test in class. Allow yourself about an hour to take the test. When you are done, check your answers in the back of the book. If you missed any answers, be sure to go back and review the appropriate sections in the chapter and do the exercises that are provided.

Multiply.

1. $a^5 \cdot a^9$

2. $3x^2 y^3 \cdot 5xy^4$

Divide.

3. $\dfrac{4x^5}{2x^2}$

4. $\dfrac{20a^3 b^5}{5a^2 b^2}$

Evaluate the following expressions if $a = 3$, $b = 4$, and $c = -5$.

5. $2a^3 - 3b^2$

6. $\dfrac{4a + 3c}{b + c}$

Use the properties of exponents to simplify. Express your answers with only positive exponents.

7. $(x^2 y^3 z^3)^3$

8. $\left(\dfrac{xy}{2}\right)^5$

9. $\dfrac{a^3 b^4 c}{a^5 b^2 c}$

10. $\dfrac{(x^{-2} y^3)^{-2}}{(xy^{-2} z^{-1})^3}$

Add.

11. $3x^2 - 7x + 2$ and $7x^2 - 5x - 9$

12. $7a^2 - 3a$ and $7a^3 + 4a^2$

Subtract.

13. $5x^2 - 2x + 5$ from $8x^2 + 9x - 7$

14. $2b^2 + 5$ from $3b^2 - 7b$

15. $5a^2 + a$ from the sum of $3a^2 - 5a$ and $9a^2 - 4a$

Add, using the vertical method.

16. $x^2 + 3$, $5x - 7$, and $3x^2 - 2$

1. _____

2. _____

3. _____

4. _____

5. _____

6. _____

7. _____

8. _____

9. _____

10. _____

11. _____

12. _____

13. _____

14. _____

15. _____

16. _____

A N S W E R S

16. _____

17. _____

18. _____

19. _____

20. _____

21. _____

22. _____

23. _____

24. _____

25. _____

26. _____

27. _____

28. _____

Add, using the vertical method.

16. $x^2 + 3$, $5x - 7$, and $3x^2 - 2$

Subtract, using the vertical method.

17. $3x^2 - 5$ from $5x^2 - 7x$

Multiply.

18. $5ab(3a^2b - 2ab + 4ab^2)$ **19.** $(x - 2)(3x + 7)$

20. $(a - 7b)(a + 7b)$

Multiply.

21. $(3m + 2n)^2$ **22.** $(2x + y)(x^2 + 3xy - 2y^2)$

Divide.

23. $\dfrac{14x^3y - 21xy^2}{7xy}$ **24.** $\dfrac{20c^3d - 30cd + 45c^2d^2}{5cd}$

25. $(x^2 - 2x - 24) \div (x + 4)$ **26.** $(2x^2 + x + 4) \div (2x - 3)$

27. $(6x^3 - 7x^2 + 3x + 9) \div (3x + 1)$

28. $(x^3 - 5x^2 + 9x - 9) \div (x - 1)$

© 1998 McGraw-Hill Companies

This test covers selected topics from the first four chapters.

Identify the property that is illustrated by each of the following statements.

1. $6 + (3 + 4) = (6 + 3) + 4$

2. $4(5 + 7) = 4 \cdot 5 + 4 \cdot 7$

Arrange the following data in ascending order and determine the range, median, and mean.

3. $6, -3, 4, 7, -5, 9$

Evaluate each of the following expressions if $x = 3$, $y = 2$, and $w = -4$.

4. $2x - y^2$

5. $3(x - 2y)$

6. $w^2 - 2xy$

7. $\dfrac{wx^2y}{6}$

8. $\dfrac{3w + 2x + 3y}{wy}$

9. $(3x - 2y)(3x + 2y)$

Solve the following equations and check your results.

10. $11x - 7 = 10x$

11. $-\dfrac{2}{3}x = 24$

12. $7x - 5 = 3x + 11$

13. $\dfrac{3}{5}x - 8 = 15 - \dfrac{2}{5}x$

Solve the following inequalities.

14. $7x - 5 > 8x + 10$

15. $6x - 9 < 3x + 6$

Perform the indicated operations.

16. $(x^2 - 3x + 5) + (2x^2 + 5x - 9)$

17. $(3x^2 - 8x - 7) - (2x^2 - 5x + 11)$

18. $4x(3x - 5)$

19. $(2x - 5)(3x + 8)$

20. $(x + 2)(x^2 - 3x + 5)$

21. $(2x + 7)(2x - 7)$

22. $(3x - 5)^2$

23. $5x(2x - 5)^2$

ANSWERS

2. _____

3. _____

4. _____

5. _____

6. _____

7. _____

8. _____

9. _____

10. _____

11. _____

12. _____

13. _____

14. _____

15. _____

16. _____

17. _____

18. _____

19. _____

20. _____

21. _____

22. _____

23. _____

24. $\dfrac{14x^3 + 63x}{7x}$

25. $\dfrac{25x^2y^3 - 15xy^2 + 30x^3y^3}{5xy^2}$

Perform the indicated long division.

26. $\dfrac{3x^2 - 2x - 4}{3x + 1}$

27. $\dfrac{4x^3 - 5x^2 + 7x - 9}{x - 2}$

Solve the following problems.

28. If 7 times a number decreased by 9 is 47, find the number.

29. The sum of two consecutive odd integers is 132. What are the two integers?

30. The length of a rectangle is 4 centimeters (cm) more than 5 times the width. If the perimeter is 56 cm, what are the dimensions of the rectangle?

Simplify and express your answer using only positive exponents.

31. $\dfrac{x^2 y^3 z^5}{x^3 y z^4}$

32. $\dfrac{(a\,b^2 c^{-2})^{-3}}{(a^2 b^{-1} c)^2}$

FACTORING POLYNOMIALS

INTRODUCTION

Developing secret codes is big business because of the widespread use of computers and the Internet. Corporations all over the world sell encryption systems that are supposed to keep data secure and safe.

In 1977, three professors from the Massachusetts Institute of Technology developed an encryption system they call RSA, a name derived from the first letters of their last names. They offered a $100 reward to anyone who could break their security code, which was based on a number that has *129 digits*. They called the code RSA-129. For the code to be broken, the 129-digit number must be factored into two prime numbers; that is, two prime numbers must be found which when multiplied together give the 129-digit number. The three professors predicted that it would take *40 quadrillion* years to find the two numbers.

In April 1994, a research scientist, 3 computer hobbyists, and more than 600 volunteers from the Internet, using 1600 computers, found the two numbers after 8 months of work and won the $100.

A data security company says that people who are using their system are safe because as yet no truly efficient algorithm for finding prime factors of massive numbers has been found, although one may someday exist. This company, hoping to test its encrypting system, now sponsors contests challenging people to factor more very large numbers into two prime numbers. RSA-150 up to RSA-500 are being worked on now.

Software companies are waging a legal battle against the U.S. government because the government does not allow any codes to be used for which it does not have the key. The software firms claim that this prohibition is costing them about $60 billion in lost sales because many companies will not buy an encryption system knowing they can be monitored by the U.S. government. _____

© Gontier / The Image Works

5.1 An Introduction to Factoring

5.1 OBJECTIVES

Factor a monomial from a polynomial

In Chapter 4 you were given factors and asked to find a product. We are now going to reverse the process. You will be given a polynomial and asked to find its factors. This is called **factoring.**

Let's start with an example from arithmetic. To *multiply* $5 \cdot 7$, you write

$$5 \cdot 7 = 35$$

To *factor* 35, you would write

$$35 = 5 \cdot 7$$

Factoring is just the *reverse* of multiplication.

Now let's look at factoring in algebra. You have used the distributive property as

$$a(b + c) = ab + ac$$

For instance,

3 and $x + 5$ are the factors of $3x + 15$.

$$3(x + 5) = 3x + 15$$

To use the distributive property in factoring, we apply that property in the opposite fashion, as

$$ab + ac = a(b + c)$$

The property lets us remove the common monomial factor a from the terms of $ab + ac$. To use this in factoring, the first step is to see whether each term of the polynomial has a common monomial factor. In our earlier example,

$$3x + 15 = 3 \cdot x + 3 \cdot 5$$
Common factor

So, by the distributive property,

$$3x + 15 = 3(x + 5)$$

Again, factoring is just the reverse of multiplication.

To check this, multiply $3(x + 5)$.

Multiplying
$$3(x + 5) = 3x + 15$$
Factoring

Here is a diagram that will relate the idea of multiplication and factoring.

The first step in factoring is to identify the **greatest common factor** (GCF) of a set of terms. This is the monomial with the largest common numerical coefficient and the largest power of each common variable.

288

• Example 1

Finding the GCF

Find the GCF for each set of terms.

(a) 9 and 12   The largest number that is a factor of both is 3.

(b) 10, 25, 150   The GCF is 5.

(c) x^4 and x^7 The largest power common to the two variables is x^4.

(d) $12a^3$ and $18a^2$ The GCF is $6a^2$.

● ● ●   CHECK YOURSELF 1

Find the GCF for each set of terms.

a. 14, 24   **b.** 9, 27, 81   **c.** a^9, a^5 **d.** $10x^5, 35x^4$

To Factor a Monomial from a Polynomial

> Checking your answer is always important and perhaps is never easier than after you have factored.

STEP 1 Find the *greatest common factor* (GCF) for all the terms.
STEP 2 Factor the GCF from each term, then apply the distributive law.
STEP 3 Mentally check your factoring by multiplication.

• Example 2

Finding the GCF of a Binomial

(a) Factor $8x^2 + 12x$.

The largest common numerical factor of 8 and 12 is 4, and x is the variable factor with the largest common power. So $4x$ is the GCF. Write

$$8x^2 + 12x = \boxed{4x} \cdot 2x + \boxed{4x} \cdot 3$$
$$\underset{\text{GCF}}{\underrightarrow{\hspace{3cm}}}$$

> It is always a good idea to check your answer by multiplying to make sure that you get the original polynomial. Try it here. Multiply $4x$ by $2x + 3$.

Now, by the distributive property, we have

$$8x^2 + 12x = 4x(2x + 3)$$

(b) Factor $6a^4 - 18a^2$.

The GCF in this case is $6a^2$. Write

$$6a^4 - 18a^2 = \boxed{6a^2} \cdot a^2 - \boxed{6a^2} \cdot 3$$
$$\underset{\text{GCF}}{\underrightarrow{\hspace{3cm}}}$$

> It is also true that
>
> $$6a^4 - 18a^2 = 3a(2a^3 - 6a)$$
>
> However, this is *not completely factored*. Do you see why? You want to find the common monomial factor with the *largest* possible coefficient and the *largest* exponent, in this case $6a^2$.

Again, using the distributive property yields

$$6a^4 - 18a^2 = 6a^2(a^2 - 3)$$

You should check this by multiplying.

● ● ● **CHECK YOURSELF 2**

Factor each of the following polynomials.

a. $5x + 20$ **b.** $6x^2 - 24x$ **c.** $10a^3 - 15a^2$

The process is exactly the same for polynomials with more than two terms. Consider Example 3.

● **Example 3**

Finding the GCF of a Polynomial

(*a*) Factor $5x^2 - 10x + 15$.

The GCF is 5.

$$5x^2 - 10x + 15 = \boxed{5} \cdot x^2 - \boxed{5} \cdot 2x + \boxed{5} \cdot 3$$
$$\underrightarrow{\hspace{3cm}} \text{GCF}$$
$$= 5(x^2 - 2x + 3)$$

The GCF is 3*a*.

(*b*) Factor $6ab + 9ab^2 - 15a^2$.

$$6ab + 9ab^2 - 15a^2 = \boxed{3a} \cdot 2b + \boxed{3a} \cdot 3b^2 - \boxed{3a} \cdot 5a$$
$$\underrightarrow{\hspace{3cm}} \text{GCF}$$
$$= 3a(2b + 3b^2 - 5a)$$

(*c*) Factor $4a^4 + 12a^3 - 20a^2$.

The GCF is $4a^2$.

$$4a^4 + 12a^3 - 20a^2 = \boxed{4a^2} \cdot a^2 + \boxed{4a^2} \cdot 3a - \boxed{4a^2} \cdot 5$$
$$\underrightarrow{\hspace{3cm}} \text{GCF}$$
$$= 4a^2(a^2 + 3a - 5)$$

(*d*) Factor $\underline{6a^2b + 9ab^2 + 3ab}$.

Mentally note that 3, *a*, and *b* are factors of each term, so

In each of these examples, you will want to check the result by multiplying the factors.

$$6a^2b + 9ab^2 + 3ab = 3ab(2a + 3b + 1)$$

● ● ● **CHECK YOURSELF 3**

Factor each of the following polynomials.

a. $8b^2 + 16b - 32$ **b.** $4xy - 8x^2y + 12x^3$
c. $7x^4 - 14x^3 + 21x^2$ **d.** $5x^2y^2 - 10xy^2 + 15x^2y$

● ● ● **CHECK YOURSELF ANSWERS**

1. (a) 2; **(b)** 9; **(c)** a^5; **(d)** $5x^4$. **2. (a)** $5(x + 4)$; **(b)** $6x(x - 4)$; **(c)** $5a^2(2a - 3)$.
3. (a) $8(b^2 + 2b - 4)$; **(b)** $4x(y - 2xy + 3x^2)$; **(c)** $7x^2(x^2 - 2x + 3)$; **(d)** $5xy(xy - 2y + 3x)$.

Find the greatest common factor for each of the following sets of terms.

1. 10, 12

2. 15, 35

3. 16, 32, 88

4. 55, 33, 132

5. x^2, x^5

6. y^7, y^9

7. a^3, a^6, a^9

8. b^4, b^6, b^8

9. $5x^4$, $10x^5$

10. $8y^9$, $24y^3$

11. $8a^4$, $6a^6$, $10a^{10}$

12. $9b^3$, $6b^5$, $12b^4$

13. $9x^2y$, $12xy^2$, $15x^2y^2$

14. $12a^3b^2$, $18a^2b^3$, $6a^4b^4$

15. $15ab^3$, $10a^2bc$, $25b^2c^3$

16. $9x^2$, $3xy^3$, $6y^3$

17. $15a^2bc^2$, $9ab^2c^2$, $6a^2b^2c^2$

18. $18x^3y^2z^3$, $27x^4y^2z^3$, $81xy^2z$

19. $(x + y)^2$, $(x + y)^3$

20. $12(a + b)^4$, $4(a + b)^3$

Factor each of the following polynomials.

21. $8a + 4$

22. $5x - 15$

23. $24m - 32n$

24. $7p - 21q$

ANSWERS
1.
2.
3.
4.
5.
6.
7.
8.
9.
10.
11.
12.
13.
14.
15.
16.
17.
18.
19.
20.
21.
22.
23.
24.

25. _____

26. _____

27. _____

28. _____

29. _____

30. _____

31. _____

32. _____

33. _____

34. _____

35. _____

36. _____

37. _____

38. _____

39. _____

40. _____

41. _____

42. _____

43. _____

44. _____

45. _____

46. _____

47. _____

48. _____

49. _____

50. _____

51. _____

52. _____

25. $12m^2 + 8m$

26. $24n^2 - 32n$

27. $10s^2 + 5s$

28. $12y^2 - 6y$

29. $12x^2 + 24x$

30. $14b^2 - 28b$

31. $15a^3 - 25a^2$

32. $36b^4 + 24b^2$

33. $6pq + 18p^2q$

34. $8ab - 24ab^2$

35. $7m^3n - 21mn^3$

36. $36p^2q^2 - 9pq$

37. $6x^2 - 18x + 30$

38. $7a^2 + 21a - 42$

39. $3a^3 + 6a^2 - 12a$

40. $5x^3 - 15x^2 + 25x$

41. $6m + 9mn - 15mn^2$

42. $4s + 6st - 14st^2$

43. $10x^2y + 15xy - 5xy^2$

44. $3ab^2 + 6ab - 15a^2b$

45. $10r^3s^2 + 25r^2s^2 - 15r^2s^3$

46. $28x^2y^3 - 35x^2y^2 + 42x^3y$

47. $9a^5 - 15a^4 + 21a^3 - 27a$

48. $8p^6 - 40p^4 + 24p^3 - 16p^2$

49. $15m^3n^2 - 20m^2n + 35mn^3 - 10mn$

50. $14ab^4 + 21a^2b^3 - 35a^3b^2 + 28ab^2$

51. $x(x - 2) + 3(x - 2)$

52. $y(y + 5) - 3(y + 5)$

292

53. $p(p - 2q) - q(p - 2q)$

54. $2c(c + d) + 3d(c + d)$

55. $3(x + y)^2 + 9(x + y)$

56. $6(a - b)^2 - 12(a - b)$

57. The GCF of $2x - 6$ is 2. The GCF of $5x + 10$ is 5. Find the greatest common factor of the product $(2x - 6)(5x + 10)$.

58. The GCF of $3z + 12$ is 3. The GCF of $4z + 8$ is 4. Find the GCF of the product $(3z + 12)(4z + 8)$.

59. The GCF of $2x^3 - 4x$ is $2x$. The GCF of $3x + 6$ is 3. Find the GCF of the product $(2x^3 - 4x)(3x + 6)$.

60. State, in a sentence, the rule that the previous three exercises illustrated.

Find the GCF for each product.

61. $(2a + 8)(3a - 6)$

62. $(5b - 10)(2b + 4)$

63. $(2x^2 + 5x)(7x - 14)$

64. $(6y^2 - 3y)(y + 7)$

65. Area of a rectangle. The area of a rectangle with width t is given by $33t - t^2$. Factor the expression and determine the length of the rectangle in terms of t.

66. Area of a rectangle. The area of a rectangle of length x is given by $3x^2 + 5x$. Find the width of the rectangle.

67. For centuries, mathematicians have found factoring numbers into prime factors a fascinating subject. A prime number is a number that cannot be written as a product of any numbers but 1 and itself. The list of postive primes begins with 2 because 1 is not considered a prime number and then goes on: 3, 5, 7, 11, . . . What are the first 10 primes? What are the primes less than 100? If you list the numbers from 1 to 100 and then cross out all numbers that are factors of 2, 3, 5, and 7, what is left? Are all the numbers not crossed out prime? Write a paragraph to explain why this might be so. You might want to investigate the Sieve of Eratosthenes, a system from 230 BC for finding prime numbers.

ANSWERS

53. _____

54. _____

55. _____

56. _____

57. _____

58. _____

59. _____

60. _____

61. _____

62. _____

63. _____

64. _____

65. _____

66. _____

67. _____

68. _____

69. _____

a. _____

b. _____

c. _____

d. _____

e. _____

f. _____

68. If we made a list of all the prime numbers, what number would be at the end of the list? Because there are an infinite number of primes numbers, there is no "largest prime number" at the end of the list. But is there some formula that will give us all the primes? Here are some formulas proposed over the centuries:

$$n^2 + n + 17 \qquad 2n^2 + 29 \qquad n - n + 14$$

In all these expressions, $n = +1, 2, 3, 4, \ldots$, that is, a positive integer beginning with 1. Investigate these expressions with a partner. Do the expressions give prime numbers when they are evaluated for these values of n? Do the expressions give _every_ prime in the range of resulting numbers? Can you put in _any_ positive number for n?

69. How are primes used in coding messages and for security? Work together to decode the messages. The messages are coded using this code: After the numbers are factored into prime factors, the power of 2 gives the number of the letter in the alphabet. This code would be easy for a code breaker to figure out, but you might make up code that would be more difficult to break.

a. 1310720, 229376, 1572864, 1760, 460, 2097152, 336

b. 786432, 143, 4608, 278528, 1344, 98304, 1835008, 352, 4718592, 5242880

c. Code a message using this rule. Exchange your message with a partner to decode it.

 Getting Ready for Section 5.2 [Section 4.7]

Multiply.

a. $(x - 1)(x + 1)$ **b.** $(a + 7)(a - 7)$

c. $(x - y)(x + y)$ **d.** $(2x - 5)(2x + 5)$

e. $(3a - b)(3a + b)$ **f.** $(5a - 4b)(5a + 4b)$

Answers

1. 2   **3.** 8   **5.** x^2 **7.** a^3 **9.** $5x^4$ **11.** $2a^4$ **13.** $3xy$ **15.** $5b$
17. $3abc^2$ **19.** $(x + y)^2$ **21.** $4(2a + 1)$ **23.** $8(3m - 4n)$
25. $4m(3m + 2)$ **27.** $5s(2s + 1)$ **29.** $12x(x + 2)$ **31.** $5a^2(3a - 5)$
33. $6pq(1 + 3p)$ **35.** $7mn(m^2 - 3n^2)$ **37.** $6(x^2 - 3x + 5)$
39. $3a(a^2 + 2a - 4)$ **41.** $3m(2 + 3n - 5n^2)$ **43.** $5xy(2x + 3 - y)$
45. $5r^2s^2(2r + 5 - 3s)$ **47.** $3a(3a^4 - 5a^3 + 7a^2 - 9)$
49. $5mn(3m^2n - 4m + 7n^2 - 2)$ **51.** $(x - 2)(x + 3)$ **53.** $(p - 2q)(p - q)$
55. $3(x + y)(x + y + 3)$ **57.** 10   **59.** $6x$ **61.** 6   **63.** $7x$
65. $33 - t$ **a.** $x^2 - 1$ **b.** $a^2 - 49$ **c.** $x^2 - y^2$ **d.** $4x^2 - 25$
e. $9a^2 - b^2$ **f.** $25a^2 - 16b^2$

The Difference of Squares

5.2

5.2 OBJECTIVES

Factor a binomial that is the difference of two squares

In Section 4.7, we introduced some special products. Recall the following formula for the product of a sum and difference of two terms:

$$(a + b)(a - b) = a^2 - b^2$$

This also means that a binomial of the form $a^2 - b^2$, called a **difference of two squares,** has as its factors $a + b$ and $a - b$.

To use this idea for factoring, we can write

$$a^2 - b^2 = (a + b)(a - b)$$

A **perfect-square** term has a coefficient that is a square (1, 4, 9, 16, 25, 36, etc.), and any variables will have exponents that are multiples of 2 (x^2, y^4, z^6, etc.).

● Example 1

Factoring the Difference of Two Squares

Factor $x^2 - 16$.

Think $x^2 - 4^2$

Since $x^2 - 16$ is a difference of squares, we have

$$x^2 - 16 = (x + 4)(x - 4)$$

You could also write $(x - 4)(x + 4)$. The order doesn't matter since multiplication is commutative.

● ● ● **CHECK YOURSELF 1**

Factor $m^2 - 49$.

Any time an expression is a difference of two squares, it can be factored.

● Example 2

Factoring the Difference of Two Squares

Factor $4a^2 - 9$.

Think $(2a)^2 - 3^2$

So $4a^2 - 9 = (2a)^2 - (3)^2$

$$= (2a + 3)(2a - 3)$$

● ● ● **CHECK YOURSELF 2**

Factor $9b^2 - 25$.

The process for factoring a difference of squares does not change when more than one variable is involved.

● Example 3

Factoring the Difference of Two Squares

Think $(5a)^2 - (4b^2)^2$

Factor $25a^2 - 16b^4$.

$$25a^2 - 16b^4 = (5a + 4b^2)(5a - 4b^2)$$

● ● ● CHECK YOURSELF 3

Factor $49c^4 - 9d^2$.

We will now consider an example that combines common-term factoring with difference-of-squares factoring. Note that the common factor is always removed as the *first step*.

● Example 4

Removing the GCF First

Factor $32x^2y - 18y^3$.
    Note that $2y$ is a common factor, so

Step 1
Remove the GCF.

$$32x^2y - 18y^3 = 2y(\underbrace{16x^2 - 9y^2})$$

Difference of squares

Step 2
Factor the remaining binomial.

$$= 2y(4x + 3y)(4x - 3y)$$

● ● ● CHECK YOURSELF 4

Factor $50a^3 - 8ab^2$.

● ● ● CHECK YOURSELF ANSWERS

1. $(m + 7)(m - 7)$. **2.** $(3b + 5)(3b - 5)$. **3.** $(7c^2 + 3d)(7c^2 - 3d)$.
4. $2a(5a + 2b)(5a - 2b)$.

For each of the following binomials, state whether the binomial is a difference of squares.

1. $3x^2 + 2y^2$

2. $5x^2 - 7y^2$

3. $16a^2 - 25b^2$

4. $9n^2 - 16m^2$

5. $16r^2 + 4$

6. $p^2 - 45$

7. $16a^2 - 12b^3$

8. $9a^2b^2 - 16c^2d^2$

9. $a^2b^2 - 25$

10. $4a^3 - b^3$

Factor the following binomials.

11. $m^2 - n^2$

12. $r^2 - 9$

13. $x^2 - 49$

14. $c^2 - d^2$

15. $49 - y^2$

16. $81 - b^2$

17. $9b^2 - 16$

18. $36 - x^2$

19. $16w^2 - 49$

20. $4x^2 - 25$

1. _____

2. _____

3. _____

4. _____

5. _____

6. _____

7. _____

8. _____

9. _____

10. _____

11. _____

12. _____

13. _____

14. _____

15. _____

16. _____

17. _____

18. _____

19. _____

20. _____

A N S W E R S

21. _____

22. _____

23. _____

24. _____

25. _____

26. _____

27. _____

28. _____

29. _____

30. _____

31. _____

32. _____

33. _____

34. _____

35. _____

36. _____

37. _____

38. _____

39. _____

40. _____

41. _____

42. _____

21. $4s^2 - 9r^2$ **22.** $64y^2 - x^2$

23. $9w^2 - 49z^2$ **24.** $25x^2 - 81y^2$

25. $16a^2 - 49b^2$ **26.** $64m^2 - 9n^2$

27. $x^4 - 36$ **28.** $y^6 - 49$

29. $x^2y^2 - 16$ **30.** $m^2n^2 - 64$

31. $25 - a^2b^2$ **32.** $49 - w^2z^2$

33. $r^4 - 4s^2$ **34.** $p^2 - 9q^4$

35. $81a^2 - 100b^6$ **36.** $64x^4 - 25y^4$

37. $18x^3 - 2xy^2$ **38.** $50a^2b - 2b^3$

39. $12m^3n - 75mn^3$ **40.** $63p^4 - 7p^2q^2$

41. $48a^2b^2 - 27b^4$ **42.** $20w^5 - 45w^3z^4$

Factor each expression.

43. $x^2(x + y) - y^2(x + y)$

44. $a^2(b - c) - 16b^2(b - c)$

45. $2m^2(m - 2n) - 18n^2(m - 2n)$

46. $3a^3(2a + b) - 27ab^2(2a + b)$

47. Find a value for k so that $kx^2 - 25$ will have the factors $2x + 5$ and $2x - 5$.

48. Find a value for k so that $9m^2 - kn^2$ will have the factors $3m + 7n$ and $3m - 7n$.

49. Find a value for k so that $2x^3 - kxy^2$ will have the factors $2x$, $x - 3y$, and $x + 3y$.

50. Find a value for k so that $20a^3b - kab^3$ will have the factors $5ab$, $2a - 3b$, and $2a + 3b$.

51. Complete the following statement in complete sentences: "To factor a number you . . . ."

52. Complete this staement: To factor an algebraic expression into prime factors means . . . .

A N S W E R S

43.

44.

45.

46.

47.

48.

49.

50.

51.

52.

Getting Ready for Section 5.3
[Section 4.6]

Multiply.

a. $(x - 1)(x + 2)$ **b.** $(a - 3)(a + 2)$

c. $(x + 4)(x + 6)$ **d.** $(w + 1)(w + 7)$

e. $(b + 1)(b + 3)$ **f.** $(a + 1)(a - 4)$

g. $(x - 1)(x - 1)$ **h.** $(p - 2)(p - 5)$

Answers

1. No   **3.** Yes   **5.** No   **7.** No   **9.** Yes   **11.** $(m + n)(m - n)$
13. $(x + 7)(x - 7)$ **15.** $(7 + y)(7 - y)$ **17.** $(3b + 4)(3b - 4)$
19. $(4w + 7)(4w - 7)$ **21.** $(2s + 3r)(2s - 3r)$ **23.** $(3w + 7z)(3w - 7z)$
25. $(4a + 7b)(4a - 7b)$ **27.** $(x^2 + 6)(x^2 - 6)$ **29.** $(xy + 4)(xy - 4)$
31. $(5 + ab)(5 - ab)$ **33.** $(r^2 + 2s)(r^2 - 2s)$ **35.** $(9a + 10b^3)(9a - 10b^3)$
37. $2x(3x + y)(3x - y)$ **39.** $3mn(2m + 5n)(2m - 5n)$
41. $3b^2(4a + 3b)(4a - 3b)$ **43.** $(x + y)^2(x - y)$
45. $2(m - 2n)(m + 3n)(m - 3n)$ **47.** 4   **49.** 18   **a.** $x^2 + x - 2$
b. $a^2 - a - 6$ **c.** $x^2 + 10x + 24$ **d.** $w^2 + 8w + 7$ **e.** $b^2 + 4b + 3$
f. $a^2 - 3a - 4$ **g.** $x^2 - 2x + 1$ **h.** $p^2 - 7p + 10$

 **Factoring by Grouping**

5.3 OBJECTIVES

1. Use the distributive property to factor
2. Factor by grouping

In Section 4.3, you learned how to find the product of two binomials by using the FOIL method. That multiplication method sometimes results in four terms that can be rewritten as a trinomial, as is the case here:

$$(x + 2)(x - 3) = x^2 - 3x + 2x - 6 = x^2 - x - 6$$

Sometimes the product of two binomials is four terms, none of which are like terms, as is the case here:

$$(x + 1)(x - y) = x^2 - xy + x - y$$

In the next two sections we wish to reverse that multiplication process by using factoring. Our first example involves factoring out a binomial by finding the greatest common factor (GCF) of a polynomial.

• Example 1

Factoring Out a Binomial

(*a*) Factor $x(x + y) + 3(x + y)$.

There are two terms, $x(x + y)$ and $3(x + y)$. They have the common binomial factor $(x + y)$. Removing that factor gives

$$x(x + y) + 3(x + y) = (x + y)(x + 3)$$

(*b*) Factor $a(a - b) - 2(a - b)$.

Here $(a - b)$ is the common binomial factor, so

$$a(a - b) - 2(a - b) = (a - b)(a - 2)$$

● ● ● **CHECK YOURSELF 1**

Remove the binomial factor.

a. $y(y - 1) - 7(y - 1)$ **b.** $a(a + b) + 3b(a + b)$

Sometimes we can find a common binomial factor for a polynomial by *grouping* the terms of the polynomial. Usually this requires that we look for a common factor for the first two terms, and then a different common factor for the second two terms. If this process results in a common binomial factor, we continue as in Example 1. Let's look at an example.

• Example 2

Factoring by Grouping

Factor each polynomial by grouping the first two terms and the last two terms.

(*a*) $a^3 + 2a^2 + 3a + 6 = (a^3 + 2a^2) + (3a + 6)$ Group the terms.

$\qquad\qquad\qquad\quad = a^2(a + 2) + 3(a + 2)$ Find the common factor for each group of terms.

$\qquad\qquad\qquad\quad = (a^2 + 3)(a + 2)$ Remove the common binomial factor.

(*b*) $6x^4 + 15x^3 - 8x - 20 = (6x^4 + 15x^3) - (8x + 20)$ Group the terms.

$\qquad\qquad\qquad\qquad\quad = 3x^3(2x + 5) - 4(2x + 5)$ Find the common factor for each group of terms.

$\qquad\qquad\qquad\qquad\quad = (2x + 5)(3x^3 - 4)$ Remove the common binomial factor.

● ● ●   **CHECK YOURSELF 2**

Factor each polynomial by grouping the first two terms and the last two terms.

a. $2a^4 + 6a^3 + a + 3$ **b.** $x^4 + 5x^3 - 2x - 10$

To effectively use the grouping method for factoring a polynomial, the terms should be written in descending order.

• Example 3

Factoring by Grouping

Rewrite each polynomial in descending order, then factor by grouping.

(*a*) $b + 2b^3 - 3 - 6b^2 = 2b^3 - 6b^2 + b - 3$ Rewrite in descending order.

$\qquad\qquad\qquad\quad = (2b^3 - 6b^2) + (b - 3)$ Group the terms.

$\qquad\qquad\qquad\quad = 2b^2(b - 3) + (b - 3)$ Find the common factor for each group of terms.

$\qquad\qquad\qquad\quad = (b - 3)(2b^2 + 1)$ Remove the common binomial factor.

(*b*) $35x^5 - 10 - 6x^3 + 21x^8 = 21x^8 + 35x^5 - 6x^3 - 10$ Rewrite in descending order.

$\qquad\qquad\qquad\qquad\quad = (21x^8 + 35x^5) - (6x^3 + 10)$ Group the terms.

$\qquad\qquad\qquad\qquad\quad = 7x^5(3x^3 + 5) - 2(3x^3 + 5)$ Find the common factor for each group of terms.

$\qquad\qquad\qquad\qquad\quad = (3x^3 + 5)(7x^5 - 2)$ Remove the common binomial factor.

● ● ● **CHECK YOURSELF 3**

Rewrite each polynomial in descending order. Then factor by grouping.

a. $15a - 2a^3 - 5 + 6a^4$ **b.** $2x^4 - 6 + 3x^3 - 4x$

In the next section, you will learn to factor trinomials using the grouping method. To prepare for that work, we will now factor polynomials that contain like terms.

●Example 4

Factoring by Grouping

Factor each polynomial by grouping. Do not combine like terms.

(a) $2a^2 + 2ab - ab - b^2 = (2a^2 + 2ab) - (ab + b^2)$

$$= 2a(a + b) - b(a + b)$$

$$= (a + b)(2a - b)$$

(b) $6x^2 - 4x + 9x - 6 = (6x^2 - 4x) + (9x - 6)$

$$= 2x(3x - 2) + 3(3x - 2)$$

$$= (3x - 2)(2x + 3)$$

CHECK YOURSELF 4

● ● ●   Factor each polynomial by grouping. Do not combine like terms.

a. $a^2 + 11a - 6a - 66$ **b.** $6x^2 + 12x - 5x - 10$

In every factoring problem, all common factors must be removed. The grouping method allows for this to be either the first or the last step, as in Example 5.

●Example 5

Removing Common Factors

Factor the given polynomial by two methods.

$x^3 + x^2y + x^2y + xy^2$

First, let's remove any common factors and then factor by grouping.

$x^3 + x^2y + x^2y + xy^2 = x(x^2 + xy + xy + y^2)$

$$= x[(x^2 + xy) + (xy + y^2)]$$

$$= x[x(x + y) + y(x + y)]$$

$$= x[(x + y)(x + y)] = x(x + y)^2$$

Let's factor the same polynomial by the grouping method as our initial step.

$$x^3 + x^2y + x^2y + xy^2 = (x^3 + x^2y) + (x^2y + xy^2)$$
$$= x^2(x + y) + xy(x + y)$$
$$= (x^2 + xy)(x + y)$$
$$= x(x + y)(x + y) = x(x + y)^2$$

● ● ● **CHECK YOURSELF 5**

Factor the given polynomial by two methods.

$$2a^3 - 6a^2 + 2a^2 - 6a$$

● ● ● **CHECK YOURSELF ANSWERS**

1. (a) $(y - 1)(y - 7)$; **(b)** $(a + b)(a + 3b)$.   **2. (a)** $(2a^3 + 1)(a + 3)$; **(b)** $(x^3 - 2)(x + 5)$.   **3. (a)** $(2a^3 + 5)(3a - 1)$; **(b)** $(x^3 - 2)(2x + 3)$.   **4. (a)** $(a + 11)(a - 6)$; **(b)** $(x + 2)(6x - 5)$.   **5.** $2a(a - 3)(a + 1)$

A N S W E R S

Use the distributive property to factor each polynomial completely.

1. $x(2x + y) + 5(2x + y)$

2. $x(x + 3y) + 7(x + 3y)$

3. $x(y - z) + 3(y - z)$

4. $2a(c - d) + b(c - d)$

5. $p(s + t) - 3(s + t)$

6. $4x(c + d) - 7y(c + d)$

7. $3y(t - s) - 2x(t - s)$

8. $2x(1 + n) - y(1 + n)$

9. $6x(a + b) + 12y(a + b)$

10. $3p(2c - d) - 15q(2c - d)$

11. $4xy(3p + q) + 8x(3p + q)$

12. $9s(4x + y) - 12st(4x + y)$

Factor each polynomial by grouping the first two terms and the last two terms.

13. $x^3 - 4x^2 + 3x - 12$

14. $x^3 - 6x^2 + 2x - 12$

15. $a^3 - 3a^2 + 5a - 15$

16. $6x^3 - 2x^2 + 9x - 3$

17. $10x^3 + 5x^2 - 2x - 1$

18. $x^5 + x^3 - 2x^2 - 2$

19. $x^4 - 2x^3 + 3x - 6$

20. $x^3 - 4x^2 + 2x - 8$

Factor each polynomial completely by removing any common factors, and then factor by grouping. Do not combine like terms.

21. $3x - 6 + xy - 2y$

22. $2x - 10 + xy - 5y$

23. $ab - ac + b^2 - bc$

24. $ax + 2a + bx + 2b$

25. $3x^2 - 2xy + 3x - 2y$

26. $xy - 5y^2 - x + 5y$

1. _____

2. _____

3. _____

4. _____

5. _____

6. _____

7. _____

8. _____

9. _____

10. _____

11. _____

12. _____

13. _____

14. _____

15. _____

16. _____

17. _____

18. _____

19. _____

20. _____

21. _____

22. _____

23. _____

24. _____

25. _____

26. _____

305

27.

28.

29.

30.

31.

32.

33.

34.

a.

b.

c.

d.

e.

f.

g.

h.

27. $5s^2 + 15st - 2st - 6t^2$

28. $3a^3 + 3ab^2 + 2a^2b + 2b^3$

29. $3x^3 + 6x^2y - x^2y - 2xy^2$

30. $2p^4 + 3p^3q - 2p^3q - 3p^2q^2$

31. $x^4 + 5x^3 - 2x^2 - 10x$

32. $x^4y - 2x^3y + x^4 - 2x^3$

33. $2x^3 - 2x^2 + 3x^2 - 3x$

34. $3b^4 - 3b^3c + 2b^3c - 2b^2c^2$

 Getting Ready for Section 5.4
[Section 4.3]

Multiply.

a. $(2x - 1)(2x + 3)$

b. $(3a - 1)(a + 4)$

c. $(x - 4)(2x - 3)$

d. $(2w - 11)(w + 2)$

e. $(y + 5)(2y + 9)$

f. $(2x + 1)(x - 12)$

g. $(p + 9)(2p + 5)$

h. $(3a - 5)(2a + 4)$

Answers

1. $(2x + y)(x + 5)$ **3.** $(y - z)(x + 3)$ **5.** $(s + t)(p - 3)$
7. $(t - s)(3y - 2x)$ **9.** $6(a + b)(x + 2y)$ **11.** $4x(3p + q)(y + 2)$
13. $(x - 4)(x^2 + 3)$ **15.** $(a - 3)(a^2 + 5)$ **17.** $(5x^2 - 1)(2x + 1)$
19. $(x - 2)(x^3 + 3)$ **21.** $(x - 2)(3 + y)$ **23.** $(b - c)(a + b)$
25. $(3x - 2y)(x + 1)$ **27.** $(s + 3t)(5s - 2t)$ **29.** $x(x + 2y)(3x - y)$
31. $x(x + 5)(x^2 - 2)$ **33.** $x(x - 1)(2x + 3)$ **a.** $4x^2 + 4x - 3$
b. $3a^2 + 11a - 4$ **c.** $2x^2 - 11x + 12$ **d.** $2w^2 - 7w - 22$
e. $2y^2 + 19y + 45$ **f.** $2x^2 - 23x - 12$ **g.** $2p^2 + 23p + 45$
h. $6a^2 + 2a - 20$

5.4 Factoring Trinomials of the Form $ax^2 + bx + c$

5.4 OBJECTIVES

1. Factor a trinomial of the form $ax^2 + bx + c$
2. Completely factor a trinomial
3. Use the *ac* test to determine factorability
4. Use the results of the *ac* test to factor

The product of two binomials of the form

$$(\_\,x + \_\,)(\_\,x + \_\,)$$

will always be a trinomial. In Section 4.6, we used the FOIL method to find the product of two binomials. In this section we will use the factoring by grouping method to find the binomial factors for a trinomial.

First let's look at some factored trinomials.

● Example 1

Matching Trinomials and Their Factors

Determine which of the following are true statements.

(*a*) $x^2 - 2x - 8 = (x - 4)(x + 2)$

This is a true statement. Using the FOIL method, we see that

$(x - 4)(x + 2) = x^2 + 2x - 4x - 8 = x^2 - 2x - 8$

(*b*) $x^2 - 6x + 5 = (x - 2)(x - 3)$

This is not a true statement.

$(x - 2)(x - 3) = x^2 - 3x - 2x + 6 = x^2 - 5x + 6$

(*c*) $x^2 + 5x - 14 = (x - 2)(x + 7)$

This is true: $(x - 2)(x + 7) = x^2 + 7x - 2x - 14 = x^2 + 5x - 14$

(*d*) $x^2 - 8x - 15 = (x - 5)(x - 3)$

This is false: $(x - 5)(x - 3) = x^2 - 3x - 5x + 15 = x^2 - 8x + 15$

● ● ● **CHECK YOURSELF 1**

Determine which of the following are true statements.

a. $2x^2 - 2x - 3 = (2x - 3)(x + 1)$
b. $3x^2 + 11x - 4 = (3x - 1)(x + 4)$
c. $2x^2 - 7x + 3 = (x - 3)(2x - 1)$

The first step in learning to factor a trinomial is to identify its coefficients. So that we are consistent, we first write the trinomial in standard $ax^2 + bx + c$ form, then label the three coefficients as *a*, *b*, and *c*.

• Example 2

Identifying the Coefficients of $ax^2 + bx + c$

First, where necessary, rewrite the trinomial in $ax^2 + bx + c$ form. Then give the values for a, b, and c, where a is the coefficient of the x^2 term, b is the coefficient of the x term, and c is the constant.

(a) $x^2 - 3x - 18$

$a = 1 \qquad b = -3 \qquad c = -18$

(b) $x^2 - 24x + 23$

$a = 1 \qquad b = -24 \qquad c = 23$

(c) $x^2 + 8 - 11x$

First rewrite the trinomial in descending order:

$x^2 - 11x + 8$

$a = 1 \qquad b = -11 \qquad c = 8$

● ● ●   CHECK YOURSELF 2

First, where necessary, rewrite the trinomials in $ax^2 + bx + c$ form. Then label a, b, and c, where a is the coefficient of the x^2 term, b is the coefficient of the x term, and c is the constant.

a. $x^2 + 5x - 14$ **b.** $x^2 - 18x + 17$ **c.** $x - 6 + 2x^2$

Not all trinomials can be factored. To discover if a trinomial is factorable, we try the **ac test.**

The *ac* Test

A trinomial of the form $ax^2 + bx + c$ is factorable if (and only if) there are two numbers, m and n, such that

$$ac = mn \qquad \text{and} \qquad b = m + n$$

In Example 3 we will look for m and n to determine whether each trinomial is factorable.

•Example 3

Using the *ac* Test

Use the *ac* test to determine which of the following trinomials can be factored. Find the values of *m* and *n* for each trinomial that can be factored.

(*a*) $x^2 - 3x - 18$

First, we find the values of *a*, *b*, and *c*, so that we can find *ac*.

$a = 1 \qquad b = -3 \qquad c = -18$

$ac = 1(-18) = -18$

Then, we look for two numbers, *m* and *n*, such that $mn = ac$, and $m + n = b$. In this case, that means

$mn = -18 \qquad$ and $\qquad m + n = -3$

We now look at all pairs of integers with a product of -18. We then look at the sum of each pair of integers.

mn	$m + n$
$1(-18) = -18$	$1 + -18 = -17$
$2(-9) = -18$	$2 + -9 = -7$
$3(-6) = -18$	$3 + -6 = -3$
$6(-3) = -18$	
$9(-1) = -18$	
$18(-1) = -18$	

We need look no further than 3 and -6.

3 and -6 are the two integers with a product of *ac* and a sum of *b*. We can say that

We could have chosen $m = -6$ and $n = 3$ as well.

$m = 3 \qquad$ and $\qquad n = -6$

(*b*) $x^2 - 24x + 23$

We find that $\qquad a = 1 \qquad b = -24 \qquad c = 23$
$\qquad\qquad\qquad\qquad ac = 1(23) = 23 \qquad$ and $\qquad b = -24$
So

$mn = 23 \qquad$ and $\qquad m + n = -24$

We now calculate integer pairs, looking for two numbers with a product of 23 and a sum of -24.

mn	$m + n$
$1(23) = 23$	$1 + 23 = 24$
$-1(-23) = 23$	$-1 + -23 = -24$

$m = -1 \qquad$ and $\qquad n = -23$

(c) $x^2 - 11x + 8$

We find that $a = 1$, $b = -11$, and $c = 8$. Therefore, $ac = 8$ and $b = -11$. Thus, $mn = 8$ and $m + n = -11$. We calculate integer pairs:

mn	$m + n$
$1(8) = 8$	$1 + 8 = 9$
$2(4) = 8$	$2 + 4 = 6$
$-1(-8) = 8$	$-1 + -8 = -9$
$-2(-4) = 8$	$-2 + -4 = -6$

There are no other pairs of integer with a product of 8, and none of these pairs has a sum of -11. The trinomial $x^2 - 11x + 8$ is not factorable.

(d) $2x^2 + 7x - 15$

We find that $a = 2$, $b = 7$, and $c = -15$. Therefore, $ac = 2(-15) = -30$ and $b = 7$. Thus $mn = -30$ and $m + n = 7$. We calculate integer pairs:

mn	$m + n$
$1(-30) = -30$	$1 + (-30) = -29$
$2(-15) = -30$	$2 + -15 = -13$
$3(-10) = -30$	$3 + -10 = -7$
$5(-6) = -30$	$5 + -6 = -1$
$6(-5) = -30$	$6 + -5 = 1$
$10(-3) = -30$	$10 + -3 = 7$

There is no need to go any further. We see that 10 and -3 have a product of -30 and a sum of 7, so

$$m = 10 \quad \text{and} \quad n = -3$$

It is not always necessary to evaluate all the products and sums in order to determine whether a trinomial is factorable. You may have noticed patterns and shortcuts that make it easier to find m and n. By all means, use them to help you find m and n. This is essential in mathematical thinking. You are taught a mathematical process that will always work for solving a problem. Such a process is called an **algorithm.** It is very easy to teach a computer to use an algorithm. It is very difficult (some would say impossible) for a computer to have insight. Shortcuts that you discover are *insights*. They may be the most important part of your mathematical education.

● ● ●   **CHECK YOURSELF 3**

Use the *ac* test to determine which of the following trinomials can be factored. Find the values of m and n for each trinomial that can be factored.

a. $x^2 - 7x + 12$
c. $3x^2 - 6x + 7$

b. $x^2 + 5x - 14$
d. $2x^2 + x - 6$

So far we have used the results of the *ac* test only to determine whether a trinomial is factorable. The results can also be used to help factor the trinomial.

• Example 4

Using the Results of the *ac* Test to Factor

Rewrite the middle term as the sum of two terms, then factor by grouping.

(*a*) $x^2 - 3x - 18$

We find that $a = 1$, $b = -3$, and $c = -18$, so $ac = -18$ and $b = -3$. We are looking for two numbers, m and n, where $mn = -18$ and $m + n = -3$. In Example 3, part (*a*) we looked at every pair of integers whose product (mn) was -18, to find a pair that had a sum $(m + n)$ of -3. We found the two integers to be 3 and -6, because $3(-6) = -18$ and $3 + (-6) = -3$, so $m = 3$ and $n = -6$. We now use that result to rewrite the middle term as the sum of $3x$ and $-6x$.

$x^2 + 3x - 6x - 18$

We then factor by grouping:

$$x^2 + 3x - 6x - 18 = x(x + 3) - 6(x + 3)$$
$$= (x + 3)(x - 6)$$

(*b*) $x^2 - 24x + 23$

We use the results from Example 3*b*, in which we found $m = -1$ and $n = -23$, to rewrite the middle term of the equation.

$x^2 - 24x + 23 = x^2 - x - 23x + 23$

Then we factor by grouping:

$$x^2 - x - 23x + 23 = (x^2 - x) - (23x - 23)$$
$$= x(x - 1) - 23(x - 1)$$
$$= (x - 1)(x - 23)$$

(*c*) $2x^2 + 7x - 15$

From Example 3*d*, we know that this trinomial is factorable, and $m = 10$ and $n = -3$. We use that result to rewrite the middle term of the trinomial.

$$2x^2 + 7x - 15 = 2x^2 + 10x - 3x - 15$$
$$= (2x^2 + 10x) - (3x + 15)$$
$$= 2x(x + 5) - 3(x + 5)$$
$$= (x + 5)(2x - 3)$$

● ● ● CHECK YOURSELF 4

Rewrite the middle term as the sum of two terms, then factor by grouping.

a. $x^2 - 7x + 12$　　　**b.** $x^2 + 5x - 14$　　　**c.** $2x^2 + x - 6$

Let's look at some examples that require us to first find m and n, then factor the trinomial.

• Example 5

Rewriting Middle Terms to Factor

Rewrite the middle term as the sum of two terms, then factor by grouping.

(a) $2x^2 - 13x - 7$

We find that $a = 2$, $b = -13$, and $c = -7$, so $mn = ac = -14$ and $m + n = b = -13$. Therefore,

mn	$m + n$
$1(-14) = -14$	$1 + (-14) = -13$

So, $m = 1$ and $n = -14$. We rewrite the middle term of the trinomial as follows:

$$2x^2 - 13x - 7 = 2x^2 + x - 14x - 7$$
$$= (2x^2 + x) - (14x + 7)$$
$$= x(2x + 1) - 7(2x + 1)$$
$$= (2x + 1)(x - 7)$$

(b) $6x^2 - 5x - 6$

We find that $a = 6$, $b = -5$, and $c = -6$, so $mn = ac = -36$ and $m + n = b = -5$. Therefore,

mn	$m + n$
$1(-36)$	-35
$2(-18)$	-16
$3(-12)$	-9
$4(-9)$	-5

So, $m = 4$ and $n = -9$. We rewrite the middle term of the trinomial:

$$6x^2 - 5x - 6 = 6x^2 + 4x - 9x - 6$$
$$= (6x^2 + 4x) - (9x + 6)$$
$$= 2x(3x + 2) - 3(3x + 2)$$
$$= (3x + 2)(2x - 3)$$

● ● ● **CHECK YOURSELF 5**

Rewrite the middle term as the sum of two terms, then factor by grouping.

a. $2x^2 - 7x - 15$ **b.** $6x^2 - 5x - 4$

Be certain to check trinomials and binomial factors for any common monomial factor. (There is no common factor in the binomial unless it is also a common factor in the original trinomial.) Example 6 shows the removal of monomial factors.

● Example 6

Removing Common Factors

Completely factor the trinomial.

$3x^2 + 12x - 15$

We could first remove the common factor of 3:

$3x^2 + 12x - 15 = 3(x^2 + 4x - 5)$

Finding m and n for the trinomial $x^2 + 4x - 5$ yields $mn = -5$ and $m + n = 4$.

mn	$m + n$
$1(-5)$	-4
$5(-1)$	4

So, $m = 5$ and $n = -1$. This gives us

$$
\begin{aligned}
3x^2 + 12x - 15 &= 3(x^2 + 4x - 5) \\
&= 3(x^2 + 5x - x - 5) \\
&= 3[(x^2 + 5x) - (x + 5)] \\
&= 3[x(x + 5) - (x + 5)] \\
&= 3[(x + 5)(x - 1)] \\
&= 3(x + 5)(x - 1)
\end{aligned}
$$

● ● ● CHECK YOURSELF 6

Completely factor the trinomial.

$6x^3 + 3x^2 - 18x$

Not all possible product pairs need to be tried to find m and n. A look at the sign pattern of the trinomial will eliminate many of the possibilities. Assuming the leading coefficient is positive, there are four possible sign patterns.

Pattern	Example	Conclusion
1. b and c are both positive.	$2x^2 + 13x + 15$	m and n must both be positive.
2. b is negative and c is positive.	$x^2 - 7x + 12$	m and n must both be negative.
3. b is positive and c is negative.	$x^2 + 3x - 10$	m and n are of opposite signs. (The value with the larger absolute value is positive.)
4. b is negative and c is negative.	$x^2 - 3x - 10$	m and n are of opposite signs. (The value with the larger absolute value is negative.)

TRIAL AND ERROR

Sometimes the factors of a trinomial seem obvious. At other times you might be certain that there are only a couple of possible sets of factors for a trinomial. It is perfectly acceptable to check these proposed factors to see if they work. If you find the factors in this manner, we say that you have used the trial-and-error method. The difficulty with using this method exclusively is found in the reason that we call this method trial and *error*.

● ● ● **CHECK YOURSELF ANSWERS**

1. **(a)** False; **(b)** True; **(c)** True.
2. **(a)** $a = 1$, $b = 5$, $c = -14$; **(b)** $a = 1$, $b = -18$, $c = 17$; **(c)** $a = 2$, $b = 1$, $c = 6$.
3. **(a)** Factorable, $m = -3$, $n = -4$; **(b)** Factorable, $m = 7$, $n = -2$;
(c) Not factorable; **(d)** Factorable, $m = 4$, $n = -3$.
4. **(a)** $x^2 - 3x - 4x + 12 = (x - 3)(x - 4)$;
(b) $x^2 + 7x - 2x - 14 = (x + 7)(x - 2)$; **(c)** $2x^2 + 4x - 3x - 6 = (2x - 3)(x + 2)$.
5. **(a)** $2x^2 - 10x + 3x - 15 = (2x + 3)(x - 5)$;
(b) $6x^2 - 8x + 3x - 4 = (3x - 4)(2x + 1)$. **6.** $3x(2x - 3)(x + 2)$.

State whether each of the following is true or false.

1. $x^2 + 2x - 3 = (x + 3)(x - 1)$

2. $y^2 - 3y - 18 = (y - 6)(y + 3)$

3. $x^2 - 10x - 24 = (x - 6)(x + 4)$

4. $a^2 + 9a - 36 = (a - 12)(a + 4)$

5. $x^2 - 16x + 64 = (x - 8)(x - 8)$

6. $w^2 - 12w - 45 = (w - 9)(w - 5)$

7. $25y^2 - 10y + 1 = (5y - 1)\,(5y + 1)$

8. $6x^2 + 5xy - 4y^2 = (6x - 2y)\,(x + 2y)$

9. $10p^2 - pq - 3q^2 = (5p - 3q)\,(2p + q)$

10. $6a^2 + 13a + 6 = (2a + 3)\,(3a + 2)$

For each of the following trinomials, label a, b, and c.

11. $x^2 + 4x - 9$

12. $x^2 + 5x + 11$

13. $x^2 - 3x + 8$

14. $x^2 + 7x - 15$

15. $3x^2 + 5x - 8$

16. $2x^2 + 7x - 9$

17. $4x^2 + 8x + 11$

18. $5x^2 + 7x - 9$

19. $-3x^2 + 5x - 10$

20. $-7x^2 + 9x - 18$

ANSWERS

1.

2.

3.

4.

5.

6.

7.

8.

9.

10.

11.

12.

13.

14.

15.

16.

17.

18.

19.

20.

21. _____

22. _____

23. _____

24. _____

25. _____

26. _____

27. _____

28. _____

29. _____

30. _____

31. _____

32. _____

33. _____

34. _____

35. _____

36. _____

37. _____

38. _____

39. _____

40. _____

41. _____

42. _____

Use the *ac* test to determine which of the following trinomials can be factored. Find the values of *m* and *n* for each trinomial that can be factored.

21. $x^2 + x - 6$

22. $x^2 + 2x - 15$

23. $x^2 + x + 2$

24. $x^2 - 3x + 7$

25. $x^2 - 5x + 6$

26. $x^2 - x + 2$

27. $2x^2 + 5x - 3$

28. $3x^2 - 14x - 5$

29. $6x^2 - 19x + 10$

30. $4x^2 + 5x + 6$

Rewrite the middle term as the sum of two terms and then factor by grouping.

31. $x^2 + 6x + 8$

32. $x^2 + 3x - 10$

33. $x^2 - 9x + 20$

34. $x^2 - 8x + 15$

35. $x^2 - 2x - 63$

36. $x^2 + 6x - 55$

Rewrite the middle term as the sum of two terms and then factor completely.

37. $x^2 + 8x + 15$

38. $x^2 - 11x + 24$

39. $x^2 - 11x + 28$

40. $y^2 - y - 20$

41. $s^2 + 13s + 30$

42. $b^2 + 14b + 33$

43. $a^2 - 2a - 48$

44. $x^2 - 17x + 60$

45. $x^2 - 8x + 7$

46. $x^2 + 7x - 18$

47. $x^2 - 6x - 40$

48. $x^2 - 11x + 10$

49. $x^2 - 14x + 49$

50. $s^2 - 4s - 32$

51. $p^2 - 10p - 24$

52. $x^2 - 11x - 60$

53. $x^2 + 5x - 66$

54. $a^2 + 2a - 80$

55. $c^2 + 19c + 60$

56. $t^2 - 4t - 60$

57. $n^2 + 5n - 50$

58. $x^2 - 16x + 63$

59. $x^2 + 7xy + 10y^2$

60. $x^2 - 8xy + 12y^2$

61. $a^2 - ab - 42b^2$

62. $m^2 - 8mn + 16n^2$

63. $x^2 - 13xy + 40y^2$

64. $r^2 - 9rs - 36s^2$

65. $6x^2 + 19x + 10$

66. $6x^2 - 7x - 3$

43. _____

44. _____

45. _____

46. _____

47. _____

48. _____

49. _____

50. _____

51. _____

52. _____

53. _____

54. _____

55. _____

56. _____

57. _____

58. _____

59. _____

60. _____

61. _____

62. _____

63. _____

64. _____

65. _____

66. _____

67.	_____
68.	_____
69.	_____
70.	_____
71.	_____
72.	_____
73.	_____
74.	_____
75.	_____
76.	_____
77.	_____
78.	_____
79.	_____
80.	_____
81.	_____
82.	_____
83.	_____
84.	_____
85.	_____
86.	_____
87.	_____
88.	_____
89.	_____
90.	_____
91.	_____
92.	_____

67. $15x^2 + x - 6$

68. $12w^2 + 19w + 4$

69. $6m^2 + 25m - 25$

70. $8x^2 - 6x - 9$

71. $9x^2 - 12x + 4$

72. $20x^2 - 23x + 6$

73. $12x^2 - 8x - 15$

74. $16a^2 + 40a + 25$

75. $3y^2 + 7y - 6$

76. $12x^2 + 11x - 15$

77. $8x^2 - 27x - 20$

78. $24v^2 + 5v - 36$

79. $2x^2 + 3xy + y^2$

80. $3x^2 - 5xy + 2y^2$

81. $5a^2 - 8ab - 4b^2$

82. $5x^2 + 7xy - 6y^2$

83. $9x^2 + 4xy - 5y^2$

84. $16x^2 + 32xy + 15y^2$

85. $6m^2 - 17mn + 12n^2$

86. $15x^2 - xy - 6y^2$

87. $36a^2 - 3ab - 5b^2$

88. $3q^2 - 17qr - 6r^2$

89. $x^2 + 4xy + 4y^2$

90. $25b^2 - 80bc + 64c^2$

91. $20x^2 - 20x - 15$

92. $24x^2 - 18x - 6$

93. $8m^2 + 12m + 4$

94. $14x^2 - 20x + 6$

95. $15r^2 - 21rs + 6s^2$

96. $10x^2 + 5xy - 30y^2$

97. $2x^3 - 2x^2 - 4x$

98. $2y^3 + y^2 - 3y$

99. $2y^4 + 5y^3 + 3y^2$

100. $4z^3 - 18z^2 - 10z$

101. $36a^3 - 66a^2 + 18a$

102. $20n^4 - 22n^3 - 12n^2$

103. $9p^2 + 30pq + 21q^2$

104. $12x^2 + 2xy - 24y^2$

Find a positive value for k for which each of the following can be factored.

105. $x^2 + kx + 8$

106. $x^2 + kx + 9$

107. $x^2 - kx + 16$

108. $x^2 - kx + 17$

109. $x^2 - kx - 5$

110. $x^2 - kx - 7$

111. $x^2 + 3x + k$

112. $x^2 + 5x + k$

113. $x^2 + 2x - k$

114. $x^2 + x - k$

93.

94.

95.

96.

97.

98.

99.

100.

101.

102.

103.

104.

105.

106.

107.

108.

109.

110.

111.

112.

113.

114.

Getting Ready for Section 5.5
[Section 4.6]

Multiply.

a. $(2x - 1)(2x + 3)$

b. $(3a - 1)(a + 4)$

c. $(x - 4)(2x - 3)$

d. $(2w - 11)(w + 2)$

e. $(y + 5)(2y + 9)$

f. $(2x + 1)(x - 12)$

g. $(p + 9)(2p + 5)$

h. $(3a - 5)(2a + 4)$

Answers

1. True   **3.** False   **5.** True   **7.** False   **9.** True

11. $a = 1, b = 4, c = -9$ **13.** $a = 1, b = -3, c = 8$

15. $a = 3, b = 5, c = -8$ **17.** $a = 4, b = 8, c = 11$

19. $a = -3, b = 5, c = -10$ **21.** Factorable; 3, −2   **23.** Not

Factorable   **25.** Factorable; −3, −2   **27.** Factorable; 6, −1

29. Factorable; −15, −4   **31.** $(x + 2)(x + 4)$ **33.** $(x - 5)(x - 4)$

35. $(x - 9)(x + 7)$ **37.** $(x + 3)(x + 5)$ **39.** $(x - 4)(x - 7)$

41. $(s + 10)(s + 3)$ **43.** $(a - 8)(a + 6)$ **45.** $(x - 1)(x - 7)$

47. $(x - 10)(x + 4)$ **49.** $(x - 7)(x - 7)$ **51.** $(p - 12)(p + 2)$

53. $(x + 11)(x - 6)$ **55.** $(c + 4)(c + 15)$ **57.** $(n + 10)(n - 5)$

59. $(x + 2y)(x + 5y)$ **61.** $(a - 7b)(a + 6b)$ **63.** $(x - 5y)(x - 8y)$

65. $(3x + 2)(2x + 5)$ **67.** $(5x - 3)(3x + 2)$ **69.** $(6m - 5)(m + 5)$

71. $(3x - 2)(3x - 2)$ **73.** $(6x + 5)(2x - 3)$ **75.** $(3y - 2)(y + 3)$

77. $(8x + 5)(x - 4)$ **79.** $(2x + y)(x + y)$ **81.** $(5a + 2b)(a - 2b)$

83. $(9x - 5y)(x + y)$ **85.** $(3m - 4n)(2m - 3n)$ **87.** $(12a - 5b)(3a + b)$

89. $(x + 2y)^2$ **91.** $5(2x - 3)(2x + 1)$ **93.** $4(2m + 1)(m + 1)$

95. $3(5r - 2s)(r - s)$ **97.** $2x(x - 2)(x + 1)$ **99.** $y^2(2y + 3)(y + 1)$

101. $6a(3a - 1)(2a - 3)$ **103.** $3(p + q)(3p + 7q)$ **105.** 6 or 9

107. 8 or 10 or 17   **109.** 4   **111.** 2   **113.** 3, 8, 15, 24, . . .

a. $4x^2 + 4x - 3$ **b.** $3a^2 + 11a - 4$ **c.** $2x^2 - 11x + 12$

d. $2w^2 - 7w - 22$ **e.** $2y^2 + 19y + 45$ **f.** $2x^2 - 23x - 12$

g. $2p^2 + 23p + 45$ **h.** $6a^2 + 2a - 20$

Solving Equations by Factoring

Note: The zero-product principle applies only if a product is equal to 0. This will be very important later on.

We are now working with equations instead of expressions. Now we are looking for values for the variable that make the statement true.

There are many applications of our work with factoring. One important use of factoring is to solve certain types of equations. First we need to review an idea from arithmetic. If the product of two factors is 0, then one or both of the factors must be equal to 0. This is called the **zero-product principle.** In symbols,

If $a \cdot b = 0$, then $a = 0$ or $b = 0$ or both.

Let's use this principle to solve an equation.

● Example 1

Using the Zero-Product Principle

Solve $(x - 3)(x + 2) = 0$.

Using the zero-product principle gives

If $(x - 3)(x + 2) = 0$, then

$x - 3 = 0$ or $x + 2 = 0$ Set each factor equal to 0.

    $x = 3$ or $x = -2$ Solve each equation.

So 3 and -2 are the solutions for the equation.

● ● ● CHECK YOURSELF 1

Solve $(x + 3)(x - 4) = 0$.

The left side of the equation of Example 1 was already in factored form. Example 2 illustrates a case in which factoring is necessary.

● Example 2

Solving Equations by Factoring

Note: Because of the x^2 term, this equation is *not linear.*

Solve $x^2 - 6x + 5 = 0$.

$x^2 - 6x + 5 = 0$

We find that $ac = 5$ and $b = -6$. We wish to find m and n, two numbers with a product of 5 and a sum of -6. The m and n values are -1 and -5; therefore,

$$x^2 - x - 5x + 5 = 0$$

$$x(x - 1) - 5(x - 1) = 0$$

$$(x - 1)(x - 5) = 0$$

Again set each of the factors equal to zero.

$$x - 5 = 0 \quad \text{or} \quad x - 1 = 0$$

$$x = 5 \qquad\qquad x = 1$$

The solutions for the equation are 5 and 1.

We can check the solutions as before by substituting the two values back into the original equation.

Letting x be 5:	Letting x be 1:
$5^2 - 6 \cdot 5 + 5 = 0$	$1^2 - 6 \cdot 1 + 5 = 0$
$25 - 30 + 5 = 0$	$1 - 6 + 5 = 0$
$0 = 0$	$0 = 0$

Both solutions are verified.

● ● ● **CHECK YOURSELF 2**

Solve $x^2 - 2x - 8 = 0$.

The equation of Example 2 has two solutions and has a special form.

Note: In standard form, the equation is *set equal to 0*, and the terms are written in **descending-exponent order.**

An equation with the form

$$ax^2 + bx + c = 0 \qquad \text{where } a \neq 0$$

is called a **quadratic equation in standard form.**

Quadratic equations must be in standard form before you factor, as Example 3 illustrates.

● Example 3

Solving Equations by Factoring

Solve $2x^2 + 5x = 3$.

Be very careful! To use the zero-product principle, one side of the equation *must be zero.* So rewrite the equation in standard form by subtracting 3 from both sides. We now have

$$2x^2 + 5x - 3 = 0$$

m and *n* are two numbers with a product of −6 and a sum of 5.

We find that $ac = -6$ and $b = 5$. The values for *m* and *n* are 6 and −1; therefore,

$$2x^2 + 6x - x - 3 = 0$$

$$2x(x + 3) - 1(x + 3) = 0$$

$$(x + 3)(2x - 1) = 0$$

Next, set each of the factors equal to zero.

$$x + 3 = 0 \qquad \text{or} \qquad 2x - 1 = 0$$
$$x = -3 \qquad\qquad\qquad 2x = 1$$
$$x = \frac{1}{2}$$

So $\frac{1}{2}$ and −3 are the two solutions for the equation. We will leave the check of these solutions to you. Be sure to return to the original equation to verify these results.

● ● ● **CHECK YOURSELF 3**

Solve.

a. $3x^2 - 5x = 2$ **b.** $2x^2 + 3 = 7x$

Example 4 shows how other factoring techniques are used in solving quadratic equations.

● Example 4

Solving Equations by Factoring

(*a*) Solve $x^2 + 5x = 0$.

Note that *x* is a common factor on the left. Factoring, we have

$$x(x + 5) = 0$$

Set each factor equal to 0.

$$x = 0 \qquad \text{or} \qquad x + 5 = 0$$
$$x = -5$$

The solutions are 0 and −5.

(*b*) Solve $x^2 = 4x$.

First, write the equation in standard form (set equal to 0).

$$x^2 - 4x = 0$$

$$x(x - 4) = 0 \qquad \text{Factor on the left.}$$

Note: When *x* is a common factor of the quadratic member, you must set *x* equal to 0 to find the zero solution of the equation.

$$x = 0 \quad \text{or} \quad x - 4 = 0$$
$$x = 4$$

The solutions are 0 and 4.

(c) Solve $x^2 + 3x = 9x$.

First, set the equation equal to 0.

$$x^2 + 3x - 9x = 0$$

Then, collect like terms.

$$x^2 - 6x = 0$$
$$x(x - 6) = 0$$
$$x = 0 \quad \text{or} \quad x = 6$$

● ● ● **CHECK YOURSELF 4**

Solve.

a. $x^2 + 8x = 0$ **b.** $x^2 = 9x$

Example 5 illustrates how the difference-of-squares factoring technique is applied in solving quadratic equations.

● Example 5

Solving Equations by Factoring

Solve $x^2 = 9$.

Again, write the equation in standard form.

$$x^2 - 9 = 0$$

The left side is a difference of squares, so we have

$$(x + 3)(x - 3) = 0$$

So

$$x + 3 = 0 \quad \text{or} \quad x - 3 = 0$$
$$x = -3 \qquad\qquad x = 3$$

The solutions are -3 and 3.

●●● CHECK YOURSELF 5

Solve $x^2 = 25$.

● Example 6

Solving Equations by Factoring

Solve $3x^2 - 3x - 6 = 0$.

Note that there is a common factor of 3 on the left. Write

The ac test can be used to factor $x^2 - x - 2$, but by now you should start to recognize some factoring patterns.

$$3(x^2 - x - 2) = 0$$
$$3(x - 2)(x + 1) = 0$$

Then, after dividing both sides by 3, we have

Note: On the right:

$\dfrac{0}{3} = 0$

$$(x - 2)(x + 1) = 0$$

So

$$
\begin{array}{lll}
x - 2 = 0 & \text{or} & x + 1 = 0 \\
\quad x = 2 & & \quad x = -1
\end{array}
$$

The solutions are 2 and -1.

●●● CHECK YOURSELF 6

Solve $4x^2 + 14x = -6$.

The following rules summarize our work in solving quadratic equations by factoring.

To Solve a Quadratic Equation by Factoring

Step 1 Add or subtract the necessary terms on both sides of the equation so that the equation is in standard form (set equal to 0).

Step 2 Factor the quadratic expression.

Step 3 Set each factor that contains a variable equal to 0.

Step 4 Solve the resulting equations to find the solutions.

Step 5 Check each solution by substituting in the original equation.

Note: If the polynomial in step 2 is not factorable, you must use other methods for solving the equation. We will discuss other approaches in Chapter 10.

Certain types of word problems will lead to quadratic equations. You will use your work from this section to solve them. Look at Example 7.

• Example 7

© 1998 McGraw-Hill Companies

Remember our five-step process for solving word problems:

1. Read the problem carefully. Then reread it to decide what you are asked to find.

2. Choose a letter to represent the unknown or unknowns.

3. Translate the problem to the language of algebra to form an equation.

4. Solve the equation.

Note that -9 and 6 are *not* the numbers asked for in the problem. The solutions are -9 and -6 *or* 6 and 9.

5. Verify your solution by returning to the original problem.

Solving an Application

One number is 3 more than another. If their product is 54, find the two numbers.

Step 1 You are asked to find the two unknown numbers.

Step 2 Let x be the smaller number.

Then $x + 3$ is the larger.

"3 more than x"

Step 3

$x(x + 3) = 54$

"Their product is 54."

Step 4

$x(x + 3) = 54$

$x^2 + 3x = 54$ Multiply on the left.

You should recognize that the equation is quadratic. Solve as follows:

$x^2 + 3x - 54 = 0$ Write the equation in standard form.

$(x + 9)(x - 6) = 0$ Factor.

$x + 9 = 0$ or $x - 6 = 0$
$x = -9$ $x = 6$

When word problems lead to quadratic equations, there may be two possible solutions to the equation. It is important to check, because one of the solutions may be eliminated by the conditions of the original problem. Here, both satisfy those conditions and so are valid solutions to the problem. The numbers are

$x = -9$ ⟵——— Smaller number ———⟶ $x = 6$

$x + 3 = -6$ ⟵——— Larger number ———⟶ $x + 3 = 9$

Step 5 Since there are two separate solutions, both must be verified in the original problem. Since $(-9)(-6)$ and $6 \cdot 9$ are both 54, both pairs of numbers are solutions.

● ● ● ● **CHECK YOURSELF 7**

The product of two consecutive integers is 90. What are the two integers? (*Hint:* Consecutive integers can be represented by x and $x + 1$.)

• Example 8

Solving an Application

The sum of a number and its square is 30. What is the number?

Step 1 We want to find the unknown number.

Step 2 Let x be the number. Then the square of the number is x^2.

Step 3 Now write the equation.

$$\underbrace{x + x^2}_{} = 30$$

The sum of the number and its square

Step 4 Writing the equation in standard form, we have

$x^2 + x - 30 = 0$

$(x + 6)(x - 5) = 0$

$x + 6 = 0 \qquad \text{or} \qquad x - 5 = 0$

$x = -6 \qquad\qquad\quad x = 5$

Possible solutions to the problem are -6 and 5.

Step 5 Since we have two possible values, both must be checked.

$-6 + (-6)^2 = 30 \qquad 5 + 5^2 = 30$

$-6 + 36 = 30 \qquad 5 + 25 = 30$

$30 = 30 \qquad\qquad 30 = 30$

Both solutions are verified.

● ● ● **CHECK YOURSELF 8**

The square of an integer is 6 less than 7 times the integer. What is the integer?

Many problems involving geometric figures will also lead to quadratic equations that can be solved by factoring, as Example 9 illustrates.

• Example 9

Solving a Geometric Application

A rectangle is 5 centimeters (cm) longer than it is wide. If the area of the rectangle is 84 cm^2, find the dimensions of the rectangle.

Step 1 You want to find the dimensions (the width and length) of the rectangle.

Step 2 Let x be the width of the rectangle; then $x + 5$ is the length. In solving geometric problems, always draw a sketch labeled with the variables assigned in this step. Here we would have

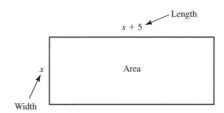

Step 3 Since the area of a rectangle is the product of its width and its length, we have

$$x(x + 5) = 84$$

Width Length Area

Step 4 Multiply and write the equation in standard form.

$$x^2 + 5x - 84 = 0$$
$$(x + 12)(x - 7) = 0$$
$$x + 12 = 0 \qquad \text{or} \qquad x - 7 = 0$$
$$x = -12 \qquad\qquad x = 7$$

This is not a possible solution—the width can't be negative!

The only possible solution is 7 cm. The width of the rectangle is 7 cm, and the length is 12 cm.

Step 5 If the width is 7 cm and the length is 12 cm, the area is 84 cm^2. We have verified the solution.

● ● ● **CHECK YOURSELF 9**

The length of a rectangle is 3 inches (in.) more than twice its width. If the area of the rectangle is 90 in.^{2}, what are its dimensions?

● ● ● **CHECK YOURSELF ANSWERS**

1. $-3, 4$. **2.** $4, -2$. **3.** (a) $2, -\dfrac{1}{3}$; (b) $3, \dfrac{1}{2}$. **4.** (a) $0, -8$; (b) $0, 9$.

5. $5, -5$. **6.** $-3, -\dfrac{1}{2}$. **7.** 9 and 10 *or* -10 and -9. **8.** 1 or 6. **9.** Width, 6 in.; length, 15 in.

Solve each of the following quadratic equations.

1. $(x - 3)(x - 4) = 0$ **2.** $(x - 7)(x + 1) = 0$

3. $(3x + 1)(x - 6) = 0$ **4.** $(5x - 4)(x - 6) = 0$

5. $x^2 - 2x - 3 = 0$ **6.** $x^2 + 5x + 4 = 0$

7. $x^2 - 7x + 6 = 0$ **8.** $x^2 + 3x - 10 = 0$

9. $x^2 + 8x + 15 = 0$ **10.** $x^2 - 3x - 18 = 0$

11. $x^2 + 4x - 21 = 0$ **12.** $x^2 - 12x + 32 = 0$

13. $x^2 - 4x = 12$ **14.** $x^2 + 8x = -15$

15. $x^2 + 5x = 14$ **16.** $x^2 = 11x - 24$

17. $2x^2 + 5x - 3 = 0$ **18.** $3x^2 + 7x + 2 = 0$

19. $4x^2 - 24x + 35 = 0$ **20.** $6x^2 + 11x - 10 = 0$

21. $4x^2 + 11x = -6$ **22.** $5x^2 + 2x = 3$

Answers:
1. ___
2. ___
3. ___
4. ___
5. ___
6. ___
7. ___
8. ___
9. ___
10. ___
11. ___
12. ___
13. ___
14. ___
15. ___
16. ___
17. ___
18. ___
19. ___
20. ___
21. ___
22. ___

ANSWERS

23. _____

24. _____

25. _____

26. _____

27. _____

28. _____

29. _____

30. _____

31. _____

32. _____

33. _____

34. _____

35. _____

36. _____

37. _____

38. _____

39. _____

40. _____

41. _____

42. _____

43. _____

44. _____

45. _____

46. _____

47. _____

48. _____

49. _____

50. _____

23. $5x^2 + 13x = 6$

24. $4x^2 = 13x + 12$

25. $x^2 - 2x = 0$

26. $x^2 + 5x = 0$

27. $x^2 = -8x$

28. $x^2 = 7x$

29. $5x^2 - 15x = 0$

30. $4x^2 + 20x = 0$

31. $x^2 - 25 = 0$

32. $x^2 = 49$

33. $x^2 = 81$

34. $x^2 = 64$

35. $2x^2 - 18 = 0$

36. $3x^2 - 75 = 0$

37. $3x^2 + 24x + 45 = 0$

38. $4x^2 - 4x = 24$

39. $6x^2 + 28x = 10$

40. $15x^2 + 27x = 6$

41. $(x + 3)(x - 2) = 14$

42. $(x - 5)(x + 2) = 18$

Simplify each equation, label the equation as linear or quadratic, and then find all solutions.

43. $3x + 4 = 2x$

44. $3x + 4 = 2$

45. $(2x + 5)(x + 1) = 0$

46. $(2x + 5) + (x + 1) = 0$

47. $(2x - 1) - (x + 5) = 0$

48. $(2x - 1)(x + 5) = 13$

49. $x^2 + 4x - 5 = x^2$

50. $x^2 + 4x = 5$

330

51. $(x^2 + 2x - 3) + (x^2 + 10x - 29) = 0$ **52.** $x^2 + 2x - 3 = x^2 + 10x - 29$

53. $(x + 1)^2 = x^2 + 4$ **54.** $(2x + 1)^2 = 3x^2 + 13$

55. $x^2 - 3x - 5 = x + 7$ **56.** $x(x + 1) = (x + 2)^2$

Translate each of the following statements to an equation. Let x represent the number in each case.

57. The square of a number minus 3 times that same number is 4.

58. The sum of the square of a number and 5 times that same number is 14.

59. If 4 times a number is added to the square of that same number, the sum is 12.

60. If a number is subtracted from 3 times the square of that number, the difference is 2.

Solve each of the following word problems. Be sure to show the equations used.

61. Integers. One integer is 5 less than another. If the product of the numbers is 66, find the numbers.

62. Integers. One integer is 7 more than another. If the product of the numbers is 60, find the two numbers.

63. Integers. One integer is 1 less than twice another. If the product of the integers is 120, what are the two integers?

64. Integers. One integer is 2 more than 3 times another. If the product of the integers is 56, find the two integers.

65. Consecutive integers. The product of two consecutive integers is 132. Find the two integers.

66. Consecutive integers. If the product of two consecutive positive even integers is 120, find the two integers.

67. Integers. The sum of an integer and its square is 72. What is the integer?

68. Integers. The square of an integer is 56 more than the integer. Find the integer.

ANSWERS

51. _____
52. _____
53. _____
54. _____
55. _____
56. _____
57. _____
58. _____
59. _____
60. _____
61. _____
62. _____
63. _____
64. _____
65. _____
66. _____
67. _____
68. _____

69.

70.

71.

72.

73.

74.

75.

76.

77.

78.

79.

80.

81.

82.

69. Integers. The square of an integer is 20 more than 8 times the integer. What is the integer?

70. Integers. An integer is added to 3 times its square. The sum is 52. What is the integer?

71. Integers. If 2 times the square of an integer is increased by that integer, the sum is 55. Find the integer.

72. Integer. If the square of an integer is 21 less than 10 times that integer, what is the integer?

73. Positive integers. One positive integer is 1 more than twice another. If the difference of their squares is 65, what are the two integers?

74. Positive integers. One positive integer is 3 less than twice another. If the difference in their squares is 24, find the two integers.

75. Consecutive integers. The sum of the squares of two consecutive positive even integers is 100. Find the two integers.

76. Consecutive integers. If the product of two consecutive positive odd integers is 63, find the two integers.

77. Sum of squares. If the sum of the squares of two consecutive integers is 61, find the integers.

78. Sum of squares. The sum of the squares of two consecutive positive even integers is 164. Find the numbers.

79. Sum of squares. The sum of the squares of three consecutive positive odd integers is 83. What are the integers?

80. Sum of squares. The sum of the squares of three consecutive integers is 50. Find the three integers.

81. Positive integers. Twice the square of a positive integer is 12 more than 5 times the integer. Find the integer.

82. Integers. Find an integer such that 10 more than the square of the integer is 40 more than the integer.

© 1998 McGraw-Hill Companies

83. Dimensions of a rectangle. The length of a rectangle is 8 feet (ft) longer than its width. If the area of the rectangle is 65 square feet (ft^2), what are the dimensions of the rectangle?

84. Dimensions of a rectangle. The length of a rectangle is 4 centimeters (cm) longer than its width. If the area of the rectangle is 140 cm^2, find the length and width of the rectangle.

85. Dimensions of a rectangle. The width of a rectangle is 3 ft less than its length. If the area of the rectangle is 70 ft^2, what are the dimensions of the rectangle?

86. Dimensions of a rectangle. The length of a rectangle is 5 cm more than its width. If the area of the rectangle is 150 cm^2, find the dimensions of the rectangle.

87. Dimensions of a rectangle. The length of a rectangle is 1 inch (in.) longer than twice its width. If the area of the rectangle is 105 in.^{2}, what are the dimensions of the rectangle?

88. Dimensions of a rectangle. The length of a rectangle is 2 cm less than 3 times its width. If the area of the rectangle is 40 cm^2, find the dimensions of the rectangle.

89. Geometry. If the sides of a square are increased by 3 in., the area is increased by 39 in.^{2}. What were the dimensions of the original rectangle?

90. Geometry. If the sides of a square are decreased by 2 cm, the area is decreased by 36 cm^2. What were the dimensions of the original square?

91. Business. The profit on a small appliance is given by $P = x^2 - 3x - 60$, where x is the number of appliances sold per day. How many appliances were sold on a day when there was a $20 loss?

92. Business. The relationship between the number x of calculators that a company can sell per month and the price of each calculator p is given by $x = 1700 - 100p$. Find the price at which a calculator should be sold to produce a monthly revenue of $7000. (*Hint:* Revenue $= xp$.)

83. _____

84. _____

85. _____

86. _____

87. _____

88. _____

89. _____

90. _____

91. _____

92. _____

93.

94.

a.

b.

c.

d.

e.

f.

93. Write a short comparison that explains the difference between $ax^2 + bx + c$ and $ax^2 + bx + c = 0$.

94. When solving quadratic equations, some people try to solve an equation in the manner shown below, but this doesn't work! Write a paragraph to explain what is wrong with this approach.

$$2x^2 + 7x + 3 = 52$$

$$(2x + 1)(x + 3) = 52$$

$$2x + 1 = 52 \text{ or } x + 3 = 52$$

$$x = \frac{51}{2} \quad \text{or} \quad x = 49$$

● Getting Ready for Section 5.6 [Section 3.4]

Solve each of the following equations for the indicated variable.

a. $2x - 3y = 12$ (for y)

b. $V - E + F = 2$ (for E)

c. $S = 2\pi rh$ (for h)

d. $s = \frac{1}{2}gt^2$ (for g)

e. $S = b^2 + \frac{1}{2}hb$ (for h)

f. $S = \pi r^2 + 2\pi rh$ (for h)

Answers

1. $3, 4$ **3.** $-\frac{1}{3}, 6$ **5.** $-1, 3$ **7.** $1, 6$ **9.** $-3, -5$ **11.** $-7, 3$

13. $-2, 6$ **15.** $-7, 2$ **17.** $-3, \frac{1}{2}$ **19.** $\frac{5}{2}, \frac{7}{2}$ **21.** $-\frac{3}{4}, -2$

23. $-3, \frac{2}{5}$ **25.** $0, 2$ **27.** $0, -8$ **29.** $0, 3$ **31.** $-5, 5$ **33.** $-9, 9$

35. $-3, 3$ **37.** $-5, -3$ **39.** $-5, \frac{1}{3}$ **41.** $4, -5$ **43.** Linear; -4

45. Quadratic; $-\frac{5}{2}, -1$ **47.** Linear; 6 **49.** Linear; $\frac{5}{4}$

51. Quadratic; $-8, 2$ **53.** Linear; $\frac{3}{2}$ **55.** Quadratic; $-2, 6$

57. $x^2 - 3x = 4$ **59.** $x^2 + 4x = 12$ **61.** $6, 11$ or $-6, -11$ **63.** $8, 15$

65. $11, 12$ or $-12, -11$ **67.** -9 or 8 **69.** -2 or 10 **71.** 5 **73.** $4, 9$

75. $6, 8$ **77.** $-6, -5$ or $5, 6$ **79.** $3, 5, 7$ **81.** 4 **83.** 5 ft by 13 ft

85. 7 ft by 10 ft **87.** 7 in. by 15 in. **89.** 5 in. by 5 in. **91.** 8

a. $\frac{2(x - 6)}{3}$ **b.** $V + F - 2$ **c.** $\frac{S}{2\pi r}$ **d.** $\frac{2s}{t^2}$ **e.** $\frac{2S - 2b^2}{b}$

f. $\frac{S - \pi r^2}{2\pi r}$

5.6 More on Literal Equations

5.6 OBJECTIVES

1. Solve literal equations involving parentheses
2. Solve literal equations by factoring

In Section 3.4 you worked with literal equations. You solved the literal equations for some particular letter. You will work with similar equations in this section.

• Example 1

Solving a Literal Equation

Solve

You may recognize this as the formula for the area of a trapezoid.

$$A = \frac{h}{2}(B + b)$$

for B.

In this case the best first step is to multiply both sides of the equation by 2 to clear fractions.

$$2A = 2 \cdot \frac{h}{2}(B + b)$$

$$2A = h(B + b) \qquad \text{Now remove the parentheses.}$$

$$2A = hB + hb$$

Remember that we want to isolate B on one side. It makes no difference whether B is on the left or the right.

$$2A - hb = hB \qquad \text{Subtract } hb \text{ from both sides.}$$

$$\frac{2A - hb}{h} = \frac{hB}{h} \qquad \text{Divide by } h \text{ to isolate } B.$$

$$\frac{2A - hb}{h} = B \qquad B = \frac{2A - hb}{h}$$

● ● ● CHECK YOURSELF 1

Solve $S = \frac{n}{2}(a + t)$ for a.

Solving literal equations may also require that you factor to isolate the specified letter. This will be the case whenever the letter that you are solving for appears in more than one term.

• Example 2

Solving a Literal Equation

Solve $ax = bx + ab$ for x.

First, subtract bx from both sides.

$$\underbrace{ax - bx}_{\uparrow} = ab$$

All terms with x are now on the left.

Since x appears in more than one term, factor.

$$x(a - b) = ab$$

Now divide both sides by $a - b$ to isolate x.

$$\frac{x(a - b)}{a - b} = \frac{ab}{a - b}$$

so

$$x = \frac{ab}{a - b}$$

●●● **CHECK YOURSELF 2**

Solve $my = mn - ny$ for y.

The following series of steps summarizes our work in solving literal equations.

To Solve a Literal Equation

STEP 1 If necessary, multiply both sides of the equation by the same factor to clear fractions.
STEP 2 Remove any parentheses by multiplying.
STEP 3 Add or subtract the same terms on both sides so that all terms involving the variable you are solving for are on one side of the equation and all other terms are on the opposite side.
STEP 4 Factor if the variable you are solving for appears in more than one term.
STEP 5 Divide both sides of the equation by the same expression to isolate the variable you are solving for.

●●● **CHECK YOURSELF ANSWERS**

1. $a = \dfrac{2S - nt}{n}$. **2.** $y = \dfrac{mn}{m + n}$.

Solve each of the following equations for the indicated variable.

1. $a(x - y) = 3$ for x

2. $m(n + p) = 5$ for p

3. $P = 2(L + W)$ for L

4. $r = 3(s - t)$ for s

5. $C = \dfrac{5}{9}(F - 32)$ for F

6. $s = \dfrac{2}{3}(a + b)$ for b

7. $ax + bx = c$ for x

8. $my - ny = p$ for y

9. $am = bm + n$ for m

10. $pq = p - 2q$ for q

11. $m(a - b) = ab$ for b

12. $s(t + v) = tv$ for t

13. $m = \dfrac{a - b}{b}$ for b

14. $s = \dfrac{c + d}{d}$ for d

15. $t = a + (n - 1)d$ for n

16. $L = a(1 + ct)$ for c

17. $S = C - rC$ for C

18. $S = C + rC$ for C

19. $A = \dfrac{1}{2}h(B + b)$ for b

20. $A = P(1 + rt)$ for t

1. _____
2. _____
3. _____
4. _____
5. _____
6. _____
7. _____
8. _____
9. _____
10. _____
11. _____
12. _____
13. _____
14. _____
15. _____
16. _____
17. _____
18. _____
19. _____
20. _____

21. Temperature. The efficient burning of fossil fuel is necessary to minimize the amount of air pollution caused by unburned fuel. Burning efficiency is related to the temperature at which the fuel is burned. If the most efficient temperature to burn coal in a large power plant is 1500° Celsius, what is this temperature in degrees Fahrenheit? $\left[C = \left(\dfrac{5}{9}\right)(F - 32).\right]$

22. Temperature. An automobile emits the least pollution when it is properly tuned because the fuel is being burned at the proper temperature and pressure. If your car burns most efficiently at 1700° Celsius, what is this temperature in degrees Fahrenheit? (See formula in Exercise 21 above.)

23. Scrubber height. The scrubber on the stack of a power plant is to be in the shape of a cylinder. It is to have a capacity of 200 cubic meters (m^3) of gas per minute. If it must fit a stack with a radius of 5 m, how high must the scrubber be?

24. Scrubber height. The scrubber on the stack of a power plant is to be in the shape of a cylinder. It is to have a capacity of 175 m^3 of gas per minute. If it must fit a stack with a radius of 4 m, how high must the scrubber be?

Getting Ready for Section 5.7 [Section 3.4]

Solve each of the following equations for the indicated variable.

a. $y = kx$ for k

b. $y = \dfrac{k}{x^2}$ for k

c. $V = cr^3$ for c

d. $V = ctn$ for t

e. $A = \dfrac{1}{2}bh$ for b

f. $V = \dfrac{1}{3}\pi r^2 h$ for h

Answers

1. $x = \dfrac{3 + ay}{a}$ **3.** $L = \dfrac{P - 2W}{2}$ **5.** $F = \dfrac{9C + 160}{5}$ **7.** $x = \dfrac{c}{a + b}$

9. $m = \dfrac{n}{a - b}$ **11.** $b = \dfrac{am}{a + m}$ **13.** $b = \dfrac{a}{m + 1}$ **15.** $n = \dfrac{t - a + d}{d}$

17. $C = \dfrac{S}{1 - r}$ **19.** $b = \dfrac{2A - hB}{h}$ **21.** 2732°F   **23.** ≈ 2.55 m

a. $k = \dfrac{y}{x}$ **b.** $k = yx^2$ **c.** $c = \dfrac{V}{r^3}$ **d.** $t = \dfrac{V}{cn}$ **e.** $b = \dfrac{2A}{h}$

f. $h = \dfrac{3V}{\pi r^2}$

Direct and Inverse Variation

5.7 OBJECTIVES

1. Write an equation for a variation
2. Solve problems of direct variation
3. Solve problems of indirect variation

Pedro makes $25 an hour as an electrician. If he works 1 hour, he makes $25; if he works 2 hours, he makes $50; and so on. We say his total pay **varies directly** with the number of hours worked.

Direct Variation

If y is a constant multiple of x, we write

$y = kx$ where k is a constant

We say that y *varies directly* as x, or that y is *directly proportional* to x. The constant k is called the **constant of variation.**

● Example 1

Writing an Equation for Direct Variation

Marina earns $9 an hour as a tutor. Write the equation that describes the relationship between the number of hours she works and her pay.

Her pay (P) is equal to the rate of pay (r) times the number of hours worked (h), so

$$P = r \cdot h \qquad \text{or} \qquad P = 9h$$

● ● ● CHECK YOURSELF 1

Sorina is driving at a constant rate of 50 m/h. Write the equation that shows the distance she travels (d) in h hours.

Remember that k is the constant of variation.

If two things vary directly and values are given for x and y, we can find k. This property is illustrated in Example 2.

● Example 2

Finding the Constant of Variation

If y varies directly with x, and $y = 30$ when $x = 6$, find k.

Since y varies directly with x, we know from the definition that

$$y = kx$$

We need to find k. We do this by substituting 30 for y and 6 for x.

$$30 = k(6) \qquad \text{or} \qquad k = 5$$

● ● ● **CHECK YOURSELF 2**

If y varies directly with x and $y = 100$ when $x = 25$, find the constant of variation.

If two quantities are related so that an *increase* in the value of the first gives a proportional *decrease* in the value of the second, we say the variables **vary inversely** with each other.

Inverse Variation

If y varies *inversely as x*, we write

$$y = \frac{k}{x} \qquad \text{where } k \text{ is a constant}$$

We also say y is *inversely proportional* to x.

● Example 3

Finding the Constant of Variation

If y varies inversely as x, and $y = 18$ when $x = \dfrac{1}{2}$, find the constant of variation. From the definition, we have

$$y = \frac{k}{x}$$

Substituting 18 for y and $\dfrac{1}{2}$ for x, we get

$$18 = \frac{k}{\dfrac{1}{2}} \qquad \text{or} \qquad k = 9$$

● ● ● **CHECK YOURSELF 3**

If y varies inversely as x, and $y = 35$ when $x = 4$, find the constant of variation.

● ● ● **CHECK YOURSELF ANSWERS**

1. $d = 50\,h$ **2.** $k = 4$ or $y = 4x$ **3.** $k = 140$ or $y = \dfrac{140}{x}$

A N S W E R S

1. **Salary.** Robin earns $12 per hour (h). How much does she earn in 8 h?

2. **Salary.** Kwang earns $9.50 per hour. How much does he earn in 40 h?

3. **Distance traveled.** Lee is traveling at a constant rate of 55 miles per hour (mi/h). How far does she travel in 8 h?

4. **Distance traveled.** An airplane is traveling at a constant rate of 450 mi/h. How far does it travel in 7 h?

Translate each of the following statements of variation to an algebraic equation using k as the constant of variation.

5. s varies directly as x

6. r is inversely proportional to s

7. V is directly proportional to t

8. m varies indirectly as n

9. y varies indirectly as the square of x

10. V varies directly as the cube of r

Find k, the constant of variation.

11. y varies directly with x; $y = 54$ when $x = 6$

12. m varies directly with n; $m = 144$ when $n = 8$

13. V is directly proportional to h; $V = 189$ when $h = 9$

14. d is directly proportional to t; $d = 750$ when $t = 15$

1. _____

2. _____

3. _____

4. _____

5. _____

6. _____

7. _____

8. _____

9. _____

10. _____

11. _____

12. _____

13. _____

14. _____

341

15. m varies inversely as p; $m = 20$ when $p = 2.5$

16. y varies inversely as x; $y = 12$ when $x = \dfrac{1}{2}$

17. w is inversely proportional to t; $w = 3$ when $t = 12$

18. r is inversely proportional to t; $r = \dfrac{1}{2}$ when $t = 14$

Answers

1. $96   **3.** 440 mi   **5.** $s = kx$ **7.** $V = kt$ **9.** $y = \dfrac{k}{x^2}$ **11.** $k = 9$

13. $k = 21$ **15.** $k = 50$ **17.** $k = 36$

Summary

Common-Term Factoring [5.1]

$4x^2$ is the greatest common monomial factor of $8x^4 - 12x^3 + 16x^2$.

Common Monomial Factor A single term that is a factor of every term of the polynomial. The greatest common factor (GCF) is the common monomial factor that has the largest possible numerical coefficient and the largest possible exponents.

Factoring a Monomial from a Polynomial

$8x^4 - 12x^3 + 16x^2$
$= 4x^2(2x^2 - 3x + 4)$

1. Determine the greatest common factor.
2. Apply the distributive law in the form

$$ab + ac = a(b + c)$$
$\uparrow$
The greatest common factor

The Difference of Squares [5.2]

To factor: $16x^2 - 25y^2$:
$\quad\quad\quad\downarrow\quad\quad\downarrow$
Think: $\quad(4x)^2 - (5y)^2$
so

Factoring a Difference of Squares Use the following form:

$$a^2 - b^2 = (a + b)(a - b)$$

$16x^2 - 25y^2$
$= (4x + 5y)(4x - 5y)$

Factoring Trinomials [5.3 and 5.4]

$4x^2 - 6x + 10x - 15$
$= 2x(2x - 3) + 5(2x - 3)$
$= (2x - 3)(2x + 5)$

Factoring by Grouping When there are four terms of a polynomial, factor the first pair and factor the last pair. If these two pairs have a common binomial factor, factor that out. The result will be the product of two binomials.

$x^2 + 3x - 28$
$ac = -28; b = 3$
$mn = -28; m + n = 3$
$m = 7, n = -4$
$x^2 + 7x - 4x - 28$
$= x(x + 7) - 4(x + 7)$

Factoring Trinomials To factor a trinomial, first use the *ac* test to determine factorability. If the trinomial is factorable, the *ac* test will yield two terms (which have as their sum the middle term) that allow the factoring to be completed by using the grouping method.

Solving Equations by Factoring [5.5]

1. Add or subtract the necessary terms on both sides of the equation so that the equation is in standard form (set equal to 0).

To solve:
$\quad\quad x^2 + 7x = 30$
$\quad x^2 + 7x - 30 = 0$
$(x + 10)(x - 3) = 0$

$x + 10 = 0 \quad$ or $\quad x - 3 = 0$
$x = -10$ and $x = 3$ are solutions.

2. Factor the quadratic expression.
3. Set each factor equal to 0.
4. Solve the resulting equations to find the solutions.
5. Check each solution by substituting in the original equation.

Solving Literal Equations [5.6]

To solve:

$$x = \frac{a + b}{a} \quad \text{for } a$$

$$ax = a + b$$

$$ax - a = b$$

1. If necessary, multiply both sides of the equation by the same term to clear fractions.
2. Remove any parentheses by multiplying.
3. Add or subtract the same terms on both sides so that all terms involving the variable you are solving for are on one side of the equation and all other terms are on the opposite side.
4. Factor if the variable you are solving for appears in more than one term.
5. Divide both sides of the equation by the same expression to isolate the specified variable.

$$a(x - 1) = b$$

$$\frac{a(x - 1)}{x - 1} = \frac{b}{x - 1}$$

$$a = \frac{b}{x - 1}$$

Direct and Inverse Variation [5.7]

Direct Variation If y is a constant multiple of x, we write

y varies directly to x

$y = 45$ when $x = 9$

$y = kx$, so

$$y = kx \quad \text{where } k \text{ is a constant}$$

$$45 = k \cdot 9$$

$$k = 5$$

We say that y *varies directly* as x, or that y is *directly proportional* to x. The constant k is called the constant of variation.

Inverse Variation If y varies *inversely* as x, we write

y varies inversely to x

$y = 5$ when $x = 6$

$y = \dfrac{k}{x}$, so

$$y = \frac{k}{x} \quad k \text{ is a constant}$$

$$5 = \frac{k}{6}$$

$$k = 30$$

We also say y is *inversely proportional* to x.

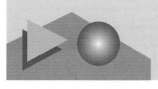
This summary exercise set is provided to give you practice with each of the objectives of the chapter. Each exercise is keyed to the appropriate chapter section. The answers are provided in the *Instructor's Manual*. Your instructor will give you guidelines on how to best use these exercises in your instructional setting.

[5.1] Factor each of the following polynomials.

1. $18a + 24$

2. $9m^2 - 21m$

3. $24s^2t - 16s^2$

4. $18a^2b + 36ab^2$

5. $35s^3 - 28s^2$

6. $3x^3 - 6x^2 + 15x$

7. $18m^2n^2 - 27m^2n + 45m^2n^3$

8. $121x^8y^3 + 77x^6y^3$

9. $8a^2b + 24ab - 16ab^2$

10. $3x^2y - 6xy^3 + 9x^3y - 12xy^2$

11. $x(2x - y) + y(2x - y)$

12. $5(w - 3z) - w(w - 3z)$

[5.2] Factor each of the following binomials completely.

13. $p^2 - 49$

14. $25a^2 - 16$

15. $m^2 - 9n^2$

16. $16r^2 - 49s^2$

17. $25 - z^2$

18. $a^4 - 16b^2$

19. $25a^2 - 36b^2$

20. $x^6 - 4y^2$

21. $3w^3 - 12wz^2$

22. $16a^4 - 49b^2$

23. $2m^2 - 72n^4$

24. $3w^3z - 12wz^3$

[5.3]   Factor the following polynomials completely.

25. $x^2 - 4x + 5x - 20$

26. $x^2 + 7x - 2x - 14$

27. $6x^2 + 4x - 15x - 10$

28. $12x^2 - 9x - 28x + 21$

29. $6x^3 + 9x^2 - 4x^2 - 6x$

30. $3x^4 + 6x^3 + 5x^3 + 10x^2$

[5.4]   Factor each of the following trinomials completely.

31. $x^2 + 9x + 20$

32. $x^2 - 10x + 24$

33. $a^2 - a - 12$

34. $w^2 - 13w + 40$

35. $x^2 + 12x + 36$

36. $r^2 - 9r - 36$

37. $b^2 - 4bc - 21c^2$

38. $m^2n + 4mn - 32n$

39. $m^3 + 2m^2 - 35m$

40. $2x^2 - 2x - 40$

41. $3y^3 - 48y^2 + 189y$

42. $3b^3 - 15b^2 - 42b$

43. $3x^2 + 8x + 5$

44. $5w^2 + 13w - 6$

45. $2b^2 - 9b + 9$

46. $8x^2 + 2x - 3$

47. $10x^2 - 11x + 3$

48. $4a^2 + 7a - 15$

49. $9y^2 - 3yz - 20z^2$

50. $8x^2 + 14xy - 15y^2$

51. $8x^3 - 36x^2 - 20x$

52. $9x^2 - 15x - 6$

53. $6x^3 - 3x^2 - 9x$

54. $5w^2 - 25wz + 30z^2$

[5.5]   Solve each of the following quadratic equations.

55. $(x - 1)(2x + 3) = 0$

56. $x^2 - 5x + 6 = 0$

57. $x^2 - 10x = 0$

58. $x^2 = 144$

59. $x^2 - 2x = 15$

60. $3x^2 - 5x - 2 = 0$

61. $4x^2 - 13x + 10 = 0$

62. $2x^2 - 3x = 5$

63. $3x^2 - 9x = 0$

64. $x^2 - 25 = 0$

65. $2x^2 - 32 = 0$

66. $2x^2 - x - 3 = 0$

[5.5] Solve each of the following applications. Be sure to show the equation used for the solution.

67. One integer is 8 less than another. If the product of the two integers is 84, what are the two integers?

68. The length of a rectangle is 3 centimeters (cm) less than twice its width, and the area of that rectangle is 35 cm². Find the length and width of the rectangle.

69. The sides of a square are increased by 3 feet (ft), and this increases the area of the square by 33 ft². What was the length of a side of the original square?

[5.6] Solve each equation for the indicated variable.

70. $A = P(1 + rt)$ for t **71.** $A = \dfrac{1}{2}h(B + b)$ for B **72.** $p = \dfrac{x - y}{y}$ for y

[5.7] Solve for k, the constant of variation.

73. y varies directly as x; $y = 20$ when $x = 40$

74. y varies inversely as x; $y = 5$ when $x = 3$

The purpose of this self-test is to help you check your progress and to review for a chapter test in class. Allow yourself about an hour to take the test. When you are done, check your answers in the back of the book. If you missed any answers, be sure to go back and review the appropriate sections in the chapter and the exercises that are provided.

Factor each of the following polynomials.

1. $12b + 18$

2. $9p^3 - 12p^2$

3. $5x^2 - 10x + 20$

4. $6a^2b - 18ab + 12ab^2$

Factor each of the following polynomials completely.

5. $a^2 - 25$

6. $64m^2 - n^2$

7. $49x^2 - 16y^2$

8. $32a^2b - 50b^3$

Factor each of the following polynomials completely.

9. $a^2 - 5a - 14$

10. $b^2 + 8b + 15$

11. $x^2 - 11x + 28$

12. $y^2 + 12yz + 20z^2$

13. $x^2 + 2x - 5x - 10$

14. $6x^2 + 2x - 9x - 3$

15. _____

16. _____

17. _____

18. _____

19. _____

20. _____

21. _____

22. _____

23. _____

24. _____

25. _____

26. _____

27. _____

Factor each of the following polynomials completely.

15. $2x^2 + 15x - 8$

16. $3w^2 + 10w + 7$

17. $8x^2 - 2xy - 3y^2$

18. $6x^3 + 3x^2 - 30x$

Solve each of the following equations for x.

19. $x^2 - 8x + 15 = 0$

20. $x^2 - 3x = 4$

21. $3x^2 + x - 2 = 0$

22. $4x^2 - 12x = 0$

Solve the following word problems.

23. One integer is 3 less than twice another. If the product of the integers is 35, what are the two integers?

24. The length of a rectangle is 2 cm more than 3 times its width. If the area of the rectangle is 33 cm^2, what are the dimensions of the rectangle?

Solve for the variable listed after each of the following equations.

25. $P = 2(L + W)$ for W

26. $a = \dfrac{b + c}{c}$ for c

27. If m varies inversely with n and $m = 3$ when $n = 6$, find k, the constant of variation.

This test covers selected topics from the first five chapters.

Simplify the expression.

1. $7x^2y + 3xy - 5x^2y + 2xy$

2. $\dfrac{27a^5b^7}{9ab}$

3. $(3x^2 - 2x + 5) + (x^2 + 3x - 2)$

4. $(5x^2 + 4x - 3) - (4x^2 - 5x - 1)$

Evaluate the expression.

5. $3(5 - 2)^2$

6. $|3| - |-4|$

Multiply.

7. $(a - 3b)(a + 3b)$

8. $(x - 2y)^2$

9. $(x - 2)(x + 5)$

10. $(a - 3)(a + 4)$

Divide.

11. $(9x^2 + 12x + 4) \div (3x + 2)$

12. $(3x^2 - 2) \div (x - 1)$

Evaluate each expression where $x = 3$, $y = -5$, and $z = 2$.

13. $\dfrac{(x^2yz)^{-3}}{x^{-6}y^{-5}z^{-3}}$

14. $\dfrac{2x + y}{y + z}$

Solve each equation and check your results.

15. $7a - 3 = 6a + 8$

16. $\dfrac{2}{3}x = -22$

17. $x + 2 = 2x + 4$

18. $x^2 - 3x = x^2 + 9$

19. $x^2 + x - 6 = 0$

20. $2x^2 - 17x + 30 = 0$

Factor each of the following expressions.

21. $12x + 20$

22. $25x^2 - 49y^2$

23. $12x^2 - 15x + 8x - 10$

24. $2x^2 - 13x + 15$

Solve the following word problems. Show the equation used for the solution.

25. 3 times a number decreased by 5 is 46. Find the number.

26. Juan's biology text cost $5 more than his mathematics text. Together they cost $81. Find the cost of the biology text.

27. A store owner finds that his daily profit is given by $P = n^2 - 10n - 50$, where n is the number of shirts sold. How many shirts must be sold for a profit of $325?

28. The square of a number plus 7 times the number is 44. Find the number.

29. Solve for the variable listed: $C = \dfrac{5}{9}(F - 32)$ for F.

30. If w varies inversely as t and $w = 4$ when $t = 7$, find k, the constant of variation.

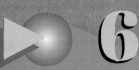

CHAPTER 6

ALGEBRAIC FRACTIONS

INTRODUCTION

In the United States, disorders of the heart and circulatory system kill more people than all other causes combined. The major risk factors for heart disease are smoking, high blood pressure, obesity, cholesterol over 240, and a family history of heart problems. Although nothing can be done about family history, everyone can affect the first four risk factors by diet and exercise.

One quick way to check your risk of heart problems is to compare your waist and hip measurements. Measure around your waist at the naval and around your hips at the largest point. These measures may be in inches or centimeters. Use the ratio w/h to assess your risk. For women, $w/h \geq 0.8$ indicates an increased health risk, and for men, $w/h \geq 0.95$ is the indicator of an increased risk.

The American Medical Association sponsored a study using Body Mass Index, or BMI, which used height and weight measurements:

$$BMI = \frac{705w}{h^2}$$

where w = weight in pounds

h = height in inches

This study concluded that people with BMI ≤ 21 had the lowest rates of heart disease, and that an increase of only 2 points in the BMI dramatically raises the risk of heart problems.

Medical professionals and researchers continue to disagree about how accurate these indicators are since each is a statistical average. One issue is how well the measures relate to the percentage of total body fat. A person may have a relatively low percentage of body fat and be in excellent health but have a BMI over 21 because of a very muscular build or large bone structure.

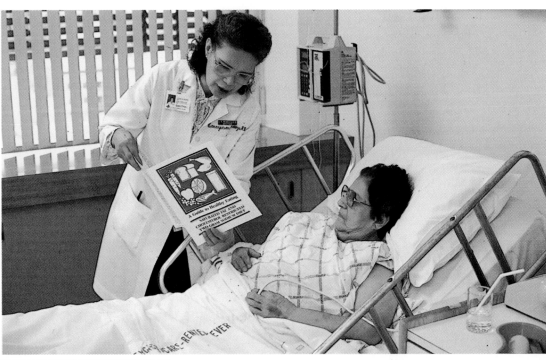

© David Young Wolff / Tony Stone Worldwide, Ltd.

Algebraic Fractions— An Introduction

6.1

6.1 OBJECTIVES

1. Review the language of fractions
2. Determine the excluded values for the variables of algebraic fraction

Algebraic fractions are also called **rational expressions.** Note the similarity to rational numbers.

In arithmetic you learned about fractions, or rational numbers. Recall that a rational number is the quotient of two integers $\frac{p}{q}$, where q is not equal to 0. For example,

$$\frac{2}{3} \qquad -\frac{4}{5} \qquad \frac{12}{7} \qquad \frac{5}{1}$$

are all rational numbers. We now want to extend the idea of fractions to algebra. All that you learned in arithmetic about fractions will be very helpful here.

An **algebraic fraction** is an expression of the form

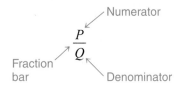

where P and Q are polynomials and Q cannot have the value 0.

The condition that Q, the polynomial in the denominator, cannot be 0 means that certain values for the variable will have to be excluded. Recall that a divisor (the denominator here) cannot have the value 0, or else the division is undefined. See Section 2.5 for details.

Use your calculator to confirm that division by zero is undefined. Compare $0 \div 5$, then try $5 \div 0$. How does your calculator tell you that division by zero is undefined?

● Example 1

Finding Excluded Values for *x*

In the following algebraic fractions, what values for x must be excluded?

(*a*) $\frac{x}{5}$. Here x can have any value, so none need to be excluded.

(*b*) $\frac{3}{x}$. If $x = 0$, then $\frac{3}{x}$ is undefined; 0 is the excluded value.

(*c*) $\frac{5}{x-2}$. If $x = 2$, then $\frac{5}{x-2} = \frac{5}{2-2} = \frac{5}{0}$, which is undefined, so 2 is the excluded value.

354

●●● **CHECK YOURSELF 1**

What values for x, if any, must be excluded?

a. $\dfrac{x}{7}$ **b.** $\dfrac{5}{x}$ **c.** $\dfrac{7}{x-5}$

If the denominator of an algebraic fraction contains a product of two or more variable factors, the zero-product principle must be used to determine the excluded values for the variable.

●Example 2

What values of x must be excluded in each fraction?

Again, if $x + 3 = 0$
$$x = -3$$
or if $x - 4 = 0$
$$x = 4$$

(a) $\dfrac{4}{(x+3)(x-4)}$. If $x = -3$, then

$$\frac{4}{(x+3)(x-4)} = \frac{4}{(-3+3)(-3-4)} = \frac{4}{0 \cdot -7} = \frac{4}{0}$$

which is undefined. Try $x = 4$; you will see that the same thing happens.
    Both -3 and 4 will make the denominator 0 and must be excluded.

(b) $\dfrac{5}{(x-1)(2x+3)}$

The denominator will be zero if $x - 1 = 0$ or if $2x + 3 = 0$.

If $x - 1 = 0$, then

$x = 1$

If $2x + 3 = 0$,

then $x = -\dfrac{3}{2}$

The excluded values are 1 and $-\dfrac{3}{2}$.

●●● **CHECK YOURSELF 2**

What values of x must be excluded in each algebraic fraction?

a. $\dfrac{2x}{(x-6)(x+1)}$ **b.** $\dfrac{3}{(3x-1)(x+5)}$

In some cases, you will have to factor the denominator to see the restrictions on the values for the variable.

• Example 3

Finding Excluded Values for *x*

What values for x must be excluded in each fraction?

(a) $\dfrac{3}{x^2 - 6x - 16}$

Factoring the denominator, we have

$$\frac{3}{x^2 - 6x - 16} = \frac{3}{(x - 8)(x + 2)}$$

Letting $x - 8 = 0$ or $x + 2 = 0$, we see that 8 and -2 make the denominator 0 so both 8 and -2 must be excluded.

(b) $\dfrac{3}{(x^2 + 2x - 48)}$

The denominator is zero when

$$x^2 + 2x - 48 = 0$$

Factoring, we find

$$(x - 6)(x + 8) = 0$$

The denominator is zero when

$$x = 6 \qquad \text{or} \qquad x = -8$$

● ● ● CHECK YOURSELF 3

What values for x must be excluded in the following fraction?

a. $\dfrac{5}{x^2 - 3x - 10}$
b. $\dfrac{7}{x^2 + 5x - 14}$

● ● ● CHECK YOURSELF ANSWERS

1. (a) None; **(b)** 0; **(c)** 5.   **2. (a)** 6, -1; **(b)** $\dfrac{1}{3}$, -5.

3. (a) 5 and -2; **(b)** 2 and -7.

6.1 Exercises

What values for x, if any, must be excluded in each of the following algebraic fractions?

1. $\dfrac{x}{15}$

2. $\dfrac{8}{x}$

3. $\dfrac{17}{x}$

4. $\dfrac{x}{8}$

5. $\dfrac{3}{x - 2}$

6. $\dfrac{x - 1}{5}$

7. $\dfrac{-5}{x + 4}$

8. $\dfrac{4}{x + 3}$

9. $\dfrac{x - 5}{2}$

10. $\dfrac{x - 1}{x - 5}$

11. $\dfrac{3x}{(x + 1)(x - 2)}$

12. $\dfrac{5x}{(x - 3)(x + 7)}$

13. $\dfrac{x - 1}{(2x - 1)(x + 3)}$

14. $\dfrac{x + 3}{(3x + 1)(x - 2)}$

15. $\dfrac{7}{x^2 - 9}$

16. $\dfrac{5x}{x^2 + x - 2}$

17. $\dfrac{x + 3}{x^2 - 7x + 12}$

18. $\dfrac{3x - 4}{x^2 - 49}$

19. $\dfrac{2x - 1}{3x^2 + x - 2}$

20. $\dfrac{3x + 1}{4x^2 - 11x + 6}$

1. _____
2. _____
3. _____
4. _____
5. _____
6. _____
7. _____
8. _____
9. _____
10. _____
11. _____
12. _____
13. _____
14. _____
15. _____
16. _____
17. _____
18. _____
19. _____
20. _____

What values for x must be excluded in each denominator?

21. $\dfrac{15}{x - y}$ 　　　　　　　　**22.** $\dfrac{x + 3y}{3x + y}$

23. $\dfrac{14 + y}{2x - y}$ 　　　　　　　**24.** $\dfrac{8}{x + y}$

25. (a) Write the value of the fraction $\dfrac{5}{n}$ when $n = 1, 2, 3, 4, 5, 6, 7, 8, \ldots$

What happens to the fraction as n gets larger? How large can n get? What do you think will eventually happen to this fraction?

(b) Write the value of the fraction $\dfrac{5}{n}$ when $n = 1, 0.5, 0.4, 0.3, 0.2, 0.1, 0.05,$ $0.04, 0.03, \ldots$

What happens to the fraction as n gets smaller? How small can n get? What do you think will eventually happen to this fraction?

26. Explain the reasoning involved in each step of reducing the fraction $\dfrac{42}{56}$.

27. Describe why $\dfrac{3}{5}$ and $\dfrac{27}{45}$ are *equivalent fractions*.

● Getting Ready for Section 6.2 [Section 4.1]

Divide.

a. $\dfrac{12a}{3}$ 　　　**b.** $\dfrac{35w}{7}$ 　　　**c.** $\dfrac{15c^5}{3c^2}$ 　　　**d.** $\dfrac{-48x^5}{3x^3}$

e. $\dfrac{56m^3}{-8m}$ 　　　**f.** $\dfrac{-72p^5}{-9p^2}$ 　　　**g.** $\dfrac{100r^3s^4}{4r^2s^3}$ 　　　**h.** $\dfrac{-84x^4y^6}{7x^2y^2}$

Answers

1. None 　　**3.** 0 　　**5.** 2 　　**7.** -4 　　**9.** None 　　**11.** $-1, 2$

13. $-3, \dfrac{1}{2}$ 　　**15.** $-3, 3$ 　　**17.** 3, 4 　　**19.** $-1, \dfrac{2}{3}$ 　　**21.** $x \neq y$

23. $x \neq \dfrac{y}{2}$ 　　**a.** $4a$ 　　**b.** $5w$ 　　**c.** $5c^3$ 　　**d.** $-16x^2$ 　　**e.** $-7m^2$ 　　**f.** $8p^3$

g. $25rs$ 　　**h.** $-12x^2y^4$

Writing Algebraic Fractions in Simplest Form

6.2 OBJECTIVE

Write an algebraic fraction in simplest form

As we pointed out in the last section, much of our work with algebraic fractions will be similar to your work in arithmetic. For instance, in algebra, as in arithmetic, many fractions name the same number. You will remember from arithmetic that

$$\frac{1}{4} = \frac{1 \cdot 2}{4 \cdot 2} = \frac{2}{8}$$

or

$$\frac{1}{4} = \frac{1 \cdot 3}{4 \cdot 3} = \frac{3}{12}$$

So $\frac{1}{4}$, $\frac{2}{8}$, and $\frac{3}{12}$ all name the same number. They are called **equivalent fractions.** These examples illustrate what is called the **fundamental principle of fractions.** In algebra it becomes

> For polynomials P, Q, and R,
>
> $$\frac{P}{Q} = \frac{PR}{QR} \qquad \text{where } Q \neq 0 \text{ and } R \neq 0$$

This principle allows us to multiply or divide the numerator and denominator of a fraction by the same nonzero polynomial. The result will be an expression that is equivalent to the original one.

Our objective in this section is to simplify algebraic fractions by using the fundamental principle. In algebra, as in arithmetic, to write a fraction in simplest form, you divide the numerator and denominator of the fraction by all common factors. The numerator and denominator of the resulting fraction will have no common factors other than 1, and the fraction is then in **simplest form.** The following rule summarizes this procedure.

Note that step 2 uses the fact that $\frac{R}{R} = 1$, if $R \neq 0$.

> **To Write Algebraic Fractions in Simplest Form**
>
> **STEP 1** Factor the numerator and denominator.
> **STEP 2** Divide the numerator and denominator by all common factors.
> **STEP 3** The resulting fraction will be in lowest terms.

• Example 1

Writing Fractions in Simplest Form

(a) Write $\dfrac{18}{30}$ in simplest form.

This is the same as dividing both the numerator and denominator of $\dfrac{18}{30}$ by 6.

$$\frac{18}{30} = \frac{2 \cdot 3 \cdot 3}{2 \cdot 3 \cdot 5} = \frac{\cancel{2} \cdot \cancel{3} \cdot 3}{\cancel{2} \cdot \cancel{3} \cdot 5} = \frac{3}{5}$$

Divide by the common factors. The slash lines indicate that we have divided the numerator and denominator by 2 and by 3.

(b) Write $\dfrac{4x^3}{6x}$ in simplest form.

$$\frac{4x^3}{6x} = \frac{2 \cdot 2 \cdot \cancel{x} \cdot x \cdot x}{2 \cdot 3 \cdot \cancel{x}} = \frac{2x^2}{3}$$

(c) Write $\dfrac{15x^3y^2}{20xy^4}$ in simplest form.

$$\frac{15x^3y^2}{20xy^4} = \frac{3 \cdot \cancel{5} \cdot \cancel{x} \cdot x \cdot x \cdot \cancel{y} \cdot \cancel{y}}{4 \cdot \cancel{5} \cdot \cancel{x} \cdot \cancel{y} \cdot \cancel{y} \cdot y \cdot y} = \frac{3x^2}{4y^2}$$

(d) Write $\dfrac{3a^2b}{9a^3b^2}$ in simplest form.

When all of the factors in the numerator have been divided by a common factor, the value of the numerator is 1.

$$\frac{3a^2b}{9a^3b^2} = \frac{\cancel{3} \cdot \cancel{a} \cdot \cancel{a} \cdot \cancel{b}}{\cancel{3} \cdot 3 \cdot \cancel{a} \cdot \cancel{a} \cdot a \cdot \cancel{b} \cdot b} = \frac{1}{3ab}$$

(e) Write $\dfrac{10a^5b^4}{2a^2b^3}$ in simplest form.

$$\frac{10a^5b^4}{2a^2b^3} = \frac{5 \cdot \cancel{2} \cdot \cancel{a} \cdot \cancel{a} \cdot a \cdot a \cdot a \cdot \cancel{b} \cdot \cancel{b} \cdot \cancel{b} \cdot b}{\cancel{2} \cdot \cancel{a} \cdot \cancel{a} \cdot \cancel{b} \cdot \cancel{b} \cdot \cancel{b}} = \frac{5a^3b}{1} = 5a^3b$$

● ● ●　CHECK YOURSELF 1

Most of the methods of this chapter build on our factoring work of the last chapter.

Write each fraction in simplest form.

a. $\dfrac{30}{66}$ **b.** $\dfrac{5x^4}{15x}$ **c.** $\dfrac{12xy^4}{18x^3y^2}$ **d.** $\dfrac{5m^2n}{10m^3n^3}$ **e.** $\dfrac{12a^4b^6}{2a^3b^4}$

In simplifying arithmetic fractions, common factors are generally easy to recognize. With algebraic fractions, the factoring techniques you studied in Chapter 5 will have to be used as the *first step* in determining those factors.

• Example 2

Writing Fractions in Simplest Form

Write each fraction in simplest form.

(a) $\dfrac{2x - 4}{x^2 - 4} = \dfrac{2(x - 2)}{(x + 2)(x - 2)}$

Factor the numerator and denominator.

$\phantom{(a) \dfrac{2x - 4}{x^2 - 4}} = \dfrac{2\cancel{(x - 2)}}{(x + 2)\cancel{(x - 2)}}$

Divide by the common factor $x - 2$. The slash lines indicate that we have divided by that common factor.

$\phantom{(a) \dfrac{2x - 4}{x^2 - 4}} = \dfrac{2}{x + 2}$

(b) $\dfrac{3x^2 - 3}{x^2 - 2x - 3} = \dfrac{3(x - 1)\cancel{(x + 1)}}{(x - 3)\cancel{(x + 1)}}$

$\phantom{(b) \dfrac{3x^2 - 3}{x^2 - 2x - 3}} = \dfrac{3(x - 1)}{x - 3}$

(c) $\dfrac{2x^2 + x - 6}{2x^2 - x - 3} = \dfrac{(x + 2)\cancel{(2x - 3)}}{(x + 1)\cancel{(2x - 3)}}$

$\phantom{(c) \dfrac{2x^2 + x - 6}{2x^2 - x - 3}} = \dfrac{x + 2}{x + 1}$

CAUTION

Pick any value, other than 0, for x and substitute. You will quickly see that

$\dfrac{x + 2}{x + 1} \neq \dfrac{2}{1}$

Be Careful! The expression $\dfrac{x + 2}{x + 1}$ is already in simplest form. Students are often tempted to divide as follows:

$\dfrac{\cancel{x} + 2}{\cancel{x} + 1}$ 　　　is *not equal* to 　　　$\dfrac{2}{1}$

The x's are *terms* in the numerator and denominator. They *cannot* be divided out. Only *factors* can be divided. The fraction

$\dfrac{x + 2}{x + 1}$

is in its simplest form.

● ● ● **CHECK YOURSELF 2**

Write each fraction in simplest form.

a. $\dfrac{5x - 15}{x^2 - 9}$　　　　　　　　　　　b. $\dfrac{a^2 - 5a + 6}{3a^2 - 6a}$

c. $\dfrac{3x^2 + 14x - 5}{3x^2 + 2x - 1}$　　　　　　　d. $\dfrac{5p - 15}{p^2 - 4}$

Remember the rules for signs in division. The quotient of a positive number and a negative number is always negative. Thus there are three equivalent ways to write such a quotient. For instance,

Note: $\dfrac{-2}{3}$, with the negative sign in the numerator, is the most common way to write the quotient.

$$\frac{-2}{3} = \frac{2}{-3} = -\frac{2}{3}$$

The quotient of two positive numbers or two negative numbers is always positive. For example,

$$\frac{-2}{-3} = \frac{2}{3}$$

● Example 3

Writing Fractions in Simplest Form

Write each fraction in simplest form.

In part (a), the final quotient is written in the most common way with the minus sign in the numerator.

(a) $\dfrac{6x^2}{-3xy} = \dfrac{2 \cdot \cancel{3} \cdot \cancel{x} \cdot x}{(-1) \cdot \cancel{3} \cdot \cancel{x} \cdot y} = \dfrac{2x}{-y} = \dfrac{-2x}{y}$

(b) $\dfrac{-5a^2b}{-10b^2} = \dfrac{\cancel{(-1)} \cdot \cancel{5} \cdot a \cdot a \cdot \cancel{b}}{\cancel{(-1)} \cdot 2 \cdot \cancel{5} \cdot \cancel{b} \cdot b} = \dfrac{a^2}{2b}$

● ● ● **CHECK YOURSELF 3**

Write each fraction in simplest form.

a. $\dfrac{8x^3y}{-4xy^2}$

b. $\dfrac{-16a^4b^2}{-12a^2b^5}$

It is sometimes necessary to factor a binomial before simplifying the fraction.

● Example 4

Writing Fractions in Simplest Form

Write each fraction in simplest form.

(a) $\dfrac{6x^2 + 2x}{2x^2 + 12x} = \dfrac{2x(3x + 1)}{2x(x + 6)} = \dfrac{3x + 1}{x + 6}$

(b) $\dfrac{x^2 - 4}{x^2 + 6x + 8} = \dfrac{(x + 2)(x - 2)}{(x + 2)(x + 4)} = \dfrac{x - 2}{x + 4}$

● ● ● ● **CHECK YOURSELF 4**

Simplify each fraction.

a. $\dfrac{3x^3 - 6x^2}{9x^4 - 3x^2}$

b. $\dfrac{x^2 - 9}{x^2 - 12x + 27}$

Reducing certain algebraic fractions will be easier with the following result. First, verify for yourself that

$$5 - 8 = -(8 - 5)$$

In general, it is true that

$$a - b = -(b - a)$$

or, by dividing both sides of the equation by $b - a$,

$$\frac{a - b}{b - a} = \frac{-(b - a)}{b - a}$$

So dividing by $b - a$ on the right, we have

Remember that a and b cannot be divided out since they are not factors.

$$\frac{a - b}{b - a} = -1$$

Let's look at some applications of that result in Example 5.

● Example 5

Writing Fractions in Simplest Form

Write each fraction in simplest form.

(a) $\dfrac{2x - 4}{4 - x^2} = \dfrac{2(x - 2)}{(2 + x)(2 - x)}$ This is equal to -1.

$$= \frac{2(-1)}{2 + x} = \frac{-2}{2 + x}$$

(b) $\dfrac{9 - x^2}{x^2 + 2x - 15} = \dfrac{(3 + x)(3 - x)}{(x + 5)(x - 3)}$ This is equal to -1.

$$= \frac{(3 + x)(-1)}{x + 5}$$

$$= \frac{-x - 3}{x + 5}$$

● ● ● **CHECK YOURSELF 5**

Write each fraction in simplest form.

a. $\dfrac{3x - 9}{9 - x^2}$

b. $\dfrac{x^2 - 6x - 27}{81 - x^2}$

● ● ● **CHECK YOURSELF ANSWERS**

1. (a) $\dfrac{5}{11}$; (b) $\dfrac{x^3}{3}$; (c) $\dfrac{2y^2}{3x^2}$; (d) $\dfrac{1}{2mn^2}$; (e) $6ab^2$.   **2.** (a) $\dfrac{5}{x + 3}$; (b) $\dfrac{a - 3}{3a}$;

(c) $\dfrac{x + 5}{x + 1}$; (d) $\dfrac{5(p - 3)}{p^2 - 4}$.   **3.** (a) $\dfrac{-2x^2}{y}$; (b) $\dfrac{4a^2}{3b^3}$.   **4.** (a) $\dfrac{x - 2}{3x^2 - 1}$; (b) $\dfrac{x + 3}{x - 9}$.

5. (a) $\dfrac{-3}{x + 3}$; (b) $\dfrac{-x - 3}{x + 9}$.

Write each fraction in simplest form.

1. $\dfrac{16}{24}$

2. $\dfrac{56}{64}$

3. $\dfrac{80}{180}$

4. $\dfrac{18}{30}$

5. $\dfrac{4x^5}{6x^2}$

6. $\dfrac{10x^2}{15x^4}$

7. $\dfrac{9x^3}{27x^6}$

8. $\dfrac{25w^6}{20w^2}$

9. $\dfrac{10a^2b^5}{25ab^2}$

10. $\dfrac{18x^4y^3}{24x^2y^3}$

11. $\dfrac{42x^3y}{14xy^3}$

12. $\dfrac{18pq}{45p^2q^2}$

13. $\dfrac{2xyw^2}{6x^2y^3w^3}$

14. $\dfrac{3c^2d^2}{6bc^3d^3}$

15. $\dfrac{10x^5y^5}{2x^3y^4}$

16. $\dfrac{3bc^6d^3}{bc^3d}$

17. $\dfrac{-4m^3n}{6mn^2}$

18. $\dfrac{-15x^3y^3}{-20xy^4}$

1. _____
2. _____
3. _____
4. _____
5. _____
6. _____
7. _____
8. _____
9. _____
10. _____
11. _____
12. _____
13. _____
14. _____
15. _____
16. _____
17. _____
18. _____

19. _____

20. _____

21. _____

22. _____

23. _____

24. _____

25. _____

26. _____

27. _____

28. _____

29. _____

30. _____

31. _____

32. _____

33. _____

34. _____

35. _____

36. _____

37. _____

38. _____

39. _____

40. _____

19. $\dfrac{-8ab^3}{-16a^3b}$

20. $\dfrac{14x^2y}{-21xy^4}$

21. $\dfrac{8r^2s^3t}{-16rs^4t^3}$

22. $\dfrac{-10a^3b^2c^3}{15ab^4c}$

23. $\dfrac{3x + 18}{5x + 30}$

24. $\dfrac{4x - 28}{5x - 35}$

25. $\dfrac{3x - 6}{5x - 15}$

26. $\dfrac{x^2 - 25}{3x - 15}$

27. $\dfrac{6a - 24}{a^2 - 16}$

28. $\dfrac{5x - 5}{x^2 - 4}$

29. $\dfrac{x^2 + 3x + 2}{5x + 10}$

30. $\dfrac{4w^2 - 20w}{w^2 - 2w - 15}$

31. $\dfrac{x^2 - 6x - 16}{x^2 - 64}$

32. $\dfrac{y^2 - 25}{y^2 - y - 20}$

33. $\dfrac{2m^2 + 3m - 5}{2m^2 + 11m + 15}$

34. $\dfrac{6x^2 - x - 2}{3x^2 - 5x + 2}$

35. $\dfrac{p^2 + 2pq - 15q^2}{p^2 - 25q^2}$

36. $\dfrac{4r^2 - 25s^2}{2r^2 + 3rs - 20s^2}$

37. $\dfrac{2x - 10}{25 - x^2}$

38. $\dfrac{3a - 12}{16 - a^2}$

39. $\dfrac{25 - a^2}{a^2 + a - 30}$

40. $\dfrac{2x^2 - 7x + 3}{9 - x^2}$

41. $\dfrac{x^2 + xy - 6y^2}{4y^2 - x^2}$

42. $\dfrac{16z^2 - w^2}{2w^2 - 5wz - 12z^2}$

43. $\dfrac{x^2 + 4x + 4}{x + 2}$

44. $\dfrac{4x^2 + 12x + 9}{2x + 3}$

45. $\dfrac{xy - 2y + 4x - 8}{2y + 6 - xy - 3x}$

46. $\dfrac{ab - 3a + 5b - 15}{15 + 3a^2 - 5b - a^2b}$

47. $\dfrac{y - 7}{7 - y}$

48. $\dfrac{5 - y}{y - 5}$

49. To work with algebraic fractions correctly, it is important to understand the difference between a *factor* and a *term* of an expression. In your own words, write definitions for both, explaining the difference between the two.

50. Give some examples of terms and factors in algebraic fractions, and explain how both are affected when a fraction is reduced.

51. Show how the following algebraic fraction can be reduced:

$$\dfrac{x^2 - 9}{4x + 12}$$

Note that your reduced fraction is equivalent. Are there other algebraic fractions equivalent to this one? Write another algebraic fraction that you think is equivalent to this one. Exchange papers with another student. Do you agree that their fraction is equivalent to yours? Why or why not?

A N S W E R S

41.

42.

43.

44.

45.

46.

47.

48.

49.

50.

51.

Getting Ready for Section 6.3 [Appendix 1]

Perform the indicated operations.

a. $\dfrac{2}{3} \cdot \dfrac{4}{5}$

b. $\dfrac{5}{6} \cdot \dfrac{4}{11}$

c. $\dfrac{4}{7} \div \dfrac{8}{5}$

d. $\dfrac{1}{6} \div \dfrac{7}{9}$

e. $\dfrac{5}{8} \cdot \dfrac{16}{15}$

f. $\dfrac{15}{21} \div \dfrac{10}{7}$

g. $\dfrac{15}{8} \cdot \dfrac{24}{25}$

h. $\dfrac{28}{16} \div \dfrac{21}{20}$

Answers

1. $\dfrac{2}{3}$ **3.** $\dfrac{4}{9}$ **5.** $\dfrac{2x^3}{3}$ **7.** $\dfrac{1}{3x^3}$ **9.** $\dfrac{2ab^3}{5}$ **11.** $\dfrac{3x^2}{y^2}$ **13.** $\dfrac{1}{3xy^2w}$

15. $5x^2y$ **17.** $\dfrac{-2m^2}{3n}$ **19.** $\dfrac{b^2}{2a^2}$ **21.** $\dfrac{-r}{2st^2}$ **23.** $\dfrac{3}{5}$ **25.** $\dfrac{3(x-2)}{5(x-3)}$

27. $\dfrac{6}{a+4}$ **29.** $\dfrac{x+1}{5}$ **31.** $\dfrac{x+2}{x+8}$ **33.** $\dfrac{m-1}{m+3}$ **35.** $\dfrac{p-3q}{p-5q}$

37. $\dfrac{-2}{x+5}$ **39.** $\dfrac{-a-5}{a+6}$ **41.** $\dfrac{-x-3y}{2y+x}$ **43.** $x+2$ **45.** $\dfrac{-(y+4)}{y+3}$

47. -1 **a.** $\dfrac{8}{15}$ **b.** $\dfrac{10}{33}$ **c.** $\dfrac{5}{14}$ **d.** $\dfrac{3}{14}$ **e.** $\dfrac{2}{3}$ **f.** $\dfrac{1}{2}$ **g.** $\dfrac{9}{5}$

h. $\dfrac{5}{3}$

6.3 Multiplying and Dividing Algebraic Fractions

6.3 OBJECTIVES

1. Write the product of two algebraic fractions in simplest form
2. Write the quotient of two algebraic fractions in simplest form

P, Q, R, and S again represent polynomials.

Divide by the common factors of 3 and 4. The alternative is to multiply *first*:

$$\frac{3}{8} \cdot \frac{4}{9} = \frac{12}{72}$$

and then reduce to lowest terms

$$\frac{12}{72} = \frac{1}{6}$$

In arithmetic, you found the product of two fractions by multiplying the numerators and the denominators. For example,

$$\frac{2}{5} \cdot \frac{3}{7} = \frac{2 \cdot 3}{5 \cdot 7} = \frac{6}{35}$$

In symbols, we have

$$\frac{P}{Q} \cdot \frac{R}{S} = \frac{PR}{QS} \qquad \text{where } Q \neq 0 \text{ and } S \neq 0$$

It is easier to divide the numerator and denominator by any common factors *before* multiplying. Consider the following.

$$\frac{3}{8} \cdot \frac{4}{9} = \frac{3 \cdot \overset{1}{4}}{\underset{2}{8} \cdot \underset{3}{9}} = \frac{1}{6}$$

In algebra, we multiply fractions in exactly the same way.

To Multiply Algebraic Fractions

STEP 1 Factor the numerators and denominators.
STEP 2 Divide the numerator and denominator by any common factors.
STEP 3 Write the product of the remaining factors in the numerator over the product of the remaining factors in the denominator.

Example 1 illustrates this property.

• Example 1

Multiplying Algebraic Fractions

Multiply the following fractions.

Divide by the common factors of 5, x^2, and y.

$(a) \quad \dfrac{2x^3}{5y^2} \cdot \dfrac{10y}{3x^2} = \dfrac{2x^3 \cdot 10y}{5y^2 \cdot 3x^2} = \dfrac{4x}{3y}$

$(b) \quad \dfrac{x}{x^2 - 3x} \cdot \dfrac{6x - 18}{9x} = \dfrac{x}{x(x - 3)} \cdot \dfrac{6(x - 3)}{9x} \quad \xleftarrow{\text{Factor}}$

Divide by the common factors of 3, x, and $x - 3$.

$\qquad\qquad = \dfrac{x \cdot \overset{2}{6}(x - 3)}{x(x - 3) \cdot \underset{3}{9x}}$

$\qquad\qquad = \dfrac{2}{3x}$

Note:

$$\frac{2 - x}{x - 2} = \frac{-(x - 2)}{x - 2} = -1$$

(c) $\dfrac{4}{x^2 - 2x} \cdot \dfrac{10 - 5x}{8} = \dfrac{4}{x(x - 2)} \cdot \dfrac{5(2 - x)}{8}$

$$= \frac{4 \cdot 5(2 - x)}{x(x - 2) \cdot 8} = \frac{-5}{2x}$$

Divide by the common factors of $x - 4$, x, and 3.

(d) $\dfrac{x^2 - 2x - 8}{3x^2} \cdot \dfrac{6x}{3x - 12} = \dfrac{(x - 4)(x + 2)}{3x^2} \cdot \dfrac{6x}{3(x - 4)}$

$$= \frac{2(x + 2)}{3x}$$

(e) $\dfrac{x^2 - y^2}{5x - 5y} \cdot \dfrac{10xy}{x^2 + 2xy + y^2} = \dfrac{(x - y)(x + y)}{5(x - y)} \cdot \dfrac{10xy}{(x + y)(x + y)}$

$$= \frac{2xy}{x + y}$$

● ● ● **CHECK YOURSELF 1**

Multiply.

a. $\dfrac{3x^2}{5y^2} \cdot \dfrac{10y^5}{15x^3}$ **b.** $\dfrac{5x + 15}{x} \cdot \dfrac{2x^2}{x^2 + 3x}$ **c.** $\dfrac{x}{2x - 6} \cdot \dfrac{3x - x^2}{2}$

d. $\dfrac{3x - 15}{6x^2} \cdot \dfrac{2x}{x^2 - 25}$ **e.** $\dfrac{x^2 - 5x - 14}{4x^2} \cdot \dfrac{8x}{x^2 - 49}$

You can also use your experience from arithmetic in dividing fractions. Recall that, to divide fractions, we *invert the divisor* (the *second* fraction) and multiply. For example,

Recall, $\dfrac{6}{5}$ is the reciprocal of $\dfrac{5}{6}$.

$$\frac{2}{3} \div \frac{5}{6} = \frac{2}{3} \cdot \frac{6}{5} = \frac{2 \cdot 6}{3 \cdot 5} = \frac{4}{5}$$

In symbols, we have

Once more P, Q, R, and S are polynomials.

$$\frac{P}{Q} \div \frac{R}{S} = \frac{P}{Q} \cdot \frac{S}{R} = \frac{PS}{QR}$$

where $Q \neq 0$, $R \neq 0$, and $S \neq 0$.

Division of algebraic fractions is done in exactly the same way.

To Divide Algebraic Fractions

STEP 1 Invert the divisor.
STEP 2 Proceed, using the steps for multiplying algebraic fractions.

Example 2 illustrates this approach.

• Example 2

Dividing Algebraic Fractions

Divide the following.

(a) $\dfrac{6}{x^2} \div \dfrac{9}{x^3} = \dfrac{6}{x^2} \cdot \dfrac{x^3}{9}$ Invert the divisor and multiply.

$= \dfrac{\overset{2}{6}}{x^2} \cdot \dfrac{\overset{x}{x^3}}{\underset{3}{9}}$ No simplification can be done until the divisor is inverted. Then divide by the common factors of 3 and x^2.

$= \dfrac{2x}{3}$

(b) $\dfrac{3x^2y}{8xy^3} \div \dfrac{9x^3}{4y^4} = \dfrac{3x^2y}{8xy^3} \cdot \dfrac{4y^4}{9x^3}$

$= \dfrac{y^2}{6x^2}$

(c) $\dfrac{2x+4y}{9x-18y} \div \dfrac{4x+8y}{3x-6y} = \dfrac{2x+4y}{9x-18y} \cdot \dfrac{3x-6y}{4x+8y}$

$= \dfrac{2(x+2y)}{\underset{3}{9}(x-2y)} \cdot \dfrac{3(x-2y)}{\underset{2}{4}(x+2y)}$

$= \dfrac{1}{6}$

Factor all numerators and denominators *before* dividing out any common factors.

(d) $\dfrac{x^2-x-6}{2x-6} \div \dfrac{x^2-4}{4x^2} = \dfrac{x^2-x-6}{2x-6} \cdot \dfrac{4x^2}{x^2-4}$

$= \dfrac{(x-3)(x+2)}{2(x-3)} \cdot \dfrac{\overset{2}{4}x^2}{(x+2)(x-2)}$

$= \dfrac{2x^2}{x-2}$

● ● ● **CHECK YOURSELF 2**

Divide.

a. $\dfrac{4}{x^5} \div \dfrac{12}{x^3}$

b. $\dfrac{5xy^2}{7x^3y} \div \dfrac{10y^2}{14x^3}$

c. $\dfrac{3x - 9y}{2x + 10y} \div \dfrac{x^2 - 3xy}{4x + 20y}$

d. $\dfrac{x^2 - 9}{4x} \div \dfrac{x^2 - 2x - 15}{2x - 10}$

Before we conclude this section, let's review why the invert-and-multiply rule works for dividing fractions. We will use an example from arithmetic for the explanation. Suppose that we want to divide as follows:

$$\frac{3}{5} \div \frac{2}{3} \tag{1}$$

We can write

$$\underbrace{\frac{3}{5} \div \frac{2}{3}}_{(1)} = \dfrac{\dfrac{3}{5}}{\dfrac{2}{3}} = \dfrac{\dfrac{3}{5} \cdot \dfrac{3}{2}}{\dfrac{2}{3} \cdot \dfrac{3}{2}} \qquad \text{We are multiplying by 1.}$$

Interpret the division as a fraction.

$$= \dfrac{\dfrac{3}{5} \cdot \dfrac{3}{2}}{1}$$

$$\frac{2}{3} \cdot \frac{3}{2} = 1$$

$$= \underbrace{\frac{3}{5} \cdot \frac{3}{2}}_{(2)}$$

We then have

$$\frac{3}{5} \overset{1}{\div} \frac{2}{3} = \frac{3}{5} \cdot \overset{2}{\frac{3}{2}}$$

Comparing expressions (1) and (2), you should see the rule for dividing fractions. Invert the fraction that follows the division symbol and multiply.

● ● ● **CHECK YOURSELF ANSWERS**

1. (a) $\dfrac{2y^3}{5x}$; **(b)** 10; **(c)** $-\dfrac{x^2}{4}$; **(d)** $\dfrac{1}{x(x + 5)}$; **(e)** $\dfrac{2(x + 2)}{x(x + 7)}$.

2. (a) $\dfrac{1}{3x^2}$; **(b)** $\dfrac{x}{y}$; **(c)** $\dfrac{6}{x}$; **(d)** $\dfrac{x - 3}{2x}$.

Multiply.

1. $\dfrac{3}{7} \cdot \dfrac{14}{27}$

2. $\dfrac{9}{20} \cdot \dfrac{5}{36}$

3. $\dfrac{x}{2} \cdot \dfrac{y}{6}$

4. $\dfrac{w}{2} \cdot \dfrac{5}{14}$

5. $\dfrac{3a}{2} \cdot \dfrac{4}{a^2}$

6. $\dfrac{5x^3}{3x} \cdot \dfrac{9}{20x}$

7. $\dfrac{3x^3y}{10xy^3} \cdot \dfrac{5xy^2}{9xy^2}$

8. $\dfrac{8xy^5}{5x^3y^2} \cdot \dfrac{15y^2}{16xy^3}$

9. $\dfrac{-4ab^2}{15a^3} \cdot \dfrac{25ab}{-16b^3}$

10. $\dfrac{-7xy^2}{12x^2y} \cdot \dfrac{24x^3y^5}{-21x^2y^7}$

11. $\dfrac{-3m^3n}{10mn^3} \cdot \dfrac{5mn^2}{-9mn^3}$

12. $\dfrac{3x}{2x-6} \cdot \dfrac{x^2-3x}{6}$

13. $\dfrac{x^2+5x}{3x^2} \cdot \dfrac{10x}{5x+25}$

14. $\dfrac{x^2-3x-10}{5x} \cdot \dfrac{15x^2}{3x-15}$

15. $\dfrac{p^2-8p}{4p} \cdot \dfrac{12p^2}{p^2-64}$

16. $\dfrac{a^2-81}{a^2+9a} \cdot \dfrac{5a^2}{a^2-7a-18}$

ANSWERS
1.
2.
3.
4.
5.
6.
7.
8.
9.
10.
11.
12.
13.
14.
15.
16.

17. _____

18. _____

19. _____

20. _____

21. _____

22. _____

23. _____

24. _____

25. _____

26. _____

27. _____

28. _____

29. _____

30. _____

31. _____

32. _____

33. _____

34. _____

35. _____

36. _____

17. $\dfrac{m^2 - 4m - 21}{3m^2} \cdot \dfrac{m^2 + 7m}{m^2 - 49}$

18. $\dfrac{2x^2 - x - 3}{3x^2 + 7x + 4} \cdot \dfrac{3x^2 - 11x - 20}{4x^2 - 9}$

19. $\dfrac{4r^2 - 1}{2r^2 - 9r - 5} \cdot \dfrac{3r^2 - 13r - 10}{9r^2 - 4}$

20. $\dfrac{a^2 + ab}{2a^2 - ab - 3b^2} \cdot \dfrac{4a^2 - 9b^2}{5a^2 - 4ab}$

21. $\dfrac{x^2 - 4y^2}{x^2 - xy - 6y^2} \cdot \dfrac{7x^2 - 21xy}{5x - 10y}$

22. $\dfrac{a^2 - 9b^2}{a^2 + ab - 6b^2} \cdot \dfrac{6a^2 - 12ab}{7a - 21b}$

23. $\dfrac{2x - 6}{x^2 + 2x} \cdot \dfrac{3x}{3 - x}$

24. $\dfrac{3x - 15}{x^2 + 3x} \cdot \dfrac{4x}{5 - x}$

Divide.

25. $\dfrac{5}{8} \div \dfrac{15}{16}$

26. $\dfrac{4}{9} \div \dfrac{12}{18}$

27. $\dfrac{5}{x^2} \div \dfrac{10}{x}$

28. $\dfrac{w^2}{3} \div \dfrac{w}{9}$

29. $\dfrac{4x^2y^2}{9x^3} \div \dfrac{8y^2}{27xy}$

30. $\dfrac{8x^3y}{27xy^3} \div \dfrac{16x^3y}{45y}$

31. $\dfrac{3x + 6}{8} \div \dfrac{5x + 10}{6}$

32. $\dfrac{x^2 - 2x}{4x} \div \dfrac{6x - 12}{8}$

33. $\dfrac{4a - 12}{5a + 15} \div \dfrac{8a^2}{a^2 + 3a}$

34. $\dfrac{6p - 18}{9p} \div \dfrac{3p - 9}{p^2 + 2p}$

35. $\dfrac{x^2 + 2x - 8}{9x^2} \div \dfrac{x^2 - 16}{3x - 12}$

36. $\dfrac{16x}{4x^2 - 16} \div \dfrac{4x - 24}{x^2 - 4x - 12}$

37. $\dfrac{x^2 - 9}{2x^2 - 6x} \div \dfrac{2x^2 + 5x - 3}{4x^2 - 1}$

38. $\dfrac{2m^2 - 5m - 7}{4m^2 - 9} \div \dfrac{5m^2 + 5m}{2m^2 + 3m}$

39. $\dfrac{a^2 - 9b^2}{4a^2 + 12ab} \div \dfrac{a^2 - ab - 6b^2}{12ab}$

40. $\dfrac{r^2 + 2rs - 15s^2}{r^3 + 5r^2s} \div \dfrac{r^2 - 9s^2}{5r^3}$

41. $\dfrac{x^2 - 16y^2}{3x^2 - 12xy} \div (x^2 + 4xy)$

42. $\dfrac{p^2 - 4pq - 21q^2}{4p - 28q} \div (2p^2 + 6pq)$

43. $\dfrac{x - 7}{2x + 6} \div \dfrac{21 - 3x}{x^2 + 3x}$

44. $\dfrac{x - 4}{x^2 + 2x} \div \dfrac{16 - 4x}{3x + 6}$

Perform the indicated operations.

45. $\dfrac{x^2 - 2x - 8}{2x - 8} \cdot \dfrac{x^2 + 5x}{x^2 + 5x + 6} \div \dfrac{x^2 + 2x - 15}{x^2 - 9}$

46. $\dfrac{14x - 7}{x^2 + 3x - 4} \cdot \dfrac{x^2 + 6x + 8}{2x^2 + 5x - 3} \div \dfrac{x^2 + 2x}{x^2 + 2x - 3}$

47. $\dfrac{x^2 + 5x}{3x - 6} \cdot \dfrac{x^2 - 4}{3x^2 + 15x} \cdot \dfrac{6x}{x^2 + 6x + 8}$

48. $\dfrac{m^2 - n^2}{m^2 - mn} \cdot \dfrac{6m}{2m^2 + mn - n^2} \cdot \dfrac{8m - 4n}{12m^2 + 12mn}$

ANSWERS

37. _____

38. _____

39. _____

40. _____

41. _____

42. _____

43. _____

44. _____

45. _____

46. _____

47. _____

48. _____

Getting Ready for Section 6.4 [Appendix]

Perform the indicated operations.

a. $\dfrac{3}{10} + \dfrac{4}{10}$

b. $\dfrac{5}{8} - \dfrac{4}{8}$

c. $\dfrac{5}{12} - \dfrac{1}{12}$

d. $\dfrac{7}{16} + \dfrac{3}{16}$

e. $\dfrac{7}{20} + \dfrac{9}{20}$

f. $\dfrac{13}{8} - \dfrac{5}{8}$

g. $\dfrac{11}{6} - \dfrac{2}{6}$

h. $\dfrac{5}{9} + \dfrac{7}{9}$

Answers

1. $\dfrac{2}{9}$ 3. $\dfrac{xy}{12}$ 5. $\dfrac{6}{a}$ 7. $\dfrac{x^2}{6y^2}$ 9. $\dfrac{5}{12a}$ 11. $\dfrac{m^2}{6n^3}$ 13. $\dfrac{2}{3}$

15. $\dfrac{3p^2}{p+8}$ 17. $\dfrac{m+3}{3m}$ 19. $\dfrac{2r-1}{3r-2}$ 21. $\dfrac{7x}{5}$ 23. $\dfrac{-6}{x+2}$ 25. $\dfrac{2}{3}$

27. $\dfrac{1}{2x}$ 29. $\dfrac{3y}{2}$ 31. $\dfrac{9}{20}$ 33. $\dfrac{a-3}{10a}$ 35. $\dfrac{x-2}{3x^2}$ 37. $\dfrac{2x+1}{2x}$

39. $\dfrac{3b}{a+2b}$ 41. $\dfrac{1}{3x^2}$ 43. $\dfrac{-x}{6}$ 45. $\dfrac{x}{2}$ 47. $\dfrac{2x}{3(x+4)}$ a. $\dfrac{7}{10}$

b. $\dfrac{1}{8}$ c. $\dfrac{1}{3}$ d. $\dfrac{5}{8}$ e. $\dfrac{4}{5}$ f. 1   g. $\dfrac{3}{2}$ h. $\dfrac{4}{3}$

Adding and Subtracting Like Fractions

6.4 OBJECTIVES

1. Write the sum of the two like fractions in simplest form
2. Write the difference of two like fractions in simplest form

The fractions have different denominators.

You probably remember from arithmetic that **like fractions** are fractions that have the same denominator. The same is true in algebra.

$\dfrac{2}{5}$, $\dfrac{12}{5}$, and $\dfrac{4}{5}$ are like fractions.

$\dfrac{x}{3}$, $\dfrac{y}{3}$, and $\dfrac{z-5}{3}$ are like fractions.

$\dfrac{3x}{2}$, $\dfrac{x}{4}$, and $\dfrac{3x}{8}$ are unlike fractions.

$\dfrac{3}{x}$, $\dfrac{2}{x^2}$, and $\dfrac{x+1}{x^3}$ are unlike fractions.

In arithmetic, the sum or difference of like fractions was found by adding or subtracting the numerators and writing the result over the common denominator. For example,

$$\frac{3}{11} + \frac{5}{11} = \frac{3+5}{11} = \frac{8}{11}$$

In symbols, we have

To Add or Subtract Like Fractions

$$\frac{P}{R} + \frac{Q}{R} = \frac{P+Q}{R} \qquad R \neq 0$$

$$\frac{P}{R} - \frac{Q}{R} = \frac{P-Q}{R} \qquad R \neq 0$$

Adding or subtracting like fractions in algebra is just as straightforward. You can use the following steps.

To Add or Subtract Like Algebraic Fractions

STEP 1 Add or subtract the numerators.
STEP 2 Write the sum or difference over the common denominator.
STEP 3 Write the resulting fraction in simplest form.

• Example 1

Adding and Subtracting Algebraic Fractions

Add or subtract as indicated. Express your results in simplest form.

Add the numerators.

(a) $\dfrac{2x}{15} + \dfrac{x}{15} = \dfrac{\overbrace{2x + x}}{15}$

$= \dfrac{3x}{15} = \dfrac{x}{5}$

Simplify.

Subtract the numerators.

(b) $\dfrac{5y}{6} - \dfrac{y}{6} = \dfrac{\overbrace{5y - y}}{6}$

$= \dfrac{4y}{6} = \dfrac{2y}{3}$

Simplify.

(c) $\dfrac{3}{x} + \dfrac{5}{x} = \dfrac{3 + 5}{x} = \dfrac{8}{x}$

(d) $\dfrac{9}{a^2} - \dfrac{7}{a^2} = \dfrac{9 - 7}{a^2} = \dfrac{2}{a^2}$

(e) $\dfrac{7}{2ab} - \dfrac{5}{2ab} = \dfrac{7 - 5}{2ab}$

$= \dfrac{2}{2ab}$

$= \dfrac{1}{ab}$

● ● ● **CHECK YOURSELF 1**

Add or subtract as indicated.

a. $\dfrac{3a}{10} + \dfrac{2a}{10}$ **b.** $\dfrac{7b}{8} - \dfrac{3b}{8}$ **c.** $\dfrac{4}{x} + \dfrac{3}{x}$ **d.** $\dfrac{5}{3xy} - \dfrac{2}{3xy}$

If polynomials are involved in the numerators or denominators, the process is exactly the same.

• Example 2

Adding and Subtracting Algebraic Fractions

Add or subtract as indicated. Express your results in simplest form.

(a) $\dfrac{5}{x+3} + \dfrac{2}{x+3} = \dfrac{5+2}{x+3} = \dfrac{7}{x+3}$

(b) $\dfrac{4x}{x-4} - \dfrac{16}{x-4} = \dfrac{4x-16}{x-4}$

Factor and simplify.

$= \dfrac{4(x-4)}{x-4} = 4$

The final answer is always written in simplest form.

(c) $\dfrac{a-b}{3} + \dfrac{2a+b}{3} = \dfrac{(a-b)+(2a+b)}{3}$

$= \dfrac{a-b+2a+b}{3}$

$= \dfrac{3a}{3} = a$

Be sure to enclose the second numerator in parentheses!

(d) $\dfrac{3x+y}{2x} - \dfrac{x-3y}{2x} = \dfrac{(3x+y)-(x-3y)}{2x}$

Change both signs.

$= \dfrac{3x+y-x+3y}{2x}$

$= \dfrac{2x+4y}{2x}$

$= \dfrac{2(x+2y)}{2x}$ Factor and divide by the common factor of 2.

$= \dfrac{x+2y}{x}$

(e) $\dfrac{3x-5}{x^2+x-2} - \dfrac{2x-4}{x^2+x-2} = \dfrac{3x-5-(2x-4)}{x^2+x-2}$ Put the second numerator in parentheses.

Change both signs.

$= \dfrac{3x-5-2x+4}{x^2+x-2}$

$= \dfrac{x-1}{x^2+x-2}$

$= \dfrac{(x-1)}{(x+2)(x-1)}$ Factor and divide by the common factor of $x-1$.

$= \dfrac{1}{x+2}$

(f) $\dfrac{2x + 7y}{x + 3y} - \dfrac{x + 4y}{x + 3y} = \dfrac{(2x + 7y) - (x + 4y)}{x + 3y}$

Change both signs.

$= \dfrac{2x + 7y - x - 4y}{x + 3y}$

$= \dfrac{x + 3y}{x + 3y} = 1$

● ● ● **CHECK YOURSELF 2**

Add or subtract as indicated.

a. $\dfrac{4}{x - 5} - \dfrac{2}{x - 5}$

b. $\dfrac{3x}{x + 3} + \dfrac{9}{x + 3}$

c. $\dfrac{5x - y}{3y} - \dfrac{2x - 4y}{3y}$

d. $\dfrac{5x + 8}{x^2 - 2x - 15} - \dfrac{4x + 5}{x^2 - 2x - 15}$

● ● ● **CHECK YOURSELF ANSWERS**

1. **(a)** $\dfrac{a}{2}$; **(b)** $\dfrac{b}{2}$; **(c)** $\dfrac{7}{x}$; **(d)** $\dfrac{1}{xy}$. **2.** **(a)** $\dfrac{2}{x - 5}$; **(b)** 3; **(c)** $\dfrac{x + y}{y}$; **(d)** $\dfrac{1}{x - 5}$.

Add or subtract as indicated. Express your results in simplest form.

1. $\dfrac{7}{18} + \dfrac{5}{18}$

2. $\dfrac{5}{18} - \dfrac{2}{18}$

3. $\dfrac{13}{16} - \dfrac{9}{16}$

4. $\dfrac{5}{12} + \dfrac{11}{12}$

5. $\dfrac{x}{8} + \dfrac{3x}{8}$

6. $\dfrac{5y}{16} + \dfrac{7y}{16}$

7. $\dfrac{7a}{10} - \dfrac{3a}{10}$

8. $\dfrac{5x}{12} - \dfrac{x}{12}$

9. $\dfrac{5}{x} + \dfrac{3}{x}$

10. $\dfrac{9}{y} - \dfrac{3}{y}$

11. $\dfrac{8}{w} - \dfrac{2}{w}$

12. $\dfrac{7}{z} + \dfrac{9}{z}$

13. $\dfrac{2}{xy} + \dfrac{3}{xy}$

14. $\dfrac{8}{ab} + \dfrac{4}{ab}$

15. $\dfrac{2}{3cd} + \dfrac{4}{3cd}$

16. $\dfrac{5}{4cd} + \dfrac{11}{4cd}$

A N S W E R S

1. _____

2. _____

3. _____

4. _____

5. _____

6. _____

7. _____

8. _____

9. _____

10. _____

11. _____

12. _____

13. _____

14. _____

15. _____

16. _____

17. _____

18. _____

19. _____

20. _____

21. _____

22. _____

23. _____

24. _____

25. _____

26. _____

27. _____

28. _____

29. _____

30. _____

31. _____

32. _____

33. _____

34. _____

35. _____

36. _____

17. $\dfrac{7}{x-5} + \dfrac{9}{x-5}$

18. $\dfrac{11}{x+7} - \dfrac{4}{x+7}$

19. $\dfrac{2x}{x-2} - \dfrac{4}{x-2}$

20. $\dfrac{7w}{w+3} + \dfrac{21}{w+3}$

21. $\dfrac{8p}{p+4} + \dfrac{32}{p+4}$

22. $\dfrac{5a}{a-3} - \dfrac{15}{a-3}$

23. $\dfrac{x^2}{x+4} + \dfrac{3x-4}{x+4}$

24. $\dfrac{x^2}{x-3} - \dfrac{9}{x-3}$

25. $\dfrac{m^2}{m-5} - \dfrac{25}{m-5}$

26. $\dfrac{s^2}{s+3} + \dfrac{2s-3}{s+3}$

27. $\dfrac{a-1}{3} + \dfrac{2a-5}{3}$

28. $\dfrac{y+2}{5} + \dfrac{4y+8}{5}$

29. $\dfrac{3x-1}{4} - \dfrac{x+7}{4}$

30. $\dfrac{4x+2}{3} - \dfrac{x-1}{3}$

31. $\dfrac{4m+7}{6m} + \dfrac{2m+5}{6m}$

32. $\dfrac{6x-y}{4y} - \dfrac{2x+3y}{4y}$

33. $\dfrac{4w-7}{w-5} - \dfrac{2w+3}{w-5}$

34. $\dfrac{3b-8}{b-6} + \dfrac{b-16}{b-6}$

35. $\dfrac{x-7}{x^2-x-6} + \dfrac{2x-2}{x^2-x-6}$

36. $\dfrac{5a-12}{a^2-8a+15} - \dfrac{3a-2}{a^2-8a+15}$

Add or subtract as indicated. Express your results in simplest form.

37. $\dfrac{5}{x-3} - \dfrac{3}{3-x}$

38. $\dfrac{-10}{5-y} + \dfrac{3}{y-5}$

39. $\dfrac{x}{9-x} + \dfrac{9}{x-9}$

40. $\dfrac{-5}{y-5} - \dfrac{y}{5-y}$

41. $\dfrac{x^2}{x^2-x-6} - \dfrac{6}{(x-3)(x+2)} + \dfrac{x}{6+x-x^2}$

42. $\dfrac{-12}{x^2+x-12} + \dfrac{x^2}{(x+4)(x-3)} - \dfrac{x}{12-x-x^2}$

43. Using the following fraction pair, explain what happens to fraction denominators when two fractions are multiplied:

$\dfrac{3}{4}$ and $\dfrac{1}{4}$

Use the following algebraic fraction pair to illustrate multiplication with algebraic fractions:

$\dfrac{3}{2x}$ and $\dfrac{1}{2x}$

Using these same two pairs illustrate what happens when two fractions are added. What is the difference in the two operations? Which is easier?

44. In Exercise 43, each fraction pair has denominators that are alike. Give two pairs of fractions, one numeric and one algebraic, that do *not* have like denominators. Explain how to multiply and how to add them. What is the difference in the two operations? Which is easier?

A N S W E R S

37. _____

38. _____

39. _____

40. _____

41. _____

42. _____

43. _____

44. _____

**Getting Ready for Section 6.5
[Appendix 1]**

a. $\dfrac{3}{4} + \dfrac{1}{2}$

b. $\dfrac{5}{6} - \dfrac{2}{3}$

c. $\dfrac{7}{10} - \dfrac{3}{5}$

d. $\dfrac{5}{8} + \dfrac{3}{4}$

e. $\dfrac{5}{6} + \dfrac{3}{8}$

f. $\dfrac{7}{8} - \dfrac{3}{5}$

g. $\dfrac{9}{10} - \dfrac{2}{15}$

h. $\dfrac{5}{12} + \dfrac{7}{18}$

Answers

1. $\dfrac{2}{3}$ **3.** $\dfrac{1}{4}$ **5.** $\dfrac{x}{2}$ **7.** $\dfrac{2a}{5}$ **9.** $\dfrac{8}{x}$ **11.** $\dfrac{6}{w}$ **13.** $\dfrac{5}{xy}$ **15.** $\dfrac{2}{cd}$

17. $\dfrac{16}{x-5}$ **19.** 2 **21.** 8 **23.** $x-1$ **25.** $m+5$ **27.** $a-2$

29. $\dfrac{x-4}{2}$ **31.** $\dfrac{m+2}{m}$ **33.** 2 **35.** $\dfrac{3}{x+2}$ **37.** $\dfrac{8}{x-3}$ **39.** -1

41. 1 **a.** $\dfrac{5}{4}$ **b.** $\dfrac{1}{6}$ **c.** $\dfrac{1}{10}$ **d.** $\dfrac{11}{8}$ **e.** $\dfrac{29}{24}$ **f.** $\dfrac{11}{40}$ **g.** $\dfrac{23}{30}$

h. $\dfrac{29}{36}$

Adding and Subtracting Unlike Fractions

6.5 OBJECTIVES

1. Write the sum of two algebraic fractions in simplest form
2. Write the difference of two algebraic fractions in simplest form

Adding or subtracting **unlike fractions** (fractions that do not have the same denominator) requires a bit more work than adding or subtracting the like fractions of the previous section. When the denominators are not the same, we must use the idea of the *lowest common denominator* (LCD). Each fraction is "built up" to an equivalent fraction having the LCD as a denominator. You can then add or subtract as before.

Let's review with an example from arithmetic.

● Example 1

Finding the LCD

Add $\dfrac{5}{9} + \dfrac{1}{6}$.

Step 1 To find the LCD, factor each denominator.

$9 = 3 \cdot 3$ ⟵── 3 appears twice.
$6 = 2 \cdot 3$

To form the LCD, include each factor the greatest number of times it appears in any single denominator. In this example, use one 2, since 2 appears only once in the factorization of 6 and two 3s, since 3 appears twice in the factorization of 9. Thus the LCD for the fractions is $2 \cdot 3 \cdot 3 = 18$.

Step 2 "Build up" each fraction to an equivalent fraction with the LCD as the denominator. Do this by multiplying the numerator and denominator of the given fractions by the same number.

Do you see that this uses the fundamental principle in the following form?

$$\frac{P}{Q} = \frac{PR}{QR}$$

$$\frac{5}{9} = \frac{5 \cdot 2}{9 \cdot 2} = \frac{10}{18}$$

$$\frac{1}{6} = \frac{1 \cdot 3}{6 \cdot 3} = \frac{3}{18}$$

Step 3 Add the fractions.

$$\frac{5}{9} + \frac{1}{6} = \frac{10}{18} + \frac{3}{18} = \frac{13}{18}$$

$\dfrac{13}{18}$ is in simplest form, and so we are done!

● ● ●   **CHECK YOURSELF 1**

Add.

a. $\dfrac{1}{6} + \dfrac{3}{8}$ **b.** $\dfrac{3}{10} + \dfrac{4}{15}$

The process of finding the LCD is exactly the same in algebra as it is in arithmetic. We can summarize the steps with the following rule:

To Add or Subtract Unlike Fractions

STEP 1 Find the lowest common denominator of all the fractions.
STEP 2 Convert each fraction to an equivalent fraction with the LCD as a denominator.
STEP 3 Add or subtract the like fractions formed in step 2.
STEP 4 Write the sum or difference in simplest form.

• Example 2

Adding Unlike Fractions

(*a*) Add $\dfrac{3}{2x} + \dfrac{4}{x^2}$.

Step 1 Factor the denominators.

$2x = 2 \cdot x$

$x^2 = x \cdot x$

Although the product of the denominators will be a common denominator, it is not necessarily the *lowest* common denominator (LCD).

The LCD must contain the factors 2 and x. The factor x must appear *twice* because it appears twice as a factor in the second denominator.

The LCD is $2 \cdot x \cdot x$, or $2x^2$.

Step 2

$$\frac{3}{2x} = \frac{3 \cdot x}{2x \cdot x} = \frac{3x}{2x^2}$$

$$\frac{4}{x^2} = \frac{4 \cdot 2}{x^2 \cdot 2} = \frac{8}{2x^2}$$

Step 3

$$\frac{3}{2x} + \frac{4}{x^2} = \frac{3x}{2x^2} + \frac{8}{2x^2} = \frac{3x + 8}{2x^2}$$

The sum is in simplest form.

(*b*) Subtract $\dfrac{4}{3x^2} - \dfrac{3}{2x^3}$.

Step 1 Factor the denominators.

$3x^2 = 3 \cdot x \cdot x$

$2x^3 = 2 \cdot x \cdot x \cdot x$ The factor x must appear *3* times. Do you see why?

The LCD must contain the factors 2, 3, and x. The LCD is

$$2 \cdot 3 \cdot x \cdot x \cdot x \quad \text{or} \quad 6x^3$$

Step 2

Both the numerator and the denominator must be multiplied by the same quantity.

$$\frac{4}{3x^2} = \frac{4 \cdot 2x}{3x^2 \cdot 2x} = \frac{8x}{6x^3}$$

$$\frac{3}{2x^3} = \frac{3 \cdot 3}{2x^3 \cdot 3} = \frac{9}{6x^3}$$

Step 3

$$\frac{4}{3x^2} - \frac{3}{2x^3} = \frac{8x}{6x^3} - \frac{9}{6x^3} = \frac{8x - 9}{6x^3}$$

The difference is in simplest form.

● ● ● **CHECK YOURSELF 2**

Add or subtract as indicated.

a. $\dfrac{5}{x^2} + \dfrac{3}{x^3}$ **b.** $\dfrac{3}{5x} - \dfrac{1}{4x^2}$

We can also add fractions with more than one variable in the denominator. Example 3 shows this property.

•Example 3

Adding Unlike Fractions

Add $\dfrac{2}{3x^2y} + \dfrac{3}{4x^3}$.

Step 1 Factor the denominators.

$$3x^2y = 3 \cdot x \cdot x \cdot y$$

$$4x^3 = 2 \cdot 2 \cdot x \cdot x \cdot x$$

The LCD is $12x^3y$. Do you see why?

Step 2

$$\frac{2}{3x^2y} = \frac{2 \cdot 4x}{3x^2y \cdot 4x} = \frac{8x}{12x^3y}$$

$$\frac{3}{4x^3} = \frac{3 \cdot 3y}{4x^3 \cdot 3y} = \frac{9y}{12x^3y}$$

Step 3

The y in the numerator and that in the denominator cannot be divided out since they are not factors.

$$\frac{2}{3x^2y} + \frac{3}{4x^3} = \frac{8x}{12x^3y} + \frac{9y}{12x^3y}$$
$$= \frac{8x + 9y}{12x^3y}$$

● ● ● CHECK YOURSELF 3

Add.

$$\frac{2}{3x^2y} + \frac{1}{6xy^2}$$

Fractions with binomials in the denominator can also be added by taking the approach shown in Example 3. Example 4 illustrates this approach with binomials.

● Example 4

Adding Unlike Fractions

(a) Add $\dfrac{5}{x} + \dfrac{2}{x-1}$.

Step 1 The LCD must have factors of x and $x-1$. The LCD is $x(x-1)$.

Step 2

$$\frac{5}{x} = \frac{5(x-1)}{x(x-1)}$$
$$\frac{2}{x-1} = \frac{2x}{x(x-1)}$$

Step 3

$$\frac{5}{x} + \frac{2}{x-1} = \frac{5(x-1)}{x(x-1)} + \frac{2x}{x(x-1)}$$
$$= \frac{5x - 5 + 2x}{x(x-1)}$$
$$= \frac{7x - 5}{x(x-1)}$$

(b) Subtract $\dfrac{3}{x-2} - \dfrac{4}{x+2}$.

Step 1 The LCD must have factors of $x-2$ and $x+2$. The LCD is $(x-2)(x+2)$.

Step 2

Multiply numerator and denominator by $x + 2$.

$$\frac{3}{x - 2} = \frac{3(x + 2)}{(x - 2)(x + 2)}$$

Multiply numerator and denominator by $x - 2$.

$$\frac{4}{x + 2} = \frac{4(x - 2)}{(x + 2)(x - 2)}$$

Step 3

$$\frac{3}{x - 2} - \frac{4}{x + 2} = \frac{3(x + 2) - 4(x - 2)}{(x + 2)(x - 2)}$$

Note the sign changes.

$$= \frac{3x + 6 - 4x + 8}{(x + 2)(x - 2)}$$

$$= \frac{-x + 14}{(x + 2)(x - 2)}$$

● ● ● ● **CHECK YOURSELF 4**

Add or subtract as indicated.

a. $\dfrac{3}{x + 2} + \dfrac{5}{x}$

b. $\dfrac{4}{x + 3} - \dfrac{2}{x - 3}$

Example 5 will show how factoring must sometimes be used in forming the LCD.

● Example 5

Adding Unlike Fractions

(a) Add $\dfrac{3}{2x - 2} + \dfrac{5}{3x - 3}$.

Step 1 Factor the denominators.

$2x - 2 = 2(x - 1)$

$3x - 3 = 3(x - 1)$

CAUTION

$x - 1$ is not used twice in forming the LCD.

The LCD must have factors of 2, 3, and $x - 1$. The LCD is $2 \cdot 3(x - 1)$, or $6(x - 1)$.

Step 2

$$\frac{3}{2x - 2} = \frac{3}{2(x - 1)} = \frac{3 \cdot 3}{2(x - 1) \cdot 3} = \frac{9}{6(x - 1)}$$

$$\frac{5}{3x - 3} = \frac{5}{3(x - 1)} = \frac{5 \cdot 2}{3(x - 1) \cdot 2} = \frac{10}{6(x - 1)}$$

Step 3

$$\frac{3}{2x - 2} + \frac{5}{3x - 3} = \frac{9}{6(x - 1)} + \frac{10}{6(x - 1)}$$

$$= \frac{9 + 10}{6(x - 1)}$$

$$= \frac{19}{6(x - 1)}$$

(*b*) Subtract $\dfrac{3}{2x - 4} - \dfrac{6}{x^2 - 4}$.

Step 1 Factor the denominators.

$$2x - 4 = 2(x - 2)$$

$$x^2 - 4 = (x + 2)(x - 2)$$

The LCD must have factors of 2, $x - 2$, and $x + 2$. The LCD is $2(x - 2)(x + 2)$.

Step 2

Multiply numerator and denominator by $x + 2$.

$$\frac{3}{2x - 4} = \frac{3}{2(x - 2)} = \frac{3(x + 2)}{2(x - 2)(x + 2)}$$

Multiply numerator and denominator by 2.

$$\frac{6}{x^2 - 4} = \frac{6}{(x + 2)(x - 2)} = \frac{6 \cdot 2}{2(x + 2)(x - 2)} = \frac{12}{2(x + 2)(x - 2)}$$

Step 3

$$\frac{3}{2x - 4} - \frac{6}{x^2 - 4} = \frac{3(x + 2) - 12}{2(x - 2)(x + 2)}$$

Remove the parentheses and combine like terms in the numerator.

$$= \frac{3x + 6 - 12}{2(x - 2)(x + 2)}$$

$$= \frac{3x - 6}{2(x - 2)(x + 2)}$$

Step 4 Simplify the difference.

Factor the numerator and divide by the common factor $x - 2$.

$$\frac{3x - 6}{2(x - 2)(x + 2)} = \frac{3(x - 2)}{2(x - 2)(x + 2)} = \frac{3}{2(x + 2)}$$

(*c*) Subtract $\dfrac{5}{x^2 - 1} - \dfrac{2}{x^2 + 2x + 1}$.

Step 1 Factor the denominators.

$$x^2 - 1 = (x - 1)(x + 1)$$

$$x^2 + 2x + 1 = (x + 1)(x + 1)$$

The LCD is $(x - 1)\underbrace{(x + 1)(x + 1)}$.

Two factors are needed.

Step 2

$$\frac{5}{(x-1)(x+1)} = \frac{5(x+1)}{(x-1)(x+1)(x+1)}$$

$$\frac{2}{(x+1)(x+1)} = \frac{2(x-1)}{(x+1)(x+1)(x-1)}$$

Step 3

Remove the parentheses and simplify in the numerator.

$$\frac{5}{x^2-1} - \frac{2}{x^2+2x+1} = \frac{5(x+1) - 2(x-1)}{(x-1)(x+1)(x+1)}$$

$$= \frac{5x+5 - 2x+2}{(x-1)(x+1)(x+1)}$$

$$= \frac{3x+7}{(x-1)(x+1)(x+1)}$$

● ● ● **CHECK YOURSELF 5**

Add or subtract as indicated.

a. $\dfrac{5}{2x+2} + \dfrac{1}{5x+5}$ **b.** $\dfrac{3}{x^2-9} - \dfrac{1}{2x-6}$

c. $\dfrac{4}{x^2-x-2} - \dfrac{3}{x^2+4x+3}$

Recall from Section 6.2 that

$$a - b = -(b - a)$$

Let's see how this can be used in adding or subtracting algebraic fractions.

●Example 6

Adding Unlike Fractions

Add $\dfrac{4}{x-5} + \dfrac{2}{5-x}$.

Rather than try a denominator of $(x-5)(5-x)$, let's simplify first.

Replace $5 - x$ with $-(x - 5)$. We now use the fact that

$$\frac{a}{-b} = -\frac{a}{b}$$

$$\frac{4}{x-5} + \frac{2}{5-x} = \frac{4}{x-5} + \frac{2}{-(x-5)}$$

$$= \frac{4}{x-5} - \frac{2}{x-5}$$

The LCD is now $x - 5$, and we can combine the fractions as

$$= \frac{4 - 2}{x - 5}$$

$$= \frac{2}{x - 5}$$

● ● ● **CHECK YOURSELF 6**

Subtract.

$$\frac{3}{x - 3} - \frac{1}{3 - x}$$

● ● ● **CHECK YOURSELF ANSWERS**

1. (a) $\dfrac{13}{24}$; (b) $\dfrac{17}{30}$.   **2.** (a) $\dfrac{5x + 3}{x^3}$; (b) $\dfrac{12x - 5}{20x^2}$.   **3.** $\dfrac{4y + x}{6x^2y^2}$.

4. (a) $\dfrac{8x + 10}{x(x + 2)}$; (b) $\dfrac{2x - 18}{(x + 3)(x - 3)}$.   **5.** (a) $\dfrac{27}{10(x + 1)}$; (b) $\dfrac{-1}{2(x + 3)}$;

(c) $\dfrac{x + 18}{(x + 1)(x - 2)(x + 3)}$.   **6.** $\dfrac{4}{x - 3}$.

Add or subtract as indicated. Express your result in simplest form.

1. $\dfrac{3}{7} + \dfrac{5}{6}$

2. $\dfrac{7}{12} - \dfrac{4}{9}$

3. $\dfrac{13}{25} - \dfrac{7}{20}$

4. $\dfrac{3}{5} + \dfrac{7}{9}$

5. $\dfrac{y}{4} + \dfrac{3y}{5}$

6. $\dfrac{5x}{6} - \dfrac{2x}{3}$

7. $\dfrac{7a}{3} - \dfrac{a}{7}$

8. $\dfrac{3m}{4} + \dfrac{m}{9}$

9. $\dfrac{3}{x} - \dfrac{4}{5}$

10. $\dfrac{5}{x} + \dfrac{2}{3}$

11. $\dfrac{5}{a} + \dfrac{a}{5}$

12. $\dfrac{y}{3} - \dfrac{3}{y}$

13. $\dfrac{5}{m} + \dfrac{3}{m^2}$

14. $\dfrac{4}{x^2} - \dfrac{3}{x}$

15. $\dfrac{2}{x^2} - \dfrac{5}{7x}$

16. $\dfrac{7}{3w} + \dfrac{5}{w^3}$

17. $\dfrac{7}{9s} + \dfrac{5}{s^2}$

18. $\dfrac{11}{x^2} - \dfrac{5}{7x}$

1.

2.

3.

4.

5.

6.

7.

8.

9.

10.

11.

12.

13.

14.

15.

16.

17.

18.

19. _____

20. _____

21. _____

22. _____

23. _____

24. _____

25. _____

26. _____

27. _____

28. _____

29. _____

30. _____

31. _____

32. _____

33. _____

34. _____

35. _____

36. _____

37. _____

38. _____

39. _____

40. _____

19. $\dfrac{3}{4b^2} + \dfrac{5}{3b^3}$

20. $\dfrac{4}{5x^3} - \dfrac{3}{2x^2}$

21. $\dfrac{x}{x+2} + \dfrac{2}{5}$

22. $\dfrac{3}{4} - \dfrac{a}{a-1}$

23. $\dfrac{y}{y-4} - \dfrac{3}{4}$

24. $\dfrac{m}{m+3} + \dfrac{2}{3}$

25. $\dfrac{4}{x} + \dfrac{3}{x+1}$

26. $\dfrac{2}{x} - \dfrac{1}{x-2}$

27. $\dfrac{5}{a-1} - \dfrac{2}{a}$

28. $\dfrac{4}{x+2} + \dfrac{3}{x}$

29. $\dfrac{4}{2x-3} + \dfrac{2}{3x}$

30. $\dfrac{7}{2y-1} - \dfrac{3}{2y}$

31. $\dfrac{2}{x+1} + \dfrac{3}{x+3}$

32. $\dfrac{5}{x-1} + \dfrac{2}{x+2}$

33. $\dfrac{4}{y-2} - \dfrac{1}{y+1}$

34. $\dfrac{5}{x+4} - \dfrac{3}{x-1}$

35. $\dfrac{2}{b-3} + \dfrac{3}{2b-6}$

36. $\dfrac{4}{a+5} - \dfrac{3}{4a+20}$

37. $\dfrac{x}{x+4} - \dfrac{2}{3x+12}$

38. $\dfrac{x}{x-3} + \dfrac{5}{2x-6}$

39. $\dfrac{4}{3m+3} + \dfrac{1}{2m+2}$

40. $\dfrac{3}{5y-5} - \dfrac{2}{3y-3}$

41. $\dfrac{4}{5x - 10} - \dfrac{1}{3x - 6}$

42. $\dfrac{2}{3w + 3} + \dfrac{5}{2w + 2}$

43. $\dfrac{7}{3c + 6} - \dfrac{2c}{7c + 14}$

44. $\dfrac{5}{3c - 12} + \dfrac{4c}{5c - 20}$

45. $\dfrac{y - 1}{y + 1} - \dfrac{y}{3y + 3}$

46. $\dfrac{x + 2}{x - 2} - \dfrac{x}{3x - 6}$

47. $\dfrac{3}{x^2 - 4} + \dfrac{2}{x + 2}$

48. $\dfrac{4}{x - 2} + \dfrac{3}{x^2 - x - 2}$

49. $\dfrac{3x}{x^2 - 3x + 2} - \dfrac{1}{x - 2}$

50. $\dfrac{a}{a^2 - 1} - \dfrac{4}{a + 1}$

51. $\dfrac{2x}{x^2 - 5x + 6} + \dfrac{4}{x - 2}$

52. $\dfrac{7a}{a^2 + a - 12} - \dfrac{4}{a + 4}$

53. $\dfrac{2}{3x - 3} - \dfrac{1}{4x + 4}$

54. $\dfrac{2}{5w + 10} - \dfrac{3}{2w - 4}$

55. $\dfrac{4}{3a - 9} - \dfrac{3}{2a + 4}$

56. $\dfrac{2}{3b - 6} + \dfrac{3}{4b + 8}$

57. $\dfrac{5}{x^2 - 16} - \dfrac{3}{x^2 - x - 12}$

58. $\dfrac{3}{x^2 + 4x + 3} - \dfrac{1}{x^2 - 9}$

59. $\dfrac{2}{y^2 + y - 6} + \dfrac{3y}{y^2 - 2y - 15}$

60. $\dfrac{2a}{a^2 - a - 12} - \dfrac{3}{a^2 - 2a - 8}$

A N S W E R S

41. _____
42. _____
43. _____
44. _____
45. _____
46. _____
47. _____
48. _____
49. _____
50. _____
51. _____
52. _____
53. _____
54. _____
55. _____
56. _____
57. _____
58. _____
59. _____
60. _____

61. $\dfrac{6x}{x^2 - 9} - \dfrac{5x}{x^2 + x - 6}$

62. $\dfrac{4y}{y^2 + 6y + 5} + \dfrac{2y}{y^2 - 1}$

63. $\dfrac{3}{a - 7} + \dfrac{2}{7 - a}$

64. $\dfrac{5}{x - 5} - \dfrac{3}{5 - x}$

65. $\dfrac{2x}{2x - 3} - \dfrac{1}{3 - 2x}$

66. $\dfrac{9m}{3m - 1} + \dfrac{3}{1 - 3m}$

Add or subtract, as indicated.

67. $\dfrac{1}{a - 3} - \dfrac{1}{a + 3} + \dfrac{2a}{a^2 - 9}$

68. $\dfrac{1}{p + 1} + \dfrac{1}{p - 3} - \dfrac{4}{p^2 - 2p - 3}$

69. $\dfrac{2x^2 + 3x}{x^2 - 2x - 63} + \dfrac{7 - x}{x^2 - 2x - 63} - \dfrac{x^2 - 3x + 21}{x^2 - 2x - 63}$

70. $-\dfrac{3 - 2x^2}{x^2 - 9x + 20} - \dfrac{4x^2 + 2x + 1}{x^2 - 9x + 20} + \dfrac{2x^2 + 3x}{x^2 - 9x + 20}$

71. Consecutive integers. Use a rational expression to represent the sum of the reciprocals of two consecutive even integers.

72. Integers. One number is two less than another. Use a rational expression to represent the sum of the reciprocals of the two numbers.

73. (a) If 1/4 of the calories in your diet should be from fat, and 3/5 are from carbohydrates (complex carbohydrates, not just sugar), what is left? If daily intake is X calories, what part is left for protein and fiber?

Simplify the following expression to get an expression for the proportion of calories left after calories from fat and carbohydrates are subtracted from your daily intake.

$$X - \frac{1}{4}X + \frac{3}{5}X$$

(b) The American Heart Association stated that, to maintain your weight at its current amount, a moderately active person needs to eat 15 calories for every pound of body weight. A sedentary person should eat only 13 calories for every pound of body weight. To lose 1 pound a week, a healthy rate of weight change, you should cut down by 500 calories a day. Make a chart of your desired daily caloric intake over a 2-day period, keeping track of the number of calories of fat, carbohydrates, and so on that you consume. Does this diet fit the recommendations of part (a)?

ANSWERS

74.

a.

b.

c.

d.

e.

f.

g.

h.

74. (a) If you have already eaten a bowl of ice cream that is 60 percent fat from calories and the total calories was 200, how many calories in fat can you eat during the rest of the day and still be under the 25 percent allowance? Solve the equation below for *a*, the percent calories in fat for the rest of the day. *If x in this equation is the amount of calories you have decided you want to eat in a day. Where does the 120 come from?*

$$\frac{120 + ax}{x} \le .25 \qquad \text{This inequality says:}$$

$$\frac{\text{Calories from fat (\%) of fat calories left)(total daily calories)}}{\text{Total daily calories}} \le 25\%$$

(b) For an afternoon snack you have a glass of 2 percent milk and two graham crackers. On the carton of milk it states that one 8-oz glass has 130 calories, and 44 of these calories are from fat. (Why is it called 2 percent?!) The graham cracker package says that two full crackers are 120 calories, and 20 of these calories are from fat. Update the equation above to reflect the additional calories from fat. Solve the new equation to find out what percentage of calories in fat may be eaten during the rest of the day. Has the percentage changed?

● Getting Ready for Section 6.6 [Section 6.3]

Multiply.

a. $\frac{3}{4} \cdot 8$

b. $\frac{7}{10} \cdot 20$

c. $\frac{4}{x^2} \cdot x^2$

d. $\frac{9}{w^2} \cdot w^3$

e. $\frac{1}{xy} \cdot xy^2$

f. $\frac{2}{a^2} \cdot a^2b^2$

g. $\frac{3}{pq} \cdot p^2q^2$

h. $\frac{2}{a^2b} \cdot a^2b^2$

© 1998 McGraw-Hill Companies

397

Answers

1. $\dfrac{53}{42}$ **3.** $\dfrac{17}{100}$ **5.** $\dfrac{17y}{20}$ **7.** $\dfrac{46a}{21}$ **9.** $\dfrac{15 - 4x}{5x}$ **11.** $\dfrac{25 + a^2}{5a}$

13. $\dfrac{5m + 3}{m^2}$ **15.** $\dfrac{14 - 5x}{7x^2}$ **17.** $\dfrac{7s + 45}{9s^2}$ **19.** $\dfrac{9b + 20}{12b^3}$

21. $\dfrac{7x + 4}{5(x + 2)}$ **23.** $\dfrac{y + 12}{4(y - 4)}$ **25.** $\dfrac{7x + 4}{x(x + 1)}$ **27.** $\dfrac{3a + 2}{a(a - 1)}$

29. $\dfrac{2(8x - 3)}{3x(2x - 3)}$ **31.** $\dfrac{5x + 9}{(x + 1)(x + 3)}$ **33.** $\dfrac{3(y + 2)}{(y - 2)(y + 1)}$ **35.** $\dfrac{7}{2(b - 3)}$

37. $\dfrac{3x - 2}{3(x + 4)}$ **39.** $\dfrac{11}{6(m + 1)}$ **41.** $\dfrac{7}{15(x - 2)}$ **43.** $\dfrac{49 - 6c}{21(c + 2)}$

45. $\dfrac{2y - 3}{3(y + 1)}$ **47.** $\dfrac{2x - 1}{(x - 2)(x + 2)}$ **49.** $\dfrac{2x + 1}{(x - 1)(x - 2)}$ **51.** $\dfrac{6}{x - 3}$

53. $\dfrac{5x + 11}{12(x - 1)(x + 1)}$ **55.** $\dfrac{-a + 43}{6(a - 3)(a + 2)}$ **57.** $\dfrac{2x + 3}{(x + 4)(x - 4)(x + 3)}$

59. $\dfrac{3y^2 - 4y - 10}{(y + 3)(y - 2)(y - 5)}$ **61.** $\dfrac{x}{(x - 3)(x - 2)}$ **63.** $\dfrac{1}{a - 7}$

65. $\dfrac{2x + 1}{2x - 3}$ **67.** $\dfrac{2}{a - 3}$ **69.** $\dfrac{x - 2}{x - 9}$ **71.** $\dfrac{2x + 2}{x(x + 2)}$ **a.** 6   **b.** 14

c. 4   **d.** $9w$ **e.** y **f.** $2b^2$ **g.** $3pq$ **h.** $2b$

398

6.6 Complex Fractions

6.6 OBJECTIVE

Simplify a complex fractional equation

A fraction that has a fraction in its numerator, in its denominator, or in both is called a **complex fraction.** For example, the following are complex fractions

$$\frac{\frac{5}{6}}{\frac{3}{4}} \qquad \frac{\frac{4}{x}}{\frac{3}{x^2}} \qquad \text{and} \qquad \frac{\frac{a+2}{3}}{\frac{a-2}{5}}$$

There are two methods for simplifying a complex fraction. To develop the first, remember that we can always multiply the numerator and the denominator of a fraction by the same nonzero term.

This is the fundamental principle of fractions.

$$\frac{P}{Q} = \frac{P \cdot R}{Q \cdot R} \qquad \text{where } Q \neq 0 \text{ and } R \neq 0$$

For our first approach to simplifying a complex fraction, multiply the numerator and denominator by the LCD of all fractions that appear within the complex fraction.

● Example 1

Simplifying Complex Fractions: Method 1

Simplify $\dfrac{\frac{3}{4}}{\frac{5}{8}}$.

The LCD of $\dfrac{3}{4}$ and $\dfrac{5}{8}$ is 8. So multiply the numerator and denominator by 8.

$$\frac{\frac{3}{4}}{\frac{5}{8}} = \frac{\frac{3}{4} \cdot 8}{\frac{5}{8} \cdot 8} = \frac{3 \cdot 2}{5 \cdot 1} = \frac{6}{5}$$

● ● ● CHECK YOURSELF 1

Simplify.

a. $\dfrac{\frac{4}{7}}{\frac{3}{7}}$
 b. $\dfrac{\frac{3}{8}}{\frac{5}{6}}$

The same method can be used to simplify a complex fraction when variables are involved in the expression. Consider Example 2.

● Example 2

Simplifying Complex Algebraic Fractions: Method 1

Simplify $\dfrac{\dfrac{5}{x}}{\dfrac{10}{x^2}}$.

The LCD of $\dfrac{5}{x}$ and $\dfrac{10}{x^2}$ is x^2, so multiply the numerator and denominator by x^2.

Be sure to write the result in simplest form.

$$\frac{\dfrac{5}{x}}{\dfrac{10}{x^2}} = \frac{\left(\dfrac{5}{x}\right)x^2}{\left(\dfrac{10}{x^2}\right)x^2} = \frac{5x}{10} = \frac{x}{2}$$

● ● ● CHECK YOURSELF 2

Simplify.

a. $\dfrac{\dfrac{6}{x^3}}{\dfrac{9}{x^2}}$

b. $\dfrac{\dfrac{m^4}{15}}{\dfrac{m^3}{20}}$

We may also have a sum or a difference in the numerator or denominator of a complex fraction. The simplification steps are exactly the same. Consider Example 3.

● Example 3

Simplifying Complex Algebraic Fractions: Method 1

Simplify $\dfrac{1 + \dfrac{x}{y}}{1 - \dfrac{x}{y}}$.

The LCD of 1, $\dfrac{x}{y}$, 1, and $\dfrac{x}{y}$ is y, so multiply the numerator and denominator by y.

Note the use of the distributive property to multiply *each term* in the numerator and in the denominator by *y*.

$$\frac{1 + \dfrac{x}{y}}{1 - \dfrac{x}{y}} = \frac{\left(1 + \dfrac{x}{y}\right)y}{\left(1 - \dfrac{x}{y}\right)y} = \frac{1 \cdot y + \dfrac{x}{y} \cdot y}{1 \cdot y - \dfrac{x}{y} \cdot y}$$

$$= \frac{y + x}{y - x}$$

● ● ● **CHECK YOURSELF 3**

Simplify.

$$\frac{\dfrac{x}{y} - 2}{\dfrac{x}{y} + 2}$$

Our second method for simplifying complex fractions uses the fact that

To divide by a fraction, we invert the divisor (it *follows* the division sign) and multiply.

$$\frac{\dfrac{P}{Q}}{\dfrac{R}{S}} = \frac{P}{Q} \div \frac{R}{S} = \frac{P}{Q} \cdot \frac{S}{R}$$

To use this method, we must write the numerator and denominator of the complex fraction as single fractions. We can then divide the numerator by the denominator as before.

●**Example 4**

Simplifying Complex Algebraic Fractions: Method 2

Simplify $\dfrac{4 - \dfrac{y^2}{x^2}}{2 + \dfrac{y}{x}}$.

In this approach, we must first work *separately* in the numerator and denominator to form single fractions.

We have written the numerator and denominator as single fractions. Be sure you see how this is done.

$$\frac{4 - \dfrac{y^2}{x^2}}{2 + \dfrac{y}{x}} = \frac{\dfrac{4x^2 - y^2}{x^2}}{\dfrac{2x + y}{x}}$$

$$= \frac{4x^2 - y^2}{x^2} \cdot \frac{x}{2x + y}$$ Invert the divisor (the denominator) and multiply.

$$= \frac{(2x - y)(2x + y)}{x^2_x} \cdot \frac{x}{2x + y}$$ Factor and divide by the common factors of $2x + y$ and x.

$$= \frac{2x - y}{x}$$

● ● ● **CHECK YOURSELF 4**

Simplify $\dfrac{\dfrac{a^2}{b^2} - 1}{\dfrac{a}{b} + 1}$.

The following algorithm summarizes our work with the two methods of simplifying complex fractions.

To Simplify Complex Fractions

Method 1

STEP 1 Multiply the numerator and denominator of the complex fraction by the LCD of all the fractions that appear within the complex fraction.

STEP 2 Write the resulting fraction in simplest form.

Method 2

STEP 1 Write the numerator and denominator of the complex fraction as single fractions, if necessary.

STEP 2 Invert the denominator and multiply as before, writing the resulting fraction in simplest form.

● ● ● **CHECK YOURSELF ANSWERS**

1. (a) $\dfrac{4}{3}$; (b) $\dfrac{9}{20}$. **2.** (a) $\dfrac{2}{3x}$; (b) $\dfrac{4m}{3}$. **3.** $\dfrac{x - 2y}{x + 2y}$.

4. $\dfrac{a - b}{b}$.

6.6 Exercises

Name

Section   Date

ANSWERS

1. _____

2. _____

3. _____

4. _____

5. _____

6. _____

7. _____

8. _____

9. _____

10. _____

11. _____

12. _____

13. _____

14. _____

Simplify each complex fraction.

1. $\dfrac{\dfrac{2}{3}}{\dfrac{6}{8}}$

2. $\dfrac{\dfrac{5}{6}}{\dfrac{10}{15}}$

3. $\dfrac{1 + \dfrac{1}{2}}{2 + \dfrac{1}{4}}$

4. $\dfrac{1 + \dfrac{3}{4}}{2 - \dfrac{1}{8}}$

5. $\dfrac{2 + \dfrac{1}{3}}{3 - \dfrac{1}{5}}$

6. $\dfrac{2 + \dfrac{3}{5}}{1 + \dfrac{3}{10}}$

7. $\dfrac{\dfrac{2}{3} + \dfrac{1}{2}}{\dfrac{3}{4} - \dfrac{1}{3}}$

8. $\dfrac{\dfrac{3}{4} + \dfrac{1}{2}}{\dfrac{7}{8} - \dfrac{1}{4}}$

9. $\dfrac{\dfrac{x}{8}}{\dfrac{x^2}{4}}$

10. $\dfrac{\dfrac{m^2}{10}}{\dfrac{m^3}{15}}$

11. $\dfrac{\dfrac{3}{a}}{\dfrac{2}{a^2}}$

12. $\dfrac{\dfrac{6}{x^2}}{\dfrac{9}{x^3}}$

13. $\dfrac{\dfrac{y + 1}{y}}{\dfrac{y - 1}{2y}}$

14. $\dfrac{\dfrac{w + 3}{4w}}{\dfrac{w - 3}{2w}}$

15. _____

16. _____

17. _____

18. _____

19. _____

20. _____

21. _____

22. _____

23. _____

24. _____

25. _____

26. _____

27. _____

28. _____

29. _____

30. _____

15. $\dfrac{2 - \dfrac{1}{x}}{2 + \dfrac{1}{x}}$

16. $\dfrac{3 + \dfrac{1}{a}}{3 - \dfrac{1}{a}}$

17. $\dfrac{3 - \dfrac{x}{y}}{\dfrac{6}{y}}$

18. $\dfrac{2 + \dfrac{x}{y}}{\dfrac{4}{y}}$

19. $\dfrac{2 + \dfrac{p}{q}}{1 + \dfrac{p}{q}}$

20. $\dfrac{\dfrac{m}{n} - 3}{\dfrac{m}{n} + 3}$

21. $\dfrac{a^2 - 1}{1 - \dfrac{1}{a}}$

22. $\dfrac{1 + \dfrac{1}{2x}}{4x^2 - 1}$

23. $\dfrac{\dfrac{x^2}{y^2} - 1}{\dfrac{x}{y} + 1}$

24. $\dfrac{\dfrac{a}{b} + 2}{\dfrac{a^2}{b^2} - 4}$

25. $\dfrac{1 + \dfrac{3}{x} - \dfrac{4}{x^2}}{1 + \dfrac{2}{x} - \dfrac{3}{x^2}}$

26. $\dfrac{1 - \dfrac{2}{r} - \dfrac{8}{r^2}}{1 - \dfrac{1}{r} - \dfrac{6}{r^2}}$

27. $\dfrac{\dfrac{1}{x} + \dfrac{1}{y}}{\dfrac{2}{x} - \dfrac{2}{y}}$

28. $\dfrac{\dfrac{3}{a} - \dfrac{3}{b}}{\dfrac{1}{a} + \dfrac{1}{b}}$

29. $\dfrac{\dfrac{2}{x} - \dfrac{1}{xy}}{\dfrac{1}{xy} + \dfrac{2}{y}}$

30. $\dfrac{\dfrac{1}{xy} + \dfrac{2}{x}}{\dfrac{3}{y} - \dfrac{1}{xy}}$

31. $\dfrac{\dfrac{x^2}{y} + 2x + y}{\dfrac{1}{y^2} - \dfrac{1}{x^2}}$

32. $\dfrac{\dfrac{x}{y} + 1 - \dfrac{2y}{x}}{\dfrac{1}{y^2} - \dfrac{4}{x^2}}$

Simplify each complex fraction.

33. $\dfrac{\dfrac{2}{x-1} + 1}{1 - \dfrac{3}{x-1}}$

34. $\dfrac{\dfrac{3}{a+2} - 1}{1 + \dfrac{2}{a+2}}$

35. $\dfrac{1 - \dfrac{1}{y-1}}{y - \dfrac{8}{y+2}}$

36. $\dfrac{1 + \dfrac{1}{x+2}}{x - \dfrac{18}{x-3}}$

37. $1 + \dfrac{1}{1 + \dfrac{1}{x}}$

38. $1 + \dfrac{1}{1 - \dfrac{1}{y}}$

39. Herbicide use. Herbicides constitute $\dfrac{2}{3}$ of all pesticides used in the United States. Insecticides are $\dfrac{1}{4}$ of all pesticides used in the United States. The ratio of herbicides to pesticides used in the United States can be written $\dfrac{2}{3} \div \dfrac{1}{4}$. Write this ratio in simplest form.

40. Pesticide use. Fungicides account for $\dfrac{1}{10}$ of the pesticides used in the United States. Insecticides account for $\dfrac{1}{4}$ of all the pesticides used in the United States. The ratio of fungicides to insecticides used in the United States can be written $\dfrac{1}{10} \div \dfrac{1}{4}$. Write this ratio in simplest form.

41. Environment. The ratio of insecticides to herbicides applied to wheat, soybeans, corn, and cotton can be expressed as $\dfrac{7X}{10} \div \dfrac{4X}{5}$. Simplify this ratio.

A N S W E R S

31. _____

32. _____

33. _____

34. _____

35. _____

36. _____

37. _____

38. _____

39. _____

40. _____

41. _____

ANSWERS

42. _____

43. _____

a. _____

b. _____

c. _____

d. _____

e. _____

f. _____

42. Electricity. The combined resistance of two resistors R_1 and R_2 in parallel, is given by the formula

$$R_T = \cfrac{1}{\cfrac{1}{R_1} + \cfrac{1}{R_2}}$$

Simplify the formula.

43. Complex fractions have some interesting patterns. Work with a partner to evaluate each complex fraction in the sequence below. This is an interesting sequence of fractions because the numerators and denominators are a famous sequence of whole numbers, and the fractions get closer and closer to a number called "the golden mean."

$$1, \quad 1 + \cfrac{1}{1}, \quad 1 + \cfrac{1}{1+\cfrac{1}{1}}, \quad 1 + \cfrac{1}{1+\cfrac{1}{1+\cfrac{1}{1}}}, \quad 1 + \cfrac{1}{1+\cfrac{1}{1+\cfrac{1}{1+\cfrac{1}{1}}}}, \ldots$$

____, ____, ____, ____, ____, ____, ____, ____

After you have evaluated these first five, you no doubt will see a pattern in the resulting fractions that allows you to go on indefinitely without having to evaluate more complex fractions. Write each of these fractions as decimals. Write your observations about the sequence of fractions and about the sequence of decimal fractions.

● Getting Ready for Section 6.7 [Section 3.4]

Solve each of the following equations.

a. $x + 8 = 10$ **b.** $5x - 4 = 2$

c. $3x + 8 = 4$ **d.** $3(x - 2) - 4 = 5$

e. $4(2x + 1) - 3 = -23$ **f.** $4(2x - 5) - 3(3x + 1) = -8$

Answers

1. $\dfrac{8}{9}$ **3.** $\dfrac{2}{3}$ **5.** $\dfrac{5}{6}$ **7.** $\dfrac{14}{5}$ **9.** $\dfrac{1}{2x}$ **11.** $\dfrac{3a}{2}$ **13.** $\dfrac{2(y+1)}{y-1}$

15. $\dfrac{2x-1}{2x+1}$ **17.** $\dfrac{3y-x}{6}$ **19.** $\dfrac{2q+p}{q+p}$ **21.** $a(a+1)$ **23.** $\dfrac{x-y}{y}$

25. $\dfrac{x+4}{x+3}$ **27.** $\dfrac{y+x}{2(y-x)}$ **29.** $\dfrac{2y-1}{1+2x}$ **31.** $\dfrac{x^2y(x+y)}{x-y}$ **33.** $\dfrac{x+1}{x-4}$

35. $\dfrac{y+2}{(y-1)(y+4)}$ **37.** $\dfrac{2x+1}{x+1}$ **39.** $\dfrac{8}{3}$ **41.** $\dfrac{7}{8}$ **a.** 2   **b.** $\dfrac{6}{5}$

c. $-\dfrac{4}{3}$ **d.** 5   **e.** -3 **f.** -15

406

Equations Involving Fractions

6.7 OBJECTIVES

1. Solve a fractional equation
2. Solve a word problem that leads to a fractional equation

The resulting equation *will* be equivalent unless a solution results that makes a denominator in the original equation 0. More about this later!

This equation has three terms: $\frac{x}{2}$, $-\frac{1}{3}$, and $\frac{2x + 3}{6}$. The sign of the term is not used to find the LCD.

By the multiplication property of equality, this equation is equivalent to the original equation, labeled (1).

In Chapter 3, you learned how to solve a variety of equations. We now want to extend that work to the solution of **fractional equations,** which are equations that involve algebraic fractions as one or more of their terms.

To solve a fractional equation, we multiply each term of the equation by the LCD of any fractions. The resulting equation should be equivalent to the original equation and be cleared of all fractions.

• Example 1

Solving Fractional Equations

Solve

$$\frac{x}{2} - \frac{1}{3} = \frac{2x + 3}{6} \tag{1}$$

The LCD for $\frac{x}{2}$, $\frac{1}{3}$, and $\frac{2x + 3}{6}$ is 6. Multiply *each* term by 6.

$$6 \cdot \frac{x}{2} - 6 \cdot \frac{1}{3} = 6\left(\frac{2x + 3}{6}\right) \quad \text{or} \quad 3x - 2 = 2x + 3 \tag{2}$$

Solving as before, we have

$$3x - 2x = 3 + 2 \quad \text{or} \quad x = 5$$

To check, substitute 5 for x in the *original* equation.

$$\frac{5}{2} - \frac{1}{3} \overset{?}{=} \frac{2 \cdot 5 + 3}{6}$$

$$\frac{13}{6} = \frac{13}{6} \quad \text{(True)}$$

CAUTION

Be Careful! Many students have difficulty because they don't distinguish between adding or subtracting *expressions* (as we did in Sections 6.4 and 6.5) and solving equations (illustrated in the above example). In the **expression**

$$\frac{x + 1}{2} + \frac{x}{3}$$

we want to add the two fractions to form a single fraction. In the **equation**

$$\frac{x + 1}{2} = \frac{x}{3} + 1$$

we want to solve for x.

407

Solve and check.

$$\frac{x}{4} - \frac{1}{6} = \frac{4x - 5}{12}$$

The steps of the solution illustrated in Example 1 are summarized in the following rule.

> **To Solve a Fractional Equation**
>
> **STEP 1** Remove the fractions in the equation by multiplying each term by the LCD of all the fractions.
> **STEP 2** Solve the equation resulting from step 1 as before.
> **STEP 3** Check your solution in the *original equation*.

The equation that is formed in step 2 can be solved by the methods of Sections 3.4 and 5.5.

We can also solve fractional equations with variables in the denominator by using the above algorithm. Example 2 illustrates this approach.

● Example 2

Solving Fractional Equations

Solve

$$\frac{7}{4x} - \frac{3}{x^2} = \frac{1}{2x^2}$$

The factor x appears twice in the LCD.

The LCD of the three terms in the equation is $4x^2$, and so we multiply each term by $4x^2$.

$$4x^2 \cdot \frac{7}{4x} - 4x^2 \cdot \frac{3}{x^2} = 4x^2 \cdot \frac{1}{2x^2}$$

Simplifying, we have

$$7x - 12 = 2$$
$$7x = 14$$
$$x = 2$$

We'll leave the check to you. Be sure to return to the original equation.

Solve and check.

$$\frac{5}{2x} - \frac{4}{x^2} = \frac{7}{2x^2}$$

The process of solving fractional equations is exactly the same when binomials are involved in the denominators.

• Example 3

Solving Fractional Equations

(*a*) Solve

There are three terms.

$$\frac{x}{x-3} - 2 = \frac{1}{x-3}$$

The LCD is $x - 3$, and so we multiply each term by $x - 3$.

Each of the terms is multiplied by $x - 3$.

$$(x-3) \cdot \left(\frac{1}{x-3}\right) - 2(x-3) = (x-3) \cdot \left(\frac{1}{x-3}\right)$$

C A U T I O N

Be careful of the signs!

Simplifying, we have

$$x - 2(x - 3) = 1$$
$$x - 2x + 6 = 1$$
$$-x = -5$$
$$x = 5$$

To check, substitute 5 for x in the original equation.

(*b*) Solve

Recall that
$x^2 - 9 = (x - 3)(x + 3)$

$$\frac{3}{x-3} - \frac{7}{x+3} = \frac{2}{x^2-9}$$

In factored form, the three denominators are $x - 3$, $x + 3$, and $(x + 3)(x - 3)$. This means that the LCD is $(x + 3)(x - 3)$, and so we multiply:

$$(x-3)(x+3)\left(\frac{3}{x-3}\right) - (x+3)(x-3)\left(\frac{7}{x+3}\right) = (x+3)(x-3)\left(\frac{2}{x^2-9}\right)$$

Simplifying, we have

$$3(x + 3) - 7(x - 3) = 2$$
$$3x + 9 - 7x + 21 = 2$$
$$-4x + 30 = 2$$
$$-4x = -28$$
$$x = 7$$

Solve and check.

a. $\dfrac{x}{x-5} - 2 = \dfrac{2}{x-5}$ **b.** $\dfrac{4}{x-4} - \dfrac{3}{x+1} = \dfrac{5}{x^2-3x-4}$

You should be aware that some fractional equations have no solutions. Example 4 shows that possibility.

● Example 4

Solving Fractional Equations

Solve

$$\frac{x}{x-2} - 7 = \frac{2}{x-2}$$

The LCD is $x-2$, and so we multiply each term by $x-2$.

$$(x-2)\left(\frac{x}{x-2}\right) - 7(x-2) = (x-2)\left(\frac{2}{x-2}\right)$$

Simplifying, we have

$$x - 7x + 14 = 2$$
$$-6x = -12$$
$$x = 2$$

Now, when we try to check our result, we have

2 is substituted for x in the original equation.

$$\frac{2}{2-2} - 7 = \frac{2}{2-2} \qquad \text{or} \qquad \frac{2}{0} - 7 = \frac{2}{0}$$

These terms are undefined.

What went wrong? Remember that two of the terms in our original equation were $\dfrac{x}{x-2}$ and $\dfrac{2}{x-2}$. The variable x cannot have the value 2 because 2 is an excluded value (it makes the denominator 0). So our original equation has *no solution*.

● ● ● CHECK YOURSELF 4

Solve, if possible.

$$\frac{x}{x+3} - 6 = \frac{-3}{x+3}$$

Equations involving fractions may also lead to quadratic equations, as Example 5 illustrates.

• Example 5

Solving Fractional Equations

Solve

$$\frac{x}{x - 4} = \frac{15}{x - 3} - \frac{2x}{x^2 - 7x + 12}$$

The LCD is $(x - 4)(x - 3)$. Multiply each term by $(x - 4)(x - 3)$.

$$\frac{x}{(x-4)}(x-4)(x-3) = \frac{15}{(x-3)}(x-4)(x-3) - \frac{2x}{(x-4)(x-3)}(x-4)(x-3)$$

Simplifying, we have

$$x(x - 3) = 15(x - 4) - 2x$$

Multiply to clear of parentheses:

$$x^2 - 3x = 15x - 60 - 2x$$

Note that this equation is *quadratic*. It can be solved by the methods of Section 5.5.

In standard form, the equation is

$$x^2 - 16x + 60 = 0 \qquad \text{or} \qquad (x - 6)(x - 10) = 0$$

Setting the factors to 0, we have

$$x - 6 = 0 \qquad \text{or} \qquad x - 10 = 0$$
$$x = 6 \qquad\qquad\qquad x = 10$$

So $x = 6$ and $x = 10$ are possible solutions. We will leave the check of *each* solution to you.

● ● ● CHECK YOURSELF 5

Solve and check.

$$\frac{3x}{x + 2} - \frac{2}{x + 3} = \frac{36}{x^2 + 5x + 6}$$

STRATEGIES IN EQUATION SOLVING

As the examples of this section illustrated, *whenever* an equation involves algebraic fractions, the *first step* of the solution is to clear the equation of fractions by multiplication.

The following algorithm summarizes our work in solving equations that involve algebraic fractions.

To Solve an Equation Involving Fractions

STEP 1 Remove the fractions appearing in the equation by multiplying each term by the LCD of all the fractions.

STEP 2 Solve the equation resulting from step 1. If the equation is linear, use the methods of Section 3.3 for the solution. If the equation is quadratic, use the methods of Section 5.5.

STEP 3 Check all solutions by substitution in the *original equation*. Be sure to discard any *extraneous* solutions, that is, solutions that would result in a zero denominator in the original equation.

Many word problems will lead to fractional equations that must be solved by using the methods above. The five steps in solving word problems are, of course, the same as you saw earlier.

• Example 6

Solving a Numerical Application

If one-third of a number is added to three-fourths of that same number, the sum is 26. Find the number.

Step 1 Read the problem carefully. You want to find the unknown number.

Step 2 Choose a letter to represent the unknown. Let x be the unknown number.

Step 3 Form an equation.

The equation expresses the relationship between the two numbers.

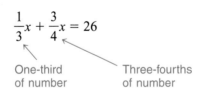

$$\frac{1}{3}x + \frac{3}{4}x = 26$$

One-third of number   Three-fourths of number

Step 4 Solve the equation. Multiply each term of the equation by 12, the LCD.

$$12 \cdot \frac{1}{3}x + 12 \cdot \frac{3}{4}x = 12 \cdot 26$$

Simplifying yields

$$4x + 9x = 312$$
$$13x = 312$$
$$x = 24$$

Be sure to answer the question raised in the problem.

The number is 24.

© 1998 McGraw-Hill Companies

Step 5 Check your solution by returning to the *original problem*. If the number is 24, we have

$$\frac{1}{3} \cdot 24 + \frac{3}{4} \cdot 24 = 8 + 18 = 26$$

and the solution is verified.

● ● ● ● **CHECK YOURSELF 6**

The sum of two-fifths of a number and one-half of that number is 18. Find the number.

Number problems that involve reciprocals can be solved by using fractional equations. Example 7 illustrates this approach.

● **Example 7**

Solving a Numerical Application

One number is twice another number. If the sum of their reciprocals is $\frac{3}{10}$, what are the two numbers?

Step 1 You want to find the two numbers.

Step 2 Let x be one number. Then $2x$ is the other number.

Twice the first

Step 3

The reciprocal of a fraction is the fraction obtained by switching the numerator and denominator.

$$\frac{1}{x} \;+\; \frac{1}{2x} \;=\; \frac{3}{10}$$

The reciprocal of the first number, x The reciprocal of the second number, $2x$

Step 4 The LCD of the fractions is $10x$, and so we multiply by $10x$.

$$10x\left(\frac{1}{x}\right) + 10x\left(\frac{1}{2x}\right) = 10x\left(\frac{3}{10}\right)$$

Simplifying, we have

$$10 + 5 = 3x$$
$$15 = 3x$$
$$5 = x$$

x was one number, and $2x$ was the other.

The numbers are 5 and 10.

Step 5

Again check the result by returning to the original problem. If the numbers are 5 and 10, we have

$$\frac{1}{5} + \frac{1}{10} = \frac{2+1}{10} = \frac{3}{10}$$

The sum of the reciprocals is $\frac{3}{10}$.

●●● **CHECK YOURSELF 7**

One number is 3 times another. If the sum of their reciprocals is $\frac{2}{9}$, find the two numbers.

___

The solution of many motion problems will also involve fractional equations. Remember that the key equation for solving all motion problems relates the distance traveled, the speed or rate, and the time:

$$d = r \cdot t$$

Often we will use this equation in different forms by solving for r or for t. So

$$r = \frac{d}{t} \quad \text{or} \quad t = \frac{d}{r}$$

● Example 8

Solving an Application Involving $r = \dfrac{d}{t}$

Vince took 1 hour (h) longer to drive 180 miles (mi) than he did on a trip of 135 mi. If his speed was the same both times, how long did each trip take?

Step 1 You want to find the times taken for the 180-mi trip and for the 135-mi trip.

Step 2 Let t be the time for the 135-mi trip (in hours).

Note: It is often helpful to choose your variable to "suggest" the unknown quantity—here t for time.

1 h longer

Then $t + 1$ is the time for the 180-mi trip.

It is often helpful to arrange the information in tabular form such as that shown.

Step 3 In forming the equation, remember that the speed (or rate) for each trip was the same. That is the *key* idea. We can equate the rates for the two trips that were

	Distance	Time	Rate
135-mi trip	135	t	$\dfrac{135}{t}$
180-mi trip	180	$t+1$	$\dfrac{180}{t+1}$

Remember that rate is distance divided by time. The rightmost column is formed by using that relationship.

found in step 2. The two rates are shown in the rightmost column of the table. Thus we can write

$$\frac{135}{t} = \frac{180}{t+1}$$

Step 4 To solve the above equation, multiply each term by $t(t+1)$, the LCD of the fractions.

$$t(t+1)\left(\frac{135}{t}\right) = t(t+1)\left(\frac{180}{t+1}\right)$$

Simplifying, we have

$$135(t+1) = 180t$$
$$135t + 135 = 180t$$
$$135 = 45t$$
$$t = 3 \text{ h}$$

The time for the 135-mi trip was 3 h, and the time for the 180-mi trip was 4 h. We'll leave the check to you.

● ● ● **CHECK YOURSELF 8**

Cynthia took 1 h longer to bicycle 60 mi than she did on a trip of 45 mi. If her speed was the same each time, find the time for each trip.

Example 9 uses the $d = r \cdot t$ relationship to find the speed.

●Example 9

Solving an Application Involving $d = r \cdot t$

A train makes a trip of 300 mi in the same time that a bus can travel 250 mi. If the speed of the train is 10 mi/h faster than the speed of the bus, find the speed of each.

Step 1 You want to find the speeds of the train and of the bus.

Step 2 Let r be the speed (or rate) of the bus (in miles per hour).

Then $r + 10$ is the rate of the train.

10 mi/h faster

Again let's form a table of the information.

Remember that time is distance divided by rate. Here the rightmost column is found by using that relationship.

	Distance	Rate	Time
Train	300	$r + 10$	$\dfrac{300}{r + 10}$
Bus	250	r	$\dfrac{250}{r}$

Step 3 To form an equation, remember that the times for the train and bus are the same. We can equate the expressions for time found in step 2. Again, working from the rightmost column, we have

$$\frac{250}{r} = \frac{300}{r + 10}$$

Step 4 We multiply each term by $r(r + 10)$, the LCD of the fractions.

$$\cancel{r}(r + 10)\left(\frac{250}{\cancel{r}}\right) = r\cancel{(r + 10)}\left(\frac{300}{\cancel{r + 10}}\right)$$

Simplifying, we have

$$250(r + 10) = 300r$$
$$250r + 2500 = 300r$$
$$2500 = 50r$$
$$r = 50 \text{ mi/h}$$

Remember to find the rates of both vehicles.

The rate of the bus is 50 mi/h, and the rate of the train is 60 mi/h. You can check this result.

● ● ● **CHECK YOURSELF 9**

A car makes a trip of 280 mi in the same time that a truck travels 245 mi. If the speed of the truck is 5 mi/h slower than that of the car, find the speed of each.

A final group of applications involves fractions in decimal form. Mixture problems often use percentages, and those percentages can be written as decimals. Example 10 illustrates this method.

• Example 10

Solving an Application Involving Solutions

A solution of antifreeze is 20% alcohol. How much pure alcohol must be added to 12 quarts (qt) of the solution to make a 40% solution?

Step 1 You want to find the number of quarts of pure alcohol that must be added.

Step 2 Let x be the number of quarts of pure alcohol to be added.

Step 3 To form our equation, note that the amount of alcohol present before mixing *must be the same* as the amount in the combined solution.

A picture will help.

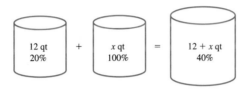

So

Express the percentages as decimals in the equation.

$$12(0.20) + x(1.00) = (12 + x)(0.40)$$

The amount of alcohol in the first solution (20% is 0.20).

The amount of pure alcohol ("pure" is 100%, or 1.00).

The amount of alcohol in the mixture.

Step 4 Most students prefer to clear the decimals at this stage. It's easy here—multiplying by 100 will move the decimal point *two places to the right*. We then have

$$12(20) + x(100) = (12 + x)(40)$$
$$240 + 100x = 480 + 40x$$
$$60x = 240$$
$$x = 4 \text{ qt}$$

● ● ● **CHECK YOURSELF 10**

How much pure alcohol must be added to 500 cubic centimeters (cm³) of a 40% alcohol mixture to make a solution that is 80% alcohol?

● ● ● **CHECK YOURSELF ANSWERS**

1. 3.   **2.** 3.   **3. (a)** 8; **(b)** -11.   **4.** No solution   **5.** $x = -5$ or $x = \dfrac{8}{3}$.   **6.** The number is 20.   **7.** The numbers are 6 and 18.   **8.** 60-mi trip: 4 h; 45-mi trip: 3 h.   **9.** Car: 40 mi/h; truck: 35 mi/h.   **10.** 1000 cm^3.

A N S W E R S

1. _____

2. _____

3. _____

4. _____

5. _____

6. _____

7. _____

8. _____

9. _____

10. _____

11. _____

12. _____

13. _____

14. _____

15. _____

16. _____

17. _____

18. _____

19. _____

20. _____

21. _____

22. _____

Solve each of the following equations for x.

1. $\dfrac{x}{2} + 3 = 6$

2. $\dfrac{x}{3} - 2 = 1$

3. $\dfrac{x}{2} - \dfrac{x}{3} = 2$

4. $\dfrac{x}{6} - \dfrac{x}{8} = 1$

5. $\dfrac{x}{5} - \dfrac{1}{3} = \dfrac{x - 7}{3}$

6. $\dfrac{x}{6} + \dfrac{3}{4} = \dfrac{x - 1}{4}$

7. $\dfrac{x}{4} - \dfrac{1}{5} = \dfrac{4x + 3}{20}$

8. $\dfrac{x}{12} - \dfrac{1}{6} = \dfrac{2x - 7}{12}$

9. $\dfrac{3}{x} + 2 = \dfrac{7}{x}$

10. $\dfrac{4}{x} - 3 = \dfrac{16}{x}$

11. $\dfrac{4}{x} + \dfrac{3}{4} = \dfrac{10}{x}$

12. $\dfrac{3}{x} = \dfrac{5}{3} - \dfrac{7}{x}$

13. $\dfrac{5}{2x} - \dfrac{1}{x} = \dfrac{9}{2x^2}$

14. $\dfrac{4}{3x} + \dfrac{1}{x} = \dfrac{14}{3x^2}$

15. $\dfrac{2}{x - 3} + 1 = \dfrac{7}{x - 3}$

16. $\dfrac{x}{x + 1} + 2 = \dfrac{14}{x + 1}$

17. $\dfrac{12}{x + 3} = \dfrac{x}{x + 3} + 2$

18. $\dfrac{5}{x - 3} + 3 = \dfrac{x}{x - 3}$

19. $\dfrac{3}{x - 5} + 4 = \dfrac{2x + 5}{x - 5}$

20. $\dfrac{24}{x + 5} - 2 = \dfrac{x + 2}{x + 5}$

21. $\dfrac{2}{x + 3} + \dfrac{1}{2} = \dfrac{x + 6}{x + 3}$

22. $\dfrac{6}{x - 5} - \dfrac{2}{3} = \dfrac{x - 9}{x - 5}$

23. $\dfrac{x}{3x + 12} + \dfrac{x - 1}{x + 4} = \dfrac{5}{3}$

24. $\dfrac{x}{4x - 12} - \dfrac{x - 4}{x - 3} = \dfrac{1}{8}$

25. $\dfrac{x}{x - 3} - 2 = \dfrac{3}{x - 3}$

26. $\dfrac{x}{x - 5} + 2 = \dfrac{5}{x - 5}$

27. $\dfrac{x - 1}{x + 3} - \dfrac{x - 3}{x} = \dfrac{3}{x^2 + 3x}$

28. $\dfrac{x}{x - 2} - \dfrac{x + 1}{x} = \dfrac{8}{x^2 - 2x}$

29. $\dfrac{1}{x - 2} - \dfrac{2}{x + 2} = \dfrac{2}{x^2 - 4}$

30. $\dfrac{1}{x + 4} + \dfrac{1}{x - 4} = \dfrac{12}{x^2 - 16}$

31. $\dfrac{5}{x - 4} = \dfrac{1}{x + 2} - \dfrac{2}{x^2 - 2x - 8}$

32. $\dfrac{11}{x + 2} = \dfrac{5}{x^2 - x - 6} + \dfrac{1}{x - 3}$

33. $\dfrac{3}{x - 1} - \dfrac{1}{x + 9} = \dfrac{18}{x^2 + 8x - 9}$

34. $\dfrac{2}{x + 2} = \dfrac{3}{x + 6} + \dfrac{9}{x^2 + 8x + 12}$

35. $\dfrac{3}{x + 3} + \dfrac{25}{x^2 + x - 6} = \dfrac{5}{x - 2}$

36. $\dfrac{5}{x + 6} + \dfrac{2}{x^2 + 7x + 6} = \dfrac{3}{x + 1}$

37. $\dfrac{7}{x - 5} - \dfrac{3}{x + 5} = \dfrac{40}{x^2 - 25}$

38. $\dfrac{3}{x - 3} - \dfrac{18}{x^2 - 9} = \dfrac{5}{x + 3}$

39. $\dfrac{2x}{x - 3} + \dfrac{2}{x - 5} = \dfrac{3x}{x^2 - 8x + 15}$

40. $\dfrac{x}{x - 4} = \dfrac{5x}{x^2 - x - 12} - \dfrac{3}{x + 3}$

41. $\dfrac{2x}{x + 2} = \dfrac{5}{x^2 - x - 6} - \dfrac{1}{x - 3}$

42. $\dfrac{3x}{x - 1} = \dfrac{2}{x - 2} - \dfrac{2}{x^2 - 3x + 2}$

43. $\dfrac{7}{x - 2} + \dfrac{16}{x + 3} = 3$

44. $\dfrac{5}{x - 2} + \dfrac{6}{x + 2} = 2$

45. $\dfrac{11}{x - 3} - 1 = \dfrac{10}{x + 3}$

46. $\dfrac{17}{x - 4} - 2 = \dfrac{10}{x + 2}$

Solve the following word problems. Be sure to write the equation used for each solution.

47. **Adding numbers.** If two-thirds of a number is added to one-half of that number, the sum is 35. Find the number.

48. **Subtracting numbers.** If one-third of a number is subtracted from three-fourths of that number, the difference is 15. What is the number?

49. **Subtracting numbers.** If one-fourth of a number is subtracted from two-fifths of a number, the difference is 3. Find the number.

50. **Adding numbers.** If five-sixths of a number is added to one-fifth of the number, the sum is 31. What is the number?

51. **Consecutive integers.** If one-third of an integer is added to one-half of the next consecutive integer, the sum is 13. What are the two integers?

52. **Consecutive integers.** If one-half of one integer is subtracted from three-fifths of the next consecutive integer, the difference is 3. What are the two integers?

53. **Reciprocals.** One number is twice another number. If the sum of their reciprocals is $\dfrac{1}{4}$, find the two numbers.

54. **Reciprocals.** One number is 3 times another. If the sum of their reciprocals is $\dfrac{1}{6}$, find the two numbers.

55. **Reciprocals.** One number is 4 times another. If the sum of their reciprocals is $\dfrac{5}{12}$, find the two numbers.

56. **Reciprocals.** One number is 3 times another. If the sum of their reciprocals is $\dfrac{4}{15}$, what are the two numbers?

57. **Reciprocals.** One number is 5 times another number. If the sum of their reciprocals is $\dfrac{6}{35}$, what are the two numbers?

58. **Reciprocals.** One number is 4 times another. The sum of their reciprocals is $\dfrac{5}{24}$. What are the two numbers?

A N S W E R S

47. _____

48. _____

49. _____

50. _____

51. _____

52. _____

53. _____

54. _____

55. _____

56. _____

57. _____

58. _____

59. _____

60. _____

61. _____

62. _____

63. _____

64. _____

65. _____

66. _____

67. _____

68. _____

69. _____

59. Reciprocals. If the reciprocal of 5 times a number is subtracted from the reciprocal of that number, the result is $\frac{4}{25}$. What is the number?

60. Reciprocals. If the reciprocal of a number is added to 4 times the reciprocal of that number, the result is $\frac{5}{9}$. Find the number.

61. Driving rate. Lee can ride his bicycle 50 miles (mi) in the same time it takes him to drive 125 mi. If his driving rate is 30 mi/h faster than his rate bicycling, find each rate.

62. Running rate. Tina can run 12 mi in the same time it takes her to bicycle 72 mi. If her bicycling rate is 20 mi/h faster than her running rate, find each rate.

63. Driving rate. An express bus can travel 275 mi in the same time that it takes a local bus to travel 225 mi. If the rate of the express bus is 10 mi/h faster than that of the local bus, find the rate for each bus.

64. Flying time. A light plane took 1 hour (h) longer to travel 450 mi on the first portion of a trip than it took to fly 300 mi on the second. If the speed was the same for each portion, what was the flying time for each part of the trip?

65. Train speed. A passenger train can travel 325 mi in the same time a freight train takes to travel 200 mi. If the speed of the passenger train is 25 mi/h faster than the speed of the freight, find the speed of each.

66. Flying time. A small business jet took 1 h longer to fly 810 mi on the first part of a flight than to fly 540 mi on the second portion. If the jet's rate was the same for each leg of the flight, what was the flying time for each leg?

67. Driving time. Charles took 2 h longer to drive 240 mi on the first day of a vacation trip than to drive 144 mi on the second day. If his average driving rate was the same on both days, what was his driving time for each of the days?

68. Driving time. Ariana took 2 h longer to drive 360 mi on the first day of a trip than she took to drive 270 mi on the second day. If her speed was the same on both days, what was the driving time each day?

69. Flying time. An airplane took 3 h longer to fly 1200 mi than it took for a flight of 480 mi. If the plane's rate was the same on each trip, what was the time of each flight?

A N S W E R S

70. _____

71. _____

72. _____

73. _____

74. _____

75. _____

76. _____

77. _____

78. _____

79. _____

80. _____

70. Traveling time. A train travels 80 mi in the same time that a light plane can travel 280 mi. If the speed of the plane is 100 mi/h faster than that of the train, find each of the rates.

71. Canoeing time. Jan and Tariq took a canoeing trip, traveling 6 mi upstream against a 2 mi/h current. They then returned to the same point downstream. If their entire trip took 4 h, how fast can they paddle in still water? [*Hint:* If r is their rate (in miles per hour) in still water, their rate upstream is $r - 2$ and their rate downstream is $r + 2$.].

72. Flying speed. A plane flies 720 mi against a steady 30 mi/h headwind and then returns to the same point with the wind. If the entire trip takes 10 h, what is the plane's speed in still air?

73. Alcohol solution. How much pure alcohol must be added to 40 ounces (oz) of a 25% solution to produce a mixture that is 40% alcohol?

74. Mixtures. How many centiliters (cL) of pure acid must be added to 200 cL of a 40% acid solution to produce a 50% solution?

Some of the following are expressions, and others are equations. In each case identify which it is and then combine or solve.

75. $\dfrac{5}{x - 2} + \dfrac{3}{x + 3} = \dfrac{8}{x^2 + x - 6}$

76. $\dfrac{7}{x + 5} + \dfrac{4}{x - 1}$

77. $\dfrac{x - 3}{2x} - \dfrac{2x + 5}{x^2}$

78. $\dfrac{x - 1}{x} - \dfrac{x + 2}{3x} = 0$

79. Write an explanation of the difference in use of the common denominator when adding algebraic fractions, and when solving equations. Use examples.

80. You have taken three tests in a class. Your scores are 50, 70, and 75 from a possible total of 100 for each test. You are obviously doing better as the term progresses. What score must you earn on the next test to raise your average grade to 80 percent? To solve, first write an expression for the average of the four test scores, using a variable for the one you have yet to take. You want this average to be at least 80 percent, so you need to write an inequality and solve it. Is it possible to achieve this average on one test?

Let x be your grade on each of the next *two* tests. Set up an inequality to find out what each of the next two test scores need to be to obtain an average of 80 percent. Is it possible? How many tests would you need to take to achieve an 80 percent average, assuming you earned 100 percent on each test? How many tests would you need to take, assuming you earned 90 percent on each test?

Getting Ready for Section 6.8
[Section 3.3]

Solve the following equations.

a. $\dfrac{x}{4} = 7$ **b.** $\dfrac{x}{8} = 9$ **c.** $\dfrac{x}{5} = \dfrac{8}{10}$ **d.** $\dfrac{x}{2} = \dfrac{3}{4}$

e. $\dfrac{x}{9} = \dfrac{7}{3}$ **f.** $\dfrac{x}{6} = \dfrac{28}{8}$ **g.** $\dfrac{2x}{6} = \dfrac{4}{3}$ **h.** $\dfrac{3x}{5} = \dfrac{9}{10}$

Answers

1. 6   **3.** 12   **5.** 15   **7.** 7   **9.** 2   **11.** 8   **13.** 3   **15.** 8

17. 2   **19.** 11   **21.** -5 **23.** -23 **25.** No solution   **27.** 6

29. 4   **31.** -4 **33.** -5 **35.** No solution   **37.** $-\dfrac{5}{2}$ **39.** $-\dfrac{1}{2}, 6$

41. $-\dfrac{1}{2}$ **43.** $-\dfrac{1}{3}, 7$ **45.** $-8, 9$ **47.** 30   **49.** 20   **51.** 15, 16

53. 6, 12   **55.** 3, 12   **57.** 7, 35   **59.** 5

61. 20 mi/h bicycling, 50 mi/h driving   **63.** 55 mi/h, 45 mi/h

65. Freight 40 mi/h, Passenger 65 mi/h   **67.** 5 h, 3 h   **69.** 5 h, 2 h

71. 4 mi/h   **73.** 10 oz   **75.** Equation; $-\dfrac{1}{8}$ **77.** Expression; $\dfrac{x^2 - 7x - 10}{2x^2}$

a. 28   **b.** 72   **c.** 4   **d.** $\dfrac{3}{2}$ **e.** 21   **f.** 21   **g.** 4   **h.** $\dfrac{3}{2}$

6.8 Ratio and Proportion

6.8 OBJECTIVES

1. Solve a proportion for an unknown
2. Apply proportions to the solution of a word problem

To begin this section, let's return to an equation that was developed in the previous section. In Example 3, we had to solve the equation

$$\frac{135}{t} = \frac{180}{t+1}$$

Such an equation is said to be in **proportion form,** or more simply it is called a **proportion.** This type of equation occurs often enough in algebra that it is worth developing some special methods for its solution. First, we will need some definitions.

A **ratio** is a means of comparing two quantities. A ratio can be written as a fraction. For instance, the ratio of 2 to 3 can be written as $\frac{2}{3}$. A statement that two ratios are equal is called a *proportion*. A proportion has the form

$$\frac{a}{b} = \frac{c}{d}$$

In the proportion above, a and d are called the **extremes** of the proportion, and b and c are called the **means.**

A useful property of proportions is easily developed. If

$$\frac{a}{b} = \frac{c}{d}$$

bd is the LCD of the denominators.

and we multiply both sides by $b \cdot d$, then

$$\left(\frac{a}{b}\right)bd = \left(\frac{c}{d}\right)bd \qquad \text{or} \qquad ad = bc$$

If $\dfrac{a}{b} = \dfrac{c}{d}$ then $ad = bc$

In words:

In any proportion, the product of the extremes (ad) is equal to the product of the means (bc).

Since a proportion is a special kind of fractional equation, this rule gives us an alternative approach to solving equations that are in the proportion form.

• Example 1

Solving a Proportion

Solve the equations for x.

The extremes are x and 15.
The means are 5 and 12.

(a) $\dfrac{x}{5} = \dfrac{12}{15}$

Set the product of the extremes equal to the product of the means.

$15x = 5 \cdot 12$

$15x = 60$

$x = 4$

Our solution is 4. You can check as before, by substituting in the original proportion.

(b) $\dfrac{x+3}{10} = \dfrac{x}{7}$

Set the product of the extremes equal to the product of the means.

$7(x + 3) = 10x$

$7x + 21 = 10x$

$21 = 3x$

$7 = x$

We will leave the checking of this result to the reader.

● ● ● CHECK YOURSELF 1

Solve for x.

a. $\dfrac{x}{8} = \dfrac{3}{4}$

b. $\dfrac{x-1}{9} = \dfrac{x+2}{12}$

There are many types of applications that lead to proportions in their solution. Typically these applications will involve a common ratio, such as miles to gallons or miles to hours, and they can be solved with three basic steps.

To Solve an Application by Using Proportions

STEP 1 Assign a variable to represent the unknown quantity.
STEP 2 Write a proportion, using the known and unknown quantities. Be sure each ratio involves the same units.
STEP 3 Solve the proportion written in step 2 for the unknown quantity.

Example 2 illustrates this approach.

•Example 2

Solving an Application Using Proportions

A car uses 3 gallons (gal) of gas to travel 105 miles (mi.). At that mileage rate, how many gallons will be used on a trip of 385 mi?

Step 1 Assign a variable to represent the unknown quantity. Let x be the number of gallons of gas that will be used on the 385-mi trip.

Step 2 Write a proportion. Note that the ratio of miles to gallons must stay the same.

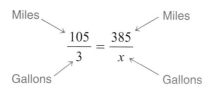

Step 3 Solve the proportion. The product of the extremes is equal to the product of the means.

$$105x = 3 \cdot 385$$

$$105x = 1155$$

$$\frac{105x}{105} = \frac{1155}{105}$$

$$x = 11 \text{ gal}$$

To verify your solution, return to the original problem and check that the two ratios are equivalent.

So 11 gal of gas will be used for the 385-mi trip.

●●● CHECK YOURSELF 2

A car uses 8 liters (L) of gasoline in traveling 100 kilometers (km). At that rate, how many liters of gas will be used on a trip of 250 km?

Proportions can also be used to solve problems in which a quantity is divided by using a specific ratio. Example 3 shows how.

•Example 3

Solving an Application Using Proportions

A piece of wire 60 inches (in.) long is to be cut into two pieces whose lengths have the ratio 5 to 7. Find the length of each piece.

Step 1 Let x represent the length of the shorter piece. Then $60 - x$ is the length of the longer piece.

A picture of the problem always helps.

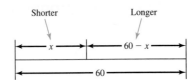

Step 2 The two pieces have the ratio $\dfrac{5}{7}$, so

$$\frac{x}{60 - x} = \frac{5}{7}$$

On the left and right, we have the ratio of the length of the shorter piece to that of the longer piece.

Step 3 Solving as before, we get

$$7x = (60 - x)5$$
$$7x = 300 - 5x$$
$$12x = 300$$
$$x = 25 \qquad \text{(Shorter piece)}$$
$$60 - x = 35 \qquad \text{(Longer piece)}$$

● ● ● **CHECK YOURSELF 3**

A board 21 feet (ft) long is to be cut into two pieces so that the ratio of their lengths is 3 to 4. Find the lengths of the two pieces.

● ● ● **CHECK YOURSELF ANSWERS**

1. (a) 6; **(b)** 10.   **2.** 20 L.   **3.** 9 ft, 12 ft.

Solve each of the following equations for x.

1. $\dfrac{x}{11} = \dfrac{12}{33}$

2. $\dfrac{4}{x} = \dfrac{16}{20}$

3. $\dfrac{5}{8} = \dfrac{20}{x}$

4. $\dfrac{x}{10} = \dfrac{9}{30}$

5. $\dfrac{x+1}{5} = \dfrac{20}{25}$

6. $\dfrac{2}{5} = \dfrac{x-2}{20}$

7. $\dfrac{3}{5} = \dfrac{x-1}{20}$

8. $\dfrac{5}{x-3} = \dfrac{15}{21}$

9. $\dfrac{x}{6} = \dfrac{x+5}{16}$

10. $\dfrac{x-2}{x+2} = \dfrac{12}{20}$

11. $\dfrac{x}{x+7} = \dfrac{10}{17}$

12. $\dfrac{x}{10} = \dfrac{x+6}{30}$

13. $\dfrac{2}{x-1} = \dfrac{6}{x+9}$

14. $\dfrac{3}{x-3} = \dfrac{4}{x-5}$

15. $\dfrac{1}{x+3} = \dfrac{7}{x^2-9}$

16. $\dfrac{1}{x+5} = \dfrac{4}{x^2+3x-10}$

17. Speed conversion. A speed of 60 miles per hour (mi/h) corresponds to 88 feet per second (ft/s). If a light plane's speed is 150 mi/h, what is its speed in feet per second?

18. Cost. If 342 cups of coffee can be made from 9 pounds (lb) of coffee, how many cups can be made from 6 lb of coffee?

19. Fuel consumption. A car uses 5 gallons (gal) of gasoline on a trip of 160 mi. At the same mileage rate, how much gasoline will a 384-mi trip require?

20. _____

21. _____

22. _____

23. _____

24. _____

25. _____

26. _____

a. _____

b. _____

c. _____

d. _____

e. _____

f. _____

20. **Fuel consumption.** A car uses 12 liters (L) of gasoline in traveling 150 kilometers (km). At that rate, how many liters of gasoline will be used in a trip of 400 km?

21. **Yearly earnings.** Sveta earns $6500 commission in 20 weeks in her new sales position. At that rate, how much will she earn in 1 year (52 weeks)?

22. **Investment earning.** Kevin earned $165 interest for 1 year on an investment of $1500. At the same rate, what amount of interest would be earned by an investment of $2500?

23. **Insect control.** A company is selling a natural insect control which mixes ladybug beetles and praying mantises in the ratio of 7 to 4. If there are a total of 110 insects per package, how many of each type of insect is in a package?

24. **Individual height.** A woman casts a shadow of 4 ft. At the same time, a 72-ft building casts a shadow of 48 ft. How tall is the woman?

25. **Consumer affairs.** A brother and sister are to divide an inheritance of $12,000 in the ratio of 2 to 3. What amount will each receive?

26. **Taxes.** In Bucks County, the property tax rate is $25.32 per $1000 of assessed value. If a house and property have a value of $128,000, find the tax the owner will have to pay.

● Getting Ready for Section 6.9

Convert each of the following to decimals.

a. $\dfrac{1}{2}$ b. $\dfrac{3}{5}$ c. $\dfrac{3}{8}$

d. $\dfrac{9}{16}$ e. $\dfrac{13}{52}$ f. $\dfrac{6}{15}$

Answers

1. 4   **3.** 32   **5.** 3   **7.** 13   **9.** 3   **11.** 10   **13.** 6   **15.** 10
17. 220 ft/s   **19.** 12 gal   **21.** $16,900
23. 70 ladybugs, 40 praying mantises   **25.** $4800, $7200
a. 0.5   **b.** 0.6   **c.** 0.375   **d.** 0.5625   **e.** 0.25   **f.** 0.4

6.9

An Introduction to Probability

6.9 OBJECTIVE

Use the definition of probability to calculate simple probabilities

An outcome that we're looking for, whether it's red on the roulette wheel, tails on the coin, or an A on a test, is called a *successful* outcome.

What are the answers to the following questions?

What are the chances that you'll ace the next math test?

What are the chances that you'll be late for your next class?

What are the chances that you'll get tails if you flip a quarter?

What are the chances that you'll win if you bet a dollar on "red" in roulette?

The answer to the first two of these questions depends entirely on your experience. The answer to the last two questions should be the same for everybody.

In mathematics, when we want to assess the chance of something happening, we calculate the **probability.** Probability is found by dividing the number of "successful" outcomes by the number of possible outcomes. The number of successful outcomes is never less than zero, so the smallest value a probability can have is zero. The number of possible outcomes (the denominator) can never be smaller than the number of successful outcomes (the numerator), so the largest possible value for a probability is 1.

A probability of zero means that an event cannot happen. A probability of 1 means that it absolutely will happen. All probabilities fall in between these extremes.

● Example 1

Calculating Probability

Use the definition of probability to answer each question.

(*a*) If you flip a fair coin, what is the probability that it will come up tails?

The probability is the number of successful outcomes divided by the number of possible outcomes. There are two possible outcomes: heads or tails. Of these, one of them (tails) is what we wanted, so the probability is $\frac{1}{2}$.

(*b*) If you roll a fair die, what is the probability of rolling a number smaller than 3?

There are six possible outcomes (1, 2, 3, 4, 5, 6). Of these, only 1 and 2 are smaller than 3, so the probability is $\frac{2}{6}$ or $\frac{1}{3}$.

(*c*) On a roulette table, what is the probability of a red number coming up?

There are 38 numbers on a roulette wheel (00, 0, 1, 2, 3, . . . , 36). Of these 38 numbers, 2 are green (00 and 0), 18 are black, and 18 are red. The probability of a red number is $\frac{18}{38}$ or $\frac{9}{19}$.

● ● ● **CHECK YOURSELF 1**

Use the definition of probability to answer each question.

a. If you flip a fair coin, what is the probability that it will come up heads?
b. If you roll a fair die, what's the probability of rolling an even number?
c. On a roulette table, what is the probability of a green number coming up?

Not all probabilities are as certain as those we saw in the first example, as Example 2 illustrates.

● Example 2

Calculating Probabilities

Use the definition of probability to answer each question.

(*a*) There are 15 males and 20 females in a classroom. If a student is selected at random, what's the probability that the student is a male?

15 of the 35 students are male, so the probability is $\dfrac{15}{35}$ or $\dfrac{3}{7}$.

(*b*) In a recent poll, 601 people were asked their opinion on a certain brand of iced tea. 153 people liked the tea, 108 didn't like the tea, and the remainder had no opinion. What's the probability that a randomly selected person polled had no opinion?

261 people had an opinion, so the remaining 340 did not. The probability that a randomly selected person had no opinion is $\dfrac{340}{601}$.

> The difference between the probabilities in Example 2 and those in Example 1 is that the probabilities in Example 2 depend on the particular classroom, or on the people that were polled. These are called **subjective probabilities.**

● ● ● **CHECK YOURSELF 2**

Use the definition of probability to answer each question.

a. There are 20 brown-eyed students in a classroom of 32 students. If a student is selected at random, what's the probability that the student has brown eyes?
b. In a recent poll, 1537 people were asked about their political preference. 452 people preferred the Whig Party candidate, 658 preferred the Tory Party candidate, and the remainder had no opinion. What's the probability that a randomly selected person polled had no opinion?

> Individual spins of a roulette wheel are **independent events.** That means that the outcome of one spin has no effect on the outcome of any other. Coin tosses and dice throws are two other examples of independent events.

Gamblers know that "dice have no memory." They know that what comes up on one roll of two dice has nothing to do with what will come up on the next roll of those same two dice, as Example 3 illustrates.

• Example 3

Calculating Probability

Find each probability.

If a total of 7 comes up once every 6 rolls of two dice, the probability of rolling a 7 is $\frac{1}{6}$.

(*a*) If a total of 7 comes up once every 6 rolls of two dice, and you've rolled a total of 7 three times in a row, what is the probability that the next roll will total 7?

The probability is $\frac{1}{6}$. The results of any previous rolls are not relevant when calculating probability.

(*b*) If $\frac{1}{2}$ of all children are boys, and you've had four girls in a row, what is the probability that the next child will be a boy?

The probability is $\frac{1}{2}$. The previous births have nothing to do with the sex of the next child.

● ● ● **CHECK YOURSELF 3**

Find each probability.

a. If heads comes up once every 2 flips of a fair coin, and you've flipped it 4 times in a row with every flip resulting in tails, what is the probability that the next flip will result in a head?

b. On a roulette table 18 of the 38 numbers are red. If black has come up 5 times in a row, what is the probability that the next number will be red?

● ● ● **CHECK YOURSELF ANSWERS**

1. (a) $\frac{1}{2}$; **(b)** $\frac{3}{6} = \frac{1}{2}$; **(c)** $\frac{2}{38} = \frac{1}{19}$.

2. (a) $\frac{20}{32} = \frac{5}{8}$; **(b)** $\frac{427}{1537}$.   **3. (a)** $\frac{1}{2}$; **(b)** $\frac{18}{38} = \frac{9}{19}$.

A single die is rolled. Find the probability of each of the following events.

1. Rolling a 3   **2.** Rolling a 5   **3.** Rolling a 7   **4.** Rolling an odd number

5. Rolling a number smaller than 5   **6.** Rolling a number greater than 1

7. Rolling any number except 4   **8.** Rolling a number divisible by 3

A card is drawn at random from a deck of 52 cards. Find the probability of drawing each of the following.

9. A 10   **10.** A black card   **11.** A red face card   **12.** A heart

13. A black 4   **14.** A jack of hearts   **15.** A queen   **16.** A face card

Find the probability of the following events coming up at a roulette table.

17. A black number   **18.** A number greater than 18

19. A number greater than 36   **20.** A number less than 37

21. A number that is at least 25   **22.** A number that is at least 33

23. There are 25 blue-eyed students in a classroom of 45 students. If a student is selected at random, what is the probability that the student has blue eyes?

24. There are 18 boys in a class of 32 students. If a student is selected at random, what is the probability that the student is a boy?

25. In a recent poll, 810 people were asked their opinion about a certain brand of coffee. 450 liked the coffee, 325 did not, and the remainder had no opinion. What's the probability that a randomly selected person polled had no opinion?

26. In a recent opinion poll, 1200 people were asked their opinion about a flat income tax. 650 favored the tax, 310 opposed it, and the rest had no opinion. What's the probability that a randomly selected individual polled opposed the flat tax?

435

ANSWERS

1. _____
2. _____
3. _____
4. _____
5. _____
6. _____
7. _____
8. _____
9. _____
10. _____
11. _____
12. _____
13. _____
14. _____
15. _____
16. _____
17. _____
18. _____
19. _____
20. _____
21. _____
22. _____
23. _____
24. _____
25. _____
26. _____

ANSWERS

27. _____

28. _____

29. _____

30. _____

31. _____

32. _____

33.

Match each probability in Column A with an appropriate expression in Column B.

Column A   *Column B*

27. 0   (*a*) Happens as often as it doesn't

28. .9   (*b*) Happens more often than not

29. .6   (*c*) Almost always happens

30. 1   (*d*) Rarely happens

31. .1   (*e*) Impossible

32. .5   (*f*) Always happens

33. (a) You and a friend decide to play a game where you each take turns throwing two fair dice. The game you devise is this: You win if the *product* of the two numbers is even. Your friend wins if the product of the two numbers is odd. Is this game fair? Do you each have the same probability of winning?

    (b) You and your friend decide to change the game. You win if the *sum* of the two numbers is even and your friend wins if the *sum* of the two numbers is odd. Is this game fair?

    (c) Now you and your friend are joined by two more friends. You play another game: You win if the sum of the numbers is 7. Your first friend wins if doubles are thrown. Your second friend wins if the sum is less than seven but not a double and your third friend wins if the sum is more than seven but not a double. Is this a fair game? Who has the best probability of winning?

Answers

1. 1/6   **3.** 0   **5.** 2/3   **7.** 5/6   **9.** 4/52   **11.** 3/26   **13.** 1/26
15. 1/13   **17.** 9/19   **19.** 0   **21.** 6/19   **23.** 5/9   **25.** 7/162   **27.** e
29. b   **31.** d

Summary

Algebraic Fractions [6.1]

Algebraic Fractions These have the form

$\dfrac{x^2 - 3x}{x - 2}$ is an algebraic fraction. The variable x cannot have the value 2.

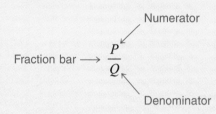

where P and Q are polynomials and Q cannot have the value 0.

Simplifying Algebraic Fractions [6.2]

Writing in Simplest Form A fraction is in simplest form if its numerator and denominator have no common factors other than 1. To write in simplest form:

$\dfrac{x + 2}{x - 1}$ is in simplest form.

1. Factor the numerator and denominator.
2. Divide the numerator and denominator by all common factors.
3. The resulting fraction will be in simplest form.

$\dfrac{x^2 - 4}{x^2 - 2x - 8}$

$= \dfrac{(x - 2)(x + 2)}{(x - 4)(x + 2)}$

$= \dfrac{(x - 2)\cancel{(x + 2)}}{(x - 4)\cancel{(x + 2)}}$

$= \dfrac{x - 2}{x - 4}$

Multiplying and Dividing Fractions [6.3]

$\dfrac{2}{3} \cdot \dfrac{4}{5} = \dfrac{2 \cdot 4}{3 \cdot 5} = \dfrac{8}{15}$

Multiplying Fractions

$$\frac{P}{Q} \cdot \frac{R}{S} = \frac{PR}{QS}$$

where $Q \neq 0$ and $S \neq 0$.

$\dfrac{2x - 4}{x^2 - 4} \cdot \dfrac{x^2 + 2x}{6x + 18}$

$= \dfrac{2(x - 2)}{(x - 2)(x + 2)} \cdot \dfrac{x(x + 2)}{6(x + 3)}$

Multiplying Algebraic Fractions

1. Factor the numerators and denominators.
2. Divide the numerator and denominator by any common factors.
3. Write the product of the remaining factors in the numerator over the product of the remaining factors in the denominator.

$= \dfrac{2\cancel{(x - 2)}}{\cancel{(x - 2)}\cancel{(x + 2)}} \cdot \dfrac{x\cancel{(x + 2)}}{6(x + 3)}$

$= \dfrac{x}{3(x + 3)}$

Dividing Fractions

$\dfrac{4}{9} \div \dfrac{8}{12}$

$$\frac{P}{Q} \div \frac{R}{S} = \frac{P}{Q} \cdot \frac{S}{R}$$

$= \dfrac{4}{9} \cdot \dfrac{12}{8} = \dfrac{2}{3}$

where $Q \neq 0$, $R \neq 0$, and $S \neq 0$. In words, invert the divisor (the second fraction) and multiply.

$\dfrac{3x}{2x-6} \div \dfrac{9x^2}{x^2-9}$

$= \dfrac{3x}{2x-6} \cdot \dfrac{x^2-9}{9x^2}$

$= \dfrac{3x}{2(x-3)} \cdot \dfrac{(x+3)(x-3)}{9x^2}$

$= \dfrac{x+3}{6x}$

Dividing Algebraic Fractions

1. Invert the fraction following the division symbol.
2. Multiply the fractions.

$\dfrac{2x}{x^2+3x} + \dfrac{6}{x^2+3x}$

$= \dfrac{2x+6}{x^2+3x}$

$= \dfrac{2(x+3)}{x(x+3)} = \dfrac{2}{x}$

For $\dfrac{2}{x^2+2x+1}$

and $\dfrac{3}{x^2+x}$

Factor:

$x^2+2x+1 = (x+1)(x+1)$

$x^2+x = x(x+1)$

The LCD is $x(x+1)(x+1)$

Adding and Subtracting Algebraic Fractions [6.4 and 6.5]

Like Fractions

1. Add or subtract the numerators.
2. Write the sum or difference over the common denominator.
3. Write the resulting fraction in simplest form.

The Lowest Common Denominator Finding the LCD:

1. Factor each denominator.
2. Write each factor the greatest number of times it appears in any single denominator.
3. The LCD is the product of the factors found in step 2.

$\dfrac{2}{x^2+2x+1} - \dfrac{3}{x^2+x}$

$= \dfrac{2x}{x(x+1)(x+1)}$

$- \dfrac{3(x+1)}{x(x+1)(x+1)}$

$= \dfrac{2x-3x-3}{x(x+1)(x+1)}$

$= \dfrac{-x-3}{x(x+1)(x+1)}$

Unlike Fractions To add or subtract unlike fractions:

1. Find the LCD.
2. Convert each fraction to an equivalent fraction with the LCD as a common denominator.
3. Add or subtract the like fractions formed.
4. Write the sum or difference in simplest form.

$\dfrac{\dfrac{x-2}{x}}{\dfrac{x^2-4}{x^2}}$ is a complex fraction.

Complex Fractions [6.6]

Complex Fractions Fractions that have a fraction in their numerator, their denominator, or both.

Simplifying To simplify a complex fraction, you can apply either of the following methods.

$$\frac{\left(\dfrac{x-2}{x}\right)x^2}{\left(\dfrac{x^2-4}{x^2}\right)x^2}$$

$$= \frac{(x-2)x}{x^2-4}$$

$$= \frac{x(x-2)}{(x+2)(x-2)}$$

$$= \frac{x}{(x+2)}$$

$$\frac{1-\dfrac{x}{y}}{1-\dfrac{x^2}{y^2}}$$

$$= \frac{\dfrac{y-x}{y}}{\dfrac{y^2-x^2}{y^2}}$$

$$= \frac{y-x}{y}\cdot\frac{y^2}{y^2-x^2}$$

$$= \frac{y-x}{y}\cdot\frac{y^2}{(y-x)(y+x)}$$

$$= \frac{y}{y+x}$$

Method 1

1. Multiply the numerator and denominator by the LCD of all fractions in the complex fraction.
2. Simplify the resulting fraction, writing the result in simplest form, if necessary.

Method 2

1. Write the numerator and denominator as single fractions if necessary.
2. Invert the denominator and multiply as before, writing the result in simplest form.

Fractional Equations [6.7]

$$\frac{2}{x-2} - \frac{3}{x+2} = \frac{2}{x^2-4}$$

Multiply by $(x-2)(x+2)$. We then have

$$2(x+2) - 3(x-2) = 2$$

Solving, we get

$$x = 8$$

Solving Fractional Equations To solve:

1. Remove the fractions in the equation by multiplying *each term* of the equation by the LCD of all the fractions.
2. Solve the resulting equation as before.
3. Check your solution in the *original equation*.

Ratio and Proportion [6.8]

Ratio A means of comparing two quantities. A ratio can be written as a fraction.

$\dfrac{2}{3}$ is the ratio of 2 to 3.

$\dfrac{a}{b}$ is the ratio of a to b.

Proportion A statement that two ratios are equal. The form is

$$\frac{2}{3} = \frac{8}{12}$$

is a proportion; 2 and 12 are the extremes, 3 and 8 are the means.

$$\frac{a}{b} = \frac{c}{d}$$

where a and d are the extremes and b and c are the means.

Solve:

$$\frac{x-2}{3} = \frac{x+2}{7}$$

Set the product of the extremes equal to the product of the means.

$7(x-2) = 3(x+2)$

$7x - 14 = 3x + 6$

$4x = 20$

$x = 5$

The Proportion Rule

If $\dfrac{a}{b} = \dfrac{c}{d}$ then $ad = bc$

In words, the product of the extremes is equal to the product of the means. This rule can be applied in solving fractional equations that are in the proportion form.

Probability [6.9]

Probability measures the chance that something will happen. The value assigned to a probability will always be between 0 and 1.

A probability of 0 means that an event cannot happen.

A probability of 1 means than an event must happen.

If every outcome is equally likely, we can calculate the probability associated with some event by dividing the number of possible successful outcomes by the number of possible outcomes.

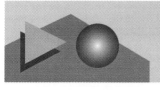

Summary Exercises

This summary exercise set is provided to give you practice with each of the objectives of the chapter. Each exercise is keyed to the appropriate chapter section. The answers are provided in the *Instructor's Manual*.

[6.1] What values for x, if any, must be excluded in the following algebraic fractions?

1. $\dfrac{x}{5}$

2. $\dfrac{3}{x - 4}$

3. $\dfrac{2}{(x + 1)(x - 2)}$

4. $\dfrac{7}{x^2 - 16}$

5. $\dfrac{x - 1}{x^2 + 3x + 2}$

6. $\dfrac{2x + 3}{3x^2 + x - 2}$

[6.2] Write each fraction in simplest form.

7. $\dfrac{6a^2}{9a^3}$

8. $\dfrac{-12x^4y^3}{18x^2y^2}$

9. $\dfrac{w^2 - 25}{2w - 8}$

10. $\dfrac{3x^2 + 11x - 4}{2x^2 + 11x + 12}$

11. $\dfrac{m^2 - 2m - 3}{9 - m^2}$

12. $\dfrac{3c^2 - 2cd - d^2}{6c^2 + 2cd}$

[6.3] Multiply or divide as indicated.

13. $\dfrac{6x}{5} \cdot \dfrac{10}{18x^2}$

14. $\dfrac{-2a^2}{ab^3} \cdot \dfrac{3ab^2}{-4ab}$

15. $\dfrac{2x + 6}{x^2 - 9} \cdot \dfrac{x^2 - 3x}{4}$

16. $\dfrac{a^2 + 5a + 4}{2a^2 + 2a} \cdot \dfrac{a^2 - a - 12}{a^2 - 16}$

17. $\dfrac{3p}{5} \div \dfrac{9p^2}{10}$

18. $\dfrac{8m^3}{5mn} \div \dfrac{12m^2n^2}{15mn^3}$

19. $\dfrac{x^2 + 7x + 10}{x^2 + 5x} \div \dfrac{x^2 - 4}{2x^2 - 7x + 6}$

20. $\dfrac{2w^2 + 11w - 21}{w^2 - 49} \div (4w - 6)$

21. $\dfrac{a^2b + 2ab^2}{a^2 - 4b^2} \div \dfrac{4a^2b}{a^2 - ab - 2b^2}$

22. $\dfrac{2x^2 + 6x}{4x} \cdot \dfrac{6x + 12}{x^2 + 2x - 3} \div \dfrac{x^2 - 4}{x^2 - 3x + 2}$

[6.4] Add or subtract as indicated.

23. $\dfrac{x}{9} + \dfrac{2x}{9}$

24. $\dfrac{7a}{15} - \dfrac{2a}{15}$

25. $\dfrac{8}{x+2} + \dfrac{3}{x+2}$

26. $\dfrac{y-2}{5} - \dfrac{2y+3}{5}$

27. $\dfrac{7r-3s}{4r} + \dfrac{r-s}{4r}$

28. $\dfrac{x^2}{x-4} - \dfrac{16}{x-4}$

29. $\dfrac{5w-6}{w-4} - \dfrac{3w+2}{w-4}$

30. $\dfrac{x+3}{x^2-2x-8} + \dfrac{2x+3}{x^2-2x-8}$

[6.5] Add or subtract as indicated.

31. $\dfrac{5x}{6} + \dfrac{x}{3}$

32. $\dfrac{3y}{10} - \dfrac{2y}{5}$

33. $\dfrac{5}{2m} - \dfrac{3}{m^2}$

34. $\dfrac{x}{x-3} - \dfrac{2}{3}$

35. $\dfrac{4}{x-3} - \dfrac{1}{x}$

36. $\dfrac{2}{s+5} + \dfrac{3}{s+1}$

37. $\dfrac{5}{w-5} - \dfrac{2}{w-3}$

38. $\dfrac{4x}{2x-1} + \dfrac{2}{1-2x}$

39. $\dfrac{2}{3x-3} - \dfrac{5}{2x-2}$

40. $\dfrac{4y}{y^2-8y+15} + \dfrac{6}{y-3}$

41. $\dfrac{3a}{a^2+5a+4} + \dfrac{2a}{a^2-1}$

42. $\dfrac{3x}{x^2+2x-8} - \dfrac{1}{x-2} + \dfrac{1}{x+4}$

[6.6] Simplify the complex fractions.

43. $\dfrac{\dfrac{x^2}{12}}{\dfrac{x^3}{8}}$

44. $\dfrac{3+\dfrac{1}{a}}{3-\dfrac{1}{a}}$

45. $\dfrac{1+\dfrac{x}{y}}{1-\dfrac{x}{y}}$

46. $\dfrac{1+\dfrac{1}{p}}{p^2-1}$

47. $\dfrac{\dfrac{1}{m}-\dfrac{1}{n}}{\dfrac{1}{m}+\dfrac{1}{n}}$

48. $\dfrac{2-\dfrac{x}{y}}{4-\dfrac{x^2}{y^2}}$

49. $\dfrac{\dfrac{2}{a+1}+1}{1-\dfrac{4}{a+1}}$

50. $\dfrac{\dfrac{a}{b}-1-\dfrac{2b}{a}}{\dfrac{1}{b^2}-\dfrac{1}{a^2}}$

[6.7]   Solve the following equations for x.

51. $\dfrac{x}{4} - \dfrac{x}{5} = 2$

52. $\dfrac{13}{4x} + \dfrac{3}{x^2} = \dfrac{5}{2x}$

53. $\dfrac{x}{x-2} + 1 = \dfrac{x+4}{x-2}$

54. $\dfrac{x}{x-4} - 3 = \dfrac{4}{x-4}$

55. $\dfrac{x}{2x-6} - \dfrac{x-4}{x-3} = \dfrac{1}{8}$

56. $\dfrac{7}{x} - \dfrac{1}{x-3} = \dfrac{9}{x^2-3x}$

57. $\dfrac{x}{x-5} = \dfrac{3x}{x^2-7x+10} + \dfrac{8}{x-2}$

58. $\dfrac{6}{x+5} + 1 = \dfrac{3}{x-5}$

59. $\dfrac{24}{x+2} - 2 = \dfrac{2}{x-3}$

[6.7]   Solve the following applications.

60. Number problem. If two-fifths of a number is added to one-half of that number, the sum is 27. Find the number.

61. Number problem. One number is 3 times another. If the sum of their reciprocals is $\dfrac{1}{3}$, what are the two numbers?

62. Reciprocals. If the reciprocal of 4 times a number is subtracted from the reciprocal of that number, the result is $\dfrac{1}{8}$. What is the number?

63. Driving speed. Robert made a trip of 240 miles (mi). Returning by a different route, he found that the distance was only 200 mi, but traffic slowed his speed by 8 miles per hour (mi/h). If the trip took the same time in both directions, what was Robert's rate each way?

64. Distance. On the first day of a vacation trip, Jovita drove 225 mi. On the second day it took her 1 h longer to drive 270 mi. If her average speed was the same both days, how long did she drive each day?

65. Plane speed. A light plane flies 700 mi against a steady 20 mi/h headwind and then returns, with the wind, to the same point. If the entire trip took 12 h, what was the speed of the plane in still air?

66. Solutions. How much pure alcohol should be added to 300 milliliters (mL) of a 30% solution to obtain a 40% solution?

67. Solutions. A chemist has a 10% acid solution and a 40% solution. How much of the 40% solution should be added to 300 mL of the 10% solution to produce a mixture with a concentration of 20%?

[6.8] Solve the following proportion problems.

68. $\dfrac{x-3}{8} = \dfrac{x-2}{10}$

69. $\dfrac{1}{x-3} = \dfrac{7}{x^2 - x - 6}$

70. Investments. Melina wants to invest a total of $10,800 in two types of savings accounts. If she wants the ratio of the amounts deposited in the two accounts to be 4 to 5, what amount should she invest in each account?

[6.9] Solve the following problems.

71. A single die is rolled. What is the probability of rolling a number greater than 4?

72. A card is drawn at random from a deck of 52 cards. What is the probability of drawing a face card or a heart?

73. In a recent poll, 1006 people were asked their opinion about Super Bowl commercials. 320 felt that they were worth watching, and 384 did not. The remaining people had no opinion. What is the probability that a person polled had no opinion?

74. There are 7 left-handed students in a class of 35. What is the probability that a student in this class is left-handed?

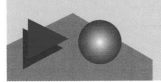

Self-Test
for Chapter 6

A N S W E R S

The purpose of this self-test is to help you check your progress and to review for a chapter test in class. Allow yourself about an hour to take the test. When you are done, check your answers in the back of the book. If you missed any answers, be sure to go back and review the appropriate sections in the chapter and the exercises that are provided.

What values for x, if any, must be excluded in the following algebraic fractions?

1. $\dfrac{8}{x-4}$

2. $\dfrac{3}{x^2-9}$

Write each fraction in simplest form.

3. $\dfrac{-21x^5y^3}{28xy^5}$

4. $\dfrac{4a-24}{a^2-6a}$

5. $\dfrac{3x^2+x-2}{3x^2-8x+4}$

Multiply or divide as indicated.

6. $\dfrac{3pq^2}{5pq^3}\cdot\dfrac{20p^2q}{21q}$

7. $\dfrac{x^2-3x}{5x^2}\cdot\dfrac{10x}{x^2-4x+3}$

8. $\dfrac{2x^2}{3xy}\div\dfrac{8x^2y}{9xy}$

9. $\dfrac{3m-9}{m^2-2m}\div\dfrac{m^2-m-6}{m^2-4}$

Add or subtract as indicated.

10. $\dfrac{3a}{8}+\dfrac{5a}{8}$

11. $\dfrac{2x}{x+3}+\dfrac{6}{x+3}$

12. $\dfrac{7x-3}{x-2}-\dfrac{2x+7}{x-2}$

13. $\dfrac{x}{3}+\dfrac{4x}{5}$

14. $\dfrac{3}{s}-\dfrac{2}{s^2}$

15. $\dfrac{5}{x-2}-\dfrac{1}{x+3}$

16. $\dfrac{6}{w-2}+\dfrac{9w}{w^2-7w+10}$

1. _____

2. _____

3. _____

4. _____

5. _____

6. _____

7. _____

8. _____

9. _____

10. _____

11. _____

12. _____

13. _____

14. _____

15. _____

16. _____

A N S W E R S

17. _____

18. _____

19. _____

20. _____

21. _____

22. _____

23. _____

24. _____

25. _____

Simplify the complex fractions.

17. $\dfrac{\dfrac{x^2}{18}}{\dfrac{x^3}{12}}$

18. $\dfrac{2 - \dfrac{m}{n}}{4 - \dfrac{m^2}{n^2}}$

Solve the following equations for x.

19. $\dfrac{x}{3} - \dfrac{x}{4} = 3$

20. $\dfrac{5}{x} - \dfrac{x-3}{x+2} = \dfrac{22}{x^2+2x}$

Solve the following applications.

21. Number problem. One number is 3 times another. If the sum of their reciprocals is $\dfrac{1}{3}$, find the two numbers.

22. Driving rate. Mark drove 250 miles (mi) to visit Sandra. Returning by a shorter route, he found that the trip was only 225 mi, but traffic slowed his speed by 5 miles per hour (mi/h). If the two trips took exactly the same time, what was his rate each way?

Solve the following proportion exercises.

23. $\dfrac{x-1}{5} = \dfrac{x+2}{8}$

24. Cable length. A cable that is 55 feet (ft) long is to be cut into two pieces whose lengths have the ratio 4 to 7. Find the lengths of the two pieces.

25. A poll of 1056 people were asked their preference for a long-distance carrier. 295 preferred TTA, 157 preferred MRI, and 142 preferred IOG. What is the probability that one of the people polled preferred none of these carriers?

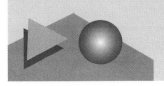
A N S W E R S

This test covers selected topics from the first six chapters.

1. _____

2. _____

Perform the indicated operation.

3. _____

1. $x^2y - 4xy - x^2y + 2xy$

2. $\dfrac{12a^3b}{9ab}$

4. _____

3. $(5x^2 - 2x + 1) - (3x^2 + 3x - 5)$

4. $(5a^2 + 6a) - (2a^2 - 1)$

5. _____

6. _____

Evaluate the expression.

7. _____

5. $4 + 3(7 - 4)^2$

6. $|3 - 5| - |-4 + 3|$

8. _____

9. _____

Multiply.

10. _____

7. $(x - 2y)(2x + 3y)$

8. $(x + 7)(x + 4)$

11. _____

12. _____

Divide.

9. $(2x^2 + 3x - 1) \div (x + 2)$

10. $(x^2 - 5) \div (x - 1)$

13. _____

14. _____

Solve each equation and check your results.

15. _____

11. $4x - 3 = 2x + 5$

12. $2 - 3(2x + 1) = 11$

16. _____

17. _____

Factor each polynomial completely.

13. $x^2 - 5x - 14$

14. $3m^2n - 6mn^2 + 9mn$

18. _____

15. $a^2 - 9b^2$

16. $2x^3 - 28x^2 + 96x$

Solve the following word problems. Show the equation used for each solution.

17. Number problem. 2 more than 4 times a number is 30. Find the number.

18. Number problem. If the reciprocal of 4 times a number is subtracted from the reciprocal of that number, the result is $\dfrac{3}{16}$. What is the number?

A N S W E R S

19. _____

20. _____

21. _____

22. _____

23. _____

24. _____

25. _____

26. _____

27. _____

28. _____

29. _____

30. _____

19. **Speed.** A speed of 60 mi/h corresponds to 88 ft/s. If a race car is traveling at 180 mi/h, what is its speed in feet per second?

20. **Rectangle dimensions.** The length of a rectangle is 3 inches (in.) less than twice its width. If the area of the rectangle is 35 square inches (in.^{2}), find the dimensions of the rectangle.

Write each fraction in simplest form.

21. $\dfrac{m^2 - 4m}{3m - 12}$

22. $\dfrac{a^2 - 49}{3a^2 + 22a + 7}$

Perform the indicated operations.

23. $\dfrac{3x^2 + 9x}{x^2 - 9} \cdot \dfrac{2x^2 - 9x + 9}{2x^3 - 3x^2}$

24. $\dfrac{4w^2 - 25}{2w^2 - 5w} \div (6w + 15)$

25. $\dfrac{4}{3r} + \dfrac{1}{2r^2}$

26. $\dfrac{2}{x - 3} - \dfrac{5}{3x + 9}$

Simplify the complex fractions.

27. $\dfrac{1 - \dfrac{1}{x}}{2 + \dfrac{1}{x}}$

28. $\dfrac{3 - \dfrac{m}{n}}{9 - \dfrac{m^2}{n^2}}$

Solve the following equations for x.

29. $\dfrac{5}{3x} + \dfrac{1}{x^2} = \dfrac{5}{2x}$

30. $\dfrac{10}{x - 3} - 2 = \dfrac{5}{x + 3}$

CHAPTER

7

GRAPHING LINEAR EQUATIONS AND INEQUALITIES

INTRODUCTION

Graphs are used to discern patterns and trends that may be difficult to see when looking at a list of numbers or other kinds of data. The word "graph" comes from Latin and Greek roots and means "to draw a picture." This is just what a graph does in mathematics: It draws a picture of a relationship between two or more variables. But, as in art, these graphs can be difficult to interpret without a little practice and training. This chapter is the beginning of that training. And the training is important because graphs are used in every field in which numbers are used.

In the field of pediatric medicine, there has been controversy about the use of somatotropin (human growth hormone) to help children whose growth has been impeded by various health problems. The reason for the controversy is that many doctors are giving this expensive drug therapy to children who are simply shorter than average or shorter than their parents want them to be. The question of which children are not growing normally because of some serious health defect and need the therapy and which children are healthy and simply small of stature and thus should not be subjected to this treatment has been vigorously argued by professionals here and in Europe, where the therapy is being used.

Some of the measures used to distinguish between the two groups are blood tests and age and height measurements. The age and height measurements are graphed and monitored over several years of a child's life in order to monitor the rate of growth. If during a certain period the child's rate of growth slows to below 4.5 centimeters per year, this indicates that something may be seriously wrong. The graph can also indicate if the child's size fits within a range considered normal at each age of the child's life. _____

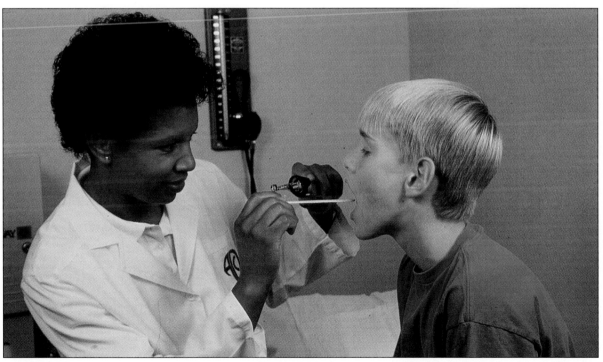

Solutions of Equations in Two Variables

7.1 OBJECTIVES

1. Find the solution(s) for an equation in two variables
2. Use the ordered pair notation to write solutions for equations in two variables

Recall that an equation is two expressions connected by an equal sign.

We discussed finding solutions for equations in Chapter 3. Recall that a solution is a value for the variable that "satisfies" the equation, or makes the equation a true statement. For instance, we know that 4 is a solution of the equation

$$2x + 5 = 13$$

We know this is true because, when we replace x with 4, we have

$$2 \cdot 4 + 5 = 13$$
$$8 + 5 = 13$$
$$13 = 13 \qquad \text{A true statement}$$

We now want to consider **equations in two variables.** An example is

$$x + y = 5$$

What will the solution look like? It is not going to be a single number, because there are two variables. Here the solution will be a pair of numbers—one value for each of the variables, x and y. Suppose that x has the value 3. In the equation $x + y = 5$, you can substitute 3 for x.

$$3 + y = 5$$

Solving for y gives

$$y = 2$$

An equation in two variables "pairs" two numbers, one for x and one for y.

So the pair of values $x = 3$ and $y = 2$ satisfies the equation because

$$3 + 2 = 5$$

That pair of numbers is then a *solution* for the equation in two variables.

How many such pairs are there? Choose any value for x (or for y). You can always find the other *paired* or *corresponding* value in an equation of this form. We say that there are an *infinite* number of pairs that will satisfy the equation. Each of these pairs is a solution. We will find some other solutions for the equation $x + y = 5$ in the following example.

● Example 1

Solving for Corresponding Values

For the equation $x + y = 5$, find (*a*) y if $x = 5$ and (*b*) x if $y = 4$.

(*a*) If $x = 5$

$$5 + y = 5 \qquad \text{or} \qquad y = 0$$

(*b*) If $y = 4$,

$$x + 4 = 5 \quad \text{or} \quad x = 1$$

So the pairs $x = 5$, $y = 0$ and $x = 1$, $y = 4$ are both solutions.

● ● ● **CHECK YOURSELF 1**

For the equation $2x + 3y = 26$,

a. If $x = 4$, $y = ?$ **b.** If $y = 0$, $x = ?$

To simplify writing the pairs that satisfy an equation, we use the **ordered-pair notation.** The numbers are written in parentheses and are separated by a comma. For example, we know that the values $x = 3$ and $y = 2$ satisfy the equation $x + y = 5$. So we write the pair as

CAUTION

(3, 2) means $x = 3$ and $y = 2$.
(2, 3) means $x = 2$ and $y = 3$.
(3, 2) and (2, 3) are entirely different. That's why we call them *ordered pairs*.

$$(3, 2)$$

The *x* coordinate   The *y* coordinate

The first number of the pair is *always* the value for x and is called the **x coordinate.** The second number of the pair is *always* the value for y and is the **y coordinate.**

Using this ordered-pair notation, we can say that (3, 2), (5, 0), and (1, 4) are all *solutions* for the equation $x + y = 5$. Each pair gives values for x and y that will satisfy the equation.

● Example 2

Identifying Solutions of Two-Variable Equations

Which of the ordered pairs (*a*) (2, 5), (*b*) (5, −1), and (*c*) (3, 4) are solutions for the equation $2x + y = 9$?

(*a*) To check whether (2, 5) is a solution, let $x = 2$ and $y = 5$ and see if the equation is satisfied.

$$2x + y = 9 \qquad \text{The original equation}$$
$$x \quad y$$
$$2 \cdot 2 + 5 = 9 \qquad \text{Substitute 2 for } x \text{ and 5 for } y.$$
$$4 + 5 = 9$$
$$9 = 9 \qquad \text{A true statement}$$

(2, 5) is a solution because a *true statement* results.

(2, 5) is a solution for the equation.

(*b*) For (5, −1), let $x = 5$ and $y = −1$.

$$2 \cdot 5 - 1 = 9$$

$$10 - 1 = 9$$

$$9 = 9 \qquad \text{A true statement}$$

So $(5, -1)$ is a solution.

(c) For $(3, 4)$, let $x = 3$ and $y = 4$. Then

$$2 \cdot 3 + 4 = 9$$

$$6 + 4 = 9$$

$$10 = 9 \qquad \textit{Not} \text{ a true statement}$$

So $(3, 4)$ is *not* a solution for the equation.

● ● ● **CHECK YOURSELF 2**

Which of the ordered pairs $(3, 4)$, $(4, 3)$, $(1, -2)$, and $(0, -5)$ are solutions for the following equation?

$$3x - y = 5$$

If the equation contains only one variable, then the missing variable can take on any value.

● Example 3

Identifying Solutions of One-Variable Equations

Which of the ordered pairs, $(2, 0)$, $(0, 2)$, $(5, 2)$, $(2, 5)$, and $(2, -1)$ are solutions for the equation $x = 2$?

A solution is any ordered pair in which the x coordinate is 2. That makes $(2, 0)$, $(2, 5)$, and $(2, -1)$ solutions for the given equation.

● ● ● **CHECK YOURSELF 3**

Which of the ordered pairs $(3, 0)$, $(0, 3)$, $(3, 3)$, $(-1, 3)$, and $(3, -1)$ are solutions for the equation $y = 3$?

Remember that, when an ordered pair is presented, the first number is always the x coordinate and the second number is always the y coordinate.

• Example 4

Completing Ordered Pair Solutions

Complete the ordered pairs (*a*) (9,), (*b*) (, −1), (*c*) (0,), and (*d*) (, 0) for the equation $x - 3y = 6$.

(*a*) The first number, 9, appearing in (9,) represents the *x* value. To complete the pair (9,), substitute 9 for *x* and then solve for *y*.

$$9 - 3y = 6$$
$$-3y = -3$$
$$y = 1$$

The *x* coordinate is sometimes called the **abscissa** and the *y* coordinate the **ordinate.**

(9, 1) is a solution.

(*b*) To complete the pair (, −1), let *y* be −1 and solve for *x*.

$$x - 3(-1) = 6$$
$$x + 3 = 6$$
$$x = 3$$

(3, −1) is a solution.

(*c*) To complete the pair (0,), let *x* be 0.

$$0 - 3y = 6$$
$$-3y = 6$$
$$y = -2$$

(0, −2) is a solution.

(*d*) To complete the pair (, 0), let *y* be 0.

$$x - 3 \cdot 0 = 6$$
$$x - 0 = 6$$
$$x = 6$$

(6, 0) is a solution.

● ● ● **CHECK YOURSELF 4**

Complete the ordered pairs below so that each is a solution for the equation $2x + 5y = 10$.

(10,), (, 4), (0,), and (, 0)

● Example 5

Finding Some Solutions of a Two-Variable Equation

Find four solutions for the equation

$$2x + y = 8$$

Generally, you'll want to pick values for x (or for y) so that the resulting equation in one variable is easy to solve.

In this case the values used to form the solutions are *up to you*. You can assign any value for x (or for y). We'll demonstrate with some possible choices.

Solution with $x = 2$:

$$2 \cdot 2 + y = 8$$
$$4 + y = 8$$
$$y = 4$$

$(2, 4)$ is a solution.

Solution with $y = 6$:

$$2x + 6 = 8$$
$$2x = 2$$
$$x = 1$$

$(1, 6)$ is a solution.

Solution with $x = 0$:

$$2 \cdot 0 + y = 8$$
$$y = 8$$

The solutions $(0, 8)$ and $(4, 0)$ will have special significance later in graphing. They are also easy to find!

$(0, 8)$ is a solution.

Solution with $y = 0$:

$$2x + 0 = 8$$
$$2x = 8$$
$$x = 4$$

$(4, 0)$ is a solution.

● ● ● CHECK YOURSELF 5

Find four solutions for $x - 3y = 12$.

● ● ● CHECK YOURSELF ANSWERS

1. (a) $y = 6$; **(b)** $x = 13$.   **2.** $(3, 4)$, $(1, -2)$, and $(0, -5)$ are solutions.
3. $(0, 3)$, $(3, 3)$, and $(-1, 3)$ are solutions.   **4.** $(10, -2)$, $(-5, 4)$, $(0, 2)$, and $(5, 0)$.
5. $(6, -2)$, $(3, -3)$, $(0, -4)$, and $(12, 0)$ are four possibilities.

A N S W E R S

1. _____

2. _____

3. _____

4. _____

5. _____

6. _____

7. _____

8. _____

9. _____

10. _____

11. _____

12. _____

13. _____

14. _____

15. _____

Determine which of the ordered pairs are solutions for the given equation.

1. $x + y = 6$ $(4, 2), (-2, 4), (0, 6), (-3, 9)$

2. $x - y = 12$ $(13, 1), (13, -1), (12, 0), (6, 6)$

3. $2x - y = 8$ $(5, 2), (4, 0), (0, 8), (6, 4)$

4. $x + 5y = 20$ $(10, -2), (10, 2), (20, 0), (25, -1)$

5. $3x + y = 6$ $(2, 0), (2, 3), (0, 2), (1, 3)$

6. $x - 2y = 8$ $(8, 0), (0, 4), (5, -1), (10, -1)$

7. $2x - 3y = 6$ $(0, 2), (3, 0), (6, 2), (0, -2)$

8. $8x + 4y = 16$ $(2, 0), (6, -8), (0, 4), (6, -6)$

9. $3x - 2y = 12$ $(4, 0), \left(\dfrac{2}{3}, -5\right), (0, 6), \left(5, \dfrac{3}{2}\right)$

10. $3x + 4y = 12$ $(-4, 0), \left(\dfrac{2}{3}, \dfrac{5}{2}\right), (0, 3), \left(\dfrac{2}{3}, 2\right)$

11. $y = 4x$ $(0, 0), (1, 3), (2, 8), (8, 2)$

12. $y = 2x - 1$ $(0, -2), (0, -1), \left(\dfrac{1}{2}, 0\right), (3, -5)$

13. $x = 3$ $(3, 5), (0, 3), (3, 0), (3, 7)$

14. $y = 5$ $(0, 5), (3, 5), (-2, -5), (5, 5)$

Complete the ordered pairs so that each is a solution for the given equation.

15. $x + y = 12$ $(4,\ \ ), (\ \ , 5), (0,\ \ ), (\ \ , 0)$

16. $x - y = 7$ (, 4), (15,), (0,), (, 0)

17. $3x + y = 9$ (3,), (, 9), (, −3), (0,)

18. $x + 5y = 20$ (0,), (, 2), (10,), (, 0)

19. $5x - y = 15$ (, 0), (2,), (4,), (, −5)

20. $x - 3y = 9$ (0,), (12,), (, 0), (, −2)

21. $3x - 2y = 12$ (, 0), (, −6), (2,), (, 3)

22. $2x + 5y = 20$ (0,), (5,), (, 0), (, 6)

23. $y = 3x + 9$ (, 0), $\left(\dfrac{2}{3}, \right)$, (0,), $\left(-\dfrac{2}{3}, \right)$

24. $3x + 4y = 12$ (0,), $\left(, \dfrac{3}{4}\right)$, (, 0), $\left(\dfrac{8}{3}, \right)$

25. $y = 3x - 4$ (0,), (, 5), (, 0), $\left(\dfrac{5}{3}, \right)$

26. $y = -2x + 5$ (0,), (, 5), $\left(\dfrac{3}{2}, \right)$, (, 1)

Find four solutions for each of the following equations. **Note:** Your answers may vary from those shown in the answer section.

27. $x - y = 7$ **28.** $x + y = 18$

29. $2x - y = 6$ **30.** $3x - y = 12$

31. $x + 4y = 8$ **32.** $x + 3y = 12$

33. $2x - 5y = 10$ **34.** $2x + 7y = 14$

35. $y = 2x + 3$ **36.** $y = 8x - 5$

37. $x = -5$ **38.** $y = 8$

An equation in three variables has an ordered triple as a solution. For example, (1, 2, 2) is a solution to the equation $x + 2y - z = 3$. Complete the ordered-triple solutions for each equation.

39. $x + y + z = 0$ (2, −3,)   **40.** $2x + y + z = 2$ (, −1, 3)

41. $x + y + z = 0$ (1, , 5)   **42.** $x + y - z = 1$ (4, , 3)

43. $2x + y + z = 2$ (−2, , 1)   **44.** $x + y - z = 1$ (−2, 1,)

45. Hourly wages. When an employee produces x units per hour, the hourly wage is given by $y = 0.75x + 8$. What are the hourly wages for the following number of units: 2, 5, 10, 15, and 20?

46. Temperature conversion. Celsius temperature readings can be converted to Fahrenheit readings using the formula $F = \dfrac{9}{5}C + 32$. What is the Fahrenheit temperature that corresponds to each of the following Celsius temperatures: −10, 0, 15, 100?

47. Area. The area of a square is given by $A = s^2$. What is the area of the squares whose sides are 5 centimeters (cm), 10 cm, 12 cm, 15 cm?

48. Unit pricing. When x number of units are sold, the price of each unit is given by $p = 5x + 12$. Find the unit price when the following quantities are sold: 2, 7, 9, 11.

49. You now have had practice solving equations with one variable and equations with two variables. Compare equations with one variable to equations with two variables. How are they alike? How are they different?

50. Each of the following sentences describes pairs of numbers that are related. After completing the sentences in parts (a) to (g), write two of your own sentences in (h) and (i).

    (a) The *number of hours you work* determines the *amount you are* _____.

    (b) The *number of gallons of gasoline* you put in your car determines *the amount you* _____.

    (c) The *amount of the* _____ in a restaurant is related to *the amount of the tip.*

    (d) The *sales amount of a purchase in a store* determines _____

    (e) The *age of an automobile* is related to _____

    (f) The *amount of electricity you use in a month* determines _____

    (g) The *cost of food for a family of four* and _____

Think of two more:

    (h) _____.

    (i) _____.

37. _____
38. _____
39. _____
40. _____
41. _____
42. _____
43. _____
44. _____
45. _____
46. _____
47. _____
48. _____
49. _____
50. _____

Getting Ready for Section 7.2 [Section 2.1]

Plot points with the following coordinates on the number line shown below.

a. -3 **b.** 7   **c.** 0   **d.** -8 **e.** $\dfrac{3}{2}$

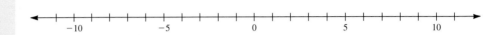

Give the coordinate of each of the following points.

f. A **g.** B **h.** C **i.** D **j.** E

Answers

1. $(4, 2), (0, 6), (-3, 9)$ **3.** $(5, 2), (4, 0), (6, 4)$ **5.** $(2, 0), (1, 3)$

7. $(3, 0), (6, 2), (0, -2)$ **9.** $(4, 0), \left(\dfrac{2}{3}, -5\right), \left(5, \dfrac{3}{2}\right)$ **11.** $(0, 0), (2, 8)$

13. $(3, 5), (3, 0), (3, 7)$ **15.** $8, 7, 12, 12$ **17.** $0, 0, 4, 9$ **19.** $3, -5, 5, 2$

21. $4, 0, -3, 6$ **23.** $-3, 11, 9, 7$ **25.** $-4, 3, \dfrac{4}{3}, 1$

27. $(0, -7), (2, -5), (4, -3), (6, -1)$ **29.** $(0, -6), (3, 0), (6, 6), (9, 12)$

31. $(8, 0), (-4, 3), (0, 2), (4, 1)$ **33.** $(-5, -4), (0, -2), (5, 0), (10, 2)$

35. $(0, 3), (1, 5), (2, 7), (3, 9)$ **37.** $(-5, 0), (-5, 1), (-5, 2), (-5, 3)$

39. $(2, -3, 1)$ **41.** $(1, -6, 5)$ **43.** $(-2, 5, 1)$

45. $9.50, 11.75, 15.50, 19.25, 23$

47. $25 \text{ cm}^2, 100 \text{ cm}^2, 144 \text{ cm}^2, 225 \text{ cm}^2$

a–e.

f. -7 **g.** -4 **h.** 4 **i.** 8 **j.** $\dfrac{19}{2}$

The Rectangular Coordinate System

7.2 OBJECTIVES

1. Graph the points corresponding to a set of ordered pairs
2. Give the coordinates of a set of points on a plane
3. Find the midpoint of two points

This system is also called the **cartesian coordinate system,** named in honor of its inventor, René Descartes (1596–1650), a French mathematician and philosopher.

In Section 7.1, we saw that ordered pairs could be used to write the solutions of equations in two variables. The next step is to graph those ordered pairs as points in a plane.

Since there are two numbers (one for x and one for y), we will need two number lines. One line is drawn horizontally, and the other is drawn vertically; their point of intersection (at their respective zero points) is called the *origin*. The horizontal line is called the **x axis,** while the vertical line is called the **y axis.** Together the lines form the **rectangular coordinate system.**

The axes divide the plane into four regions called **quadrants,** which are numbered (usually by Roman numerals) counterclockwise from the upper right.

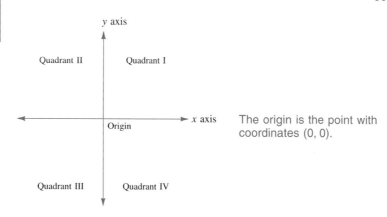

The origin is the point with coordinates (0, 0).

We now want to establish correspondences between ordered pairs of numbers (x, y) and points in the plane.

For any ordered pair

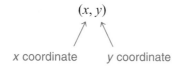

the following are true:

1. If the x coordinate is

Positive, the point corresponding to that pair is located x units to the *right* of the y axis.

Negative, the point is x units to the *left* of the y axis.

Zero, the point is on the y axis.

2. If the y coordinate is

Positive, the point is y units *above* the x axis.

Negative, the point is y units *below* the x axis.

Zero, the point is on the x axis.

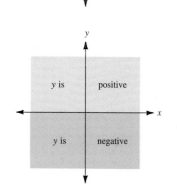

459

Example 1 illustrates how to use these guidelines to give coordinates to points in the plane.

● Example 1

Identifying the Coordinates for a Given Point

Remember: The *x* coordinate gives the *horizontal* distance from the origin. The *y* coordinate gives the *vertical* distance from the *x* axis.

Give the coordinates for the given points.

(*a*)

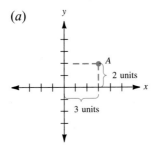

Point *A* is 3 units to the *right* of the origin and 2 units *above* the *x* axis. Point *A* has coordinates (3, 2).

(*b*)

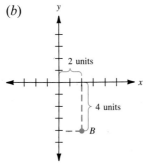

Point *B* is 2 units to the *right* of the origin and 4 units *below* the *x* axis. Point *B* has coordinates (2, −4).

(*c*)

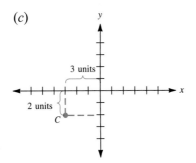

Point *C* is 3 units to the *left* of the origin and 2 units *below* the *x* axis. *C* has coordinates (−3, −2).

(*d*)

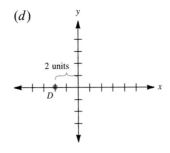

Point *D* is 2 units to the *left* of the origin and *on* the *x* axis. Point *D* has coordinates (−2, 0).

● ● ●   **C H E C K   Y O U R S E L F   1**

Give the coordinates of points *P*, *Q*, *R*, and *S*.

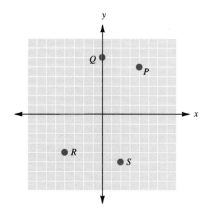

P _____

Q _____

R _____

S _____

Reversing the process above will allow us to graph (or plot) a point in the plane given the coordinates of the point. You can use the following steps.

The graphing of individual points is sometimes called **point plotting.**

To Graph a Point in the Plane

STEP 1   Start at the origin.
STEP 2   Move right or left according to the value of the *x* coordinate.
STEP 3   Move up or down according to the value of the *y* coordinate.

● Example 2

Graphing Points

(*a*) Graph the point corresponding to the ordered pair (4, 3).

Move 4 units to the right on the *x* axis. Then move 3 units up from the point you stopped at on the *x* axis. This locates the point corresponding to (4, 3).

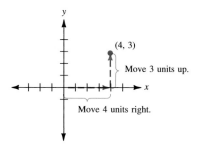

(*b*) Graph the point corresponding to the ordered pair $(-5, 2)$.

In this case move 5 units *left* (because the *x* coordinate is negative) and then 2 units *up*.

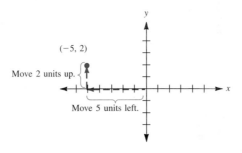

(*c*) Graph the point corresponding to $(-4, -2)$.

Here move 4 units *left* and then 2 units *down* (the *y* coordinate is negative).

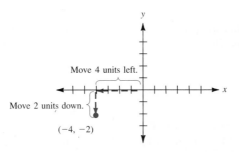

Any point on an axis will have 0 for one of its coordinates.

(*d*) Graph the point corresponding to $(0, -3)$.

There is *no* horizontal movement because the *x* coordinate is 0. Move 3 units *down*.

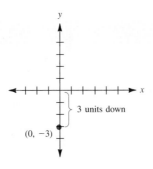

(*e*) Graph the point corresponding to $(5, 0)$.

Move 5 units *right*. The desired point is on the *x* axis because the *y* coordinate is 0.

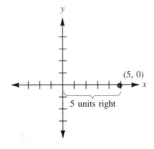

● ● ● **CHECK YOURSELF 2**

Graph the points corresponding to $M(4, 3)$, $N(-2, 4)$, $P(-5, -3)$, and $Q(0, -3)$.

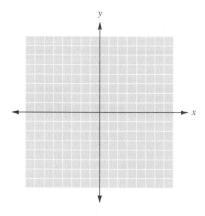

Every two points have a **midpoint.** The midpoint of A and B on line $\overleftrightarrow{AB}$ is the point on the line that is an equal distance from A and B. The following formula can be used to find the midpoint.

The *x* coordinate for the midpoint is the average of the *x*'s. The *y* coordinate for the midpoint is the average of the *y*'s.

The midpoint M of points $A(x_1, y_1)$ and $B(x_2, y_2)$ is found with the formula

$$M = \left(\frac{x_1 + x_2}{2}, \frac{y_1 + y_2}{2} \right)$$

●Example 3

Finding the Midpoint

(*a*) Find the midpoint of $(2, 0)$ and $(10, 0)$.

$$M = \left(\frac{2 + 10}{2}, \frac{0 + 0}{2} \right) = (6, 0)$$

(*b*) Find the midpoint of $(5, 7)$ and $(-1, -3)$.

$$M = \left(\frac{5 + (-1)}{2}, \frac{7 + (-3)}{2} \right) = (2, 2)$$

(*c*) Find the midpoint of $(3, -5)$ and $(-2, -2)$.

$$M = \left(\frac{3 + (-2)}{2}, \frac{(-5) + (-2)}{2} \right) = \left(\frac{1}{2}, \frac{-7}{2} \right)$$

● ● ● CHECK YOURSELF 3

Find the midpoint for each pair of points.

a. $(0, 6)$ and $(0, -4)$.

b. $(3, -6)$ and $(-5, 4)$.

c. $(-1, -5)$ and $(-2, 8)$.

● ● ● CHECK YOURSELF ANSWERS

1. $P(4, 5)$, $Q(0, 6)$, $R(-4, -4)$, and $S(2, -5)$.

2.

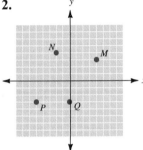

3. **(a)** $(0, 1)$; **(b)** $(-1, -1)$; **(c)** $\left(-\dfrac{3}{2}, \dfrac{3}{2}\right)$.

7.2 Exercises

Name

Section   Date

Give the coordinates of the points graphed below.

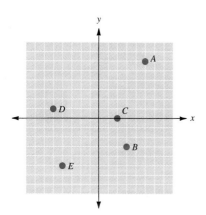

1. *A*   **2.** *B*

3. *C*   **4.** *D*

5. *E*

Give the coordinates of the points graphed below.

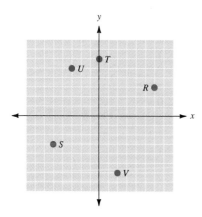

6. *R*   **7.** *S*

8. *T*   **9.** *U*

10. *V*

1. _____

2. _____

3. _____

4. _____

5. _____

6. _____

7. _____

8. _____

9. _____

10. _____

11. _____

12. _____

13. _____

14. _____

15. _____

16. _____

Find the midpoint for each pair of points.

11. $(0, 9)$ and $(0, -5)$

12. $(0, 6)$ and $(6, 0)$

13. $(1, -2)$ and $(5, -8)$

14. $(-2, 8)$ and $(-4, -2)$

15. $(2, -8)$ and $(-1, -5)$

16. $(-3, 5)$ and $(2, -6)$

Plot points with the following coordinates on the graph below.

17. $M(5, 3)$ **18.** $N(0, -3)$

19. $P(-2, 6)$ **20.** $Q(5, 0)$

21. $R(-4, -6)$ **22.** $S(-3, -4)$

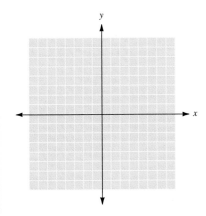

Plot points with the following coordinates on the graph below.

23. $F(-3, -1)$ **24.** $G(4, 3)$

25. $H(5, -2)$ **26.** $I(-3, 0)$

27. $J(-5, 3)$ **28.** $K(0, 6)$

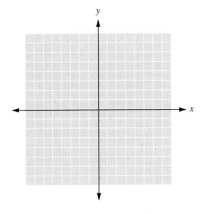

ANSWERS

29. _____

30. _____

31. _____

32. _____

33. _____

29. Graph points with coordinates (2, 3), (3, 4), and (4, 5) below. What do you observe? Can you give the coordinates of another point with the same property?

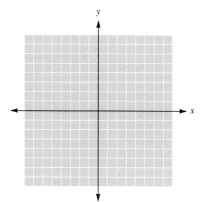

30. Graph points with coordinates (−1, 4), (0, 3), and (1, 2) below. What do you observe? Can you give the coordinates of another point with the same property?

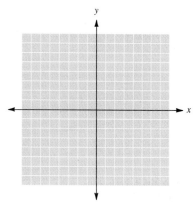

31. Graph points with coordinates (−1, 3), (0, 0), and (1, −3) below. What do you observe? Can you give the coordinates of another point with the same property?

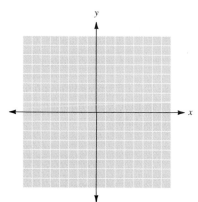

32. Graph points with coordinates (1, 5), (−1, 3), and (−3, 1) below. What do you observe? Can you give the coordinates of another point with the same property?

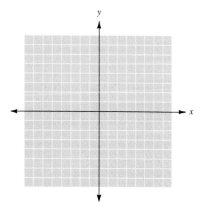

33. Environment. A local plastics company is sponsoring a plastics recycling contest for the local community. The focus of the contest is collecting plastic milk, juice, and water jugs. The company will award $200 plus the current market price of the jugs collected to the group that collects the most jugs in a single month. The number of jugs collected and the amount of money won can be represented as an ordered pair.

a. In April, group *A* collected 1500 pounds (lb) of jugs to win first place. The prize for the month was $350. On the graph on the next page, *x* represents the pounds of jugs and *y* represents the amount of money that the group won. Graph the point that represents the winner for April.

b. In May, group *B* collected 2300 lb of jugs to win first place. The prize for the month was $430. Graph the point that represents the May winner on the same axis you used in part (a).

c. In June, group *C* collected 1200 lb of jugs to win the contest. The prize for the month was $320. Graph the point that represents the June winner on the same axis as used before.

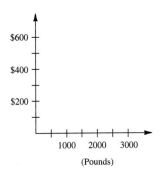

(Pounds)

34. Education. The table gives the hours, *x*, that Damien studied for five different math exams and the resulting grades, *y*. Plot the data given in the table.

x	4	5	5	2	6
y	83	89	93	75	95

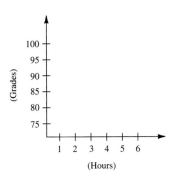

(Hours)

35. Science. The table gives the average temperature *y* (in degrees Fahrenheit) for the first 6 months of the year, *x*. The months are numbered 1 through 6, with 1 corresponding to January. Plot the data given in the table.

x	1	2	3	4	5	6
y	4	14	26	33	42	51

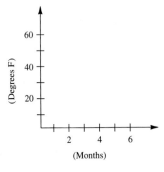

(Months)

36. Business. The table gives the total salary of a salesperson, y, for each of the four quarters of the year, x. Plot the data given in the table.

x	1	2	3	4
y	\$6000	\$5000	\$8000	\$9000

\$10000 —

\$6000 —

\$2000 —

2　4

(Quarter)

37. How would you describe a rectangular coordinate system? Explain what information is needed to locate a point in a coordinate system.

38. Some newspapers have a special day that they devote to automobile wants ads. Use this special section or the Sunday classified ads from your local newspaper to find all the want ads for a particular automobile model. Make a list of the model year and asking price for 10 ads, being sure to get a variety of ages for this model. After collecting the information, make a scatter plot of the age and the asking price for the car.

　　Describe your graph, including an explanation of how you decided which variable to put on the vertical axis and which on the horizontal axis. What trends or other information are given by the graph?

● **Getting Ready for Section 7.3**
　[Section 3.3]

Solve each of the following equations.

a. $2x - 2 = 6$　　　　　**b.** $2 - 5x = 12$

c. $7y + 10 = -11$　　　　**d.** $-3 + 5x = 1$

e. $6 - 3x = 8$　　　　　**f.** $-4y + 6 = 3$

Answers

1. $(5, 6)$ **3.** $(2, 0)$ **5.** $(-4, -5)$ **7.** $(-5, -3)$ **9.** $(-3, 5)$

11. $(0, 2)$ **13.** $(3, -5)$ **15.** $\left(\dfrac{1}{2}, \dfrac{-13}{2}\right)$

17–27. **29.** The points lie on a line; $(1, 2)$

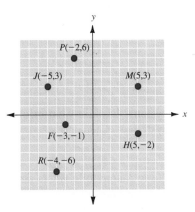

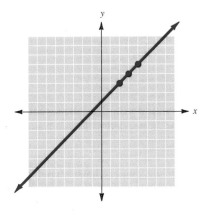

31. The points lie on a line; $(2, -6)$

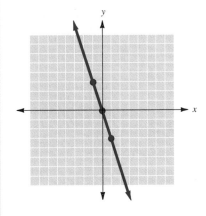

33. $(1500, 350)$

35.

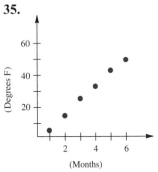

a. 4 **b.** -2 **c.** -3 **d.** $\dfrac{4}{5}$ **e.** $-\dfrac{2}{3}$ **f.** $\dfrac{3}{4}$

7.3 Graphing Linear Equations

7.3 OBJECTIVES

1. Graph a linear equation by plotting points
2. Graph a linear equation by the intercept method
3. Graph a linear equation by solving the equation for y

We are now ready to combine our work of the last two sections. In Section 7.1 you learned to write the solutions of equations in two variables as ordered pairs. Then, in Section 7.2, these ordered pairs were graphed in the plane. Putting these ideas together will let us graph certain equations. Example 1 illustrates this approach.

● Example 1

Graphing a Linear Equation

Graph $x + 2y = 4$.

We are going to find *three* solutions for the equation. We'll point out why shortly.

Step 1 Find some solutions for $x + 2y = 4$. To find solutions, we choose any convenient values for x, say $x = 0$, $x = 2$, and $x = 4$. Given these values for x, we can substitute and then solve for the corresponding value for y. So

If $x = 0$, then $y = 2$, so $(0, 2)$ is a solution.
If $x = 2$, then $y = 1$, so $(2, 1)$ is a solution.
If $x = 4$, then $y = 0$, so $(4, 0)$ is a solution.

A handy way to show this information is in a table such as this:

The table is just a convenient way to display the information. It is the same as writing $(0, 2)$, $(2, 1)$, and $(4, 0)$.

x	y
0	2
2	1
4	0

Step 2 We now graph the solutions found in step 1.

$x + 2y = 4$

x	y
0	2
2	1
4	0

What pattern do you see? It appears that the three points lie on a straight line, and that is in fact the case.

Step 3 Draw a straight line through the three points graphed in step 2.

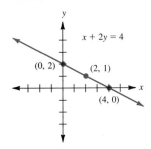

The arrows on the end of the line mean that the line extends indefinitely in either direction.

The graph is a "picture" of the solutions for the given equation.

The line shown is the **graph** of the equation $x + 2y = 4$. It represents *all* of the ordered pairs that are solutions (an infinite number) for that equation.

Every ordered pair that is a solution will have its graph on this line. Any point on the line will have coordinates that are a solution for the equation.

Note: Why did we suggest finding *three* solutions in step 1? Two points determine a line, so technically you need only two. The third point that we find is a check to catch any possible errors.

● ● ● **CHECK YOURSELF 1**

Graph $2x - y = 6$, using the steps shown in Example 1.

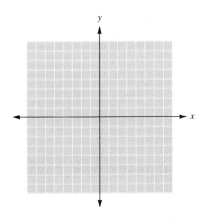

Let's summarize. An equation that can be written in the form

$$Ax + By = C$$

where A, B, and C are real numbers and A and B cannot both be 0 is called a **linear equation in two variables.** The graph of this equation is a *straight line*.

The steps of graphing follow.

To Graph a Linear Equation

STEP 1 Find at least three solutions for the equation, and put your results in tabular form.

STEP 2 Graph the solutions found in step 1.

STEP 3 Draw a straight line through the points determined in step 2 to form the graph of the equation.

● Example 2

Graphing a Linear Equation

Graph $y = 3x$.

Step 1 Some solutions are

Let $x = 0$, 1, and 2, and substitute to determine the corresponding y values. Again the choices for x are simply convenient. Other values for x would serve the same purpose.

x	y
0	0
1	3
2	6

Step 2 Graph the points.

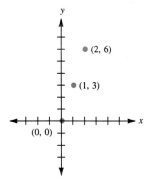

Step 3 Draw a line through the points.

Notice that connecting any two of these points produces the same line.

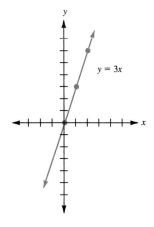

● ● ● CHECK YOURSELF 2

Graph the equation $y = -2x$ after completing the table of values.

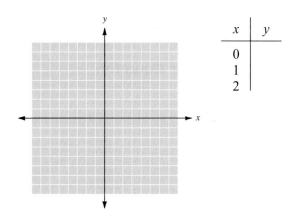

x	y
0	
1	
2	

Let's work through another example of graphing a line from its equation.

• Example 3

Graphing a Linear Equation

Graph $y = 2x + 3$.

Step 1 Some solutions are

x	y
0	3
1	5
2	7

Step 2 Graph the points corresponding to these values.

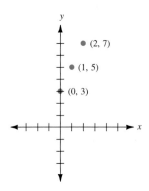

Step 3 Draw a line through the points.

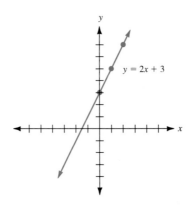

●●● **CHECK YOURSELF 3**

Graph the equation $y = 3x - 2$ after completing the table of values.

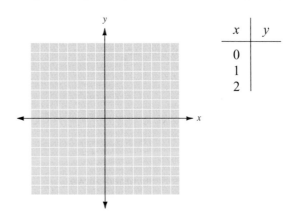

x	y
0	
1	
2	

In graphing equations, particularly when fractions are involved, a careful choice of values for x can simplify the process. Consider Example 4.

●Example 4

Graphing a Linear Equation

Graph

$$y = \frac{3}{2}x - 2$$

As before, we want to find solutions for the given equation by picking convenient values for x. Note that in this case, choosing *multiples of 2* will avoid fractional values for y and make the plotting of those solutions much easier. For instance, here we might choose values of -2, 0, and 2 for x.

Step 1

If $x = -2$:

$$y = \frac{3}{2}(-2) - 2$$

$$= -3 - 2 = -5$$

If $x = 0$:

Suppose we do *not* choose a multiple of 2, say, $x = 3$. Then

$$y = \frac{3}{2}(3) - 2$$

$$= \frac{9}{2} - 2$$

$$= \frac{5}{2}$$

$\left(3, \dfrac{5}{2}\right)$ is still a valid solution,

but we must graph a point with fractional coordinates.

$$y = \frac{3}{2}(0) - 2$$

$$= 0 - 2 = -2$$

If $x = 2$:

$$y = \frac{3}{2}(2) - 2$$

$$= 3 - 2 = 1$$

In tabular form, the solutions are

x	y
-2	-5
0	-2
2	1

Step 2 Graph the points determined above.

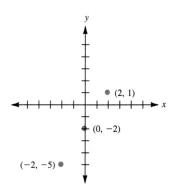

Step 3 Draw a line through the points.

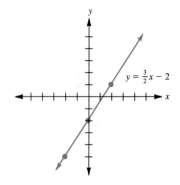

● ● ● **CHECK YOURSELF 4**

Graph the equation $y = -\dfrac{1}{3}x + 3$ after completing the table of values.

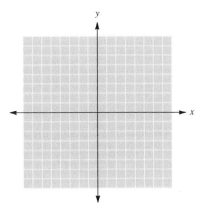

x	y
-3	
0	
3	

Some special cases of linear equations are illustrated in Examples 5 and 6.

● Example 5

Graphing an Equation That Results in a Vertical Line

Graph $x = 3$.

 The equation $x = 3$ is equivalent to $x + 0 \cdot y = 3$. Let's look at some solutions.

If $y = 1$:	If $y = 4$:	If $y = -2$:
$x + 0 \cdot 1 = 3$	$x + 0 \cdot 4 = 3$	$x + 0(-2) = 3$
$x = 3$	$x = 3$	$x = 3$

In tabular form,

x	y
3	1
3	4
3	-2

What do you observe? The variable x has the value 3, regardless of the value of y. Look at the graph on the following page.

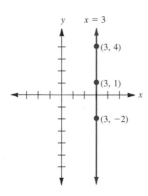

The graph of $x = 3$ is a vertical line crossing the x axis at $(3, 0)$.

Note that graphing (or plotting) points in this case is not really necessary. Simply recognize that the graph of $x = 3$ *must* be a vertical line (parallel to the y axis) which intercepts the x axis at 3.

● ● ● **CHECK YOURSELF 5**

Graph the equation $x = -2$.

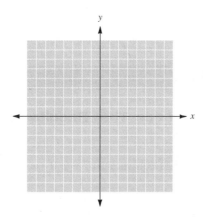

Example 6 is a related example involving a horizontal line.

● Example 6

Graphing an Equation That Results in a Horizontal Line

Graph $y = 4$.

Since $y = 4$ is equivalent to $0 \cdot x + y = 4$, any value for x paired with 4 for y will form a solution. A table of values might be

x	y
-2	4
0	4
2	4

Here is the graph.

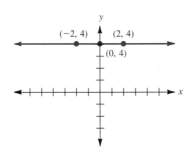

This time the graph is a horizontal line that crosses the y axis at $(0, 4)$. Again the graphing of points is not required. The graph of $y = 4$ *must* be horizontal (parallel to the x axis) and intercepts the y axis at 4.

●●● **CHECK YOURSELF 6**

Graph the equation $y = -3$.

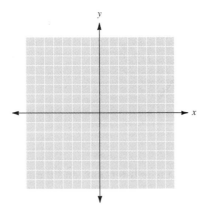

The following box summarizes our work in the previous two examples:

Vertical and Horizontal Lines

1. The graph of $x = a$ is a *vertical line* crossing the x axis at $(a, 0)$.
2. The graph of $y = b$ is a *horizontal line* crossing the y axis at $(0, b)$.

To simplify the graphing of certain linear equations, some students prefer the **intercept method** of graphing. This method makes use of the fact that the solutions that are easiest to find are those with an x coordinate or a y coordinate of 0. For instance, let's graph the equation

$$4x + 3y = 12$$

With practice, all this can be done mentally, which is the big advantage of this method.

First, let $x = 0$ and solve for y.

$$4 \cdot 0 + 3y = 12$$

$$3y = 12$$

$$y = 4$$

So $(0, 4)$ is one solution. Now we let $y = 0$ and solve for x.

$$4x + 3 \cdot 0 = 12$$

$$4x = 12$$

$$x = 3$$

A second solution is $(3, 0)$.

The two points corresponding to these solutions can now be used to graph the equation.

Remember, only two points are needed to graph a line. A third point is used only as a check.

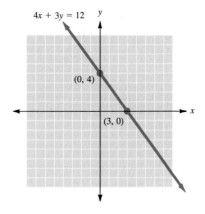

The intercepts are the points where the line cuts the x and y axes.

The number 3 is called the **x intercept,** and the number 4 is the **y intercept** of the graph. Using these points to draw the graph gives the name to this method. Let's look at a second example of graphing by the intercept method.

● Example 7

Using the Intercept Method to Graph a Line

Graph $3x - 5y = 15$, using the intercept method.
To find the x intercept, let $y = 0$.

$$3x - 5 \cdot 0 = 15$$

$$x = 5$$

The x intercept

To find the y intercept, let $x = 0$.

$$3 \cdot 0 - 5y = 15$$

$$y = -3$$

The y intercept

So $(5, 0)$ and $(0, -3)$ are solutions for the equation, and we can use the corresponding points to graph the equation.

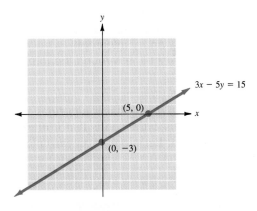

● ● ●   **CHECK YOURSELF 7**

Graph $4x + 5y = 20$, using the intercept method.

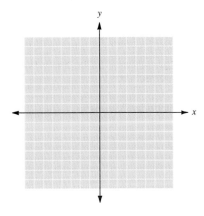

Finding the third "checkpoint" is always a good idea.

This all looks quite easy, and for many equations it is. What are the drawbacks? For one, you don't have a third checkpoint, and it is possible for errors to occur. You can, of course, still find a third point (other than the two intercepts) to be sure your graph is correct. A second difficulty arises when the x and y intercepts are very close to one another (or are actually the same point—the origin). For instance, if we have the equation

$$3x + 2y = 1$$

the intercepts are $\left(\dfrac{1}{3}, 0\right)$ and $\left(0, \dfrac{1}{2}\right)$. It is hard to draw a line accurately through these intercepts, so choose other solutions farther away from the origin for your points.

Let's summarize the steps of graphing by the intercept method for appropriate equations.

Graphing a Line by the Intercept Method

STEP 1 To find the *x* intercept: Let *y* = 0, then solve for *x*.
STEP 2 To find the *y* intercept: Let *x* = 0, then solve for *y*.
STEP 3 Graph the *x* and *y* intercepts.
STEP 4 Draw a straight line through the intercepts.

A third method of graphing linear equations involves **solving the equation for y.** The reason we use this extra step is that it often will make finding solutions for the equation much easier. Let's look at an example.

● Example 8

Graphing a Linear Equation

Graph $2x + 3y = 6$.

Rather than finding solutions for the equation in this form, we solve for *y*.

Remember that solving for *y* means that we want to leave *y* isolated on the left.

$$2x + 3y = 6$$
$$3y = 6 - 2x \quad \} \quad \text{Subtract } 2x.$$
$$y = \frac{6 - 2x}{3} \quad \} \quad \text{Divide by 3.}$$
or $\quad y = 2 - \frac{2}{3}x$

Now find your solutions by picking convenient values for *x*.

Again, to pick convenient values for *x*, we suggest you look at the equation carefully. Here, for instance, picking multiples of 3 for *x* will make the work much easier.

If $x = -3$:

$$y = 2 - \frac{2}{3}(-3)$$
$$= 2 + 2 = 4$$

So $(-3, 4)$ is a solution.

If $x = 0$:

$$y = 2 - \frac{2}{3} \cdot 0$$
$$= 2$$

So $(0, 2)$ is a solution.

If $x = 3$:

$$y = 2 - \frac{2}{3} \cdot 3$$
$$= 2 - 2 = 0$$

So $(3, 0)$ is a solution.

We can now plot the points that correspond to these solutions and form the graph of the equation as before.

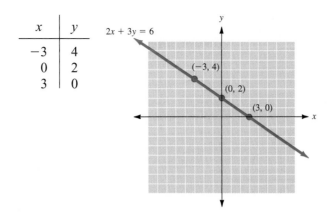

x	y
−3	4
0	2
3	0

CHECK YOURSELF 8

Graph the equation $5x + 2y = 10$. Solve for y to determine solutions.

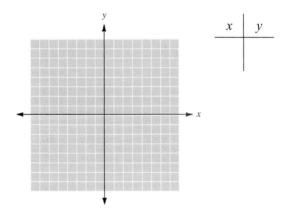

x	y

CHECK YOURSELF ANSWERS

1.

x	y
1	−4
2	−2
3	0

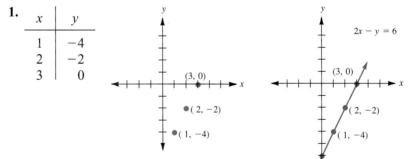

2.

x	y
0	0
1	−2
2	−4

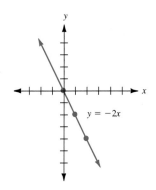

$y = -2x$

3.

x	y
0	−2
1	1
2	4

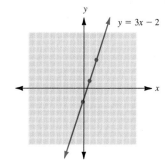

$y = 3x - 2$

4.

x	y
−3	4
0	3
3	2

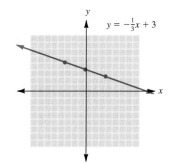

$y = -\frac{1}{3}x + 3$

5.

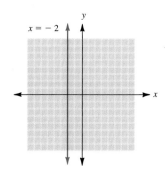

$x = -2$

6.

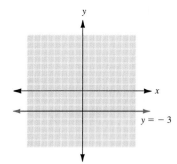

$y = -3$

7.

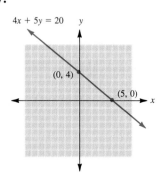

$4x + 5y = 20$

$(0, 4)$

$(5, 0)$

8.

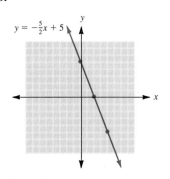

$y = -\frac{5}{2}x + 5$

Name

Section   Date

Graph each of the following equations.

1. $x + y = 6$

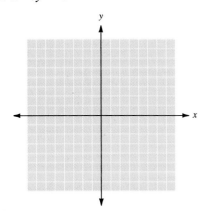

2. $x - y = 5$

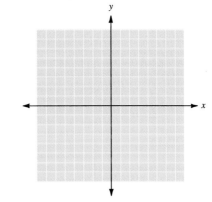

3. $x - y = -3$

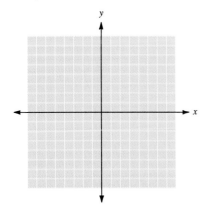

4. $x + y = -3$

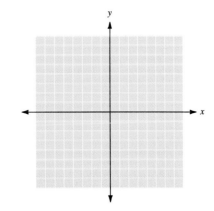

5. $2x + y = 2$

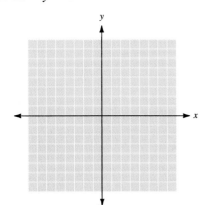

6. $x - 2y = 6$

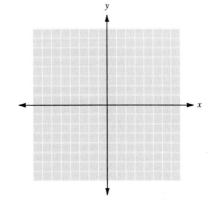

7. $3x + y = 0$

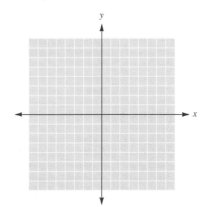

8. $3x - y = 6$

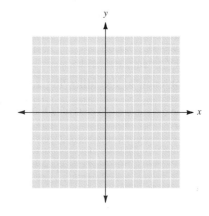

9. $x + 4y = 8$

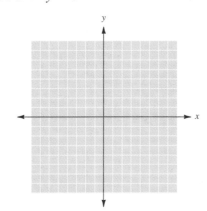

10. $2x - 3y = 6$

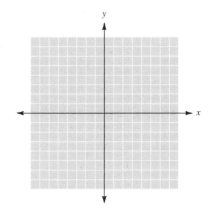

11. $y = 5x$

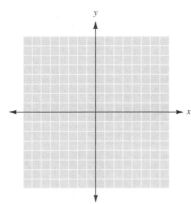

12. $y = -4x$

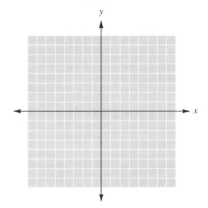

13. $y = 2x - 1$

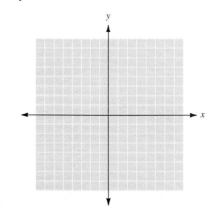

14. $y = 4x + 3$

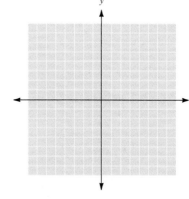

15. $y = -3x + 1$

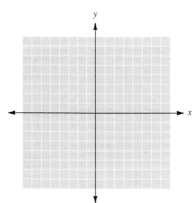

16. $y = -3x - 3$

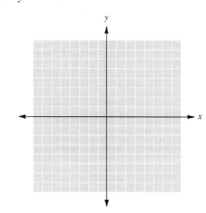

17. $y = \dfrac{1}{3}x$

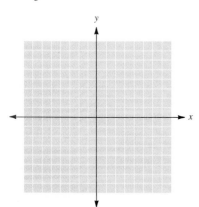

18. $y = -\dfrac{1}{4}x$

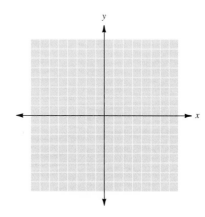

ANSWERS

13. _____

14. _____

15. _____

16. _____

17. _____

18. _____

19. _____

20. _____

21. _____

22. _____

23. _____

24. _____

19. $y = \dfrac{2}{3}x - 3$

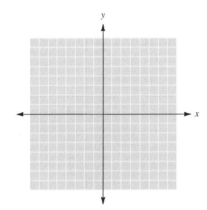

20. $y = \dfrac{3}{4}x + 2$

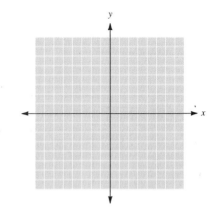

21. $x = 5$

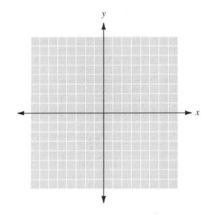

22. $y = -3$

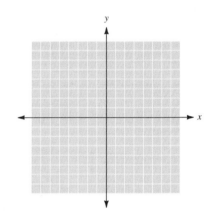

23. $y = 1$

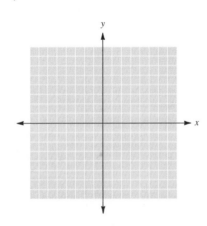

24. $x = -2$

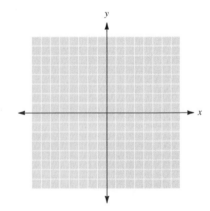

Graph each of the following equations, using the intercept method.

25. $x - 2y = 4$

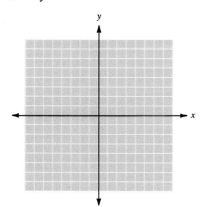

26. $6x + y = 6$

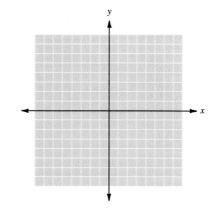

27. $5x + 2y = 10$

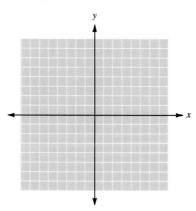

28. $2x + 3y = 6$

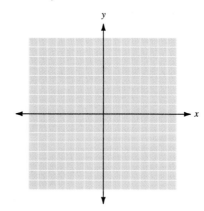

29. $3x + 5y = 15$

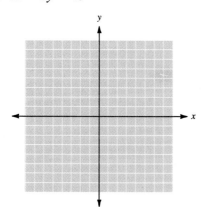

30. $4x + 3y = 12$

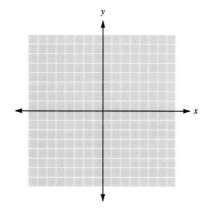

A N S W E R S

25. _____

26. _____

27. _____

28. _____

29. _____

30. _____

31. _____

32. _____

33. _____

34. _____

35. _____

36. _____

Graph each of the following equations by first solving for y.

31. $x + 3y = 6$

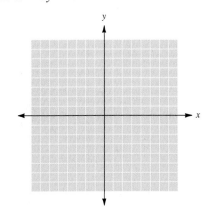

32. $x - 2y = 6$

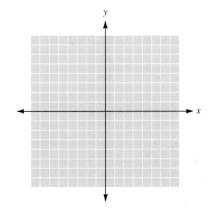

33. $3x + 4y = 12$

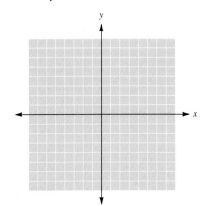

34. $2x - 3y = 12$

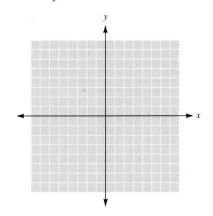

35. $5x - 4y = 20$

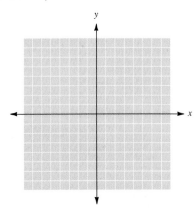

36. $7x + 3y = 21$

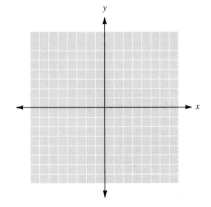

Write an equation that describes the following relationships between x and y. Then graph each relationship.

37. y is twice x.

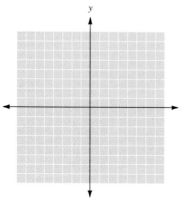

38. y is 3 times x.

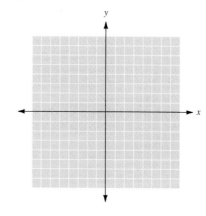

39. y is 3 more than x.

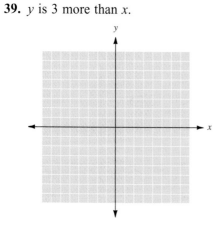

40. y is 2 less than x.

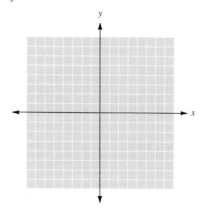

41. y is 3 less than 3 times x.

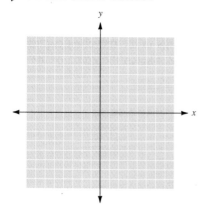

42. y is 4 more than twice x.

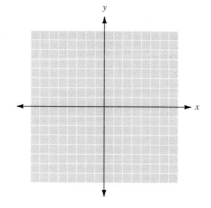

ANSWERS

37. _____

38. _____

39. _____

40. _____

41. _____

42. _____

43. _____

44. _____

45. _____

46. _____

47. _____

43. The difference of x and the product of 4 and y is 12.

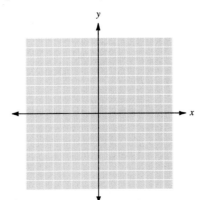

44. The difference of twice x and y is 6.

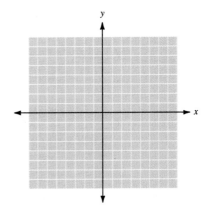

Graph each pair of equations on the same axes. Give the coordinates of the point where the lines intersect.

45. $x + y = 4$
$x - y = 2$

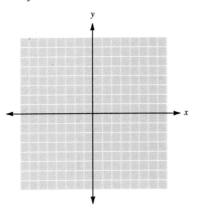

46. $x - y = 3$
$x + y = 5$

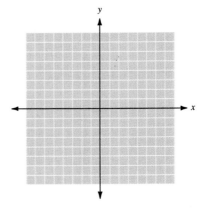

47. Graph of winnings. The equation $y = 0.10x + 200$ describes the amount of winnings a group earns for collecting plastic jugs in the recycling contest described in Exercise 33 at the end of Section 7.2. Sketch the graph of the line on the axis below.

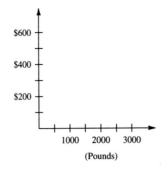

48. Minimum values. The contest sponsor will award a prize only if the winning group in the contest collects 100 lb of jugs or more. Use your graph in Exercise 47 to determine the minimum prize possible.

49. Fundraising. A high school class wants to raise some money by recycling newspapers. They decide to rent a truck for a weekend and to collect the newspapers from homes in the neighborhood. The market price for recycled newsprint is currently $11 per ton. The equation $y = 11x - 100$ describes the amount of money the class will make, where y is the amount of money made in dollars, x is the number of tons of newsprint collected, and 100 is the cost in dollars to rent the truck.

a. Using the axes below, draw a graph that represents the relationship between newsprint collected and money earned.

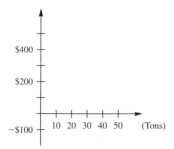

b. The truck is costing the class $100. How many tons of newspapers must the class collect to break even on this project?

c. If the class members collect 16 tons of newsprint, how much money will they earn?

d. Six months later the price of newsprint is $17 dollars a ton, and the cost to rent the truck has risen to $125. Write the equation that describes the amount of money the class might make at that time.

50. Production costs. The cost of producing a number of items x is given by $C = mx + b$, where b is the fixed cost and m is the variable cost (the cost of producing one item).

a. If the fixed cost is $40 and the variable cost is $10, write the cost equation.

b. Graph the cost equation.

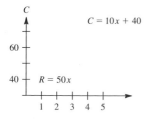

c. The revenue generated from the sale of x items is given by $R = 50x$. Graph the revenue equation on the same set of axes as the cost equation.

d. How many items must be produced in order for the revenue to equal the cost (the break-even point)?

Graph each set of equations on the same coordinate system. Do the lines intersect? What are the *y* intercepts?

51. _____

52. _____

a. _____

b. _____

c. _____

d. _____

51. $y = 3x$
$y = 3x + 4$
$y = 3x - 5$

52. $y = -2x$
$y = -2x + 3$
$y = -2x - 5$

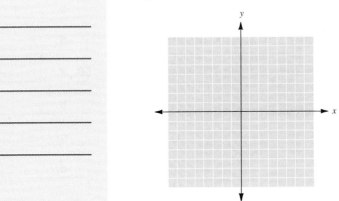

Getting Ready for Section 7.4 [Section 2.5]

Evaluate the following expressions.

a. $\dfrac{7 - 3}{8 - 4}$ **b.** $\dfrac{-9 - 5}{-4 - 3}$ **c.** $\dfrac{4 - (-2)}{6 - 2}$ **d.** $\dfrac{-4 - (-4)}{8 - 2}$

Answers

1. $x + y = 6$ **3.** $x - y = -3$ **5.** $2x + y = 2$

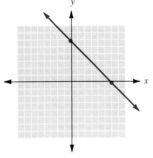 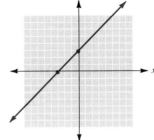 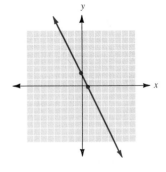

7. $3x + y = 0$ **9.** $x + 4y = 8$ **11.** $y = 5x$

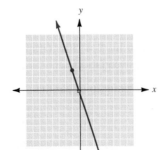 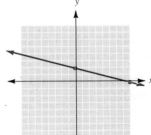 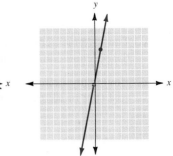

13. $y = 2x - 1$

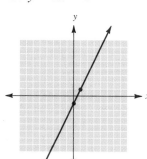

15. $y = -3x + 1$

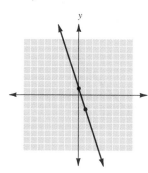

17. $y = \dfrac{1}{3}x$

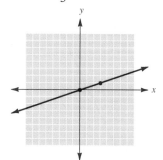

19. $y = \dfrac{2}{3}x - 3$

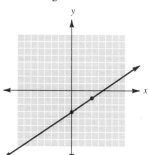

21. $x = 5$

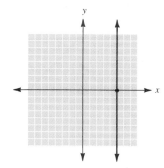

23. $y = 1$

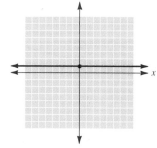

25. $x - 2y = 4$

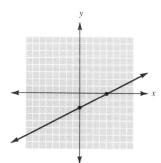

27. $5x + 2y = 10$

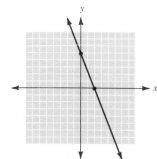

29. $3x + 5y = 15$

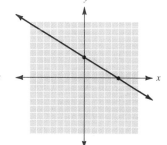

31. $y = 2 - \dfrac{x}{3}$

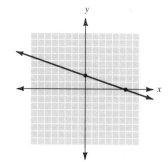

33. $y = 3 - \dfrac{3}{4}x$

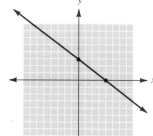

35. $y = -5 + \dfrac{5}{4}x$

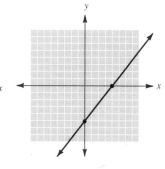

37. $y = 2x$

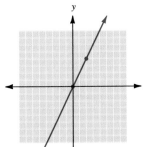

39. $y = 3 + x$

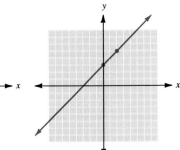

41. $y = 3x - 3$

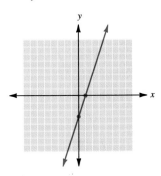

43. $x - 4y = 12$

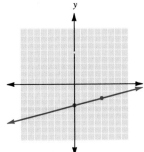

45. $(3, 1)$

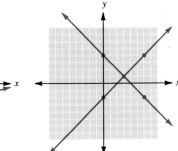

47. Graph

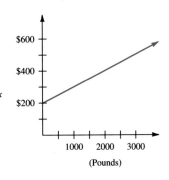
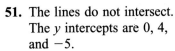

(Pounds)

49. (a) Graph, **(b)** $9\dfrac{1}{11} \approx 9$ tons,

(c) \$76, **(d)** $y = 17x - 125$

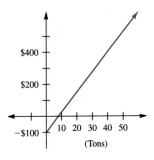

(Tons)

51. The lines do not intersect. The y intercepts are 0, 4, and -5.

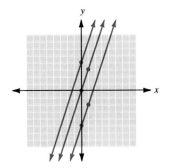

a. 1   **b.** 2   **c.** $\dfrac{3}{2}$ **d.** 0

 **The Slope of a Line**

7.4 OBJECTIVES

1. Find the slope of a line through two given points
2. Rewrite the equation of a line in the slope-intercept form

Recall that an equation such as $y = 2x + 3$ is a *linear equation in two variables*. Its graph is always a straight line.

Note: x_1 is read "x sub 1," x_2 is read "x sub 2," and so on. The 1 in x_1 and the 2 in x_2 are called **subscripts.**

The difference $x_2 - x_1$ is sometimes called the **run** between points P and Q. The difference $y_2 - y_1$ is called the **rise.** So the slope may be thought of as "rise over run."

We saw in Section 7.3 that the graph of an equation such as

$$y = 2x + 3$$

is a straight line. In this section we want to develop an important idea related to the equation of a line and its graph, called the **slope** of a line. Finding the slope of a line gives us a numerical measure of the "steepness" or inclination of that line.

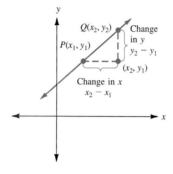

To find the slope of a line, we first let $P(x_1, y_1)$ and $Q(x_2, y_2)$ be any two distinct points on that line. The **horizontal change** (or the change in x) between the points is $x_2 - x_1$. The **vertical change** (or the change in y) between the points is $y_2 - y_1$.

We call the ratio of the vertical change, $y_2 - y_1$, to the horizontal change, $x_2 - x_1$, the *slope* of the line as we move along the line from P to Q. That ratio is usually denoted by the letter m, and so we have the following formula:

The Slope of a Line

If $P(x_1, y_1)$ and $Q(x_2, y_2)$ are any two points on a line, then m, the slope of the line, is given by

$$m = \frac{\text{vertical change}}{\text{horizontal change}} = \frac{y_2 - y_1}{x_2 - x_1} \qquad \text{where } x_2 \neq x_1$$

This definition provides exactly the numerical measure of "steepness" that we want. If a line "rises" as we move from left to right, the slope will be positive—the steeper the line, the larger the numerical value of the slope. If the line "falls" from left to right, the slope will be negative.

Let's proceed to some examples.

• Example 1

Finding the Slope

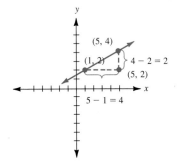

Find the slope of the line containing points with coordinates $(1, 2)$ and $(5, 4)$.

Let $P(x_1, y_1) = (1, 2)$ and $Q(x_2, y_2) = (5, 4)$. By the definition above, we have

$$m = \frac{y_2 - y_1}{x_2 - x_1} = \frac{4 - 2}{5 - 1} = \frac{2}{4} = \frac{1}{2}$$

Note: We would have found the same slope if we had reversed P and Q and subtracted in the other order. In that case, $P(x_1, y_1) = (5, 4)$ and $Q(x_2, y_2) = (1, 2)$, so

$$m = \frac{2 - 4}{1 - 5} = \frac{-2}{-4} = \frac{1}{2}$$

It makes no difference which point is labeled (x_1, y_1) and which is (x_2, y_2), the resulting slope will be the same. You must simply stay with your choice once it is made and *not* reverse the order of the subtraction in your calculations.

● ● ● CHECK YOURSELF 1

Find the slope of the line containing points with coordinates $(2, 3)$ and $(5, 5)$.

By now you should be comfortable subtracting negative numbers. Let's apply that skill to finding a slope.

• Example 2

Finding the Slope

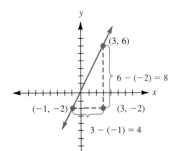

Find the slope of the line containing points with the coordinates $(-1, -2)$ and $(3, 6)$.

Again, applying the definition, we have

$$m = \frac{6 - (-2)}{3 - (-1)} = \frac{6 + 2}{3 + 1} = \frac{8}{4} = 2$$

The figure below compares the slopes found in the two previous examples. Line l_1, from Example 1, had slope $\dfrac{1}{2}$. Line l_2, from Example 2, had slope 2. Do you see the idea of slope measuring steepness? The greater the slope, the more steeply the line is inclined upward.

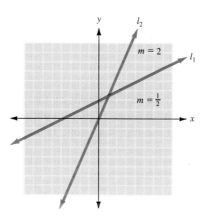

●●● **CHECK YOURSELF 2**

Find the slope of the line containing points with coordinates $(-1, 2)$ and $(2, 7)$. Draw a sketch of this line and the line of Check Yourself 1. Compare the lines and the two slopes.

Let's look at lines with a negative slope.

●**Example 3**

Finding the Slope

Find the slope of the line containing points with coordinates $(-2, 3)$ and $(1, -3)$.
    By the definition,

$$m = \frac{-3 - 3}{1 - (-2)} = \frac{-6}{3} = -2$$

This line has a *negative* slope. The line *falls* as we move from left to right.

●●● **CHECK YOURSELF 3**

Find the slope of the line containing points with coordinates $(-1, 3)$ and $(1, -3)$.

We have seen that lines with positive slope rise from left to right and lines with negative slope fall from left to right. What about lines with a slope of zero? A line with a slope of 0 is especially important in mathematics.

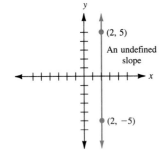

● Example 4

Finding the Slope

Find the slope of the line containing points with coordinates $(-5, 2)$ and $(3, 2)$.

By the definition,

$$m = \frac{2 - 2}{3 - (-5)} = \frac{0}{8} = 0$$

The slope of the line is 0. In fact, that will be the case for any horizontal line. Since any two points on the line have the same y coordinate, the vertical change $y_2 - y_1$ must always be 0, and so the resulting slope is 0.

● ● ● **CHECK YOURSELF 4**

Find the slope of the line containing points with coordinates $(-2, -4)$ and $(3, -4)$.

Since division by 0 is undefined, it is possible to have a line with an undefined slope.

● Example 5

Finding the Slope

Find the slope of the line containing points with coordinates $(2, -5)$ and $(2, 5)$.

By the definition,

$$m = \frac{5 - (-5)}{2 - 2} = \frac{10}{0}$$

Remember that division by zero is undefined.

We say that the vertical line has an undefined slope. On a vertical line, any two points have the same x coordinate. This means that the horizontal change $x_2 - x_1$ must always be 0 and since division by 0 is undefined, the slope of a vertical line will always be undefined.

● ● ● **CHECK YOURSELF 5**

Find the slope of the line containing points with the coordinates $(-3, -5)$ and $(-3, 2)$.

The following sketch summarizes the results of our previous examples.

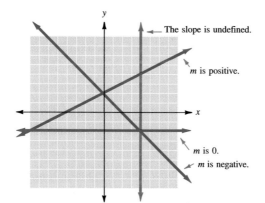

As the slope gets closer to 0, the line gets "flatter."

Four lines are illustrated in the figure. Note that

1. The slope of a line that rises from left to right is positive.
2. The slope of a line that falls from left to right is negative.
3. The slope of a horizontal line is 0.
4. A vertical line has an undefined slope.

We now want to consider finding the equation of a line when its slope and *y* intercept are known. Suppose that the *y* intercept of a line is *b*. Then the point at which the line crosses the *y* axis must have coordinates (0, *b*). Look at the sketch below.

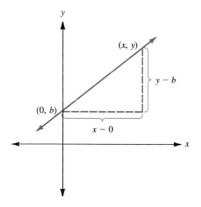

Now, using any other point (*x*, *y*) on the line and using our definition of slope, we can write

Change in *y*.

$$m = \frac{y - b}{x - 0}$$ (1)

Change in *x*.

or

$$m = \frac{y - b}{x}$$ (2)

Multiplying both sides of equation (2) by x, we have

$$mx = y - b \tag{3}$$

Finally, adding b to both sides of equation (3) gives

$$mx + b = y$$

or

$$y = mx + b \tag{4}$$

We can summarize the above discussion as follows:

In this form, the equation is *solved for y.* The coefficient of x will give you the slope of the line, and the constant term gives the y intercept.

The Slope-Intercept Form for a Line

An equation of the line with slope m and y intercept b is

$y = mx + b$

• Example 6

Finding the Slope and *y* Intercept

(a) Find the slope and y intercept for the graph of the equation

$$y = 3x + 4$$

The graph has slope 3 and y intercept 4.

(b) Find the slope and y intercept for the graph of the equation

$$y = -\frac{2}{3}x - 5$$

The slope of the line is $-\dfrac{2}{3}$; the y intercept is -5.

● ● ●   **CHECK YOURSELF 6**

Find the slope and y intercept for the graph of each of the following equations.

a. $y = -3x - 7$ 　　　　　　　　　　　　**b.** $y = \dfrac{3}{4}x + 5$

As Example 7 illustrates, we may have to solve for y as the first step in determining the slope and the y intercept for the graph of an equation.

● Example 7

Finding the Slope and y Intercept

Find the slope and y intercept for the graph of the equation

$$3x + 2y = 6$$

First, we must solve the equation for y.

If we write the equation as
$$y = \frac{-3x + 6}{2}$$
it is more difficult to identify the slope and the intercept.

$$3x + 2y = 6$$
$$2y = -3x + 6 \qquad \text{Subtract } 3x \text{ from both sides.}$$
$$y = -\frac{3}{2}x + 3 \qquad \text{Divide each term by 2.}$$

The equation is now in slope-intercept form. The slope is $-\dfrac{3}{2}$, and the y intercept is 3.

● ● ● **C H E C K   Y O U R S E L F   7**

Find the slope and y intercept for the graph of the equation

$$2x - 5y = 10$$

As we mentioned earlier, knowing certain properties of a line (namely, its slope and y intercept) will also allow us to write the equation of the line by using the slope-intercept form. Example 8 illustrates this approach.

● Example 8

Writing the Equation of a Line

(*a*) Write the equation of a line with slope 3 and y intercept 5.

We know that $m = 3$ and $b = 5$. Using the slope-intercept form, we have

$$y = 3x + 5$$
$$\quad\;\; m \quad\; b$$

which is the desired equation.

(b) Write the equation of a line with slope $-\dfrac{3}{4}$ and y intercept -3.

We know that $m = -\dfrac{3}{4}$ and $b = -3$. In this case,

$$y = \overset{\overset{\displaystyle m}{\downarrow}}{-\dfrac{3}{4}} x + \overset{\overset{\displaystyle b}{\downarrow}}{(-3)}$$

or

$$y = -\dfrac{3}{4}x - 3$$

which is the desired equation.

● ● ● **CHECK YOURSELF 8**

Write the equation of a line with the following:

a. slope -2 and y intercept 7   **b.** slope $\dfrac{2}{3}$ and y intercept -3

We can also use the slope and y intercept of a line in drawing its graph. Consider Example 9.

● Example 9

Graphing a Line

Graph the line with slope $\dfrac{2}{3}$ and y intercept 2.

Since the y intercept is 2, we begin by plotting the point $(0, 2)$. Since the horizontal change (or run) is 3, we move 3 units to the right *from that y intercept.* Then since the vertical change (or rise) is 2, we move 2 units up to locate another point on the desired graph. Note that we will have located that second point at $(3, 4)$. The final step is to simply draw a line through that point and the y intercept.

Note: $m = \dfrac{2}{3} = \dfrac{\text{rise}}{\text{run}}$

The line rises from left to right because the slope is positive.

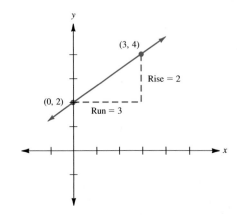

The equation of this line is $y = \dfrac{2}{3}x + 2$.

● ● ● ● CHECK YOURSELF 9

Graph the equation of a line with slope $\dfrac{3}{5}$ and y intercept -2.

We summarize the use of graphing by the slope-intercept form with the following algorithm.

Graphing by Using the Slope-Intercept Form

Step 1 Write the original equation of the line in slope-intercept form.
Step 2 Determine the slope m and the y intercept b.
Step 3 Plot the y intercept at $(0, b)$.
Step 4 Use m (the change in y over the change in x) to determine a second point on the desired line.
Step 5 Draw a line through the two points determined above to complete the graph.

You have now seen two methods for graphing lines: the slope-intercept method (Section 7.4) and the intercept method (Section 7.3). When you graph a linear equation, you should first decide which is the appropriate method.

● **Example 10**

Selecting an Appropriate Graphing Method

Decide which of the two methods for graphing lines—the intercept method or the slope-intercept method—is more appropriate for graphing equations (a), (b), and (c).

(a) $2x - 5y = 10$

Because both intercepts are easy to find, you should choose the intercept method to graph this equation.

(b) $2x + y = 6$

This equation can be quickly graphed by either method. As it is written, you might choose the intercept method. It can, however, be rewritten as $y = -2x + 6$. In that case the slope-intercept method is more appropriate.

(c) $y = \dfrac{1}{4}x - 4$

Since the equation is in slope-intercept form, that is the more appropriate method to choose.

● ● ●   **CHECK YOURSELF 10**

Which would be more appropriate for graphing each equation, the intercept method or the slope-intercept method?

a. $x + y = -2$ **b.** $3x - 2y = 12$ **c.** $y = -\dfrac{1}{2}x - 6$

● ● ●   **CHECK YOURSELF ANSWERS**

1. $m = \dfrac{2}{3}$.   **2.** $m = \dfrac{5}{3}$.

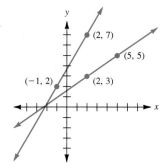

3. $m = -3$.   **4.** $m = 0$.   **5.** m is undefined.   **6.** **(a)** $m = -3, b = -7$;

(b) $m = \dfrac{3}{4}, b = 5$.   **7.** $y = \dfrac{2}{5}x - 2$; the slope is $\dfrac{2}{5}$; the y intercept is -2.

8. **(a)** $y = -2x + 7$; **(b)** $y = \dfrac{2}{3}x - 3$.

9.

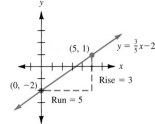

10. **(a)** Either; **(b)** intercept; **(c)** slope-intercept.

Find the slope of the line through the following pairs of points.

1. $(5, 7)$ and $(9, 11)$

2. $(4, 9)$ and $(8, 17)$

3. $(-2, -5)$ and $(2, 15)$

4. $(-3, 2)$ and $(0, 17)$

5. $(-2, 3)$ and $(3, 7)$

6. $(-3, -4)$ and $(3, -2)$

7. $(-3, 2)$ and $(2, -8)$

8. $(-6, 1)$ and $(2, -7)$

9. $(3, 3)$ and $(5, 0)$

10. $(-2, 4)$ and $(3, 1)$

11. $(5, -4)$ and $(5, 2)$

12. $(-5, 4)$ and $(2, 4)$

13. $(-4, -2)$ and $(3, 3)$

14. $(-5, -3)$ and $(-5, 2)$

15. $(-3, -4)$ and $(2, -4)$

16. $(-5, 7)$ and $(2, -2)$

17. $(-1, 7)$ and $(2, 3)$

18. $(-4, -2)$ and $(6, 4)$

Find the slope and y intercept of the line represented by each of the following equations.

19. $y = 3x + 5$

20. $y = -7x + 3$

21. $y = -2x - 5$

22. $y = 5x - 2$

23. $y = \dfrac{3}{4}x + 1$

24. $y = -4x$

A N S W E R S

1.
2.
3.
4.
5.
6.
7.
8.
9.
10.
11.
12.
13.
14.
15.
16.
17.
18.
19.
20.
21.
22.
23.
24.

25. _____

26. _____

27. _____

28. _____

29. _____

30. _____

31. _____

32. _____

33. _____

34. _____

35. _____

36. _____

25. $y = \dfrac{2}{3}x$

26. $y = -\dfrac{3}{5}x - 2$

27. $4x + 3y = 12$

28. $2x + 5y = 10$

29. $y = 9$

30. $2x - 3y = 6$

31. $3x - 2y = 8$

32. $x = 5$

Write the equation of the line with given slope and y intercept. Then graph each line, using the slope and y intercept.

33. $m = 3, b = 5$

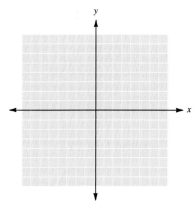

34. $m = -2, b = 4$

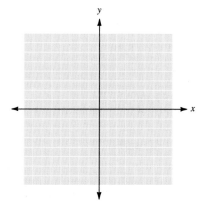

35. $m = -3, b = 4$

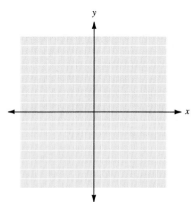

36. $m = 5, b = -2$

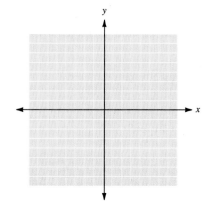

37. $m = \dfrac{1}{2}, b = -2$

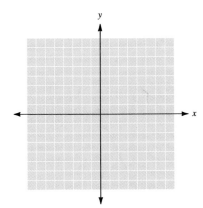

38. $m = -\dfrac{3}{4}, b = 8$

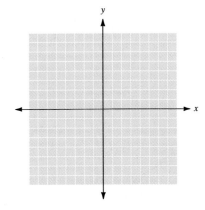

39. $m = -\dfrac{2}{3}, b = 0$

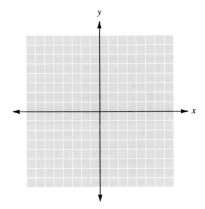

40. $m = \dfrac{2}{3}, b = -2$

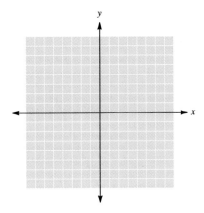

41. $m = \dfrac{3}{4}, b = 3$

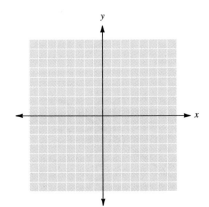

42. $m = -3, b = 0$

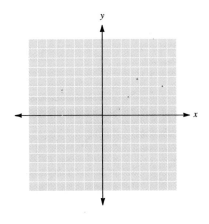

ANSWERS

37. _____

38. _____

39. _____

40. _____

41. _____

42. _____

In Exercises 43 to 50, match the graph with one of the equations below.

(a) $y = 2x$,　**(b)** $y = x + 1$,　**(c)** $y = -x + 3$,　**(d)** $y = 2x + 1$,　**(e)** $y = -3x - 2$,

(f) $y = \dfrac{2}{3}x + 1$,　**(g)** $y = -\dfrac{3}{4}x + 1$,　**(h)** $y = -4x$

43.

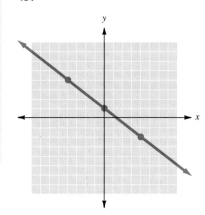

44.

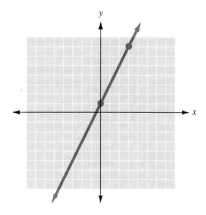

45.

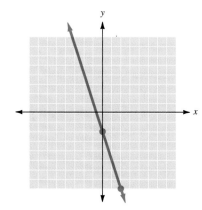

46.

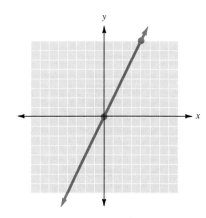

47.

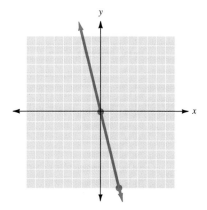

48.

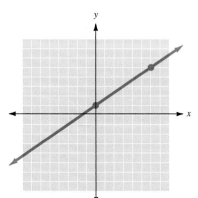

49.

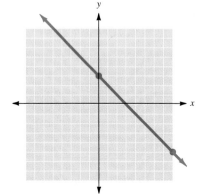

50.

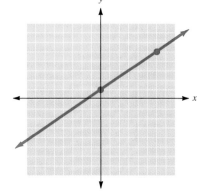

In which quadrant(s) are there no solutions for each line?

51. $y = 2x + 1$

52. $y = 3x + 2$

53. $y = -x + 1$

54. $y = -2x + 5$

55. $y = -2x - 5$

56. $y = -5x - 7$

57. $y = 3$

58. $x = -2$

59. Recycling. The equation $y = 0.10x + 200$ was used in Section 7.3 to describe the award money in a recycling contest. What are the slope and the y intercept for this equation? What does the slope of the line represent in the equation? What does the y intercept represent?

60. Fundraising. The equation $y = 11x - 100$ was used in Section 7.3 to describe the amount of money a high school class might earn from a paper drive. What are the slope and y intercept for this equation?

61. Fundraising. In the equation in Exercise 60, what does the slope of the line represent? What does the y intercept represent?

62. Slope of a roof. A roof rises 8.75 feet (ft) in a horizontal distance of 15.09 ft. Find the slope of the roof to the nearest hundredth.

63. Slope of airplane descent. An airplane covered 15 miles (mi) of its route while decreasing its altitude by 24,000 ft. Find the slope of the line of descent that was followed. (1 mi = 5280 ft.) Round to the nearest hundredth.

64. Slope of road descent. Driving down a mountain, Tom finds that he has descended 1800 ft in elevation by the time he is 3.25 mi horizontally away from the top of the mountain. Find the slope of his descent to the nearest hundredth.

ANSWERS

51. _____

52. _____

53. _____

54. _____

55. _____

56. _____

57. _____

58. _____

59. _____

60. _____

61. _____

62. _____

63. _____

64. _____

65. Complete the following statement: "The difference between undefined slope and zero slope is . . . ."

66. Complete the following: "The slope of a line tells you . . . ."

67. In a study on nutrition conducted in 1984, 18 normal adults aged 23 to 61 years old were measured for body fat, which is given as percentage of weight. The mean (average) body fat percentage for women 40 years old was 28.6 percent, and for women 53 years old it was 38.4 percent. Work with a partner to decide how to show this information on a scatterplot. Try to find a linear equation that will tell you percentage of body fat based on a woman's age. What does your equation give for 20 years of age? For 60? Do you think a linear model works well for predicting body fat percentage in women as they age?

68. On two occasions last month, Sam Johnson rented a car on a business trip. Both times it was the same model from the same company, and both times it was in San Francisco. Sam now has to fill out an expense account form and needs to know how much he was charged per mile and the base rate. On both occasions he dropped the car at the airport booth and just got the total charge, not the details. All Sam knows is that he was charged $210 for 625 miles on the first occasion and $133.50 for 370 miles on the second trip. Sam has called accounting to ask for help. Plot these two points on a graph, and draw the line that goes through them. What question does the slope of the line answer for Sam? How does the y intercept help? Write a memo to Sam explaining the answers to his question and how a knowledge of algebra and graphing has helped you find the answers.

**Getting Ready for Section 7.5
[Section 3.6]**

Graph each of the following inequalities.

a. $x < 3$

⟵———|——|————→
　　　0

b. $x \geq -2$

⟵————|————→
　　　0

c. $2x \leq 8$

⟵————|————→
　　　0

d. $3x > -9$

⟵————|————→
　　　0

e. $-3x < 12$

⟵————|————→
　　　0

f. $-2x \leq 10$

⟵————|————→
　　　0

g. $\dfrac{2}{3}x \leq 4$

⟵————|————→
　　　0

h. $-\dfrac{3}{4}x \geq 6$

⟵————|————→
　　　0

Answers

1. 1　　**3.** 5　　**5.** $\dfrac{4}{5}$　　**7.** -2　　**9.** $-\dfrac{3}{2}$　　**11.** Undefined　　**13.** $\dfrac{5}{7}$

15. 0　　**17.** $-\dfrac{4}{3}$　　**19.** Slope 3, y intercept 5　　**21.** Slope -2, y intercept -5

23. Slope $\dfrac{3}{4}$, y intercept 1　　**25.** Slope $\dfrac{2}{3}$, y intercept 0

27. Slope $-\dfrac{4}{3}$, y intercept 4　　**29.** Slope 0, y intercept 9

31. Slope $\dfrac{3}{2}$, y intercept -4

33. $y = 3x + 5$

35. $y = -3x + 4$

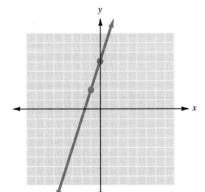

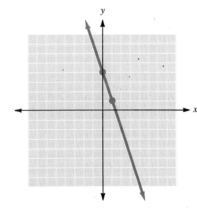

37. $y = \dfrac{1}{2}x - 2$

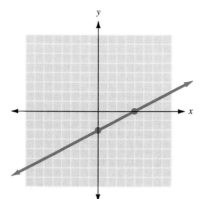

39. $y = -\dfrac{2}{3}x$

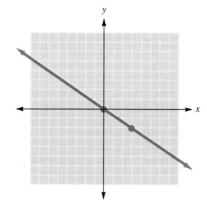

41. $y = \dfrac{3}{4}x + 3$

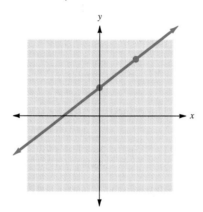

43. g **45.** e **47.** h **49.** c **51.** IV   **53.** III   **55.** I

57. III and IV

59. $m = 0.10$, market price of jugs; y intercept $= 200$, the 200 award.

61. Slope represents the price of newsprint; the y intercept the cost of the truck.

63. -0.30

a.

b.

c.

d.

e.

f.

g.

h.

Graphing Linear Inequalities

7.5 OBJECTIVE

Graph a linear inequality in two variables

The inequality symbols ≤, >, and ≥ can also be used.

In Section 3.6 you learned to graph inequalities in one variable on a number line. We now want to extend our work with graphing to include linear inequalities in two variables. We begin with a definition.

> An inequality that can be written in the form
>
> $Ax + By < C$
>
> where A and B are not both 0, is called a **linear inequality in two variables.**

Some examples of linear inequalities in two variables are

$$x + 3y > 6 \qquad y \le 3x + 1 \qquad 2x - y \ge 3$$

The *graph* of a linear inequality is always a region (actually a half plane) of the plane whose boundary is a straight line. Let's look at an example of graphing such an inequality.

• Example 1

Graphing a Linear Inequality

Graph $2x + y < 4$.

First, replace the inequality symbol ($<$) with an equals sign. We then have $2x + y = 4$. This equation forms the **boundary line** of the graph of the original inequality. You can graph the line by any of the methods discussed earlier in this chapter.

The boundary line for our inequality is shown below.

The dotted line indicates that the points on the line $2x + y = 4$ are *not* part of the solution to the inequality $2x + y < 4$.

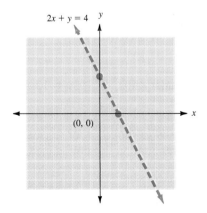

We see that the boundary line separates the plane into two regions, each of which is called a **half plane.**

You can always use the origin for a test point unless the boundary line passes through the origin.

We now need to choose the correct half plane. Choose any convenient test point not on the boundary line. The origin $(0, 0)$ is a good choice because it makes for easy calculation.

Substitute $x = 0$ and $y = 0$ into the inequality.

$$2 \cdot 0 + 0 < 4$$
$$0 + 0 < 4$$
$$0 < 4 \qquad \text{A true statement}$$

Since the inequality is *true* for the test point, we shade the half plane containing that test point (here the origin). The origin and all other points *below* the boundary line then represent solutions for our original inequality.

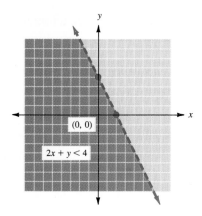

●●● **CHECK YOURSELF 1**

Graph the inequality $x + 3y < 3$.

The process is similar when the boundary line is included in the solution.

● Example 2

Graphing a Linear Inequality

Graph $4x - 3y \geq 12$.

First, graph the boundary line, $4x - 3y = 12$.

Again, we replace the inequality symbol ($\geq$) with an equals sign to write the equation for our boundary line.

> **Note:** When equality *is included* ($\leq$ or $\geq$), use a *solid line* for the graph of the boundary line. This means the line is included in the graph of the linear inequality.

The graph of our boundary line (a solid line here) is shown on the facing page.

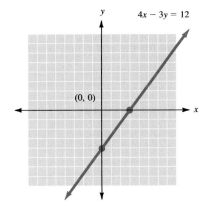

Although any of our graphing methods can be used here, the intercept method is probably the most efficient.

Again, we use $(0, 0)$ as a convenient test point. Substituting 0 for x and for y in the original inequality, we have

$$4 \cdot 0 - 3 \cdot 0 \geq 12$$
$$0 \geq 12 \qquad \text{A false statement}$$

Since the inequality is *false* for the test point, we shade the half plane that does *not* contain that test point, here $(0, 0)$.

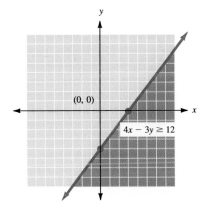

All points *on and below* the boundary line represent solutions for our original inequality.

● ● ● **CHECK YOURSELF 2**

Graph the inequality $3x + 2y \geq 6$.

Some applications involve horizontal or vertical boundary lines.

● Example 3

Graphing a Linear Inequality

Graph $x \leq 5$.

The boundary line is $x = 5$. Its graph is a solid line because equality is included. Using $(0, 0)$ as a test point, we substitute 0 for x with the result

$0 \le 5$ A true statement

Since the inequality is *true* for the test point, we shade the half plane containing the origin.

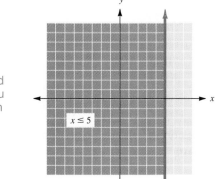

If the correct half plane is obvious, you may not need to use a test point. Did you know without testing which half plane to shade in this example?

● ● ● CHECK YOURSELF 3

Graph the inequality $y < 2$.

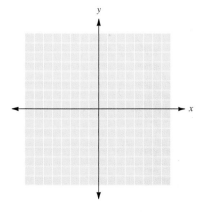

As we mentioned earlier, we may have to use a point other than the origin as our test point. Example 4 illustrates this approach.

● Example 4

Graphing a Linear Inequality

Graph $2x + 3y < 0$.

The boundary line is $2x + 3y = 0$. Its graph is shown on the facing page.

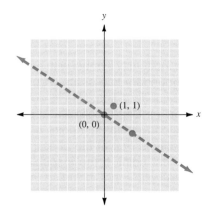

We use a dotted line for our boundary line since equality is not included.

We cannot use (0, 0) as our test point in this case. Do you see why?

Choose any other point *not* on the line. For instance, we have picked (1, 1) as a test point. Substituting 1 for x and 1 for y gives

$$2 \cdot 1 + 3 \cdot 1 < 0$$
$$2 + 3 < 0$$
$$5 < 0 \qquad \text{A false statement}$$

Since the inequality is *false* at our test point, we shade the half plane *not* containing (1, 1). This is shown in the following.

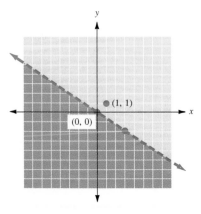

● ● ● **CHECK YOURSELF 4**

Graph the inequality $x - 2y < 0$.

The following steps summarize our work in graphing linear inequalities in two variables.

To Graph a Linear Inequality

STEP 1 Replace the inequality symbol with an equals sign to form the equation of the boundary line of the graph.

STEP 2 Graph the boundary line. Use a dotted line if equality is not included ($<$ or $>$). Use a solid line if equality is included ($\leq$ or $\geq$).

STEP 3 Choose any convenient test point *not* on the line.

STEP 4 If the inequality is *true* at the checkpoint, shade the half plane including the test point. If the inequality is *false* at the checkpoint, shade the half plane not including the test point.

● ● ● **CHECK YOURSELF ANSWERS**

1.

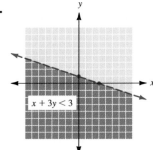

$x + 3y < 3$

2.

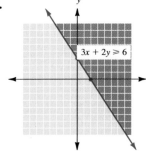

$3x + 2y \geq 6$

3.

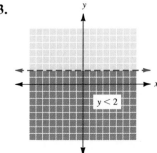

$y < 2$

4.

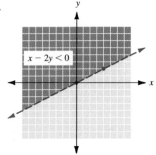

$x - 2y < 0$

A N S W E R S

1. _____
2. _____
3. _____
4. _____
5. _____
6. _____
7. _____
8. _____

In Exercises 1 to 8, we have graphed the boundary line for the linear inequality. Determine the correct half plane in each case, and complete the graph.

1. $x + y < 5$

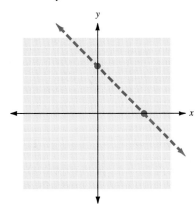

2. $x - y \geq 4$

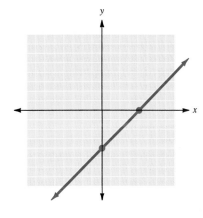

3. $x - 2y \geq 4$

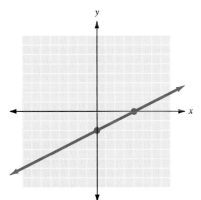

4. $2x + y < 6$

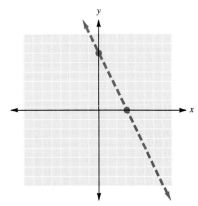

5. $x \leq -3$

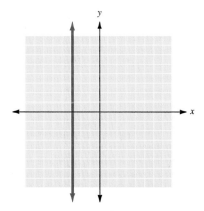

6. $y \geq 2x$

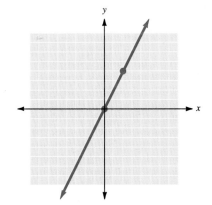

7. $y < 2x - 6$

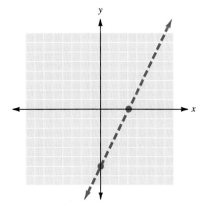

8. $y > 3$

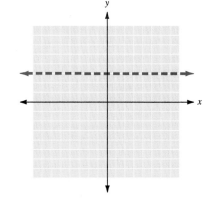

Graph each of the following inequalities.

9. $x + y < 3$

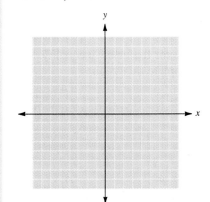

10. $x - y \geq 4$

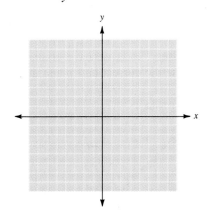

11. $x - y \leq 5$

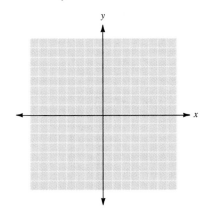

12. $x + y > 5$

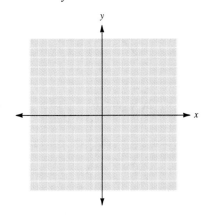

13. $2x + y < 6$

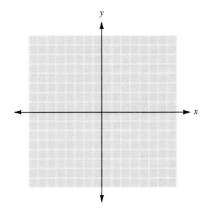

14. $3x + y \geq 6$

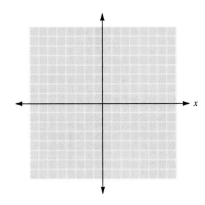

15. $x \leq 3$

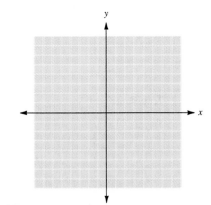

16. $4x + y \geq 4$

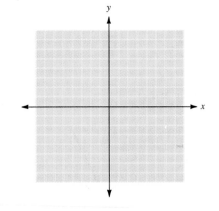

17. $x - 5y < 5$

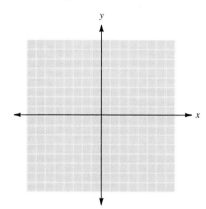

18. $y > 3$

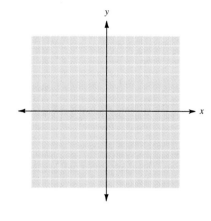

A N S W E R S

17. _____

18. _____

19. _____

20. _____

21. _____

22. _____

23. _____

24. _____

19. $y < -4$

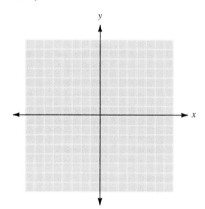

20. $4x + 3y > 12$

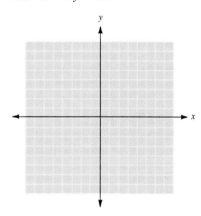

21. $2x - 3y \geq 6$

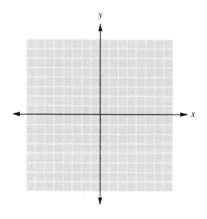

22. $x \geq -2$

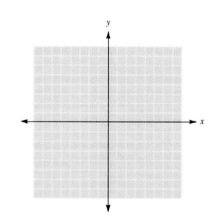

23. $3x + 2y \geq 0$

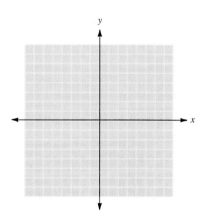

24. $3x + 5y < 15$

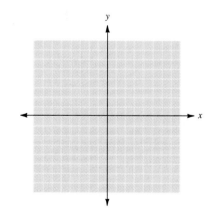

25. _____

26. _____

27. _____

28. _____

29. _____

30. _____

31. _____

32. _____

25. $5x + 2y > 10$

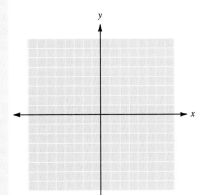

26. $x - 3y \geq 0$

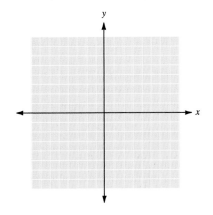

27. $y \leq 2x$

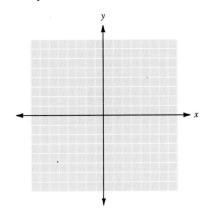

28. $3x - 4y < 12$

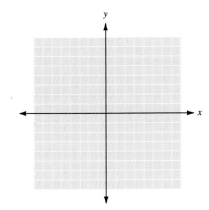

29. $y > 2x - 3$

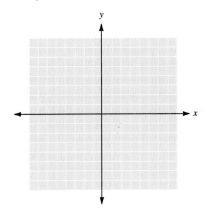

30. $y \geq -2x$

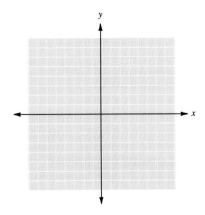

31. $y < -2x - 3$

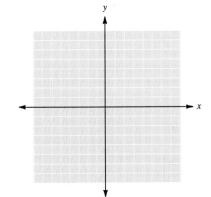

32. $y \leq 3x + 4$

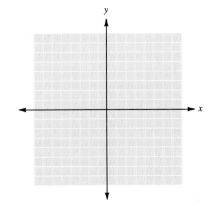

Graph each of the following inequalities.

33. $2(x + y) - x > 6$

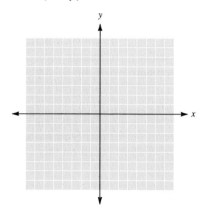

34. $3(x + y) - 2y < 3$

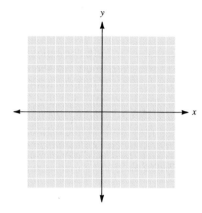

35. $4(x + y) - 3(x + y) \leq 5$

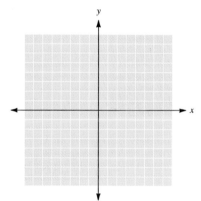

36. $5(2x + y) - 4(2x + y) \geq 4$

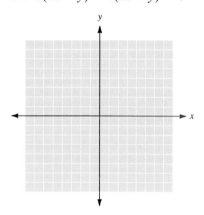

37. Hours worked. Suppose you have two part-time jobs. One is at a video store that pays $6 per hour and the other is at a convenience store that pays $5 per hour. Between the two jobs, you want to earn at least $160 per week. Write an inequality that shows the various number of hours you can work at each job.

38. Money problem. You have at least $30 in change in your drawer, consisting of dimes and quarters. Write an inequality that shows the different number of coins in your drawer.

39. Linda Williams has just begun a nursery business and seeks your advice. She has limited funds to spend and wants to stock two kinds of fruit-bearing plants. She lives in the northeastern part of Texas and thinks that blueberry bushes and peach trees would sell well there. Linda can buy blueberry bushes from a supplier for $2.50 each and young peach trees for $5.50 each. She wants to know what combination she should buy and keep her outlay to $500 or less. Write an equation and draw a graph to depict what combinations of blueberry and peach trees she can buy for the amount of money she has. Explain the graph and her options.

A N S W E R S

33. _____

34. _____

35. _____

36. _____

37. _____

38. _____

39. _____

40. After reading an article on the front page of *The New York Times* titled "You Have to be Good at Algebra to Figure Out the Best Deal for Long Distance," Rafaella De La Cruz decided to apply her skills in algebra to try to decide between two competing long-distance companies. It was difficult at first to get the companies to explain their charge policies. They both kept repeating that they were 25 percent cheaper than their competition. Finally, Rafaella found someone who explained that the charge depended on when she called, where she called, how long she talked, and how often she called. "Too many variables!" she exclaimed. So she decided to ask one company what they charged as a base amount, just for using the service.

Company A said that they charged $5 for the privilege of using their long-distance service whether or not she made any phone calls, and that because of this fee they were able to allow her to call anywhere in the United States after 6 PM for only $0.15 a minute. Complete this table of charges based on this company's plan:

Total Minutes Long Distance in 1 Month (after 6 P.M.)	Total Charge
0 minutes	
10 minutes	
30 minutes	
60 minutes	
120 minutes	

Use this table to make a whole-page graph of the monthly charges from Company A based on the number of minutes of long distance.

Rafaella wanted to compare this offer to Company B, which she was currently using. She looked at her phone bill and saw that one month she had been charged $7.50 for 30 minutes and another month she had been charged $11.25 for 45 minutes of long-distance calling. These calls were made after 6 PM to her relatives in Indiana and in Arizona. Draw a graph on the same set of axes you made for Company A's figures. Use your graph and what you know about linear inequalities to advise Rafaella about which company is best.

Answers

1. $x + y < 5$ **3.** $x - 2y \geq 4$ **5.** $x \leq -3$

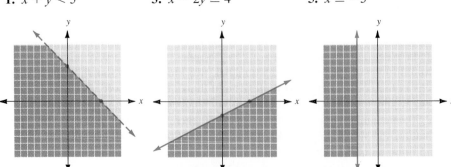

7. $y < 2x - 6$

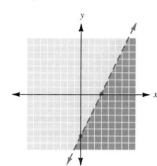

9. $x + y < 3$

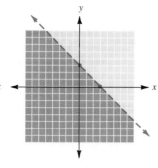

11. $x - y \leq 5$

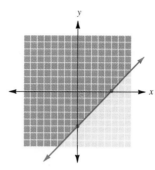

13. $2x + y < 6$

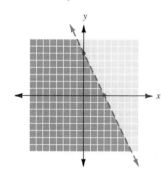

15. $x \leq 3$

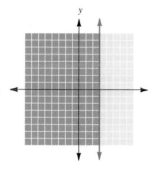

17. $x - 5y < 5$

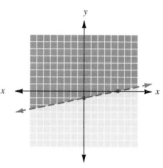

19. $y < -4$

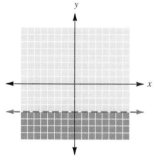

21. $2x - 3y \geq 6$

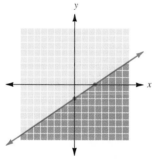

23. $3x + 2y \geq 0$

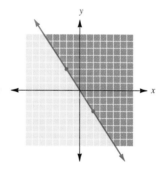

25. $5x + 2y > 10$

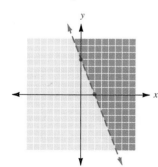

27. $y \leq 2x$

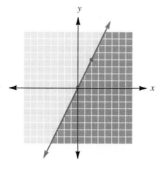

29. $y > 2x - 3$

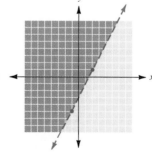

31. $y < -2x - 3$

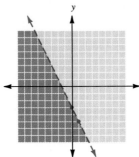

33. $x + 2y > 6$

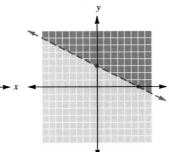

35. $x + y \le 5$

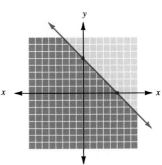

37. $6x + 5y \ge 160$

Scatter Plots and Line Graphs

7.6 OBJECTIVES

1. Create a scatter plot from a set of points
2. Interpret a scatter plot
3. Create a line graph from a set of points
4. Interpret a line graph

In Section 7.2, we discussed the graphing of individual points. Graphing one point at a time is called **point plotting.** Many applications of mathematics, particularly statistical applications, start with point plotting.

Let's assume we're interested in looking at how a small group of students did on the first two math tests of the semester. Their scores are presented in the following table.

Student	Test 1	Test 2
Abdul	92	94
Ben	63	65
Carlos	81	76
Deann	68	79
Elise	72	73
Francine	91	93
Garth	88	90

The information is interesting, but it's difficult to see the relationship between the first and second test scores. Their relationship is easier to see if we make each pair of scores an ordered pair, then plot the resulting points. Such a graph is called a **scatter plot.**

• Example 1

Creating a Scatter Plot

Use the test scores in the table above to create a scatter plot.

Abdul's scores become the ordered pair (92, 94). To plot this point, we go to 92 on the x axis and up 94 units.

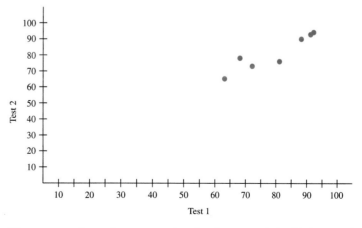

You can see from the scatter plot that in general the higher students' score on the first test, the better they did on the second test.

529

● ● ● **CHECK YOURSELF 1**

Use the scores in this table to create a scatter plot.

Name	Lab 1	Lab 2
Henri	22	25
Juan	18	16
Isabell	24	25
Kandace	19	20
Le	25	23
Merri	14	16
Nhan	17	18

As we just noted, a graph that displays a series of related points is called a scatter plot. The points are related by the fact that they have the same **units.** There units are displayed on the *x* and *y* axes. It is important to note these labels when reading a scatter plot. Let's look at an example.

● **Example 2**

Reading a Scatter Plot

Find the ordered pairs associated with the points on the scatter plot below.

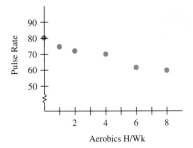

The broken line on the *y* axis indicates that we have omitted the values from 0 to 50. The ordered pairs are (0, 80), (1, 75), (2, 72), (4, 70), (6, 65), and (8, 62). In table form, we have the following.

Aerobic Hours/Week	Pulse Rate
0	80
1	75
2	72
4	70
6	65
8	62

● ● ● **CHECK YOURSELF 2**

Find the ordered pairs associated with the points on the scatter plot.

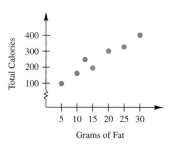

Note that, in Example 1, the *y* value of the points tends to increase as the *x* value increases. We say that there is a **positive relationship** between the two test scores. In Example 2, the *y* values tends to decrease as the *x* value increases. We say there is a **negative relationship** between aerobic hours and pulse rate. That is, as one goes up, the other goes down.

●**Example 3**

Interpreting Scatter Plots

Describe the relationship displayed in each graph.

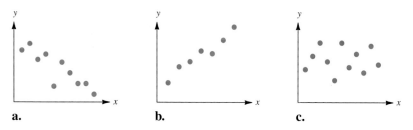

a.　　　　　　　　b.　　　　　　　　c.

(*a*) There is a negative relationship between the *x* and *y* values.
(*b*) There is a positive relationship between the *x* and *y* values.
(*c*) There is no obvious relationship between the *x* and *y* values.

● ● ●   **CHECK YOURSELF 3**

Describe the relationship displayed in each graph.

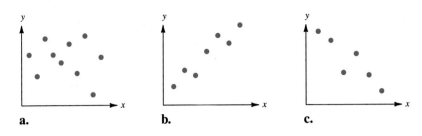

a.   b.   c.

If the *x* value of a set of points represents time, we frequently connect the plotted points. Such a graph is called a **line graph.**

● Example 4

Creating a Line Graph

Create a line graph from the following table:

Age	Weight (kilograms)
0	3
1	7
2	9
3	12
4	16
5	18
6	20

There is no need to make any adjustments of the scale on the axes. The age values go from 0 to 6, and the weight values go from 0 to 20 by fives.

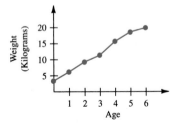

● ● ●   **CHECK YOURSELF 4**

Create a line graph from the following table:

Height (centimeters)	Weight (kilograms)
140	60
150	64
160	70
170	73
180	75

As was the case with scatter plots, both the label and the scales on the axes must be considered when interpreting a graph.

● Example 5

Interpreting a Line Graph

Interpret the information presented in the following graph, which shows new car prices for a Mazda Miata:

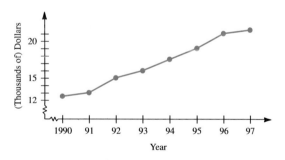

The price of a new Miata has increased each year over a 7-year period. Here is the information from the graph in table form:

Year	1990	1991	1992	1993	1994	1995	1996	1997
Price	$12,500	$13,000	$15,000	$16,000	$17,500	$19,000	$21,000	$21,500

● ● ● **CHECK YOURSELF 5**

Interpret the information presented in the following graph:

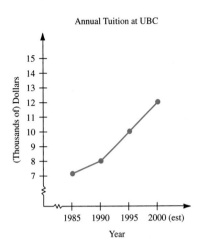

Annual Tuition at UBC

● ● ● **CHECK YOURSELF ANSWERS**

1.

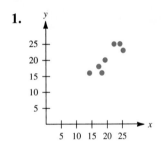

The ordered pairs are (22, 25), (18, 16), (24, 25), (19, 20), (25, 23), (14, 16), and (17, 18).

2. The ordered pairs are (5, 100), (10, 160), (12, 250), (15, 200), (20, 300), (25, 325), and (30, 400). Your answers may vary slightly from these points.

3. **(a)** There is no obvious relationship; **(b)** There is a positive relationship; **(c)** There is a negative relationship.

4.

Year	Tuition
1985	$ 7,000
1990	$ 8,000
1995	$10,000
2000	$12,000

5.

Exercises

Draw a scatter diagram for each of the following tables. State if you think there is a positive relationship, a negative relationship, or no relationship.

1. _____

2. _____

1.

Name	Test 1	Test 2
Maritza	86	89
Kathy	65	70
Frank	83	87
Damien	75	77
Sean	82	78
Ting	56	43

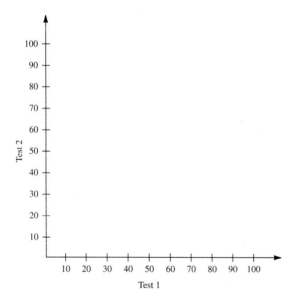

2.

Name	IQ	Hours Watching TV
Tomas	125	5
Ian	116	14
Sam	97	30
Jusef	114	16
Peter	85	41
Colin	107	25
Demi	128	10

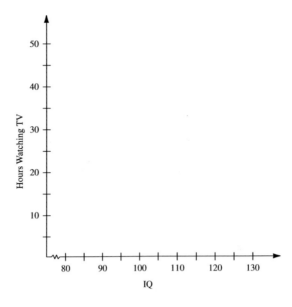

3.

Name	Mid-Term Grade	Final
Tom	66	80
Inez	71	75
Dick	80	95
Gerry	76	83
Ari	66	72
Nicole	85	73
Jenny	89	85

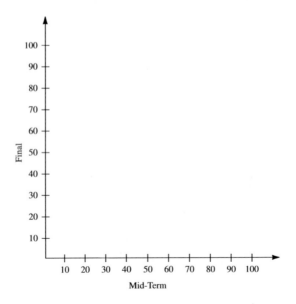

4.

Name	Mid-Term Grade	Final
Juan	56	71
Merri	65	68
Hana	85	89
Amy	77	82
Sue	85	91
Aaron	76	81

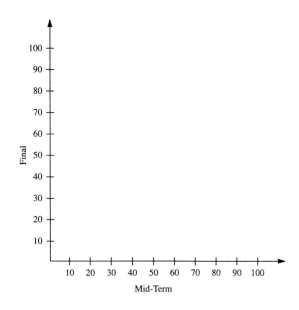

Describe the relationship displayed in each graph.

5.

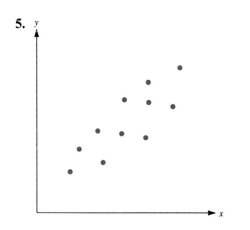

6.

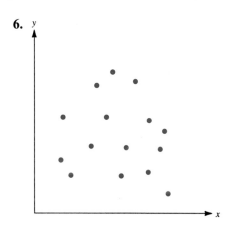

7.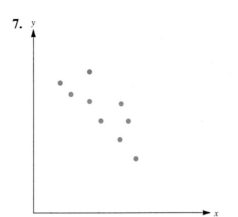

8.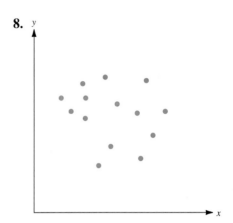

Create a line graph for each of the following.

9.

Credits Taken	Number of People
6	4
12	3
18	6
24	3
30	5
36	9

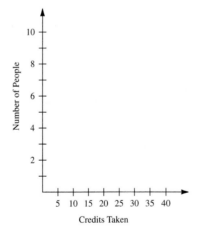

10.

Year	Price
1990	$250
1992	$350
1994	$390
1996	$450
1998	$525

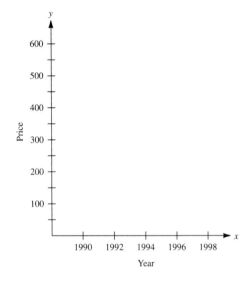

11. Here is a table of numbers of males and females who earned bachelor degrees in the years 1965–1990.

Year	Men Earning Bachelor Degree (in thousands)	Women Earning Bachelor Degree (in thousands)
1965	289	213
1970	451	341
1973	518	404
1975	505	418
1978	487	434
1980	474	456
1985	483	497
1990	491	558

Make one scatter plot for the men and one for the women. What trends do you see? Can you make predictions for the year 2000? Explain.

12.

12. Ben and Jerry's ice cream has many loyal fans and is known to be very rich. It is sold only in pints and is relatively expensive. Is there some relationship between the price of ice cream and the amount of fat in the ice cream? Work with a small group of four to five students to collect information from as many different brands of ice cream as possible. (Look at the nutritional information label on the ice cream; it will indicate the serving size, amount of fat in grams, and total calories in one serving.) You should pick one flavor, such as chocolate or vanilla, and investigate only that one. You will need to record the price and information from the nutrition label for each brand.

Compute the number of calories of fat in each serving by multiplying grams of fat by 9 calories per gram. What percentage of a serving is fat? What is cost per serving? If you find two different prices for a particular brand, use both prices, or compute the mean price. Make a scatter plot of percentage of fat in a serving and cost of a serving.

Write about any conclusions you draw from your scatter plot. Does the graph raise more questions? State your new questions and what might be done to try to answer them.

Answers

1. Positive relationship

3. No relationship

5. Positive relationship

7. Negative relationship

9. See exercise

11.

Summary

The Rectangular Coordinate System [7.1 and 7.2]

If $2x - y = 10$, $(6, 2)$ is a solution for the equation, because substituting 6 for x and 2 for y gives a true statement.

Solutions of Linear Equations A pair of values that satisfy the equation. Solutions for linear equations in two variables are written as *ordered pairs*. An ordered pair has the form

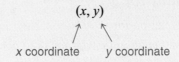

$$(x, y)$$

x coordinate y coordinate

The Rectangular Coordinate System A system formed by two perpendicular axes which intersect at a point called the **origin.** The horizontal line is called the **x axis.** The vertical line is called the **y axis.**

Graphing Points from Ordered Pairs The coordinates of an ordered pair allow you to associate a point in the plane with every ordered pair.
    To graph a point in the plane,

To graph the point corresponding to $(2, 3)$:

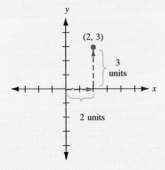

1. Start at the origin.
2. Move right or left according to the value of the x coordinate: to the right if x is positive or to the left if x is negative.
3. Then move up or down according to the value of the y coordinate: up if y is positive and down if y is negative.

Midpoint The midpoint of A and B is the point on line $\overleftrightarrow{AB}$ that is equal distance from A and B.

Graphing Linear Equations [7.3]

$2x - 3y = 4$ is a linear equation.

Linear Equation An equation that can be written in the form

$$Ax + By = C$$

where A and B are not both 0.

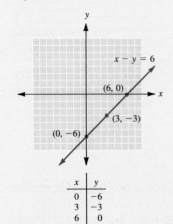

Graphing Linear Equations

1. Find at least three solutions for the equation, and put your results in tabular form.
2. Graph the solutions found in step 1.
3. Draw a straight line through the points determined in step 2 to form the graph of the equation.

541

x and y Intercepts of a Line The *x* **intercept** is the *x* coordinate of the point where the line intersects the *x* axis. The *y* **intercept** is the *y* coordinate of the point where the line intersects the *y* axis.

If $2x + 4y = 8$, $(4, 0)$ gives the *x* intercept and $(0, 2)$ gives the *y* intercept.

Graphing by the Intercept Method

1. Find the *x* intercept by letting $y = 0$. Then solve for *x*.
2. Find the *y* intercept by letting $x = 0$. Then solve for *y*.
3. Graph the *x* and *y* intercepts.
4. Draw a straight line through the intercepts.

To graph $x + 2y = 6$, we can solve for *y*.

$$y = -\frac{1}{2}x + 3$$

Graphing by Solving for y

1. Solve the given equation for *y*.
2. Use the equivalent equation (solved for *y*) to determine solutions.
3. Graph as before.

The Slope of a Line [7.4]

To find the slope of the line through $(-2, -3)$ and $(4, 6)$,

$$m = \frac{6 - (-3)}{4 - (-2)}$$

$$= \frac{6 + 3}{4 + 2}$$

$$= \frac{9}{6} = \frac{3}{2}$$

Slope The slope of a line gives a numerical measure of the steepness of the line. The slope *m* of a line containing the distinct points in the plane $P(x_1, y_1)$ and $Q(x_2, y_2)$ is given by

$$m = \frac{y_2 - y_1}{x_2 - x_1} \qquad \text{where } x_2 \neq x_1$$

For the equation

$$y = \frac{2}{3}x - 3$$

the slope *m* is $\frac{2}{3}$ and *b*, the *y* intercept, is -3.

Slope-Intercept Form The slope-intercept form for the equation of a line is

$$y = mx + b$$

where the line has slope *m* and *y* intercept *b*.

Graphing Linear Inequalities [7.5]

The Graphing Steps

To graph $x - 2y < 4$:
$x - 2y = 4$ is the boundary line. Using $(0, 0)$ as the checkpoint, we have

$$0 - 2 \cdot 0 < 4$$

$$0 < 4 \qquad \text{(True)}$$

Shade the half plane that includes $(0, 0)$.

1. Replace the inequality symbol with an equals sign to form the equation of the boundary line of the graph.
2. Graph the boundary line. Use a dotted line if equality is not included ($<$ or $>$). Use a solid line if equality is included ($\leq$ or $\geq$).
3. Choose any convenient test point not on the line.
4. If the inequality is *true* at the checkpoint, shade the half plane including the test point. If the inequality is *false* at the checkpoint, shade the half plane that does not include the checkpoint.

Scatter Plots and Line Graphs [7.6]

If the points in a scatter plot tend to rise from left to right, a **positive relationship** exists between the *x* and *y* values.

If the points in a scatter plot tend to fall from left to right, a **negative relationship** exists between the *x* and *y* values.

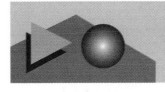

Summary Exercises

This summary exercise set is provided to give you practice with each of the objectives of the chapter. Each exercise is keyed to the appropriate chapter section. The answers are provided in the instructor's manual.

[7.1] Determine which of the ordered pairs are solutions for the given equations.

1. $x - y = 6$ $(6, 0), (3, 3), (3, -3), (0, -6)$

2. $2x + y = 8$ $(4, 0), (2, 2), (2, 4), (4, 2)$

3. $2x + 3y = 6$ $(3, 0), (6, 2), (-3, 4), (0, 2)$

4. $2x - 5y = 10$ $(5, 0), \left(\dfrac{5}{2}, -1\right), \left(2, \dfrac{2}{5}\right), (0, -2)$

[7.1] Complete the ordered pairs so that each is a solution for the given equation.

5. $x + y = 8$ $(4, \ \ ), (\ \ , 8), (8, \ \ ), (6, \ \ )$

6. $x - 2y = 10$ $(0, \ \ ), (12, \ \ ), (\ \ , -2), (8, \ \ )$

7. $2x + 3y = 6$ $(3, \ \ ), (6, \ \ ), (\ \ , -4), (-3, \ \ )$

8. $y = 3x + 4$ $(2, \ \ ), (\ \ , 7), \left(\dfrac{1}{3}, \ \ \right), \left(\dfrac{4}{3}, \ \ \right)$

[7.1] Find four solutions for each of the following equations.

9. $x + y = 10$ **10.** $2x + y = 8$

11. $2x - 3y = 6$ **12.** $y = -\dfrac{3}{2}x + 2$

[7.2] Give the coordinates of the points graphed below.   [7.2] Plot points with the coordinates shown.

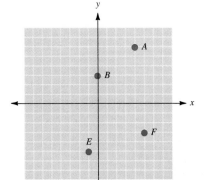

13. A

14. B

15. E

16. F

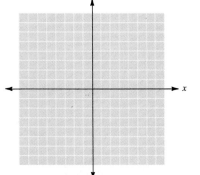

17. $P(6, 0)$

18. $Q(5, 4)$

19. $T(-2, 4)$

20. $U(4, -2)$

[7.2]   Find the midpoint for each pair of points.

21. (0, 3) and (0, 9)

22. (2, 4) and (−6, 8)

23. (1, 5) and (−3, −5)

24. (2, −7) and (−3, −1)

[7.3]   Graph each of the following equations.

25. $x + y = 5$ **26.** $x - y = 6$ **27.** $y = 2x$

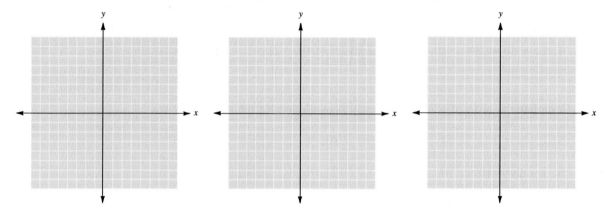

28. $y = -3x$ **29.** $y = \dfrac{3}{2}x$ **30.** $y = 3x + 2$

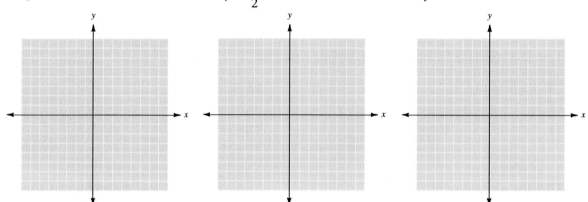

31. $y = 2x - 3$

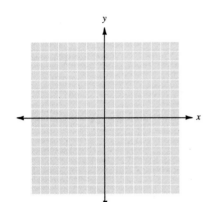

32. $y = -3x + 4$

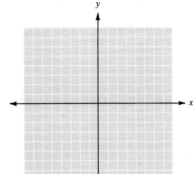

33. $y = \dfrac{2}{3}x + 2$

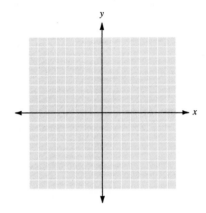

34. $3x - y = 3$

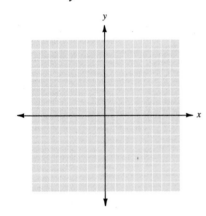

35. $2x + y = 6$

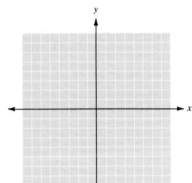

36. $3x + 2y = 12$

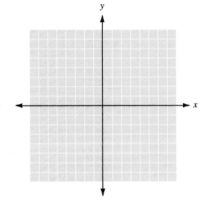

37. $3x - 4y = 12$

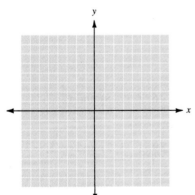

38. $x = 3$

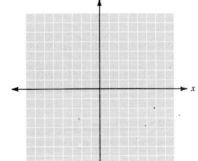

39. $y = -2$

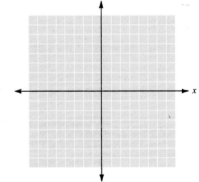

[7.3]   Graph each of the following equations.

40. $5x - 3y = 15$

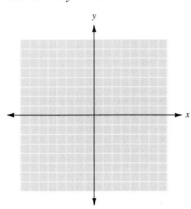

41. $4x + 3y = 12$

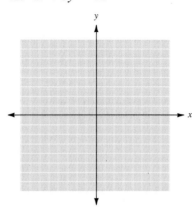

[7.3]   Graph each equation by first solving for y.

42. $2x + y = 6$

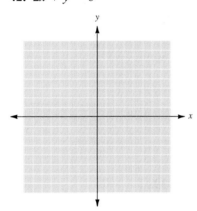

43. $3x + 2y = 6$

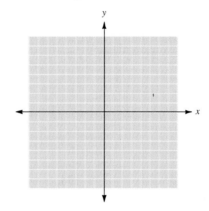

[7.4]   Find the slope of the line through each of the following pairs of points.

44. $(3, 4)$ and $(5, 8)$

45. $(-2, 3)$ and $(1, -6)$

46. $(-2, 5)$ and $(2, 3)$

47. $(-5, -2)$ and $(1, 2)$

48. $(-2, 6)$ and $(5, 6)$

49. $(-3, 2)$ and $(-1, -3)$

50. $(-3, -6)$ and $(5, -2)$

51. $(-6, -2)$ and $(-6, 3)$

[7.4]   Find the slope and y intercept of the line represented by each of the following equations.

52. $y = 2x + 5$

53. $y = -4x - 3$

54. $y = -\dfrac{3}{4}x$

55. $y = \dfrac{2}{3}x + 3$

56. $2x + 3y = 6$ **57.** $5x - 2y = 10$ **58.** $y = -3$ **59.** $x = 2$

[7.4]   Write the equation of the line with the given slope and y intercept. Then graph each line, *using* the slope and y intercept.

60. $m = 2, b = 3$ **61.** $m = \dfrac{3}{4}, b = -2$ **62.** $m = -\dfrac{2}{3}, b = 2$

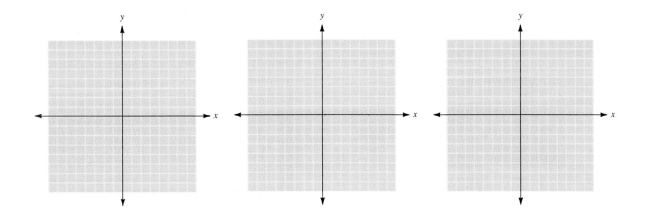

[7.5]   Graph each of the following inequalities.

63. $x + y \leq 4$ **64.** $x - y > 5$ **65.** $2x + y < 6$

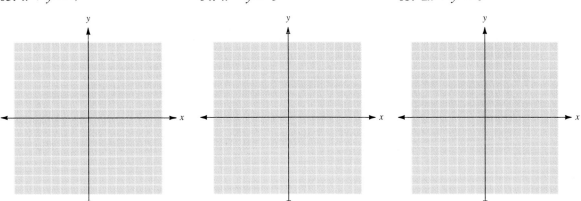

66. $2x - y \geq 6$

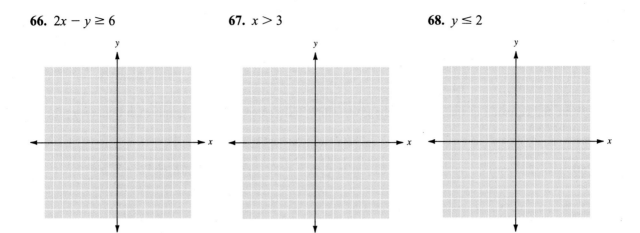

67. $x > 3$

68. $y \leq 2$

69. The following data represent the living area (in hundreds of square feet) of a home and the selling price (in thousands of dollars) of the home. Draw a scatter diagram to represent the data.

Living Area	14	36	23	17	17	13	21	25
Selling Price	145	228	150	130	160	114	142	165

70. Use the scores in the following table to create a scatter plot. Indicate if there is a positive relationship, a negative relationship, or no relationship.

Student	Placement Test Score	1st Test Grade
Amy	13	75
Trinh	15	80
Joshua	10	70
Tom	20	90
Inci	8	60
Branabas	17	75
Ruth	22	88

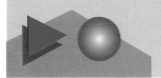

Self-Test
for Chapter 7

Name _____

Section _____ Date _____

A N S W E R S

1. _____
2. _____
3. _____
4. _____
5. _____
6. _____
7. _____
8. _____
9. _____
10. _____
11. _____
12. _____
13. _____
14. _____
15. _____

The purpose of this self-test is to help you check your progress and to review for a chapter test in class. Allow yourself about an hour to take the test. When you are done, check your answers in the back of the book. If you missed any answers, be sure to go back and review the appropriate sections in the chapter.

Determine which of the ordered pairs are solutions for the given equations.

1. $x + y = 9$ $(3, 6), (9, 0), (3, 2)$

2. $4x - y = 16$ $(4, 0), (3, -1), (5, 4)$

Complete the ordered pairs so that each is a solution for the given equation.

3. $x + 3y = 12$ $(3, \ ), (\ , 2), (9, \ )$

4. $4x + 3y = 12$ $(3, \ ), (\ , 4), (\ , 3)$

Find four solutions for each of the following equations.

5. $x - y = 7$ **6.** $5x - 6y = 30$

Give the coordinates of the points graphed below.

Plot points with the coordinates shown.

7. A

8. B

9. C

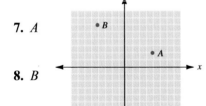

10. $S(1, -2)$

11. $T(0, 3)$

12. $U(-2, -3)$

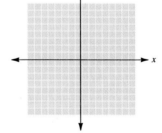

Graph each of the following equations.

13. $x + y = 4$ **14.** $y = 3x$ **15.** $y = \dfrac{3}{4}x - 4$

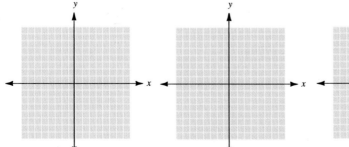

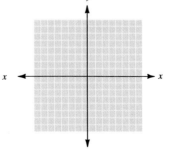

16. $x + 3y = 6$ **17.** $2x + 5y = 10$ **18.** $y = -4$

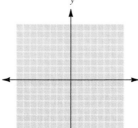 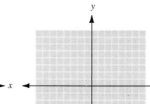 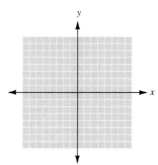

Find the slope of the line through the following pairs of points.

19. $(-3, 5)$ and $(2, 10)$ **20.** $(-2, 6)$ and $(2, 9)$

Write the equation of the line with the given slope and y intercept. Then graph each line, *using* the slope and y intercept.

21. $m = -3, b = 6$ **22.** $m = \dfrac{2}{5}, b = -3$

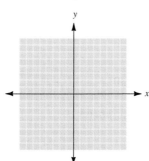 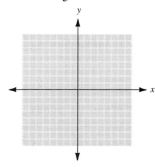

Graph each of the following inequalities.

23. $x + y < 3$ **24.** $3x + y \geq 9$ **25.** $x \leq 7$

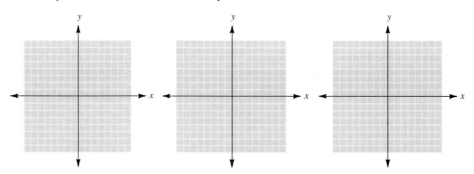

This review covers selected topics from the first seven chapters.

Perform the indicated operation.

1. $3x^2y^2 - 5xy - 2x^2y^2 + 2xy$

2. $\dfrac{36m^5n^2}{27m^2n}$

3. $(x^2 - 3x + 5) - (x^2 - 2x - 4)$

4. $(5z^2 - 3z) - (2z^2 - 5)$

Multiply.

5. $(2x - 3)(x + 7)$

6. $(2a - 2b)(a + 4b)$

Divide.

7. $(x^2 + 3x + 2) \div (x - 3)$

8. $(x^4 - 2x) \div (x + 2)$

Solve each equation and check your results.

9. $5x - 2 = 2x - 6$

10. $3(x - 2) = 2(3x + 1) - 2$

Factor each polynomial completely.

11. $x^2 - x - 56$

12. $4x^3y - 2x^2y^2 + 8x^4y$

13. $8a^3 - 18ab^2$

14. $15x^2 - 21xy + 6y^2$

Find the slope of the line through the following pairs of points.

15. $(2, -4)$ and $(-3, -9)$

16. $(-1, 7)$ and $(3, -2)$

A N S W E R S

1. _____

2. _____

3. _____

4. _____

5. _____

6. _____

7. _____

8. _____

9. _____

10. _____

11. _____

12. _____

13. _____

14. _____

15. _____

16. _____

Graph each of the following equations.

17. $x + y = 4$

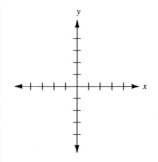

18. $y = 2x - 5$

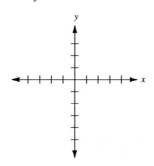

19. If the reciprocal of 4 times a number is subtracted from the reciprocal of that number, the result is $\dfrac{3}{16}$. What is the number?

20. The length of a rectangle is 3 in less than twice its width. If the area of the rectangle is 35 in.^{2}, find the dimensions of the rectangle.

CHAPTER

8

Systems of Linear Equations

INTRODUCTION

In the United States, almost all electricity is generated by the burning of the fossil fuels (coal, oil, or gas); by nuclear fission; or by water-powered turbines in hydroelectric dams. About 65 percent of the electric power we use comes from burning fossil fuels. Because of this dependence on a nonrenewable resource and concern over pollution caused by burning fossil fuels, there has been some urgency in developing ways to utilize other power sources. Some of the most promising projects have been in solar- and wind-generated energy.

Alternative sources of energy are expensive compared to the cost of the traditional methods of generating electricity described above. But alternative energy sources are looking more promising as the average price per kilowatt hour (kwh) of electric power sold to residential users has been going up—about $0.0028 per kwh—since 1970. The costs of manufacturing and installing banks of wind turbines in windy locations has declined.

When will the cost of generating electricity for residential use using wind power be equal to or less than the cost of using the traditional energy mix? Economists use equations such as the following to make projections and then advise about the feasibility of investing in wind power plants for large cities:

$C_1 = \$0.054 + 0.0028t$
$C_2 = \$0.25 - 0.0154t$

where C = cost per kwh in 1980
    C_1 = cost of present mix of energy sources*
    C_2 = cost of wind-powered electricity

*Of course, the true cost of burning fossil fuels also includes the damage to the environment and people's health.

Charles Thatcher © Tony Stone

Solving Systems of Linear Equations by Graphing

8.1 OBJECTIVE

Find the solution(s) for a set of linear equations by graphing

From our work in Section 7.3, we know that an equation of the form $x + y = 3$ is a linear equation. Remember that its graph is a straight line. Often we will want to consider two equations together. They then form a **system of linear equations.** An example of such a system is

$$x + y = 3$$
$$3x - y = 5$$

A solution for a linear equation in two variables is any ordered pair that satisfies the equation. Often you must find a single ordered pair that satisfies both equations of the system. It is called the **solution for the system.** For instance, the solution for the system above is (2, 1) because, replacing x with 2 and y with 1, we have

$x + y = 3$	$3x - y = 5$
$2 + 1 \overset{?}{=} 3$	$3 \cdot 2 - 1 \overset{?}{=} 5$
$3 = 3$	$6 - 1 \overset{?}{=} 5$
	$5 = 5$

There is no other ordered pair that satisfies both equations.

Since both statements are true, the ordered pair (2, 1) satisfies both equations.

One approach to finding the solution for a system of linear equations is the **graphical method.** To use this, we graph the two lines on the same coordinate system. The coordinates of the point where the lines intersect is the solution for the system.

● Example 1

Solving by Graphing

Solve the system by graphing.

$$x + y = 6$$
$$x - y = 4$$

Use the intercept method to graph each equation.

First, we determine solutions for the equations of our system. For $x + y = 6$, two solutions are (6, 0) and (0, 6). For $x - y = 4$, two solutions are (4, 0) and (0, −4). Using these intercepts, we graph the two equations. The lines intersect at the point (5, 1).

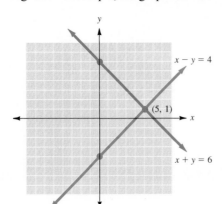

(5, 1) is the solution of the system. It is the only point that lies on both lines.

Note: By substituting 5 for x and 1 for y into the two original equations, we can check that $(5, 1)$ is indeed the solution for our system.

Both statements must be true for (5, 1) to be a solution for the system.

$$
\begin{array}{ll}
x + y = 6 & x - y = 4 \\
\hline
5 + 1 \overset{?}{=} 6 & 5 - 1 \overset{?}{=} 4 \\
6 = 6 & 4 = 4
\end{array}
$$

● ● ● **CHECK YOURSELF 1**

Solve the system by graphing.

$2x - y = 4$

$x + y = 5$

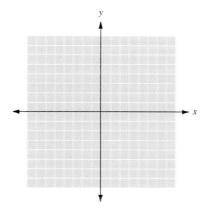

Example 2 shows how to graph a system when one of the equations represents a horizontal line.

●Example 2

Solving by Graphing

Solve the system by graphing.

$3x + 2y = 6$

$y = 6$

For $3x + 2y = 6$, two solutions are $(2, 0)$ and $(0, 3)$. These represent the x and y intercepts of the graph of the equation. The equation $y = 6$ represents a horizontal line that crosses the y axis at the point $(0, 6)$. Using these intercepts, we graph the two equations. The lines will intersect at the point $(-2, 6)$. So this is a solution to our system.

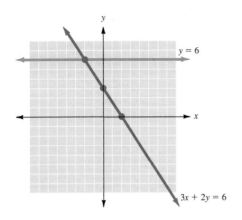

● ● ● **CHECK YOURSELF 2**

Solve the system by graphing.

$$4x + 5y = 20$$
$$y = 8$$

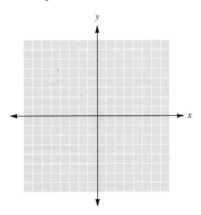

The systems in Examples 1 and 2 both had exactly one solution. A system with one solution is called a **consistent system.** It is possible that a system of equations will have no solution. Such a system is called an **inconsistent system.** We present such a system here.

● Example 3

Solving an Inconsistent System

Solve by graphing.

$$2x + y = 2$$
$$2x + y = 4$$

We can graph the two lines as before. For $2x + y = 2$, two solutions are $(0, 2)$ and $(1, 0)$. For $2x + y = 4$, two solutions are $(0, 4)$ and $(2, 0)$. Using these intercepts, we graph the two equations.

Note: In slope-intercept form, our equations are

$y = -2x + 2$

and

$y = -2x + 4$

Both lines have slope -2.

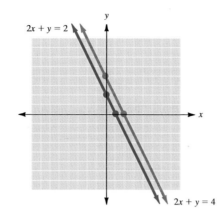

Notice that the slope for each of these lines is -2, but they have different y intercepts. This means that the lines are parallel (they will never intersect). Since the lines have no points in common, there is no ordered pair that will satisfy both equations. The system has no solution. It is *inconsistent*.

● ● ● **CHECK YOURSELF 3**

Solve by graphing (if possible).

$x - 3y = 3$

$x - 3y = 6$

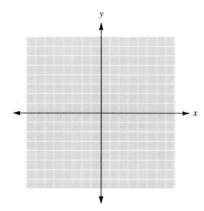

There is one more possibility for linear systems, as Example 4 illustrates.

• Example 4

Solving a Dependent System

Solve by graphing.

$$x - 2y = 4$$

$$2x - 4y = 8$$

Note that multiplying the first equation by 2 results in the second equation.

Graphing as before and using the intercept method, we find

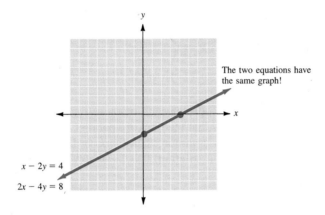

The two equations have the same graph!

$x - 2y = 4$

$2x - 4y = 8$

Since the graphs coincide, there are *infinitely many* solutions for this system. Every point on the graph of $x - 2y = 4$ is also on the graph of $2x - 4y = 8$, so any ordered pair satisfying $x - 2y = 4$ also satisfies $2x - 4y = 8$. This is called a *dependent* system, and any point on the line is a solution.

● ● ●   **CHECK YOURSELF 4**

Solve by graphing.

$$x + \ y = 4$$

$$2x + 2y = 8$$

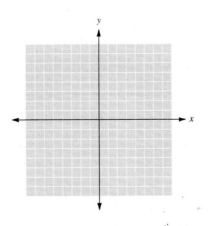

The following summarizes our work in this section.

To Solve a System of Equations by Graphing

STEP 1 Graph both equations on the same coordinate system.
STEP 2 Determine the solution to the system as follows.
  a. If the lines intersect at one point, the solution is the ordered pair corresponding to that point. This is called a *consistent system*.

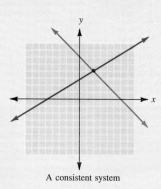

A consistent system

b. If the lines are parallel, it is called an **inconsistent system**.

There is no ordered pair that lies on both lines.

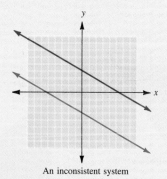

An inconsistent system

c. If the two equations have the same graph, then the system has infinitely many solutions. This is called a **dependent system**.

Any ordered pair that corresponds to a point on the line is a solution.

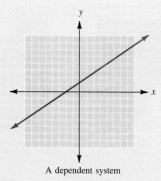

A dependent system

STEP 3 Check the solution in both equations, if necessary.

● ● ● **CHECK YOURSELF ANSWERS**

1.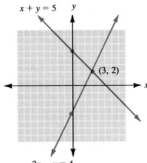

2.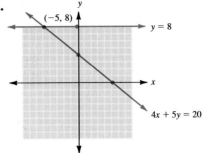

3. There is no solution. The lines are parallel, so the system is inconsistent.

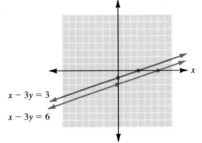

4.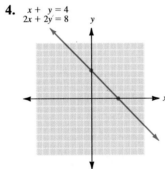

A dependent system

Solve each of the following systems by graphing.

1. $x + y = 6$
$x - y = 4$

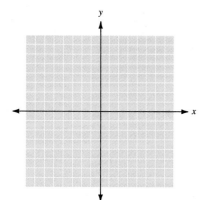

2. $x - y = 8$
$x + y = 2$

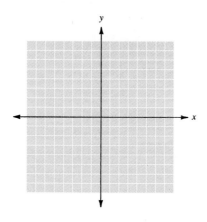

3. $-x + y = 3$
$x + y = 5$

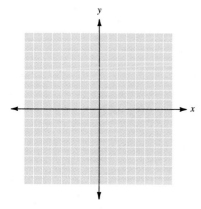

4. $x + y = 7$
$-x + y = 3$

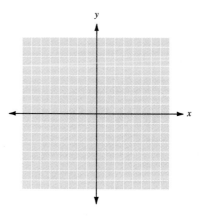

5. $x + 2y = 4$
$x - y = 1$

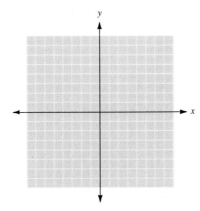

6. $3x + y = 6$
$x + y = 4$

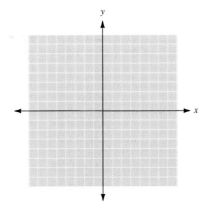

7. $2x + y = 8$
$2x - y = 0$

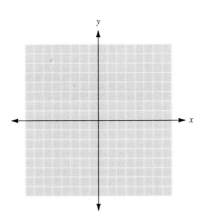

8. $x - 2y = -2$
$x + 2y = 6$

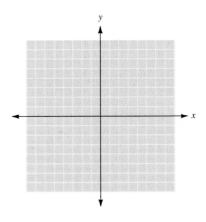

9. $x + 3y = 12$
$2x - 3y = 6$

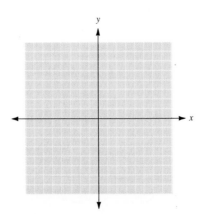

10. $2x - y = 4$
$2x - y = 6$

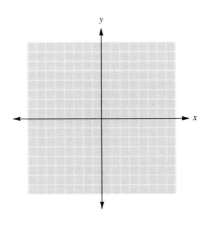

11. $3x + 2y = 12$
$\quad\quad\quad y = 3$

12. $x - 2y = 8$
$\quad\quad 3x - 2y = 12$

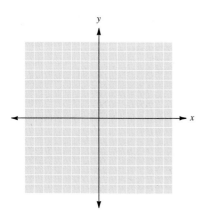

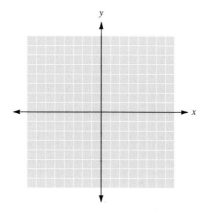

13. $x - y = 4$
$\quad\quad 2x - 2y = 8$

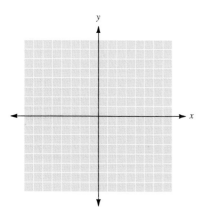

14. $2x - y = 8$
$\quad\quad\quad x = 2$

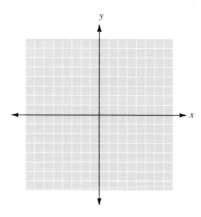

15. $x - 4y = -4$
$\quad\; x + 2y = 8$

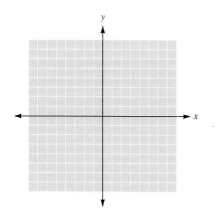

16. $x - 6y = 6$
$\quad -x + y = 4$

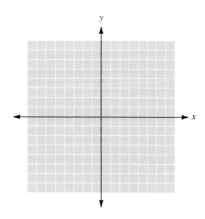

ANSWERS

17. _____

18. _____

19. _____

20. _____

21. _____

22. _____

17. $3x - 2y = 6$
$2x - y = 5$

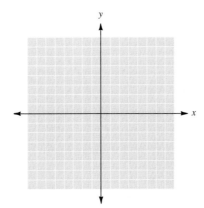

18. $4x + 3y = 12$
$x + y = 2$

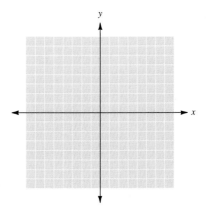

19. $3x - y = 3$
$3x - y = 6$

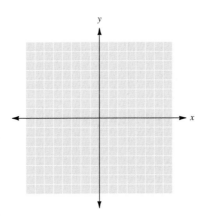

20. $3x - 6y = 9$
$x - 2y = 3$

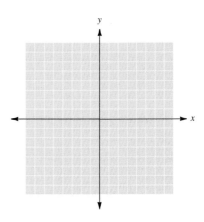

21. $2y = 3$
$x - 2y = -3$

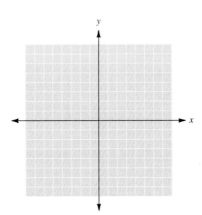

22. $x + y = -6$
$-x + 2y = 6$

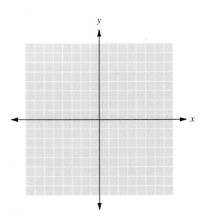

23. $x = 4$
$y = -6$

24. $x = -3$
$y = 5$

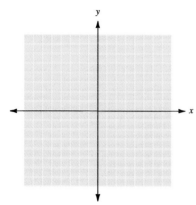

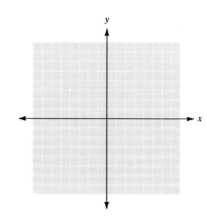

25. Find values for m and b in the following system so that the solution to the system is $(1, 2)$.

$mx + 3y = 8$
$-3x + 4y = b$

26. Find values for m and b in the following system so that the solution to the system is $(-3, 4)$.

$5x + 7y = b$
$mx + \ y = 22$

27. Complete the following statements in your own words:

"To solve an equation means to . . . ."
"To solve a system of equations means to . . . ."

28. A system of equations such as the one below is sometimes called a "2-by-2" system of linear equations."

$3x + 4y = 1$
$x - 2y = 6$

Explain this term.

29. Complete this statement in your own words: "All the points on the graph of the equation $2x + 3y = 6$ . . . ." Exchange statements with other students. Do you agree with other student's statements?

30. Does a system of linear equations always have a solution? How can you tell without graphing that a system of two equations graphs into two parallel lines? Give some examples to explain your reasoning.

A N S W E R S

23.

24.

25.

26.

27.

28.

29.

30.

Getting Ready for Section 8.2
[Section 1.4]

Simplify each of the following expressions.

a. $(2x + y) + (x - y)$ **b.** $(x + y) + (-x + y)$

c. $(3x + 2y) + (-3x - 3y)$ **d.** $(x - 5y) + (2x + 5y)$

e. $2(x + y) + (3x - 2y)$ **f.** $2(2x - y) + (-4x - 3y)$

g. $3(2x + y) + 2(-3x + y)$ **h.** $3(2x - 4y) + 4(x + 3y)$

Answers

1. $\left.\begin{array}{l} x + y = 6 \\ x - y = 4 \end{array}\right\}(5, 1)$ **3.** $\left.\begin{array}{l} -x + y = 3 \\ x + y = 5 \end{array}\right\}(1, 4)$

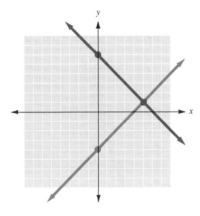
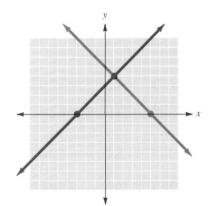

5. $\left.\begin{array}{l} x + 2y = 4 \\ x - y = 1 \end{array}\right\}(2, 1)$ **7.** $\left.\begin{array}{l} 2x + y = 8 \\ 2x - y = 0 \end{array}\right\}(2, 4)$

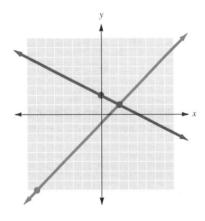
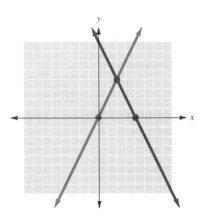

9. $\left.\begin{array}{l} x + 3y = 12 \\ 2x - 3y = 6 \end{array}\right\}(6, 2)$

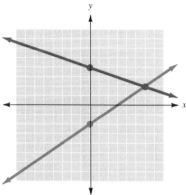

11. $\left.\begin{array}{l} 3x + 2y = 12 \\ y = 3 \end{array}\right\}(2, 3)$

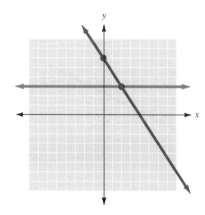

13. $\left.\begin{array}{l} x - y = 4 \\ 2x - 2y = 8 \end{array}\right\}$ Dependent

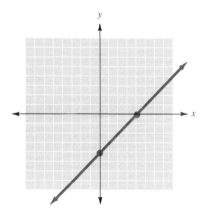

15. $\left.\begin{array}{l} x - 4y = -4 \\ x + 2y = 8 \end{array}\right\}(4, 2)$

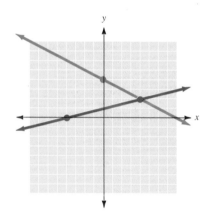

17. $\left.\begin{array}{l} 3x - 2y = 6 \\ 2x - y = 5 \end{array}\right\}(4, 3)$

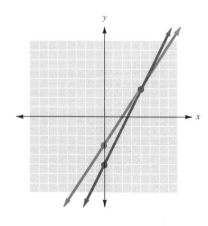

19. $\left.\begin{array}{l} 3x - y = 3 \\ 3x - y = 6 \end{array}\right\}$ Inconsistent

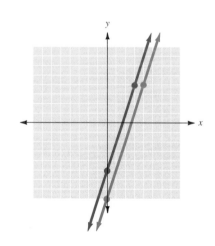

21. $\left.\begin{array}{r} 2y = 3 \\ x - 2y = -3 \end{array}\right\} \left(0, \dfrac{3}{2}\right)$

23. $\left.\begin{array}{r} x = 4 \\ y = -6 \end{array}\right\} (4, -6)$

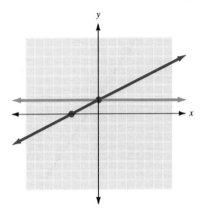

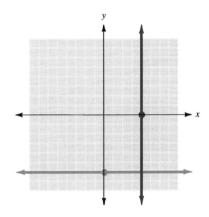

25. $m = 2, b = 5$

a. $3x$ **b.** $2y$ **c.** $-y$ **d.** $3x$ **e.** $5x$ **f.** $-5y$ **g.** $5y$ **h.** $10x$

Solving Systems of Linear Equations by Addition

8.2 OBJECTIVES

1. Find the solution(s) for a set of linear equations by addition
2. Solve applications using the addition method

The graphical method of solving equations, shown in Section 8.1, has two definite disadvantages. First, it is time-consuming to graph each system that you want to solve. More importantly, the graphical method is not precise. For instance, look at the graph of the system

$$x - 2y = 4$$
$$3x + 2y = 6$$

which is shown below.

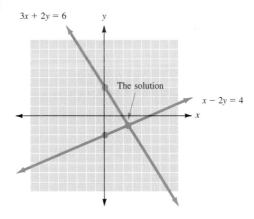

The exact solution for the system happens to be $\left(\dfrac{5}{2}, -\dfrac{3}{4}\right)$, but that would be difficult to read from the graph. Fortunately, there are algebraic methods that do not have this disadvantage and will allow you to find exact solutions for a system of equations.

Let's illustrate an algebraic method of finding a solution. It is called the **addition method.**

● Example 1

Solving a System by the Addition Method

This method uses the fact that if

$a = b$ and $c = d$

then

$a + c = b + d$

This is the **additive property** of equality. Note that by the additive property, if equals are added to equals, the resulting sums are equal.

This is also called **solution by elimination** for this reason.

Solve the system.

$$x + y = 8$$
$$x - y = 2$$

Note that the coefficients of the y terms are the *additive inverses* of one another (1 and -1) and that adding the two equations will "eliminate" the variable y. That addition step is shown here.

$$\left.\begin{array}{r} x + y = 8 \\ x - y = 2 \end{array}\right\}$$

By adding, we eliminate the variable y. The resulting equation contains *only* the variable x.

$$\begin{array}{r} 2x = 10 \\ x = 5 \end{array}$$

We now know that 5 is the x coordinate of our solution. Substitute 5 for x into *either* of the original equations.

$x + y = 8$

$5 + y = 8$

$y = 3$

So $(5, 3)$ is the solution.

To check, replace x and y with these values in *both* of the original equations.

$$\frac{x + y = 8}{5 + 3 = 8}$$ $$\frac{x - y = 2}{5 - 3 = 2}$$

$8 = 8$ (True) $2 = 2$ (True)

Since $(5, 3)$ satisfies both equations, it is the solution.

● ● ● **CHECK YOURSELF 1**

Solve the system by adding.

$x - y = -2$

$x + y = 6$

● Example 2

Solving a System by the Addition Method

Solve the system.

$-3x + 2y = 12$

$3x - y = -9$

In this case, adding will eliminate the x terms.

Note that we don't care which variable is eliminated. Choose the one that requires the least work.

$$\frac{\begin{array}{l}-3x + 2y = 12 \\ 3x - y = -9\end{array}}{y = 3}$$

Now substitute 3 for y in either equation. From the first equation

$-3x + 2 \cdot 3 = 12$

$-3x = 6$

$x = -2$

and $(-2, 3)$ is the solution.

Show that you get the same x coordinate by substituting 3 for y in the second equation rather than in the first. Then check the solution.

● ● ● **CHECK YOURSELF 2**

Solve the system by adding.

$$5x - 2y = 9$$
$$-5x + 3y = -11$$

Note that in both Examples 1 and 2 we found an equation in a single variable by adding. We could do this because the coefficients of one of the variables were opposites. This gave 0 as a coefficient for one of the variables after we added the two equations. In some systems, you will not be able to directly eliminate either variable by adding. However, an equivalent system can always be written by multiplying one or both of the equations by a nonzero constant so that the coefficients of x (or of y) are opposites. Example 3 illustrates this approach.

● Example 3

Solving a System by the Addition Method

Solve the system.

$$2x + y = 13 \tag{1}$$
$$3x + y = 18 \tag{2}$$

Remember that multiplying both sides of an equation by some nonzero number does not change the solutions. So even though we have "altered" the equations, they are equivalent and will have the same solutions.

Note that adding the equations in this form will not eliminate either variable. You will still have terms in x and in y. However, look at what happens if we multiply both sides of equation (2) by -1 as the first step.

$$2x + y = 13 \longrightarrow 2x + y = 13$$
$$3x + y = 18 \xrightarrow{\text{Multiply by } -1} -3x - y = -18$$

Now we can add.

$$\begin{array}{rcl} 2x + y &=& 13 \\ -3x - y &=& -18 \\ \hline -x &=& -5 \\ x &=& 5 \end{array}$$

Substitute 5 for x in equation (1).

$$2 \cdot 5 + y = 13$$
$$y = 3$$

$(5, 3)$ is the solution. We will leave it to the reader to check this solution.

● ● ● **CHECK YOURSELF 3**

Solve the system by adding.

$$x - 2y = 9$$

$$x + 3y = -1$$

To summarize, multiplying both sides of one of the equations by a nonzero constant can yield an equivalent system in which the coefficients of the x terms or the y terms are opposites. This means that a variable can be eliminated by adding. Let's look at another example.

● Example 4

Solving a System by the Addition Method

Solve the system.

$$x + 4y = 2 \tag{1}$$

$$3x - 2y = -22 \tag{2}$$

One approach is to multiply both sides of equation (2) by 2. Do you see that the coefficients of the y terms will then be opposites?

$$x + 4y = 2 \longrightarrow x + 4y = 2$$

$$3x - 2y = -22 \xrightarrow[\text{by 2}]{\text{Multiply}} 6x - 4y = -44$$

If we add the resulting equations, the variable y will be eliminated and we can solve for x.

Note that the coefficients of the y terms are opposites.

$$
\begin{aligned}
x + 4y &= 2 \\
6x - 4y &= -44 \\
\hline
7x &= -42 \\
x &= -6
\end{aligned}
$$

Now substitute -6 for x in equation (1) to find y.

Also, -6 could be substituted for x in equation (2) to find y.

$$-6 + 4y = 2$$

$$4y = 8$$

$$y = 2$$

So $(-6, 2)$ is the solution.

Again you should check this result. As is often the case, there are several ways to solve the system. For example, what if we multiply both sides of equation (1) by -3? The coefficients of the x terms will then be opposites, and adding will eliminate the variable x so that we can solve for y. Try that for yourself in the following Check Yourself exercise.

●●● CHECK YOURSELF 4

Solve the system by eliminating x.

$$x + 4y = \quad 2$$
$$3x - 2y = -22$$

It may be necessary to multiply each equation separately so that one of the variables will be eliminated when the equations are added. Example 5 illustrates this approach.

● Example 5

Solving a System by the Addition Method

Solve the system.

$$4x + 3y = 11 \tag{1}$$
$$3x - 2y = \ 4 \tag{2}$$

Do you see that multiplying in one equation will not help in this case? We will have to multiply in both equations.

To eliminate x, we can multiply both sides of equation (1) by 3 and both sides of equation (2) by -4. The coefficients of the x terms will then be opposites.

The minus sign is used with the 4 so that the coefficients of the x term are opposites.

$$4x + 3y = 11 \xrightarrow[\text{by 3}]{\text{Multiply}} 12x + 9y = \quad 33$$

$$3x - 2y = \ 4 \xrightarrow[\text{by } -4]{\text{Multiply}} -12x + 8y = -16$$

Adding the resulting equations gives

$$17y = 17$$
$$y = \quad 1$$

Now substituting 1 for y in equation (1), we have

$$4x + 3 \cdot 1 = 11$$
$$4x = \ 8$$
$$x = \ 2$$

Check (2, 1) in both equations of the original system.

and (2, 1) is the solution.

●●● CHECK YOURSELF 5

Solve the system by eliminating y.

$$4x + 3y = 11$$
$$3x - 2y = \ 4$$

Let's summarize the solution steps that we have illustrated.

To Solve a System of Linear Equations by Adding

STEP 1 If necessary, multiply both sides of one or both equations by nonzero numbers to form an equivalent system in which the coefficients of one of the variables are opposites.

STEP 2 Add the equations of the new system.

STEP 3 Solve the resulting equation for the remaining variable.

STEP 4 Substitute the value found in step 3 into either of the original equations to find the value of the second variable.

STEP 5 Check your solution in both of the original equations.

In Section 8.1 we saw that some systems had *infinitely* many solutions. Let's see how this is indicated when we are using the addition method of solving equations.

•Example 6

Solving a Dependent System

Solve

$$x + 3y = -2 \qquad (1)$$

$$3x + 9y = -6 \qquad (2)$$

We multiply both sides of equation (1) by -3.

$$x + 3y = -2 \xrightarrow[\text{by } -3]{\text{Multiply}} -3x - 9y = 6$$

$$3x + 9y = -6 \xrightarrow{\hspace{3cm}} \underline{3x + 9y = -6}$$

$$0 = 0$$

Adding, we see that both variables have been eliminated, and we have the true statement $0 = 0$.

The lines coincide. That will be the case whenever *adding eliminates both variables* and a true statement results.

Look at the graph of the system.

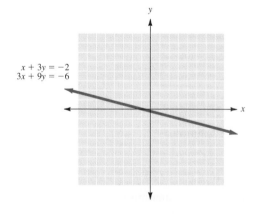

$$x + 3y = -2$$
$$3x + 9y = -6$$

As we see, the two equations have the *same* graph. This means that the system is *dependent,* and there are *infinitely many solutions.* Any (x, y) that satisfies $x + 3y = -2$ will also satisfy $3x + 9y = -6$.

● ● ● CHECK YOURSELF 6

Solve the system by adding.

$$x - 2y = 3$$
$$-2x + 4y = -6$$

Earlier we encountered systems that had *no* solutions. Example 7 illustrates what happens when we try to solve such a system with the addition method.

● Example 7

Solving an Inconsistent System

Solve the system.

$$3x - y = 4 \tag{1}$$
$$-6x + 2y = -5 \tag{2}$$

We multiply both sides of equation (1) by 2.

Be sure to multiply the 4 by 2.

$$3x - y = 4 \xrightarrow{\substack{\text{Multiply} \\ \text{by 2}}} 6x - 2y = 8 \quad \text{We now add the two equations}$$
$$-6x + 2y = -5 \xrightarrow{} \underline{-6x + 2y = -5}$$
$$0 = 3$$

Again both variables have been eliminated by addition. But this time we have the *false* statement $0 = 3$ because we tried to solve a system whose graph consists of two parallel lines, as we see in the graph below. Since the two lines do not intersect, there is *no* solution for the system. It is *inconsistent.*

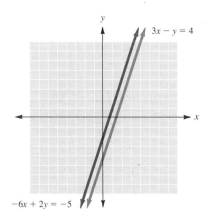

● ● ● CHECK YOURSELF 7

Solve the system by adding.

$5x + 15y = 20$

$x + 3y = 3$

Remember that, in Chapter 3, all the unknowns in the problem had to be expressed in terms of that single variable.

In Chapter 3 we solved word problems by using equations in a single variable. Now that you have the background to use two equations in two variables to solve word problems, let's see how they can be applied. The five steps for solving word problems stay the same (in fact, we give them again for reference in our first application example). Many students find that using two equations and two variables makes writing the necessary equation much easier, as Example 8 illustrates.

● Example 8

Solving an Application with Two Equations

Ryan bought 8 pens and 7 pencils and paid a total of $14.80. Ashleigh purchased 2 pens and 10 pencils and paid $7. Find the cost for a single pen and a single pencil.

Here are the steps for using a single variable:

1. Read the problem carefully. What do you want to find?

Step 1 You want to find the cost of a single pen and the cost of a single pencil.

2. Assign variables to the unknown quantities.

Step 2 Let x be the cost of a pen and y be the cost of a pencil.

3. Write the equation for the solution.

Step 3 Write the two necessary equations.

$8x + 7y = 14.80$ In the first equation, $8x$ is the total cost   (1)
of the pens Ryan bought and $7y$ is total
$2x + 10y = 7.00$ cost of the pencils Ryan bought. The second   (2)
equation is formed in a similar fashion.

4. Solve the equation.

Step 4 Solve the system formed in step 3. We multiply equation (2) by -4. Adding will then eliminate the variable x.

$8x + 7y = 14.80$

$-8x - 40y = -28.00$

Now adding the equations, we have

$-33y = -13.20$

$y = 0.40$

Substituting 0.40 for y in equation (1), we have

$8x + 7(0.40) = 14.80$

$8x + 2.80 = 14.80$

$8x = 12.00$

$x = 1.50$

5. Verify your result by returning to the original problem.

Step 5 From the results of step 4 we see that the pens are $1.50 each and that the pencils are 40¢ each.

To check these solutions, replace x with $1.50 and y with 0.40 in equation (1).

$$8(1.50) + 7(0.40) = 14.80$$
$$12.00 + 2.80 = 14.80$$
$$14.80 = 14.80 \quad \text{(True)}$$

We leave it to you to check these values in equation (2).

● ● ● **CHECK YOURSELF 8**

Alana bought three digital tapes and two compact disks on sale for $66. At the same sale, Chen bought three digital tapes and four compact disks for $96. Find the individual price for a tape and a disk.

Example 9 shows how sketches can be helpful in setting up a problem.

●**Example 9**

Using a Sketch to Help Solve an Application

An 18-foot board is cut into two pieces, one of which is 4 ft longer than the other. How long is each piece?

Step 1 You want to find the two lengths.

Step 2 Let x be the length of the longer piece and y the length of the shorter piece.

Step 3 Write the equations for the solution.

You should always draw a sketch of the problem when it is appropriate.

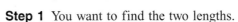

$x + y = 18 \leftarrow$ The total length is 18.

Our second equation could also be written as

$x = y + 4$

$x - y = 4 \quad$ The difference in
$\leftarrow$ lengths is 4.

Step 4 To solve the system, add:

$$
\begin{array}{ll}
x + y = 18 & \qquad\qquad (1) \\
\underline{x - y = 4} & \qquad\qquad (2) \\
2x = 22 & \\
x = 11 &
\end{array}
$$

Replace x with 11 in equation (1).

$$11 + y = 18$$
$$y = 7$$

The longer piece has length 11 ft, the shorter piece 7 ft.

Step 5 We leave it to you to check this result in the original problem.

● ● ● **CHECK YOURSELF 9**

A 20-ft board is cut into two pieces, one of which is 6 ft longer than the other. How long is each piece?

Using two equations in two variables also helps in solving **mixture problems.**

● Example 10

Solving a Mixture Problem Involving Coins

Winnifred has collected $4.50 in nickels and dimes. If she has 55 coins, how many of each kind of coin does she have?

Step 1 You want to find the number of nickels and the number of dimes.

Step 2 Let

Again we choose appropriate variables—*n* for nickels, *d* for dimes.

n = number of nickels

d = number of dimes

Step 3 Write the equations for the solution.

$$n + d = 55 \longleftarrow \text{There are 55 coins in all.}$$

Remember: The value of a number of coins is the value per coin times the number of coins: 5*n*, 10*d*, etc.

$$5n + 10d = 450$$

Value of nickels · Value of dimes · Total value (in cents)

Step 4 We now have the system

$$n + d = 55 \qquad (1)$$
$$5n + 10d = 450 \qquad (2)$$

Let's solve this system by addition. Multiply equation (1) by -5. We then add the equation to eliminate the variable n.

$$
\begin{aligned}
-5n - 5d &= -275 \\
5n + 10d &= 450 \\
\hline
5d &= 175 \\
d &= 35
\end{aligned}
$$

We now substitute d for 35 in equation (1).

$$n + 35 = 55$$
$$n = 20$$

There are 20 nickels and 35 dimes.

Step 5 We leave it to you to check this result. Just verify that the value of these coins is $4.50.

● ● ● **CHECK YOURSELF 10**

Tickets for a play cost $8 or $6. If 350 tickets were sold in all and receipts were $2500, how many of each price ticket were sold?

We can also solve mixture problems that involve percentages by using two equations in two unknowns. Look at Example 11.

● Example 11

Solving a Mixture Problem Involving Chemicals

In a chemistry lab are two solutions: a 20% acid solution and a 60% acid solution. How many milliliters of each should be mixed to produce 200 milliliters (mL) of a 44% acid solution?

Step 1 You need to know the amount of each solution to use.

Step 2 Let

x = amount of 20% acid solution

y = amount of 60% acid solution

Step 3 A drawing will help. Note that a 20% acid solution is 20% acid and 80% water.

We can write equations from the total amount of the solution, here 200 mL, and from the amount of acid in that solution. Many students find a table helpful in organizing the information at this point. Here, for example, we might have

Note: The amount of acid is the amount of solution times the percentage of acid (as a decimal). That is the key to forming the third column of our table.

	Amount of Solution	% Acid	Amount of Acid
	x	0.20	$0.20x$
	y	0.60	$0.60y$
Totals	200	0.44	$(0.44)(200)$

Now we are ready to form our system.

Equation (1) is the total amount of the solution from the first column of our table.

$$x + y = 200 \qquad (1)$$

Equation (2) is the amount of acid from the third column of our table.

$$0.20x + 0.60y = \underline{0.44(200)} \qquad (2)$$

↑ Acid in 20% solution. ↖ Acid in 60% solution. ↖ Acid in mixture.

Step 4 If we multiply equation (2) by 100 to clear it of decimals, we have

$$x + y = 200 \xrightarrow[\text{by} -20]{\text{Multiply}} -20x - 20y = -4000$$

$$20x + 60y = 8800 \xrightarrow{\hspace{3cm}} \underline{20x + 60y = 8800}$$

$$40y = 4800$$

$$y = 120$$

Substituting 120 for y in equation (1), we have

$$x + 120 = 200$$
$$x = 80$$

The amounts to be mixed are 80 mL (20% acid solution) and 120 mL (60% acid solution).

Step 5 You can check this solution by verifying that the amount of acid from the 20% solution and the amount from the 60% solution are equal to the amount of acid in the mixture.

● ● ● **CHECK YOURSELF 11**

You have a 30% alcohol solution and a 50% alcohol solution. How much of each solution should be combined to make 400 mL of a 45% alcohol solution?

A related kind of application involves interest. The key equation involves the *principal* (the amount invested), the annual *interest rate,* the *time* (in years) that the money is invested, and the amount of *interest* you receive.

$$I = P \cdot r \cdot t$$

Interest Principal Rate Time

For 1 year we have

$$I = P \cdot r \qquad \text{since } t = 1$$

● **Example 12**

Solving an Investment Application

Jeremy inherits $20,000 and invests part of the money in bonds with an interest rate of 11 percent. The remainder of the money is in savings at a 9 percent rate. What amount has he invested at each rate if he receives $2040 in interest for 1 year?

Step 1 You want to find the amounts invested at 11 and at 9 percent.

Step 2 Let x = the amount invested at 11 percent and y = the amount invested at 9 percent. Once again you may find a table helpful at this point.

The amount invested at 11 percent could have been represented by y and the amount invested at 9 percent by x.

Note: The formula $I = P \cdot r$ (interest equals principal times rate) is the key to forming the third column of our table.

	Principal	Rate	Interest
	x	11%	0.11x
	y	9%	0.09y
Totals	20,000		2040

Step 3 Form the equations for the solution, using the first and second columns of the above table.

$x + y = 20,000$ ⟵ He has $20,000 invested in all.

$0.11x + 0.09y = 2040$

The interest at 11% (rate · principal)   The interest at 9%   The total interest

Step 4 To solve the following system, use addition.

$$x + \quad y = 20,000 \qquad (1)$$
$$0.11x + 0.09y = 2,040 \qquad (2)$$

To do this, multiply both sides of equation (1) by -9. Multiplying both sides of equation (2) by 100 will clear decimals. Adding the resulting equations will eliminate y.

$$\begin{array}{r} -9x - 9y = -180,000 \\ 11x + 9y = 204,000 \\ \hline 2x = 24,000 \\ x = 12,000 \end{array}$$

Now, substitute 12,000 for x in equation (1) and solve for y.

$$12,000 + y = 20,000$$
$$y = 8,000$$

Jeremy has $12,000 invested at 11 percent and $8000 invested at 9 percent.

Step 5 To check, the interest at 11 percent is ($12,000)(0.11), or $1320. The interest at 9 percent is ($8000)(0.09), or $720. The total interest is $2040, and the solution is verified.

● ● ●   **CHECK YOURSELF 12**

Jan has $2000 more invested in a stock that pays 9 percent interest than in a savings account paying 8 percent. If her total interest for 1 year is $860, how much does she have invested at each rate?

Another group of applications is called **motion problems;** they involve a distance traveled, the rate, and the time of travel. Example 13 shows the use of $d = r \cdot t$ in forming a system of equations to solve a motion problem.

● **Example 13**

Solving a Motion Problem

A boat can travel 36 miles (mi) downstream in 2 hours (h). Coming back upstream, the trip takes 3 h. Find the rate of the boat in still water and the rate of the current.

Step 1 You want to find the two rates (of the boat and the current).

Step 2 Let

x = rate of boat in still water

y = rate of current

Step 3 To write the equations, think about the following: What is the effect of the current? Suppose the boat's rate in still water is 10 mi/h and the current is 2 mi/h.

The current *increases* the rate *downstream* to 12 mi/h (10 + 2). The current *decreases* the rate *upstream* to 8 mi/h (10 − 2). So here the rate downstream will be $x + y$, and the rate upstream will be $x - y$. At this point a table of information is helpful.

	Distance	Rate	Time
Downstream	36	$x + y$	2
Upstream	36	$x - y$	3

From the relationship $d = r \cdot t$ we can now use our table to write the system

$36 = 2(x + y)$ (From line 1 of our table)

$36 = 3(x - y)$ (From line 2 of our table)

Step 4 Removing the parentheses in the equations of step 3, we have

$2x + 2y = 36$

$3x - 3y = 36$

By either of our earlier methods, this system gives values of 15 for x and 3 for y. The rate in still water is 15 mi/h, and the rate of the current is 3 mi/h. We leave the check to you.

● ● ● **CHECK YOURSELF 13**

A plane flies 480 mi with the wind in 4 h. In returning against the wind, the trip takes 6 h. What is the rate of the plane in still air? What was the rate of the wind?

● ● ● **CHECK YOURSELF ANSWERS**

1. $(2, 4)$.   **2.** $(1, -2)$.   **3.** $(5, -2)$.   **4.** $(-6, 2)$.   **5.** $(2, 12)$.
6. A dependent system.   **7.** There is no solution. The system is inconsistent.
8. Tape $12, disk $15.   **9.** 7 ft, 13 ft.   **10.** 150 $6 tickets, 200 $8 tickets.
11. 100 mL (30%), 300 mL (50%).   **12.** $4000 at 8%, $6000 at 9%.
13. Plane's rate in still air, 100 mi/h; wind's rate, 20 mi/h.

Name

Section   Date

A N S W E R S

Solve each of the following systems by addition.

1. $x + y = 6$
$x - y = 4$

2. $x - y = 8$
$x + y = 2$

3. $-x + y = 3$
$x + y = 5$

4. $x + y = 7$
$-x + y = 3$

5. $2x - y = 1$
$-2x + 3y = 5$

6. $x - 2y = 2$
$x + 2y = -14$

7. $x + 3y = 12$
$2x - 3y = 6$

8. $-3x + y = 8$
$3x - 2y = -10$

9. $x + 2y = -2$
$3x + 2y = -12$

10. $4x - 3y = 22$
$4x + 5y = 6$

11. $4x - 3y = 6$
$4x + 5y = 22$

12. $2x + 3y = 1$
$5x + 3y = 16$

13. $2x + y = 8$
$2x + y = 2$

14. $5x + 4y = 7$
$5x - 2y = 19$

15. $3x - 5y = 2$
$2x - 5y = -2$

16. $2x - y = 4$
$2x - y = 6$

17. $x + y = 3$
$3x - 2y = 4$

18. $x - y = -2$
$2x + 3y = 21$

19. $-5x + 2y = -3$
$x - 3y = -15$

20. $x + 5y = 10$
$-2x - 10y = -20$

21. $7x + y = 10$
$2x + 3y = -8$

22. $3x - 4y = 2$
$4x - y = 20$

23. $5x + 2y = 28$
$x - 4y = -23$

24. $7x + 2y = 17$
$x - 5y = 13$

1. _____
2. _____
3. _____
4. _____
5. _____
6. _____
7. _____
8. _____
9. _____
10. _____
11. _____
12. _____
13. _____
14. _____
15. _____
16. _____
17. _____
18. _____
19. _____
20. _____
21. _____
22. _____
23. _____
24. _____

25.

26.

27.

28.

29.

30.

31.

32.

33.

34.

35.

36.

37.

38.

39.

40.

41.

42.

43.

44.

45.

46.

47.

48.

25. $3x - 4y = 2$
$-6x + 8y = -4$

26. $-x + 5y = 19$
$4x + 3y = -7$

27. $5x - 2y = 31$
$4x + 3y = 11$

28. $7x + 3y = -13$
$5x + 2y = -8$

29. $3x - 2y = 12$
$5x - 3y = 21$

30. $-4x + 5y = -6$
$5x - 2y = 16$

31. $-2x + 7y = 2$
$3x - 5y = -14$

32. $3x + 4y = 0$
$5x - 3y = -29$

33. $7x + 4y = 20$
$5x + 6y = 19$

34. $5x + 4y = 5$
$7x - 6y = 36$

35. $2x - 7y = 6$
$-4x + 3y = -12$

36. $3x + 2y = -18$
$7x - 6y = -42$

37. $5x - y = 20$
$4x + 3y = 16$

38. $3x + y = -5$
$5x - 4y = 20$

39. $3x + y = 1$
$5x + y = 2$

40. $2x - y = 2$
$2x + 5y = -1$

41. $3x + 4y = 3$
$6x - 2y = 1$

42. $3x + 3y = 1$
$2x + 4y = 2$

43. $5x - 2y = \dfrac{9}{5}$

$3x + 4y = -1$

44. $2x + 3y = -\dfrac{1}{12}$

$5x + 4y = \dfrac{2}{3}$

Solve the following systems by adding.

45. $\dfrac{x}{3} - \dfrac{y}{4} = -\dfrac{1}{2}$

$\dfrac{x}{2} - \dfrac{y}{5} = \dfrac{3}{10}$

46. $\dfrac{1}{3}x - \dfrac{1}{2}y = \dfrac{5}{6}$

$\dfrac{1}{2}x - \dfrac{2}{5}y = \dfrac{9}{10}$

47. $0.4x - 0.2y = 0.6$
$0.5x - 0.6y = 9.5$

48. $0.2x + 0.37y = 0.8$
$-0.6x + 1.4y = 2.62$

Solve each of the following problems. Be sure to show the equations used for the solution.

49. **Number problem.** The sum of two numbers is 40. Their difference is 8. Find the two numbers.

50. **Cost of stamps.** Eight eagle stamps and two raccoon stamps cost $2.80. Three eagle stamps and four raccoon stamps cost $2.35. Find the cost of each kind of stamp.

51. **Cost of food.** Robin bought four chocolate bars and a pack of gum and paid $2.75. Meg bought two chocolate bars and three packs of gum and paid $2.25. Find the cost of each.

52. **Cost of apples.** Xavier bought five red delicious apples and four Granny Smith apples at a cost of $4.81. Dean bought one of each of the two types at a cost of $1.08. Find the cost for each kind of apple.

53. **Cost of disks.** Four single-sided disks and two double-sided disks cost a total of $5.10. Two single-sided and four double-sided disks cost $5.40. Find the unit cost for each.

54. **Length.** A 30-meter (m) rope is cut into two pieces so that one piece is 6 m longer than the other. How long is each piece?

55. **Length.** An 18-foot (ft) board is cut into two pieces, one of which is twice as long as the other. How long is each piece?

56. **Number of coins.** Jill has $3.50 in nickels and dimes. If she has 50 coins, how many of each type of coin does she have?

57. **Number of coins.** Richard has 22 coins with a total value of $4. If the coins are all quarters and dimes, how many of each type of coin does he have?

58. **Tickets sold.** Theater tickets are $4 for general admission and $5 for students. During one evening 240 tickets were sold, and the receipts were $1040. How many of each kind of ticket were sold?

59. **Tickets sold.** 400 tickets were sold for a concert. The receipts from ticket sales were $3100, and the ticket prices were $7 and $9. How many of each price ticket were sold?

49.

50.

51.

52.

53.

54.

55.

56.

57.

58.

59.

ANSWERS

60.

61.

62.

63.

64.

65.

66.

67.

68.

60. Coffee mixture. A coffee merchant has coffee beans that sell for $3 per pound (lb) and $5 per pound. The two types are to be mixed to create 100 pounds of a mixture that will sell for $4.50 per pound. How much of each type of bean should be used in the mixture?

61. Nut mixture. Peanuts are selling for $2 per pound, and cashews are selling for $5 per pound. How much of each type of nut would be needed to create 20 lb of a mixture that would sell for $2.75 per pound?

62. Acid solution. A chemist has a 25% and a 50% acid solution. How much of each solution should be used to form 200 milliliters (mL) of a 35% acid solution?

63. Alcohol solution. A pharmacist wishes to prepare 150 mL of a 20% alcohol solution. She has a 30% solution and a 15% solution in her stock. How much of each should be used in forming the desired mixture?

64. Alcohol solution. You have two alcohol solutions, one a 15% solution and one a 45% solution. How much of each solution should be used to obtain 300 mL of a 25% solution?

65. Investment. Otis has a total of $12,000 invested in two accounts. One account pays 8 percent and the other 9 percent. If his interest for 1 year is $1010, how much does he have invested at each rate?

66. Investment. Amy invests a part of $8000 in bonds paying 12 percent interest. The remainder is in a savings account at 8 percent. If she receives $840 in interest for 1 year, how much does she have invested at each rate?

67. Motion problem. A plane flys 450 miles (mi) with the wind in 3 hours (h). Flying back against the wind, the plane takes 5 h to make the trip. What was the rate of the plane in still air? What was the rate of the wind?

68. Motion problem. An airliner made a trip of 1800 mi in 3 h, flying east across the country with the jetstream directly behind it. The return trip, against the jetstream, took 4 h. Find the speed of the plane in still air and the speed of the jetstream.

Each of the following applications can be solved by the use of a system of linear equations. Match the application with the system on the right that could be used for its solution.

69. Number problem. One number is 4 less than 3 times another. If the sum of the numbers is 36, what are the two numbers?

(a) $12x + 5y = 116$
$8x + 12y = 112$

(b) $x + y = 8000$
$0.06x + 0.09y = 600$

70. Tickets sold. Suppose that a movie theater sold 300 adult and student tickets for a showing with a revenue of $1440. If the adult tickets were $6 and the student tickets $4, how many of each type of ticket were sold?

(c) $x + y = 200$
$0.20x - 0.60y = 90$

(d) $x + y = 36$
$y = 3x - 4$

71. Dimensions of a rectangle. The length of a rectangle is 3 centimeters (cm) more than twice its width. If the perimeter of the rectangle is 36 cm, find the dimensions of the rectangle.

(e) $2(x + y) = 36$
$3(x - y) = 36$

(f) $x + y = 300$
$6x + 4y = 1440$

72. Cost of pens. An order of 12 dozen roller-ball pens and 5 dozen ballpoint pens cost $116. A later order for 8 dozen roller-ball pens and 12 dozen ballpoint pens cost $112. What was the cost of 1 dozen of each of the pens?

(g) $L = 2W + 3$
$2L + 2W = 36$

(h) $x + y = 140$
$2x + 5.5y = 420$

73. Nut mixture. A candy merchant wishes to mix peanuts selling at $2/lb with cashews selling for $5.50/lb to form 140 lb of a mixed-nut blend that will sell for $3/lb. What amount of each type of nut should be used?

74. Investments. Rolando has investments totaling $8000 in two accounts, one a savings account paying 6 percent interest and the other a bond paying 9 percent. If the annual interest from the two investments was $600, how much did he have invested at each rate?

75. Alcohol solution. A chemist wants to combine a 20% alcohol solution with a 60% solution to form 200 milliliters (mL) of a 45% solution. How much of each of the solutions should be used to form the mixture?

76. Motion problem. Marcus was able to make a downstream trip of 36 mi in 2 h. In returning upstream, it took 3 h to make the trip. How fast can his boat travel in still water? What was the rate of the river's current?

ANSWERS

69.

70.

71.

72.

73.

74.

75.

76.

77. Writing for reflection. Write in response to the questions below.

Many people find word problems easier to do when two variables and two equations are used to model the problem. Compare the problems in this section with the problems in Sections 3.3 and 3.5. How does this method help you in solving application problems? In general, how would you evaluate your ability to solve application or word problems? What can you do to improve?

78. Work with a partner to solve the following problems.

Your friend, Valerie, has contacted you about going into business with her. She wants to start a small manufacturing business making and selling sweaters to specialty boutiques. She explains that the initial investment for each of you will be $1500 for a knitting machine. She has worked hard to come up with an estimate for expenses and thinks that they will be close to $1600 a month for overhead. She says that each sweater manufactured will cost $28 to produce and that the sweaters will sell for at least $70. She wants to know if you are willing to invest the money you have saved for college costs. You have faith in Valerie's ability to carry out her plan. But, you have worked hard to save this money. Use graphs and equations to help you decide if this is a good opportunity. Think about whether you need more information from Valerie. Write a letter summarizing your thoughts.

● Getting Ready for Section 8.3 [Section 3.3]

Solve each of the following equations.

a. $2x + 3(x + 1) = 13$ **b.** $3(y - 1) + 4y = 18$

c. $x + 2(3x - 5) = 25$ **d.** $3x - 2(x - 7) = 12$

Answers

1. (5, 1)   **3.** (1, 4)   **5.** (2, 3)   **7.** (6, 2)   **9.** $\left(-5, \dfrac{3}{2}\right)$ **11.** (3, 2)

13. Inconsistent   **15.** (4, 2)   **17.** (2, 1)   **19.** (3, 6)   **21.** (2, −4)

23. $\left(3, \dfrac{13}{2}\right)$ **25.** Dependent   **27.** (5, −3)   **29.** (6, 3)   **31.** (−8, −2)

33. $\left(2, \dfrac{3}{2}\right)$ **35.** (3, 0)   **37.** (4, 0)   **39.** $\left(\dfrac{1}{2}, -\dfrac{1}{2}\right)$ **41.** $\left(\dfrac{1}{3}, \dfrac{1}{2}\right)$

43. $\left(\dfrac{1}{5}, -\dfrac{2}{5}\right)$ **45.** (3, 6)   **47.** (−11, −25)   **49.** (24, 16)

51. Chocolate 60¢, gum 35¢   **53.** Single-sided 80¢, double-sided 95¢

55. 12 ft, 6 ft   **57.** 10 dimes, 12 quarters   **59.** 250 at $7, 150 at $9

61. 15 lb peanuts, 5 lb cashews   **63.** 50 mL of 30%, 100 mL of 15%

65. $7000 at 8%, $5000 at 9%   **67.** 120 mi/h, 30 mi/h

69. _d_   **71.** _g_   **73.** _h_   **75.** _c_   **a.** 2   **b.** 3   **c.** 5   **d.** −2

8.3 Solving Systems of Linear Equations by Substitution

8.3 OBJECTIVES

1. Find the solution(s) for a set of linear equations by substitution
2. Solve applications using the substitution method

In Sections 8.1 and 8.2, we looked at graphing and addition as methods of solving linear systems. A third method is called **solution by substitution.**

● Example 1

Solving a System by Substitution

Solve by substitution.

$$x + y = 12 \qquad (1)$$
$$y = 3x \qquad (2)$$

Notice that equation (2) says that y and $3x$ name the same quantity. So we may substitute $3x$ for y in equation (1). We then have

Replace y with $3x$ in equation (1).

$$x + 3x = 12$$
$$4x = 12$$
$$x = 3$$

The resulting equation contains only the variable x, so substitution is just another way of eliminating one of the variables from our system.

We can now substitute 3 for x in equation (1) to find the corresponding y coordinate of the solution.

$$3 + y = 12$$
$$y = 9$$

The solution for a system is written as an ordered pair.

So $(3, 9)$ is the solution.

This last step is identical to the one you saw in Section 8.2. As before, you can substitute the known coordinate value back into either of the original equations to find the value of the remaining variable. The check is also identical.

● ● ● CHECK YOURSELF 1

Solve by substitution.

$$x - y = 9$$
$$y = 4x$$

The same technique can be readily used any time one of the equations is *already solved* for x or for y, as Example 2 illustrates.

• Example 2

Solving a System by Substitution

Solve by substitution.

$$2x + 3y = 3 \tag{1}$$

$$y = 2x - 7 \tag{2}$$

Since Equation (2) tells us that y is $2x - 7$, we can replace y with $2x - 7$ in equation (1). This gives

Now y is eliminated from the equation, and we can proceed to solve for x.

$$2x + 3\overbrace{(2x - 7)}^{y} = 3$$

$$2x + 6x - 21 = 3$$

$$8x = 24$$

$$x = 3$$

We now know that 3 is the x coordinate for the solution. So substituting 3 for x in equation (2), we have

$$y = 2 \cdot 3 - 7$$

$$= 6 - 7$$

$$= -1$$

And $(3, -1)$ is the solution. Once again you should verify this result by letting $x = 3$ and $y = -1$ in the original system.

● ● ● CHECK YOURSELF 2

Solve by substitution.

$$2x - 3y = 6$$

$$x = 4y - 2$$

As we have seen, the substitution method works very well when one of the given equations is already solved for x or for y. It is also useful if you can readily solve for x or for y in one of the equations.

• Example 3

Solving a System by Substitution

Solve by substitution.

$$x - 2y = 5 \tag{1}$$

$$3x + y = 8 \tag{2}$$

Neither equation is solved for a variable. That is easily handled in this case. Solving for x in equation (1), we have

$$x = 2y + 5$$

Equation (2) could have been solved for y with the result substituted into equation (1).

Now substitute $2y + 5$ for x in equation (2).

$$\overbrace{3(2y + 5)}^{x} + y = 8$$

$$6y + 15 + y = 8$$

$$7y = -7$$

$$y = -1$$

Substituting -1 for y in equation (2) yields

$$3x + (-1) = 8$$

$$3x = 9$$

$$x = 3$$

So $(3, -1)$ is the solution. You should check this result by substituting 3 for x and -1 for y in the equations of the original system.

● ● ● **CHECK YOURSELF 3**

Solve by substitution.

$$3x - y = 5$$
$$x + 4y = 6$$

Inconsistent systems and dependent systems will show up in a fashion similar to that which we saw in Section 8.2. Example 4 illustrates this approach.

● Example 4

Solving an Inconsistent System

Solve the following systems by substitution.

(a) $4x - 2y = 6$ (1)

       $y = 2x - 3$ (2)

From equation (2) we can substitute $2x - 3$ for y in equation (1).

$$4x - 2(2x - 3) = 6$$

Don't forget to change both signs in the parentheses.

$$4x - 4x + 6 = 6$$

$$6 = 6$$

Both variables have been eliminated, and we have the true statement $6 = 6$.

Recall from the last section that a true statement tells us that the lines coincide. We call this system dependent. There are an infinite number of solutions.

(*b*) $3x - 6y = 9$ (3)

$x = 2y + 2$ (4)

Substitute $2y + 2$ for x in equation (3).

$$3(2y + 2) - 6y = 9$$

$$6y + 6 - 6y = 9$$

$$6 = 9$$

This time we have a false statement.

This means that the system is *inconsistent* and that the graphs of the two equations are parallel lines. There is no solution.

● ● ● CHECK YOURSELF 4

Indicate whether the systems are inconsistent (no solution) or dependent (an infinite number of solutions).

a. $5x + 15y = 10$
$x = -3y + 1$

b. $12x - 4y = 8$
$y = 3x - 2$

The following summarizes our work in this section.

To Solve a System of Linear Equations by Substitution

STEP 1 Solve one of the given equations for *x* or *y*. If this is already done, go on to step 2.
STEP 2 Substitute this expression for *x* or for *y* into the other equation.
STEP 3 Solve the resulting equation for the remaining variable.
STEP 4 Substitute the known value into either of the original equations to find the value of the second variable.
STEP 5 Check your solution in both of the original equations.

STRATEGIES FOR SOLVING SYSTEMS OF EQUATIONS

You have now seen three different ways to solve systems of linear equations: by graphing, adding, and substitution. The natural question is, Which method should I use in a given situation?

Graphing is the least exact of the methods, and solutions may have to be estimated.

The algebraic methods—addition and substitution—give exact solutions, and both will work for any system of linear equations. In fact, you may have noticed that several examples in this section could just as easily have been solved by adding (Example 3, for instance).

The choice of which algebraic method (substitution or addition) to use is yours and depends largely on the given system. Here are some guidelines designed to help you choose an appropriate method for solving a linear system.

Choosing an Appropriate Method for Solving a System

1. If one of the equations is already solved for x (or for y), then substitution is the preferred method.
2. If the coefficients of x (or of y) are the same, or opposites, in the two equations, then addition is the preferred method.
3. If solving for x (or for y) in either of the given equations will result in fractional coefficients, then addition is the preferred method.

• Example 5

Choosing an Appropriate Method for Solving a System

Select the most appropriate method for solving each of the following systems.

(a) $5x + 3y = 9$

$2x - 7y = 8$

Addition is the most appropriate method since solving for a variable will result in fractional coefficients.

(b) $7x + 26 = 8$

$x = 3y - 5$

Substitution is the most appropriate method since the second equation is already solved for x.

(c) $8x - 9y = 11$

$4x + 9y = 15$

Addition is the most appropriate method since the coefficients of y are opposites.

●●● **CHECK YOURSELF 5**

Select the most appropriate method for solving each of the following systems.

a. $2x + 5y = 3$
$8x - 5y = -13$

b. $4x - 3y = 2$
$y = 3x - 4$

c. $3x - 5y = 2$
$x = 3y - 2$

d. $5x - 2y = 19$
$4x + 6y = 38$

Number problems, such as those presented in Chapter 3, are sometimes more easily solved by the methods presented in this section. Example 6 illustrates this approach.

● Example 6

Solving a Number Problem by Substitution

The sum of two numbers is 25. If the second number is 5 less than twice the first number, what are the two numbers?

1. What do you want to find?

Step 1 You want to find the two unknown numbers.

2. Assign variables. This time we use two letters, x and y.

Step 2 Let x = the first number and y = the second number.

3. Write equations for the solution. Here two equations are needed because we have introduced two variables.

Step 3

$\underbrace{x + y} = 25$

The sum   is 25.

$y = \underbrace{2x - 5}$

The second   is 5 less than
number   twice the first.

4. Solve the system of equations.

Step 4

$$x + y = 25 \tag{1}$$
$$y = 2x - 5 \tag{2}$$

We use the substitution method because equation (2) is already solved for y.

Substitute $2x - 5$ for y in equation (1).

$$x + (2x - 5) = 25$$
$$3x - 5 = 25$$
$$x = 10$$

From equation (1),

$$10 + y = 25$$
$$y = 25$$

The two numbers are 10 and 15.

5. Check the result.

Step 5 The sum of the numbers is 25. The second number, 15, is 5 less than twice the first number, 10. The solution checks.

●●● **CHECK YOURSELF 6**

The sum of two numbers is 28. The second number is 4 more than twice the first number. What are the numbers?

Sketches are always helpful in solving applications from geometry. Let's look at such an example.

● Example 7

Solving an Application from Geometry

The length of a rectangle is 3 meters (m) more than twice its width. If the perimeter of the rectangle is 42 m, find the dimensions of the rectangle.

Step 1 You want to find the dimensions (length and width) of the rectangle.

We used x and y as our two variables in the previous examples. Use whatever letters you want. The process is the same, and sometimes it helps you remember what letter stands for what. Here L = length and W = width.

Step 2 Let L be the length of the rectangle and W the width. Now draw a sketch of the problem.

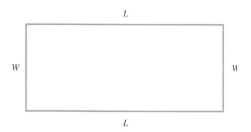

Step 3 Write the equations for the solution.

$$L = \underbrace{2W + 3}$$
3 more than twice
the width

$$\underbrace{2L + 2W} = 42$$
The perimeter

Step 4 Solve the system.

$$L = 2W + 3 \tag{1}$$
$$2L + 2W = 42 \tag{2}$$

Substitution is used since one equation is already solved for a variable.

From equation (1) we can substitute $2W + 3$ for L in equation (2).

$$2(2W + 3) + 2W = 42$$
$$4W + 6 + 2W = 42$$
$$6W = 36$$
$$W = 6$$

Replace W with 6 in equation (1) to find L.

$$L = 2 \cdot 6 + 3$$
$$= 12 + 3$$
$$= 15$$

The length is 15 m, the width is 6 m.

Step 5 Check these results. The perimeter is $2L + 2W$, which should give us 42 m.

$$2(15) + 2(6) \stackrel{?}{=} 42$$
$$30 + 12 \stackrel{\checkmark}{=} 42$$

● ● ● **CHECK YOURSELF 7**

The length of the two equal legs of an isosceles triangle is 5 in less than the length of the base. If the perimeter of the triangle is 50 in, find the lengths of the legs and the base.

● ● ● **CHECK YOURSELF ANSWERS**

1. $(-3, -12)$.   **2.** $(6, 2)$.   **3.** $(2, 1)$.   **4. (a)** Inconsistent; **(b)** Dependent.
5. (a) Addition; **(b)** Substitution; **(c)** Substitution; **(d)** Addition.
6. The numbers are 8 and 20.   **7.** The legs have length 15 in.; the base is 20 in.

Name

Section   Date

Solve each of the following systems by substitution.

1. $x + y = 10$
$\quad\quad y = 4x$

2. $x - y = 4$
$\quad\quad x = 3y$

3. $2x - y = 10$
$\quad\quad x = -2y$

4. $x + 3y = 10$
$\quad\quad 3x = y$

5. $3x + 2y = 12$
$\quad\quad y = 3x$

6. $4x - 3y = 24$
$\quad\quad y = -4x$

7. $x + y = 5$
$\quad\quad y = x - 3$

8. $x + y = 9$
$\quad\quad x = y + 3$

9. $x - y = 4$
$\quad\quad x = 2y - 2$

10. $x - y = 7$
$\quad\quad y = 2x - 12$

11. $2x + y = 7$
$\quad\quad y - x = -8$

12. $3x - y = -15$
$\quad\quad x = y - 7$

13. $2x - 5y = 10$
$\quad\quad x - y = 8$

14. $4x - 3y = 0$
$\quad\quad y = x + 1$

15. $3x + 4y = 9$
$\quad\quad y - 3x = 1$

16. $5x - 2y = -5$
$\quad\quad y - 5x = 3$

17. $3x - 18y = 4$
$\quad\quad x = 6y + 2$

18. $4x + 5y = 6$
$\quad\quad y = 2x - 10$

19. $5x - 3y = 6$
$\quad\quad y = 3x - 6$

20. $8x - 4y = 16$
$\quad\quad y = 2x - 4$

21. $8x - 5y = 16$
$\quad\quad y = 4x - 5$

22. $6x - 5y = 27$
$\quad\quad x = 5y + 2$

23. $x + 3y = 7$
$\quad\quad x - y = 3$

24. $2x - y = -4$
$\quad\quad x + y = -5$

1. _____
2. _____
3. _____
4. _____
5. _____
6. _____
7. _____
8. _____
9. _____
10. _____
11. _____
12. _____
13. _____
14. _____
15. _____
16. _____
17. _____
18. _____
19. _____
20. _____
21. _____
22. _____
23. _____
24. _____

25. $6x - 3y = 9$
$-2x + y = -3$

26. $5x - 6y = 21$
$x - 2y = 5$

27. $x - 7y = 3$
$2x - 5y = 15$

28. $4x - 12y = 5$
$-x + 3y = -1$

29. $4x + 3y = -11$
$5x + y = -11$

30. $5x - 4y = 5$
$4x - y = -7$

Solve each of the following systems by using either addition or substitution. If a unique solution does not exist, state whether the system is dependent or inconsistent.

31. $2x + 3y = -6$
$x = 3y + 6$

32. $7x + 3y = 31$
$y = -2x + 9$

33. $2x - y = 1$
$-2x + 3y = 5$

34. $x + 3y = 12$
$2x - 3y = 6$

35. $6x + 2y = 4$
$y = -3x + 2$

36. $3x - 2y = 15$
$-x + 5y = -5$

37. $x + 2y = -2$
$3x + 2y = -12$

38. $10x + 2y = 7$
$y = -5x + 3$

39. $2x - 3y = 14$
$4x + 5y = -5$

40. $2x + 3y = 1$
$5x + 3y = 16$

41. $4x - 2y = 0$
$x = \dfrac{3}{2}$

42. $4x - 3y = \dfrac{11}{2}$
$y = -\dfrac{3}{2}$

Solve each system.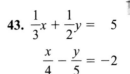

43. $\dfrac{1}{3}x + \dfrac{1}{2}y = 5$

$\dfrac{x}{4} - \dfrac{y}{5} = -2$

44. $\dfrac{5x}{2} - y = \dfrac{9}{10}$

$\dfrac{3x}{4} + \dfrac{5y}{6} = \dfrac{2}{3}$

45. $0.4x - 0.2y = 0.6$
$2.5x - 0.3y = 4.7$

46. $0.4x - 0.1y = 5$
$6.4x + 0.4y = 60$

Solve each of the following problems. Be sure to show the equation used for the solution.

47. **Number problem.** The sum of two numbers is 100. The second is three times the first. Find the two numbers.

48. **Number problem.** The sum of two numbers is 70. The second is 10 more than 3 times the first. Find the numbers.

49. **Number problem.** The sum of two numbers is 56. The second is 4 less than twice the first. What are the two numbers?

50. **Number problem.** The difference of two numbers is 4. The larger is 8 less than twice the smaller. What are the two numbers?

51. **Number problem.** The difference of two numbers is 22. The larger is 2 more than 3 times the smaller. Find the two numbers.

52. **Number problem.** One number is 18 more than another, and the sum of the smaller number and twice the larger number is 45. Find the two numbers.

53. **Number problem.** One number is 5 times another. The larger number is 9 more than twice the smaller. Find the two numbers.

54. **Package weight.** Two packages together weigh 32 kilograms (kg). The smaller package weighs 6 kg less than the larger. How much does each package weigh?

55. **Appliance costs.** A washer-dryer combination costs $400. If the washer costs $40 more than the dryer, what does each appliance cost separately?

56. **Voting trends.** In a town election, the winning candidate had 220 more votes than the loser. If 810 votes were cast in all, how many votes did each candidate receive?

57. **Cost of furniture.** An office desk and chair together cost $250. If the desk cost $20 less than twice as much as the chair, what did each cost?

58. **Dimensions of a rectangle.** The length of a rectangle is 2 inches (in.) more than twice its width. If the perimeter of the rectangle is 34 in., find the dimensions of the rectangle.

59. **Perimeter.** The perimeter of an isosceles triangle is 37 in. The lengths of the two equal legs are 6 in. less than 3 times the length of the base. Find the lengths of the three sides.

ANSWERS

47.

48.

49.

50.

51.

52.

53.

54.

55.

56.

57.

58.

59.

599

60. You have a part-time job writing the *Consumer Concerns* column for your local newspaper. Your topic for this week is clothes dryers, and you are planning to compare the Helpmate and the Whirlgarb dryers, both readily available in stores in your area. The information you have is that the Helpmate dryer is listed at $520, and it costs 22.5¢ to dry an average size load at the utility rates in your city. The Whirlgarb dryer is listed at $735, and it costs 15.8¢ to run for each normal load. The maintenance costs for both dryers is about the same. Working with a partner, write a short article giving your readers helpful advice about these appliances. What should they consider when buying one of these clothes dryers?

Answers

1. (2, 8)　　**3.** (4, −2)　　**5.** $\left(\frac{4}{3}, 4\right)$　　**7.** (4, 1)　　**9.** (10, 6)　　**11.** (5, −3)

13. (10, 2)　　**15.** $\left(\frac{1}{3}, 2\right)$　　**17.** Inconsistent　　**19.** (3, 3)　　**21.** $\left(\frac{3}{4}, -2\right)$

23. (4, 1)　　**25.** Dependent　　**27.** (10, 1)　　**29.** (−2, −1)　　**31.** (0, −2)

33. (2, 3)　　**35.** Dependent　　**37.** $\left(-5, \frac{3}{2}\right)$　　**39.** $\left(\frac{5}{2}, -3\right)$　　**41.** $\left(\frac{3}{2}, 3\right)$

43. (0, 10)　　**45.** (2, 1)　　**47.** 25, 75　　**49.** 20, 36　　**51.** 32, 10

53. 3, 15　　**55.** Washer $220, dryer $180　　**57.** Desk $160, chair $90

59. 7 in., 15 in., 15 in.

Summary

Systems of Linear Equations [8.1–8.3]

A System of Equations Two or more equations considered together.

Solution The solution of a system of two equations in two unknowns is an ordered pair that satisfies each equation of the system.

Solving by Graphing

1. Graph both equations on the same coordinate system.
2. The system may have
   a. *One solution*. The lines intersect at one point (a consistent system). The solution is the ordered pair corresponding to that point.
   b. *No solution*. The lines are parallel (an inconsistent system).
   c. *Indefinitely many solutions*. The two equations have the same graph (a dependent system). Any ordered pair corresponding to a point on the line is a solution.

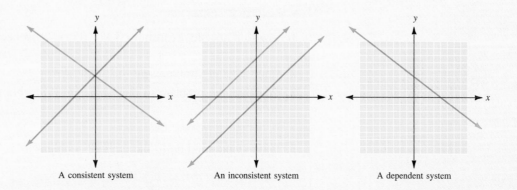

A consistent system   An inconsistent system   A dependent system

Solving by Adding

1. If necessary, multiply both sides of one or both equations by nonzero numbers to form an equivalent system in which the coefficients of one of the variables are opposites.
2. Add the equations of the new system.
3. Solve the resulting equation for the remaining variable.
4. Substitute the value found in step 3 into either of the original equations to find the value of the second variable.
5. Check your solution in both of the original equations.

$2x - y = 4$ (1)
$3x + 2y = 13$ (2)

Multiply equation (1) by 2.

$4x - 2y = 8$
$3x + 2y = 13$

Add.

$7x = 21$
$x = 3$

In equation (1),

$2 \cdot 3 - y = 4$
$y = 2$

$(3, 2)$ is the solution.

$x - 2y = 3$ (1)

$2x + 3y = 13$ (2)

From equation (1),

$x = 2y + 3$

Substitute in equation (2):

$2(2y + 3) + 3y = 13$

$4y + 6 + 3y = 13$

$7y + 6 = 13$

$7y = 7$

$y = 1$

Solving by Substitution

1. Solve one of the given equations for x or for y. If this is already done, go on to step 2.
2. Substitute this expression for x or for y into the other equation.
3. Solve the resulting equation for the remaining variable.
   Steps 4 and 5 are the same as above.

Continue as before.

Solving Word Problems by Using Systems of Equations [8.2–8.3]

Applying Systems of Equations Often word problems can be solved by using two variables and two equations to represent the unknowns and the given relationships in the problem.

The Solution Steps

1. Read the problem carefully. Then reread it to decide what you are asked to find.
2. Choose letters to represent the unknowns.
3. Translate the problem to the language of algebra to form a system of equations.
4. Solve the system.
5. Verify your solution in the original problem.

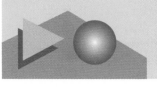

Summary Exercises

This summary exercise set is provided to give you practice with all the objectives of the chapter. Each exercise is keyed to the appropriate chapter section. The answers are provided in the *Instructor's Manual*.

[8.1]   Solve each of the following systems by graphing.

1. $x + y = 6$
$x - y = 2$

2. $x - y = 8$
$2x + y = 7$

3. $x + 2y = 4$
$x + 2y = 6$

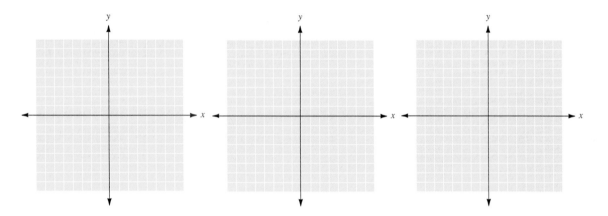

4. $2x - y = 8$
$y = 2$

5. $2x - 4y = 8$
$x - 2y = 4$

6. $3x + 2y = 6$
$4x - y = 8$

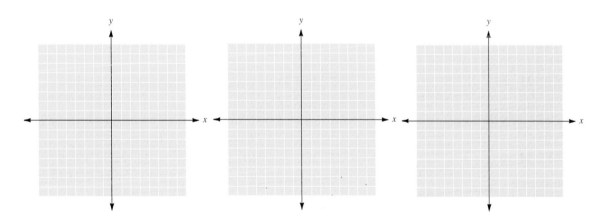

[8.2]   Solve each of the following systems by adding.

7. $x + y = 8$
$x - y = 2$

8. $-x - y = 4$
$x - y = -8$

9. $2x - 3y = 16$
$5x + 3y = 19$

10. $2x + y = 7$
$3x - y = 3$

11. $3x - 5y = 14$
$3x + 2y = 7$

12. $2x - 4y = 8$
$x - 2y = 4$

13. $4x - 3y = -22$
 $4x + 5y = -6$

14. $5x - 2y = 17$
 $3x - 2y = 9$

15. $4x - 3y = 10$
 $2x - 3y = 6$

16. $2x + 3y = -10$
 $-2x + 5y = 10$

17. $3x + 2y = 3$
 $6x + 4y = 5$

18. $3x - 2y = 23$
 $x + 5y = -15$

19. $5x - 2y = -1$
 $10x + 3y = 12$

20. $x - 3y = 9$
 $5x - 15y = 45$

21. $2x - 3y = 18$
 $5x - 6y = 42$

22. $3x + 7y = 1$
 $4x - 5y = 30$

23. $5x - 4y = 12$
 $3x + 5y = 22$

24. $6x + 5y = -6$
 $9x - 2y = 10$

25. $4x - 3y = 7$
 $-8x + 6y = -10$

26. $3x + 2y = 8$
 $-x - 5y = -20$

27. $3x - 5y = -14$
 $6x + 3y = -2$

[8.3] Solve each of the following systems by substitution.

28. $x + 2y = 10$
 $y = 2x$

29. $x - y = 10$
 $x = -4y$

30. $2x - y = 10$
 $x = 3y$

31. $2x + 3y = 2$
 $y = x - 6$

32. $4x + 2y = 4$
 $y = 2 - 2x$

33. $x + 5y = 20$
 $x = y + 2$

34. $6x + y = 2$
 $y = 3x - 4$

35. $2x + 6y = 10$
 $x = 6 - 3y$

36. $2x + y = 9$
 $x - 3y = 22$

37. $x - 3y = 17$
 $2x + y = 6$

38. $2x + 3y = 4$
 $y = 2$

39. $4x - 5y = -2$
 $x = -3$

40. $-6x + 3y = -4$
 $y = -\dfrac{2}{3}$

41. $5x - 2y = -15$
 $y = 2x + 6$

42. $3x + y = 15$
 $x = 2y + 5$

[8.3]   Solve each of the following systems by either addition or substitution.

43. $x - 4y = 0$
$4x + y = 34$

44. $2x + y = 2$
$y = -x$

45. $3x - 3y = 30$
$x = -2y - 8$

46. $5x + 4y = 40$
$x + 2y = 11$

47. $x - 6y = -8$
$2x + 3y = 4$

48. $4x - 3y = 9$
$2x + y = 12$

49. $9x + y = 9$
$x + 3y = 14$

50. $3x - 2y = 8$
$-6x + 4y = -16$

51. $3x - 2y = 8$
$2x - 3y = 7$

[8.2–8.3]   Solve the following problems. Be sure to show the equations used.

52. Number problem. The sum of two numbers is 40. If their difference is 10, find the two numbers.

53. Number problem. The sum of two numbers is 17. If the larger number is 1 more than 3 times the smaller, what are the two numbers?

54. Number problem. The difference of two numbers is 8. The larger number is 2 less than twice the smaller. Find the numbers.

55. Appliance cost. Five writing tablets and three pencils cost $8.25. Two tablets and two pencils cost $3.50. Find the cost for each item.

56. Cable length. A cable 200 ft long is cut into two pieces so that one piece is 12 feet (ft) longer than the other. How long is each piece?

57. Cost. An amplifier and a pair of speakers cost $925. If the amplifier costs $75 more than the speakers, what does each cost?

58. Cost. A sofa and chair cost $850 as a set. If the sofa costs $100 more than twice as much as the chair, what is the cost of each?

59. Rectangular dimensions. The length of a rectangle is 4 centimeters (cm) more than its width. If the perimeter of the rectangle is 64 cm, find the dimensions of the rectangle.

60. Isosceles triangles. The perimeter of an isosceles triangle is 29 inches (in.). The lengths of the two equal legs are 2 in. more than twice the length of the base. Find the lengths of the three sides.

61. Coin problem. Darryl has 30 coins with a value of $5.50. If they are all nickels and quarters, how many of each kind of coin does he have?

62. Ticket sales. Tickets for a concert sold for $11 and $8. If 600 tickets were sold for one evening and the receipts were $5550, how many of each kind of ticket were sold?

63. Acid solution. A laboratory has a 20% acid solution and a 50% acid solution. How much of each should be used to produce 600 milliliters (mL) of a 40% acid solution?

64. Antifreeze mixture. A service station wishes to mix 40 L of a 78% antifreeze solution. How many liters of a 75% solution and a 90% solution should be used in forming the mixture?

65. Investment rates. Martha has $18,000 invested. Part of the money is invested in a bond that yields 11 percent interest. The remainder is in her savings account, which pays 7 percent. If she earns $1660 in interest for 1 year, how much does she have invested at each rate?

66. Motion problem. A boat travels 24 miles (mi) upstream in 3 hours (h). It then takes 3 h to go 36 mi downstream. Find the speed of the boat in still water and the speed of the current.

67. Motion problem. A plane flying with the wind makes a trip of 2200 mi in 4 h. Returning against the wind, it can travel only 1800 mi in 4 h. What is the plane's rate in still air? What is the wind speed?

Name

Section   Date

The purpose of this self-test is to help you check your progress and to review for a chapter test in class. Allow yourself about an hour to take the test. When you are done, check your answers in the back of the book. If you missed any answers, be sure to go back and review the appropriate sections in the chapter and the exercises that are provided.

Solve each of the following systems by graphing.

1. $x + y = 5$
$x - y = 3$

2. $x + 2y = 8$
$x - y = 2$

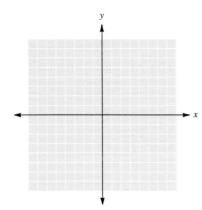

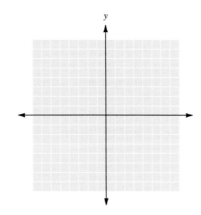

3. $x - 3y = 3$
$x - 3y = 6$

4. $4x - y = 4$
$x - 2y = -6$

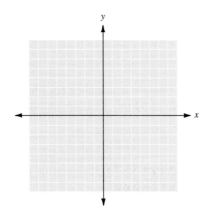

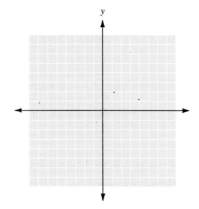

Solve each of the following systems by addition.

5. $x + y = 5$
$x - y = 3$

6. $x + 2y = 8$
$x - y = 2$

7. _____

8. _____

9. _____

10. _____

11. _____

12. _____

13. _____

14. _____

15. _____

16. _____

17. _____

18. _____

19. _____

20. _____

21. _____

22. _____

23. _____

24. _____

25. _____

7. $3x + y = 6$
$-3x + 2y = 3$

8. $3x + 2y = 11$
$5x + 2y = 15$

9. $3x - 6y = 12$
$x - 2y = 4$

10. $4x + y = 2$
$8x - 3y = 9$

11. $2x - 5y = 2$
$3x + 4y = 26$

12. $x + 3y = 6$
$3x + 9y = 9$

Solve each of the following systems by substitution.

13. $x + y = 8$
$y = 3x$

14. $x - y = 9$
$x = -2y$

15. $2x - y = 10$
$x = y + 4$

16. $x - 3y = -7$
$y = x - 1$

17. $3x + y = -6$
$y = 2x + 9$

18. $4x + 2y = 8$
$y = 3 - 2x$

19. $5x + y = 10$
$x + 2y = -7$

20. $3x - 2y = 5$
$2x + y = 8$

Solve each of the following problems. Be sure to show the equations used.

21. Number problem. The sum of two numbers is 30, and their difference is 6. Find the two numbers.

22. Rope length. A rope 50 meters (m) long is cut into two pieces so that one piece is 8 m longer than the other. How long is each piece?

23. Dimensions of a rectangle. The length of a rectangle is 4 inches (in.) less than twice its width. If the perimeter of the rectangle is 64 in., what are the dimensions of the rectangle?

24. Coin problem. Murray has 30 coins with a value of $5.70. If the coins are all dimes and quarters, how many of each coin does he have?

25. Motion problem. Jackson was able to travel 36 miles (mi) downstream in 2 hours (h). In returning upstream, it took 3 h to make the trip. How fast can his boat travel in still water? What was the rate of the river current?

This test is provided to help you in the process of review of the previous chapters. Answers are provided in the back of the book. If you missed any answers, be sure to go back and review the appropriate chapter sections.

Perform each of the indicated operations.

1. $(5x^2 - 9x + 3) + (3x^2 + 2x - 7)$

2. Subtract $9w^2 + 5w$ from the sum of $8w^2 - 3w$ and $2w^2 - 4$.

3. $7xy(4x^2y - 2xy + 3xy^2)$

4. $(3s - 7)(5s + 4)$

5. $\dfrac{5x^3y - 10x^2y^2 + 15xy^2}{-5xy}$

6. $\dfrac{4x^2 + 6x - 4}{2x - 1}$

Solve the following equation for x.

7. $5 - 3(2x - 7) = 8 - 4x$

Solve the following applications.

8. A bank teller has 83 $5 and $10 bills with a value of $695. How many bills of each denomination does she have?

9. A light plane makes a trip between two cities, against a steady headwind, in 7 hours (h). Returning with the wind, the plane can travel 20 mi/h faster and makes the trip in 6 h. What is the plane's speed in each direction?

Factor each of the following polynomials completely.

10. $24a^3 - 16a^2$

11. $7m^2n - 21mn - 49mn^2$

12. $a^2 - 64b^2$

13. $5p^3 - 80pq^2$

14. _____

15. _____

16. _____

17. _____

18. _____

19. _____

20. _____

21. _____

22. _____

23. _____

24. _____

25. _____

14. $a^2 - 14a + 48$ **15.** $2w^3 - 8w^2 - 42w$

Solve each of the following equations.

16. $x^2 - 9x + 20 = 0$ **17.** $2x^2 - 32 = 0$

Solve the following applications.

18. Twice the square of a positive integer is 35 more than 9 times that integer. What is the integer?

19. The length of a rectangle is 2 inches (in.) more than 3 times its width. If the area of the rectangle is 85 square inches (in.^{2}), find the dimensions of the rectangle.

Write each fraction in simplest form.

20. $\dfrac{m^2 - 4m}{3m - 12}$ **21.** $\dfrac{a^2 - 49}{3a^2 + 22a + 7}$

Perform the indicated operations.

22. $\dfrac{3x^2 + 9x}{x^2 - 9} \cdot \dfrac{2x^2 - 9x + 9}{2x^3 - 3x^2}$ **23.** $\dfrac{4w^2 - 25}{2w^2 - 5w} \div (6w + 15)$

Graph each of the following equations.

24. $x - y = 5$ **25.** $y = \dfrac{2}{3}x + 3$

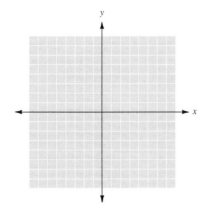

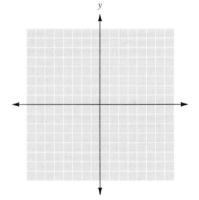

26. $x + 2y = 6$

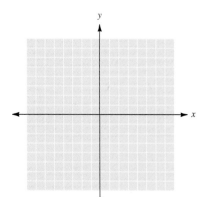

27. $2x - 5y = 10$

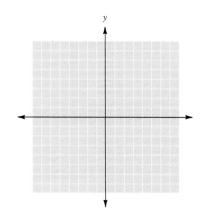

28. $y = -5$

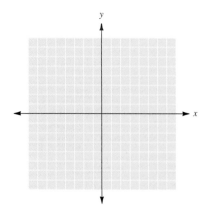

29. Find the slope of the line through the pair of points $(-2, -3)$ and $(5, 7)$.

30. Find the slope and y intercept of the line described by the equation
$5x - 3y = 15$.

31. Given the slope and y intercept for the following line, write the equation of the line. Then graph the line.

$m = 2, b = -5$

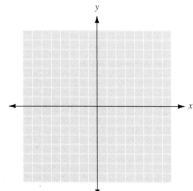

ANSWERS

26. _____

27. _____

28. _____

29. _____

30. _____

31. _____

Graph each of the following inequalities.

32. $x + 2y < 6$

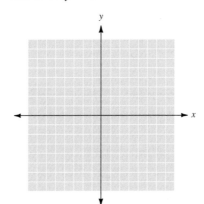

33. $3x - 4y \geq 12$

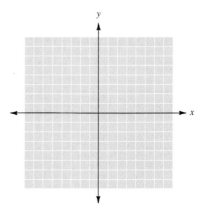

Solve each of the following systems by graphing.

34. $x - y = 2$
$x + 3y = 6$

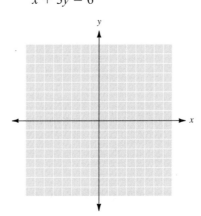

35. $3x + 2y = 6$
$x + 2y = -2$

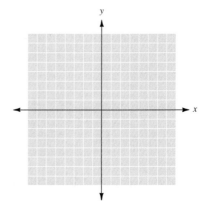

Solve each of the following systems. If a unique solution does not exist, state whether the system is inconsistent or dependent.

36. $2x - 3y = 6$
$x - 3y = 2$

37. $2x + y = 4$
$y = 2x - 8$

38. $5x + 2y = 30$
$x - 4y = 17$

39. $2x - 6y = 8$
$x = 3y + 4$

40. $4x - 5y = 20$
$2x + 3y = 10$

41. $5x - 4y = -7$
$3x + 5y = -19$

42. $4x + 2y = 11$
$2x + y = 5$

43. $4x - 3y = 7$
$6x + 6y = 7$

44. $5x - 3y = 11$

$y = 10x - 7$

45. $2x - 5y = -17$

$x = \dfrac{3}{2}$

ANSWERS

44. _____

45. _____

46. _____

47. _____

48. _____

49. _____

50. _____

51. _____

Solve each of the following applications. Be sure to show the system of equations used for your solution.

46. One number is 4 less than 5 times another. If the sum of the numbers is 26, what are the two numbers?

47. Cynthia bought five blank VHS tapes and four cassette tapes for $28.50. Charlie bought four VHS tapes and two cassette tapes for $21.00. Find the cost of each type of tape.

48. Receipts for a concert, attended by 450 people, were $2775. If reserved-seat tickets were $7 and general-admission tickets were $4, how many of each type of ticket were sold?

49. Anthony invested part of his $12,000 inheritance in a bond paying 9 percent and the other part in a savings account paying 6 percent. If his interest from the two investments was $930 in the first year, how much did he have invested at each rate?

50. A chemist has a 30% acid solution and a 60% acid solution already prepared. How much of each of the two solutions should be mixed in order to form 300 milliliters (mL) of a 50% acid solution?

51. Andrew was able to travel 75 miles (mi) downstream in 3 hours (h). Returning upstream, he took 5 h to make the trip. How fast can his boat travel in still water, and what was the rate of the current?

CHAPTER 9

RADICALS

INTRODUCTION

In designing a public building, an engineer or an architect must include a plan for safety. The Uniform Building Code states size and location requirements for exits: "If two exits are required in a building, they must be placed apart a distance not less than one-half the length of the maximum overall diagonal dimension of the building . . . ." Stated in algebraic terms, if the building is rectangular and if d is the distance between exits, l is the length of the building, and w is the width of the building, then

$$d \geq \frac{1}{2}\sqrt{l^2 + w^2}$$

So, for example, if a rectangular building is 50 by 40 feet, the diagonal dimension is $\sqrt{50^2 + 40^2}$, and the distance d between the exits must be equal to or more than half of the following equation:

$$d \geq \frac{1}{2}\sqrt{50^2 + 40^2}$$

Thus, the distance between the exits must be 32 ft or more.

The use of a radical sign often shows up in the measurement of distances and is based on the Pythagorean Theorem, which demonstrates the relationship between the sides of a right triangle: $a^2 + b^2 = c^2$. Using algebra to interpret statements such as the one in the building code quoted above is an example of how algebra can make complicated statements clearer and easier to understand.

© Brett Palmer / The Stock Market

Roots and Radicals

9.1 OBJECTIVES

1. Use the radical notation to represent roots
2. Distinguish between rational and irrational numbers

The symbol $\sqrt{}$ first appeared in print in 1525. In Latin, "radix" means **root,** and this was contracted to a small *r*. The present symbol may have evolved from the manuscript form of that small *r*.

In Chapter 4, we discussed the properties of exponents. Over the next four sections, we will work with a new notation that "reverses" the process of raising to a power.

From our work in Chapter 1, we know that when we have a statement such as

$$x^2 = 9$$

it is read as "*x* squared equals 9."

Here we are concerned with the relationship between the variable *x* and the number 9. We call that relationship the **square root** and say, equivalently, that "*x* is the square root of 9."

We know from experience that *x* must be 3 (since $3^2 = 9$) or -3 [since $(-3)^2 = 9$]. We see that 9 has two square roots, 3 and -3. In fact, every positive number will have *two* square roots. In general, if $x^2 = a$, we call *x* the *square root of a*.

We are now ready for our new notation. The symbol $\sqrt{}$ is called a **radical sign.** We saw above that 3 was the positive square root of 9. We also call 3 the **principal square root** of 9 and can write

$$\sqrt{9} = 3$$

to indicate that 3 is the principal square root of 9.

To summarize:

$\sqrt{9}$ asks, "What positive number must we square to get 9?"

$\sqrt{9}$ is read the "*square root*" of 9, and since $3^2 = 9$,

$\sqrt{9} = 3$

This leads us to the following definition.

Definition

$\sqrt{a}$ is the *positive* (or *principal*) square root of *a*. It is the positive number whose square is *a*.

● Example 1

Finding Principal Square Roots

Find the following square roots.

(*a*) $\sqrt{49} = 7$ Since 7 is the positive number, we must square to get 49.

(*b*) $\sqrt{81} = 9$

(*c*) $\sqrt{\dfrac{4}{9}} = \dfrac{2}{3}$ Since $\dfrac{2}{3}$ is the positive number, we must square to get $\dfrac{4}{9}$.

616

● ● ● **CHECK YOURSELF 1**

Find the following square roots.

a. $\sqrt{64}$ **b.** $\sqrt{144}$ **c.** $\sqrt{\dfrac{16}{25}}$

Note: When you use the radical sign, you will get only the *positive square root:*

$\sqrt{25} = 5$

Each positive number has two square roots. For instance, 25 has square roots of 5 and −5 because

$5^2 = 25$ and $(-5)^2 = 25$

If you want to indicate the negative square root, you must use a minus sign in front of the radical.

$-\sqrt{25} = -5$

● Example 2

Finding Square Roots

Find the following square roots.

(*a*) $\sqrt{100} = 10$ The principal root
(*b*) $-\sqrt{100} = -10$ The negative square root
(*c*) $-\sqrt{\dfrac{9}{16}} = -\dfrac{3}{4}$

● ● ● **CHECK YOURSELF 2**

Find the following square roots.

a. $\sqrt{16}$ **b.** $-\sqrt{16}$ **c.** $-\sqrt{\dfrac{16}{25}}$

The square roots of negative numbers are *not* real numbers. For instance, $\sqrt{-9}$ is *not* a real number because there is *no* real number x such that

$x^2 = -9$

CAUTION

Be Careful! Do not confuse

$-\sqrt{9}$ with $\sqrt{-9}$

The expression $-\sqrt{9}$ is −3, while $\sqrt{-9}$ is not a real number.
Example 3 summarizes our discussion thus far.

• Example 3

Finding Square Roots

Evaluate each of the following square roots.

(a) $\sqrt{36} = 6$

(b) $\sqrt{121} = 11$

(c) $-\sqrt{64} = -8$

(d) $\sqrt{-64}$ is not a real number.

(e) $\sqrt{0} = 0$ (Because $0 \cdot 0 = 0$)

● ● ●   **CHECK YOURSELF 3**

Evaluate, if possible.

a. $\sqrt{81}$ **b.** $\sqrt{49}$ **c.** $-\sqrt{49}$ **d.** $\sqrt{-49}$

All calculators have square root keys, but the calculator gives the exact value of the square root only for perfect square integers. For all other positive integers, *a calculator gives only an approximation of the correct answer.* In Example 4 you will use your calculator to approximate square roots.

• Example 4

Approximating Square Roots

Use your calculator to approximate each square root to the nearest hundredth.

The ≈ sign means "is approximately equal to."

(a) $\sqrt{45} \approx 6.708203932 \approx 6.71$

(b) $\sqrt{8} \approx 2.83$

(c) $\sqrt{20} \approx 4.47$

(d) $\sqrt{273} \approx 16.52$

● ● ●   **CHECK YOURSELF 4**

Use your calculator to approximate each square root to the nearest hundredth.

a. $\sqrt{3}$ **b.** $\sqrt{14}$ **c.** $\sqrt{91}$ **d.** $\sqrt{756}$

As we mentioned earlier, finding the square root of a number is the reverse of squaring a number. We can extend that idea to work with other roots of numbers. For instance, the *cube root* of a number is the number we must cube (or raise to the third power) to get that number. For example, the cube root of 8 is 2 since $2^3 = 8$, and we write

$\sqrt[3]{8}$ is read "the cube root of 8."

$\sqrt[3]{8} = 2$

We give special names to the parts of a radical expression. These are summarized as follows.

The index for $\sqrt[3]{a}$ is 3.

The index of 2 for square roots is generally not written. We understand that $\sqrt{a}$ is the principal square root of a.

Every radical expression contains three parts as shown below. The principal *n*th root of *a* is written as

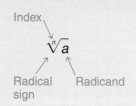

To illustrate, the *cube root* of 64 is written

$\text{Index} \longrightarrow \sqrt[3]{64}$
$\text{of } 3$

and it represents the number we must cube (or raise to the third power) to get 64.

$$\sqrt[3]{64} = 4$$

because $4^3 = 64$. And

$\text{Index} \longrightarrow \sqrt[4]{81}$
$\text{of } 4$

is the *fourth root* of 81. It represents the number we must raise to the fourth power to get 81.

$$\sqrt[4]{81} = 3$$

because $3^4 = 81$.

We can find roots of negative numbers as long as the index is *odd* (3, 5, etc.). For example,

$$\sqrt[3]{-64} = -4$$

because $(-4)^3 = -64$.

If the index is *even* (2, 4, etc.), roots of negative numbers are *not* real numbers. For example,

$$\sqrt[4]{-16}$$

The *even power* of a real number is always *positive* or *zero*.

is not a real number because there is no real number x such that $x^4 = -16$.

The following table shows the most common roots.

It would be helpful for your work here and in future mathematics classes to memorize these roots.

Square Roots		Cube Roots	Fourth Roots
$\sqrt{1} = 1$	$\sqrt{49} = 7$	$\sqrt[3]{1} = 1$	$\sqrt[4]{1} = 1$
$\sqrt{4} = 2$	$\sqrt{64} = 8$	$\sqrt[3]{8} = 2$	$\sqrt[4]{16} = 2$
$\sqrt{9} = 3$	$\sqrt{81} = 9$	$\sqrt[3]{27} = 3$	$\sqrt[4]{81} = 3$
$\sqrt{16} = 4$	$\sqrt{100} = 10$	$\sqrt[3]{64} = 4$	$\sqrt[4]{256} = 4$
$\sqrt{25} = 5$	$\sqrt{121} = 11$	$\sqrt[3]{125} = 5$	$\sqrt[4]{625} = 5$
$\sqrt{36} = 6$	$\sqrt{144} = 12$		

You can use the table in Example 5, which summarizes the discussion above.

● Example 5

Evaluating Cube Roots and Fourth Roots

Evaluate each of the following.

The cube root of a negative number will be negative.

The fourth root of a negative number is not a real number.

(a) $\sqrt[3]{125} = 5$ because $5^3 = 125$.

(b) $\sqrt[5]{32} = 2$ because $2^5 = 32$.

(c) $\sqrt[3]{-125} = -5$ because $(-5)^3 = -125$.

(d) $\sqrt[4]{-81}$ is not a real number.

● ● ● CHECK YOURSELF 5

Evaluate, if possible.

a. $\sqrt[3]{64}$ **b.** $\sqrt[4]{16}$ **c.** $\sqrt[4]{-256}$ **d.** $\sqrt[3]{-8}$

The radical notation allows us to distinguish between two important types of numbers: rational numbers and irrational numbers.

A **rational number** can be represented by a fraction whose numerator and denominator are integers and whose denominator is nonzero. The form of a rational number is

$$\frac{a}{b} \qquad a \text{ and } b \text{ are integers, } b \neq 0$$

Some examples of rational numbers are $\dfrac{-2}{3}$, $\dfrac{4}{5}$, 2, and $\dfrac{7}{3}$. Certain square roots are rational numbers also. For example,

Note that each radicand is a **perfect-square integer** (that is, an integer which is the square of another integer).

$$\sqrt{4} \qquad \sqrt{25} \qquad \text{and} \qquad \sqrt{64}$$

represent the rational numbers 2, 5, and 8, respectively.

An **irrational number** is a number that represents a point on the number line but *cannot* be written as the ratio of two integers. These are called **irrational numbers.** For example, the square root of any positive number which is not itself a perfect square is an irrational number. Because the radicands are *not* perfect squares, the expressions $\sqrt{2}$, $\sqrt{3}$, and $\sqrt{5}$ represent irrational numbers.

Note: The fact that the square root of 2 is irrational will be proved in later mathematics courses and was known to Greek mathematicians over 2000 years ago.

● Example 6

Identifying Rational Numbers

Which of the following numbers are rational and which are irrational?

$$\sqrt{\frac{2}{3}} \qquad \sqrt{\frac{4}{9}} \qquad \sqrt{7} \qquad \sqrt{16} \qquad \sqrt{25}$$

Here $\sqrt{7}$ and $\sqrt{\dfrac{2}{3}}$ are irrational numbers. And $\sqrt{16}$ and $\sqrt{25}$ are rational numbers because 16 and 25 are perfect squares. Also $\sqrt{\dfrac{4}{9}}$ is rational because $\sqrt{\dfrac{4}{9}} = \dfrac{2}{3}$.

● ● ● **CHECK YOURSELF 6**

Which of the following numbers are rational and which are irrational?

a. $\sqrt{26}$ **b.** $\sqrt{49}$ **c.** $\sqrt{\dfrac{6}{7}}$

d. $\sqrt{100}$ **e.** $\sqrt{105}$ **f.** $\sqrt{\dfrac{16}{9}}$

> The decimal representation of a rational number always terminates or repeats. For instance,
>
> $$\frac{3}{8} = 0.375$$
>
> $$\frac{5}{11} = 0.454545\ldots$$
>
> $$\approx 0.45$$

An important fact about the irrational numbers is that their decimal representations are always *nonterminating* and *nonrepeating*. We can therefore only approximate irrational numbers with a terminating decimal. A table of roots is at the end of this book, or a calculator can be used to find roots. However, note that the values found for the irrational roots are only approximations. For instance, $\sqrt{2}$ is approximately 1.414 (to three decimal places), and we can write

$$\sqrt{2} \approx 1.414$$

> 1.414 is an approximation to the number whose square is 2.

With a calculator we find that

$$(1.414)^2 = 1.999396$$

The set of all rational numbers and the set of all irrational numbers together form the set of *real numbers*. The real numbers will represent every point that can be pictured on the number line. Some examples are shown below.

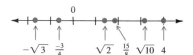

> For this reason we refer to the number line as the **real number line.**

The following diagram summarizes the relationships among the various numeric sets that have been introduced here and in Chapter 1.

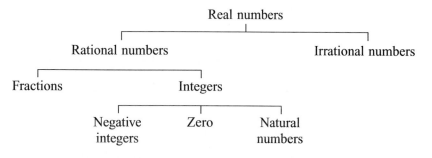

We conclude our work in this section by developing a general result that we will need later. Let's start by looking at two numerical examples.

$$\sqrt{2^2} = \sqrt{4} = 2 \tag{1}$$

$$\sqrt{(-2)^2} = \sqrt{4} = 2 \qquad \text{since } (-2)^2 = 4 \tag{2}$$

Consider the value of $\sqrt{x^2}$ where x is positive or negative.

> This is because the principal square root of a number is always positive or zero.

In (1) where $x = 2$:

$$\sqrt{2^2} = 2$$

In (2) where $x = -2$:

$$\sqrt{(-2)^2} \neq -2$$

$$\sqrt{(-2)^2} = -(-2) = 2.$$

Comparing the results of (1) and (2), we see that $\sqrt{x^2}$ is x if x is positive (or 0) and $\sqrt{x^2}$ is $-x$ if x is negative. We can write

$$\sqrt{x^2} = \begin{cases} x & \text{where } x \geq 0 \\ -x & \text{where } x < 0 \end{cases}$$

From your earlier work with absolute values you will remember that

$$|x| = \begin{cases} x & \text{where } x \geq 0 \\ -x & \text{where } x < 0 \end{cases}$$

and we can summarize the discussion by writing

$$\sqrt{x^2} = |x| \qquad \text{for any real number } x$$

● Example 7

Evaluating Radical Expressions

Evaluate each of the following.

(a) $\sqrt{5^2} = 5$

(b) $\sqrt{(-4)^2} = |-4| = 4$

Note: Alternatively in (b), we could write

$$\sqrt{(-4)^2} = \sqrt{16} = 4$$

● ● ● **CHECK YOURSELF 7**

Evaluate.

a. $\sqrt{6^2}$ **b.** $\sqrt{(-6)^2}$

● ● ● **CHECK YOURSELF ANSWERS**

1. (a) 8; **(b)** 12; **(c)** $\dfrac{4}{5}$. **2. (a)** 4; **(b)** -4; **(c)** $-\dfrac{4}{5}$. **3. (a)** 9; **(b)** 7; **(c)** -7;

(d) not a real number. **4. (a)** 1.73; **(b)** 3.74; **(c)** 9.54; **(d)** 27.50. **5. (a)** 4;

(b) 2; **(c)** not a real number; **(d)** -2. **6. (a)** Irrational; **(b)** rational (since

$\sqrt{49} = 7$); **(c)** irrational; **(d)** rational (since $\sqrt{100} = 10$); **(e)** irrational;

(f) rational $\left(\text{since } \sqrt{\dfrac{16}{9}} = \dfrac{4}{3} \right)$. **7. (a)** 6; **(b)** 6.

9.1 Exercises

A N S W E R S

1. _____

2. _____

3. _____

4. _____

5. _____

6. _____

7. _____

8. _____

9. _____

10. _____

11. _____

12. _____

13. _____

14. _____

15. _____

16. _____

17. _____

18. _____

19. _____

20. _____

21. _____

22. _____

23. _____

24. _____

Evaluate, if possible.

1. $\sqrt{16}$

2. $\sqrt{121}$

3. $\sqrt{400}$

4. $\sqrt{64}$

5. $-\sqrt{100}$

6. $\sqrt{-100}$

7. $\sqrt{-81}$

8. $-\sqrt{81}$

9. $\sqrt{\dfrac{16}{9}}$

10. $-\sqrt{\dfrac{1}{25}}$

11. $\sqrt{-\dfrac{4}{5}}$

12. $\sqrt{\dfrac{4}{25}}$

13. $\sqrt[3]{27}$

14. $\sqrt[4]{81}$

15. $\sqrt[3]{-27}$

16. $\sqrt[4]{-16}$

17. $\sqrt[4]{-81}$

18. $-\sqrt[3]{64}$

19. $-\sqrt[3]{27}$

20. $-\sqrt[3]{-8}$

21. $\sqrt[4]{625}$

22. $\sqrt[3]{1000}$

23. $\sqrt[3]{\dfrac{1}{27}}$

24. $\sqrt[3]{-\dfrac{8}{27}}$

25. _____

26. _____

27. _____

28. _____

29. _____

30. _____

31. _____

32. _____

33. _____

34. _____

35. _____

36. _____

37. _____

38. _____

39. _____

40. _____

41. _____

42. _____

43. _____

44. _____

45. _____

46. _____

47. _____

48. _____

49. _____

50. _____

Which of the following roots are rational numbers and which are irrational numbers?

25. $\sqrt{19}$

26. $\sqrt{36}$

27. $\sqrt{100}$

28. $\sqrt{7}$

29. $\sqrt[3]{9}$

30. $\sqrt[3]{8}$

31. $\sqrt[4]{16}$

32. $\sqrt{\dfrac{4}{9}}$

33. $\sqrt{\dfrac{4}{7}}$

34. $\sqrt[3]{5}$

35. $\sqrt[3]{-27}$

36. $-\sqrt[4]{81}$

Use your calculator to approximate the square root to the nearest hundredth.

37. $\sqrt{11}$

38. $\sqrt{14}$

39. $\sqrt{7}$

40. $\sqrt{23}$

41. $\sqrt{46}$

42. $\sqrt{78}$

43. $\sqrt{\dfrac{2}{5}}$

44. $\sqrt{\dfrac{3}{4}}$

45. $\sqrt{\dfrac{8}{9}}$

46. $\sqrt{\dfrac{7}{15}}$

47. $-\sqrt{18}$

48. $-\sqrt{31}$

49. $-\sqrt{27}$

50. $-\sqrt{65}$

For Exercises 51 to 56, find the two expressions that are equivalent.

51. $\sqrt{-16}$, $-\sqrt{16}$, -4

52. $-\sqrt{25}$, -5, $\sqrt{-25}$

53. $\sqrt[3]{-125}$, $-\sqrt[3]{125}$, $|-5|$

54. $\sqrt[5]{-32}$, $-\sqrt[5]{32}$, $|-2|$

55. $\sqrt[4]{10,000}$, 100, $\sqrt[3]{1000}$

56. 10^2, $\sqrt{10,000}$, $\sqrt[3]{100,000}$

57. **Dimensions of a square.** The area of a square is 32 square feet (ft^2). Find the length of a side to the nearest hundredth.

58. **Dimensions of a square.** The area of a square is 83 ft^2. Find the length of the side to the nearest hundredth.

59. **Radius of a circle.** The area of a circle is 147 ft^2. Find the radius to the nearest hundredth.

60. **Area of a circle.** If the area of a circle is 72 square centimeters (cm^2), find the radius to the nearest hundredth.

61. **Freely falling objects.** The time in seconds (s) that it takes for an object to fall from rest is given by $t = \frac{1}{4}\sqrt{s}$, where s is the distance fallen. Find the time required for an object to fall from a building that is 800 ft high.

62. **Freely falling objects.** Find the time required for an object to fall from a building that is 1400 ft high. (Use the formula in Exercise 61.)

63. Complete the following: "The square root of a number is . . . ."

64. Look up the words "rational" and "irrational" in a dictionary. Why are some numbers called "rational" and some are called "irrational"?

65. Write this algebraic expression in words:

$(\sqrt{n})^2$

What is it equal to? Explain.

66. The number 1 is a rational number and so is the number 2. How many rational numbers are between 1 and 2? How many irrational numbers are there? Provide some examples of each. Exchange papers with your partner. Are your answers the same?

ANSWERS

51. _____
52. _____
53. _____
54. _____
55. _____
56. _____
57. _____
58. _____
59. _____
60. _____
61. _____
62. _____
63. _____
64. _____
65. _____
66. _____

Getting Ready for Section 9.2
[Section 4.1]

Find each of the following products.

a. $(4x^2)(2x)$ **b.** $(9a^4)(5a)$ **c.** $(16m^2)(3m)$ **d.** $(8b^3)(2b)$

e. $(27p^6)(3p)$ **f.** $(81s^4)(s^3)$ **g.** $(100y^4)(2y)$ **h.** $(49m^6)(2m)$

Answers

1. 4   **3.** 20   **5.** -10 **7.** Not a real number   **9.** $\dfrac{4}{3}$

11. Not a real number   **13.** 3   **15.** -3 **17.** Not a real number

19. -3 **21.** 5   **23.** $\dfrac{1}{3}$ **25.** Irrational   **27.** Rational   **29.** Irrational

31. Rational   **33.** Irrational   **35.** Rational   **37.** 3.32   **39.** 2.65

41. 6.78   **43.** 0.63   **45.** 0.94   **47.** -4.24 **49.** -5.20
51. $-\sqrt{16}, -4$ **53.** $\sqrt[3]{-125}, -\sqrt[3]{125}$ **55.** $\sqrt[4]{10,000}, \sqrt[3]{1000}$
57. 5.66 ft   **59.** 6.84 ft   **61.** 7.07 s   **a.** $8x^3$ **b.** $45a^5$ **c.** $48m^3$
d. $16b^4$ **e.** $81p^7$ **f.** $81s^7$ **g.** $200y^5$ **h.** $98m^7$

9.2 Simplifying Radical Expressions

9.2 OBJECTIVE

Simplify expressions involving radicals

In Section 9.1, we introduced the radical notation. For most applications, we will want to make sure that all radical expressions are in *simplest form*. To accomplish this, the following three conditions must be satisfied.

An expression involving square roots is in *simplest form* if

1. There are no perfect-square factors in a radical.
2. No fraction appears inside a radical.
3. No radical appears in the denominator.

For instance, considering condition 1,

$\sqrt{17}$ is in simplest form since 17 has *no* perfect-square factors

while

$\sqrt{12}$ is *not* in simplest form

because it does not contain a perfect-square factor.

$$\sqrt{12} = \sqrt{4 \cdot 3}$$

A perfect square

To simplify radical expressions, we'll need to develop two important properties. First, look at the following expressions:

$$\sqrt{4 \cdot 9} = \sqrt{36} = 6$$
$$\sqrt{4} \cdot \sqrt{9} = 2 \cdot 3 = 6$$

Since this tells us that $\sqrt{4 \cdot 9} = \sqrt{4} \cdot \sqrt{9}$, the following general rule for radicals is suggested.

Property 1 of Radicals

For any positive real numbers a and b,

$$\sqrt{ab} = \sqrt{a} \cdot \sqrt{b}$$

In words, the square root of a product is the product of the square roots.

Let's see how this property is applied in simplifying expressions when radicals are involved.

● Example 1

Simplifying Radical Expressions

Perfect-square factors are 1, 4, 9, 16, 25, 36, 49, 64, 81, 100, and so on.

Simplify each expression.

(a) $\sqrt{12} = \sqrt{4 \cdot 3}$

A perfect square

Apply Property 1.

Note that we have removed the perfect-square factor from inside the radical, so the expression is in simplest form.

$$= \sqrt{4} \cdot \sqrt{3}$$
$$= 2\sqrt{3}$$

It would not have helped to write

$$\sqrt{45} = \sqrt{15 \cdot 3}$$

since neither factor is a perfect square.

(b) $\sqrt{45} = \sqrt{9 \cdot 5}$

A perfect square

$$= \sqrt{9} \cdot \sqrt{5}$$
$$= 3\sqrt{5}$$

We look for the *largest* perfect-square factor, here 36.

(c) $\sqrt{72} = \sqrt{36 \cdot 2}$

A perfect square

Then apply Property 1.

$$= \sqrt{36} \cdot \sqrt{2}$$
$$= 6\sqrt{2}$$

(d) $5\sqrt{18} = 5\sqrt{9 \cdot 2}$

A perfect square

$$= 5 \cdot \sqrt{9} \cdot \sqrt{2} = 5 \cdot 3\sqrt{2} = 15\sqrt{2}$$

CAUTION

Be Careful! Even though

$$\sqrt{a \cdot b} = \sqrt{a} \cdot \sqrt{b}$$

$$\sqrt{a + b} \quad \text{is } not \text{ the same as} \quad \sqrt{a} + \sqrt{b}$$

Let $a = 4$ and $b = 9$, and substitute.

$$\sqrt{a + b} = \sqrt{4 + 9} = \sqrt{13}$$

$$\sqrt{a} + \sqrt{b} = \sqrt{4} + \sqrt{9} = 2 + 3 = 5$$

Since $\sqrt{13} \neq 5$, we see that the expressions $\sqrt{a + b}$ and $\sqrt{a} + \sqrt{b}$ are not in general the same.

● ● ● **CHECK YOURSELF 1**

Simplify.

a. $\sqrt{20}$ **b.** $\sqrt{75}$ **c.** $\sqrt{98}$ **d.** $\sqrt{48}$

The process is the same if variables are involved in a radical expression. In our remaining work with radicals, we will assume that all variables represent positive real numbers.

●Example 2

Simplifying Radical Expressions

Simplify each of the following radicals.

(a) $\sqrt{x^3} = \sqrt{x^2 \cdot x}$

          A perfect square

By our first rule for radicals.

Note: $\sqrt{x^2} = x$ (as long as x is positive).

$= \sqrt{x^2} \cdot \sqrt{x}$

$= x\sqrt{x}$

(b) $\sqrt{4b^3} = \sqrt{4 \cdot b^2 \cdot b}$

          Perfect squares

$= \sqrt{4b^2} \cdot \sqrt{b}$

$= 2b\sqrt{b}$

Note that we want the perfect-square factor to have the largest possible even exponent, here 4. Keep in mind that

$a^2 \cdot a^2 = a^4$

(c) $\sqrt{18a^5} = \sqrt{9 \cdot a^4 \cdot 2a}$

          Perfect squares

$= \sqrt{9a^4} \cdot \sqrt{2a}$

$= 3a^2\sqrt{2a}$

● ● ● **CHECK YOURSELF 2**

Simplify.

a. $\sqrt{9x^3}$ **b.** $\sqrt{27m^3}$ **c.** $\sqrt{50b^5}$

To develop a second property for radicals, look at the following expressions:

$$\sqrt{\frac{16}{4}} = \sqrt{4} = 2$$

$$\frac{\sqrt{16}}{\sqrt{4}} = \frac{4}{2} = 2$$

Since $\sqrt{\dfrac{16}{4}} = \dfrac{\sqrt{16}}{\sqrt{4}}$, a second general rule for radicals is suggested.

Property 2 of Radicals

For any positive real numbers a and b,

$$\sqrt{\frac{a}{b}} = \frac{\sqrt{a}}{\sqrt{b}}$$

In words, the square root of a quotient is the quotient of the square roots.

This property is used in a fashion similar to Property 1 in simplifying radical expressions. Remember that our second condition for a radical expression to be in simplest form states that no fraction should appear inside a radical. Example 3 illustrates how expressions that violate that condition are simplified.

● Example 3

Simplifying Radical Expressions

Write each expression in simplest form.

Apply Property 2 to write the numerator and denominator as separate radicals.

(a) $\sqrt{\dfrac{9}{4}} = \dfrac{\sqrt{9}}{\sqrt{4}}$ $\quad\begin{cases}\text{Remove any}\\ \text{perfect squares}\\ \text{from the radical.}\end{cases}$

$= \dfrac{3}{2}$

Apply Property 2.

(b) $\sqrt{\dfrac{2}{25}} = \dfrac{\sqrt{2}}{\sqrt{25}}$

$= \dfrac{\sqrt{2}}{5}$

Apply Property 2.

(c) $\sqrt{\dfrac{8x^2}{9}} = \dfrac{\sqrt{8x^2}}{\sqrt{9}}$

Factor $8x^2$ as $4x^2 \cdot 2$.

$= \dfrac{\sqrt{4x^2 \cdot 2}}{3}$

Apply Property 1 in the numerator.

$= \dfrac{\sqrt{4x^2} \cdot \sqrt{2}}{3}$

$= \dfrac{2x\sqrt{2}}{3}$

● ● ● **CHECK YOURSELF 3**

Simplify.

a. $\sqrt{\dfrac{25}{16}}$ **b.** $\sqrt{\dfrac{7}{9}}$ **c.** $\sqrt{\dfrac{12x^2}{49}}$

In our previous examples, the denominator of the fraction appearing in the radical was a perfect square, and we were able to write each expression in simplest radical form by removing that perfect square from the denominator.

If the denominator of the fraction in the radical is *not* a perfect square, we can still apply Property 2 of radicals. As we will see in Example 4, the third condition for a radical to be in simplest form is then violated, and a new technique is necessary.

●Example 4

Simplifying Radical Expressions

Write each expression in simplest form.

We begin by applying Property 2.

(a) $\sqrt{\dfrac{1}{3}} = \dfrac{\sqrt{1}}{\sqrt{3}} = \dfrac{1}{\sqrt{3}}$

Do you see that $\dfrac{1}{\sqrt{3}}$ is still not in simplest form because of the radical in the denominator? To solve this problem, we multiply the numerator and denominator by $\sqrt{3}$. Note that the denominator will become

$$\sqrt{3} \cdot \sqrt{3} = \sqrt{9} = 3$$

In general, if $a \geq 0$, then $\sqrt{a} \cdot \sqrt{a} = a$. We then have

We can do this because we are multiplying the fraction by $\dfrac{\sqrt{3}}{\sqrt{3}}$ or 1, which does not change its value.

$$\dfrac{1}{\sqrt{3}} = \dfrac{1 \cdot \sqrt{3}}{\sqrt{3} \cdot \sqrt{3}} = \dfrac{\sqrt{3}}{3}$$

The expression $\dfrac{\sqrt{3}}{3}$ is now in simplest form since all three of our conditions are satisfied.

Note:

$\sqrt{2} \cdot \sqrt{5} = \sqrt{2 \cdot 5} = \sqrt{10}$

$\sqrt{5} \cdot \sqrt{5} = 5$

(b) $\sqrt{\dfrac{2}{5}} = \dfrac{\sqrt{2}}{\sqrt{5}}$

$\phantom{(b)\ \sqrt{\dfrac{2}{5}}} = \dfrac{\sqrt{2} \cdot \sqrt{5}}{\sqrt{5} \cdot \sqrt{5}}$

$\phantom{(b)\ \sqrt{\dfrac{2}{5}}} = \dfrac{\sqrt{10}}{5}$

and the expression is in simplest form since again our three conditions are satisfied.

(c) $\sqrt{\dfrac{3x}{7}} = \dfrac{\sqrt{3x}}{\sqrt{7}}$

We multiply numerator and denominator by $\sqrt{7}$ to "clear" the denominator of the radical.

$\qquad = \dfrac{\sqrt{3x} \cdot \sqrt{7}}{\sqrt{7} \cdot \sqrt{7}}$

$\qquad = \dfrac{\sqrt{21x}}{7}$

The expression is in simplest form.

● ● ● **CHECK YOURSELF 4**

Simplify.

a. $\sqrt{\dfrac{1}{2}}$ **b.** $\sqrt{\dfrac{2}{3}}$ **c.** $\sqrt{\dfrac{2y}{5}}$

Both of the properties of radicals given in this section are true for cube roots, fourth roots, and so on. Here we have limited ourselves to simplifying expressions involving square roots.

● ● ● **CHECK YOURSELF ANSWERS**

1. (a) $2\sqrt{5}$; (b) $5\sqrt{3}$; (c) $7\sqrt{2}$; (d) $4\sqrt{3}$. **2.** (a) $3x\sqrt{x}$; (b) $3m\sqrt{3m}$; (c) $5b^2\sqrt{2b}$. **3.** (a) $\dfrac{5}{4}$; (b) $\dfrac{\sqrt{7}}{3}$; (c) $\dfrac{2x\sqrt{3}}{7}$. **4.** (a) $\dfrac{\sqrt{2}}{2}$; (b) $\dfrac{\sqrt{6}}{3}$; (c) $\dfrac{\sqrt{10y}}{5}$.

Use Property 1 to simplify each of the following radical expressions. Assume that all variables represent positive real numbers.

1. $\sqrt{18}$

2. $\sqrt{50}$

3. $\sqrt{28}$

4. $\sqrt{108}$

5. $\sqrt{45}$

6. $\sqrt{80}$

7. $\sqrt{48}$

8. $\sqrt{125}$

9. $\sqrt{200}$

10. $\sqrt{96}$

11. $\sqrt{147}$

12. $\sqrt{300}$

13. $3\sqrt{12}$

14. $5\sqrt{24}$

15. $\sqrt{5x^2}$

16. $\sqrt{7a^2}$

17. $\sqrt{3y^4}$

18. $\sqrt{10x^6}$

19. $\sqrt{2r^3}$

20. $\sqrt{5a^5}$

1. _____

2. _____

3. _____

4. _____

5. _____

6. _____

7. _____

8. _____

9. _____

10. _____

11. _____

12. _____

13. _____

14. _____

15. _____

16. _____

17. _____

18. _____

19. _____

20. _____

21. _____

22. _____

23. _____

24. _____

25. _____

26. _____

27. _____

28. _____

29. _____

30. _____

31. _____

32. _____

33. _____

34. _____

35. _____

36. _____

37. _____

38. _____

39. _____

40. _____

41. _____

42. _____

21. $\sqrt{27b^2}$

22. $\sqrt{98m^4}$

23. $\sqrt{24x^4}$

24. $\sqrt{72x^3}$

25. $\sqrt{54a^5}$

26. $\sqrt{200y^6}$

27. $\sqrt{x^3y^2}$

28. $\sqrt{a^2b^5}$

Use Property 2 to simplify each of the following radical expressions.

29. $\sqrt{\dfrac{4}{25}}$

30. $\sqrt{\dfrac{64}{9}}$

31. $\sqrt{\dfrac{9}{16}}$

32. $\sqrt{\dfrac{49}{25}}$

33. $\sqrt{\dfrac{3}{4}}$

34. $\sqrt{\dfrac{5}{9}}$

35. $\sqrt{\dfrac{5}{36}}$

36. $\sqrt{\dfrac{10}{49}}$

Use the properties for radicals to simplify each of the following expressions. Assume that all variables represent positive real numbers.

37. $\sqrt{\dfrac{8a^2}{25}}$

38. $\sqrt{\dfrac{12y^2}{49}}$

39. $\sqrt{\dfrac{1}{5}}$

40. $\sqrt{\dfrac{1}{7}}$

41. $\sqrt{\dfrac{3}{2}}$

42. $\sqrt{\dfrac{5}{3}}$

43. $\sqrt{\dfrac{3a}{5}}$

44. $\sqrt{\dfrac{2x}{7}}$

45. $\sqrt{\dfrac{2x^2}{3}}$

46. $\sqrt{\dfrac{5m^2}{2}}$

47. $\sqrt{\dfrac{8s^3}{7}}$

48. $\sqrt{\dfrac{12x^3}{5}}$

Decide whether each of the following is already written in simplest form. If it is not, explain what needs to be done.

49. $\sqrt{10mn}$

50. $\sqrt{18ab}$

51. $\dfrac{\sqrt{98x^2y}}{7x}$

52. $\dfrac{\sqrt{6xy}}{3x}$

53. Find the area and perimeter of this square:

$$\begin{array}{c} \sqrt{3} \;\square \\ \sqrt{3} \end{array}$$

One of these measures, the area, is a rational number, and the other is an irrational number. Explain how this happened. Will the area always be a rational number? Explain.

54. Part (a) is a repeat of Exercise 70, Section 1.4. You may refer to that problem, or re-create the table here.

(a) Evaluate the three expressions $\dfrac{n^2 - 1}{2}$, n, $\dfrac{n^2 + 1}{2}$ using odd values of n:

1, 3, 5, 7, etc. Make a chart like the one below and complete it.

n	$a = \dfrac{n^2 - 1}{2}$	$b = n$	$c = \dfrac{n^2 + 1}{2}$	a^2	b^2	c^2
1						
3						
5						
7						
9						
11						
13						
15						

ANSWERS

43. _____

44. _____

45. _____

46. _____

47. _____

48. _____

49. _____

50. _____

51. _____

52. _____

53. _____

54. _____

(b) Check for each of these sets of three numbers to see if this statement is true: $\sqrt{a^2 + b^2} = \sqrt{c^2}$. For how many of your sets of three did this work? Sets of three numbers for which this statement are true are called "Pythagorean triples" because $a^2 + b^2 = c^2$. Can the radical equation be written in this way: $\sqrt{a^2 + b^2} = a^2 + b^2$? Explain your answer.

Getting Ready for Section 9.3
[Section 1.3]

Use the distributive property to combine the like terms in each of the following expressions.

a. $5x + 6x$ **b.** $8a - 3a$ **c.** $10y - 12y$ **d.** $7m + 10m$

e. $9a + 7a - 12a$ **f.** $5s - 8s + 4s$ **g.** $12m + 3n - 6m$ **h.** $8x + 5y - 4x$

Answers

1. $3\sqrt{2}$ **3.** $2\sqrt{7}$ **5.** $3\sqrt{5}$ **7.** $4\sqrt{3}$ **9.** $10\sqrt{2}$ **11.** $7\sqrt{3}$

13. $6\sqrt{3}$ **15.** $x\sqrt{5}$ **17.** $y^2\sqrt{3}$ **19.** $r\sqrt{2r}$ **21.** $3b\sqrt{3}$

23. $2x^2\sqrt{6}$ **25.** $3a^2\sqrt{6a}$ **27.** $xy\sqrt{x}$ **29.** $\dfrac{2}{5}$ **31.** $\dfrac{3}{4}$ **33.** $\dfrac{\sqrt{3}}{2}$

35. $\dfrac{\sqrt{5}}{6}$ **37.** $\dfrac{2a\sqrt{2}}{5}$ **39.** $\dfrac{\sqrt{5}}{5}$ **41.** $\dfrac{\sqrt{6}}{2}$ **43.** $\dfrac{\sqrt{15a}}{5}$ **45.** $\dfrac{x\sqrt{6}}{3}$

47. $\dfrac{2s\sqrt{14s}}{7}$ **49.** Simplest form

51. Remove the perfect-square factors from the radical and simplify.

a. $11x$ **b.** $5a$ **c.** $-2y$ **d.** $17m$ **e.** $4a$ **f.** s **g.** $6m + 3n$

h. $4x + 5y$

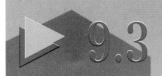

Adding and Subtracting Radicals

9.3 OBJECTIVE

Add and subtract expressions involving radicals

"Indices" is the plural of "index."

Two radicals that have the same index and the same radicand (the expression inside the radical) are called **like radicals.** For example,

$2\sqrt{3}$ and $5\sqrt{3}$ are like radicals.

$\sqrt{2}$ and $\sqrt{5}$ are not like radicals—they have different radicands.

$\sqrt{2}$ and $\sqrt[3]{2}$ are not like radicals—they have different indices (2 and 3, representing a square root and a cube root).

Like radicals can be added (or subtracted) in the same way as like terms. We apply the distributive property and then combine the coefficients:

$$2\sqrt{5} + 3\sqrt{5} = (2 + 3)\sqrt{5} = 5\sqrt{5}$$

• Example 1

Adding and Subtracting Like Radicals

Simplify each expression.

Apply the distributive property, then combine the coefficients.

(a) $5\sqrt{2} + 3\sqrt{2} = (5 + 3)\sqrt{2} = 8\sqrt{2}$

(b) $7\sqrt{5} - 2\sqrt{5} = (7 - 2)\sqrt{5} = 5\sqrt{5}$

(c) $8\sqrt{7} - \sqrt{7} + 2\sqrt{7} = (8 - 1 + 2)\sqrt{7} = 9\sqrt{7}$

● ● ● **CHECK YOURSELF 1**

Simplify.

a. $2\sqrt{5} + 7\sqrt{5}$ **b.** $9\sqrt{7} - \sqrt{7}$ **c.** $5\sqrt{3} - 2\sqrt{3} + \sqrt{3}$

If a sum or difference involves terms that are *not* like radicals, we may be able to combine terms after simplifying the radicals according to our earlier methods.

• Example 2

Adding and Subtracting Radicals

Simplify each expression.

(a) $3\sqrt{2} + \sqrt{8}$

We do not have like radicals, but we can simplify $\sqrt{8}$. Remember that

$$\sqrt{8} = \sqrt{4 \cdot 2} = 2\sqrt{2}$$

so

$$\sqrt{8}$$
$$3\sqrt{2} + \sqrt{8} = 3\sqrt{2} + \overbrace{2\sqrt{2}}$$
$$= (3 + 2)\sqrt{2} = 5\sqrt{2}$$

Simplify $\sqrt{12}$.

The radicals can now be combined. Do you see why?

(b) $5\sqrt{3} - \sqrt{12} = 5\sqrt{3} - \sqrt{4 \cdot 3}$
$$= 5\sqrt{3} - \sqrt{4} \cdot \sqrt{3}$$
$$= 5\sqrt{3} - 2\sqrt{3}$$
$$= (5 - 2)\sqrt{3} = 3\sqrt{3}$$

● ● ●   **CHECK YOURSELF 2**

Simplify.

a. $\sqrt{2} + \sqrt{18}$ **b.** $5\sqrt{3} - \sqrt{27}$

If variables are involved in radical expressions, the process of combining terms proceeds in a fashion similar to that shown in previous examples. Consider Example 3. We again assume that all variables represent positive real numbers.

● Example 3

Simplifying Expressions Involving Variables

Simplify each expression.

Since like radicals are involved, we apply the distributive property and combine terms as before.

Simplify the first term.

The radicals can now be combined.

(a) $5\sqrt{3x} - 2\sqrt{3x} = (5 - 2)\sqrt{3x} = 3\sqrt{3x}$

(b) $2\sqrt{3a^3} + 5a\sqrt{3a}$
$$= 2\sqrt{a^2 \cdot 3a} + 5a\sqrt{3a}$$
$$= 2\sqrt{a^2} \cdot \sqrt{3a} + 5a\sqrt{3a}$$
$$= 2a\sqrt{3a} + 5a\sqrt{3a}$$
$$= (2a + 5a)\sqrt{3a} = 7a\sqrt{3a}$$

● ● ●   **CHECK YOURSELF 3**

Simplify each expression.

a. $2\sqrt{7y} + 3\sqrt{7y}$ **b.** $\sqrt{20a^2} - a\sqrt{45}$

● ● ●   **CHECK YOURSELF ANSWERS**

1. (a) $9\sqrt{5}$; **(b)** $8\sqrt{7}$; **(c)** $4\sqrt{3}$.   **2. (a)** $4\sqrt{2}$; **(b)** $2\sqrt{3}$.   **3. (a)** $5\sqrt{7y}$;
(b) $-a\sqrt{5}$.

Simplify by combining like terms.

1. $2\sqrt{2} + 4\sqrt{2}$

2. $\sqrt{3} + 5\sqrt{3}$

3. $11\sqrt{7} - 4\sqrt{7}$

4. $5\sqrt{3} - 3\sqrt{2}$

5. $5\sqrt{7} + 3\sqrt{6}$

6. $3\sqrt{5} - 5\sqrt{5}$

7. $2\sqrt{3} - 5\sqrt{3}$

8. $2\sqrt{11} + 5\sqrt{11}$

9. $2\sqrt{3x} + 5\sqrt{3x}$

10. $7\sqrt{2a} - 3\sqrt{2a}$

11. $2\sqrt{3} + \sqrt{3} + 3\sqrt{3}$

12. $3\sqrt{5} + 2\sqrt{5} + \sqrt{5}$

13. $5\sqrt{7} - 2\sqrt{7} + \sqrt{7}$

14. $3\sqrt{10} - 2\sqrt{10} + \sqrt{10}$

15. $2\sqrt{5x} + 5\sqrt{5x} - 2\sqrt{5x}$

16. $5\sqrt{3b} - 2\sqrt{3b} + 4\sqrt{3b}$

17. $2\sqrt{3} + \sqrt{12}$

18. $5\sqrt{2} + \sqrt{18}$

19. _____

20. _____

21. _____

22. _____

23. _____

24. _____

25. _____

26. _____

27. _____

28. _____

29. _____

30. _____

31. _____

32. _____

33. _____

34. _____

35. _____

36. _____

37. _____

38. _____

19. $\sqrt{20} - \sqrt{5}$

20. $\sqrt{98} - 3\sqrt{2}$

21. $2\sqrt{6} - \sqrt{54}$

22. $2\sqrt{3} - \sqrt{27}$

23. $\sqrt{72} + \sqrt{50}$

24. $\sqrt{27} - \sqrt{12}$

25. $3\sqrt{12} - \sqrt{48}$

26. $5\sqrt{8} + 2\sqrt{18}$

27. $2\sqrt{45} - 2\sqrt{20}$

28. $2\sqrt{98} - 4\sqrt{18}$

29. $\sqrt{12} + \sqrt{27} - \sqrt{3}$

30. $\sqrt{50} + \sqrt{32} - \sqrt{8}$

31. $3\sqrt{24} - \sqrt{54} + \sqrt{6}$

32. $\sqrt{63} - 2\sqrt{28} + 5\sqrt{7}$

33. $2\sqrt{50} + 3\sqrt{18} - \sqrt{32}$

34. $3\sqrt{27} + 4\sqrt{12} - \sqrt{300}$

Simplify by combining like terms.

35. $a\sqrt{27} - 2\sqrt{3a^2}$

36. $5\sqrt{2y^2} - 3y\sqrt{8}$

37. $5\sqrt{3x^3} + 2\sqrt{27x}$

38. $7\sqrt{2a^3} - \sqrt{8a}$

Use a calculator to find a decimal approximation for each of the following. Round your answer to the nearest hundredth.

39. $\sqrt{3} - \sqrt{2}$

40. $\sqrt{7} + \sqrt{11}$

41. $\sqrt{5} + \sqrt{3}$

42. $\sqrt{17} - \sqrt{13}$

43. $4\sqrt{3} - 7\sqrt{5}$

44. $8\sqrt{2} + 3\sqrt{7}$

45. $5\sqrt{7} + 8\sqrt{13}$

46. $7\sqrt{2} - 4\sqrt{11}$

47. Perimeter of a rectangle. Find the perimeter of the rectangle shown in the figure.

48. Perimeter of a rectangle. Find the perimeter of the rectangle shown in the figure.

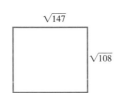

49. Perimeter of a triangle. Find the perimeter of the triangle shown in the figure.

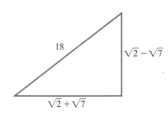

50. Perimeter of a triangle. Find the perimeter of the triangle shown in the figure.

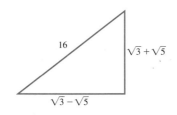

ANSWERS

39. _____

40. _____

41. _____

42. _____

43. _____

44. _____

45. _____

46. _____

47. _____

48. _____

49. _____

50. _____

a. _____

b. _____

c. _____

d. _____

e. _____

f. _____

g. _____

h. _____

 Getting Ready for Section 9.4
[Section 4.6]

Perform the indicated multiplication.

a. $2(x + 5)$ **b.** $3(a - 3)$ **c.** $m(m - 8)$ **d.** $y(y + 7)$

e. $(w + 2)(w - 2)$ **f.** $(x - 3)(x + 3)$ **g.** $(x + y)(x + y)$ **h.** $(b - 7)(b - 7)$

Answers

1. $6\sqrt{2}$ **3.** $7\sqrt{7}$ **5.** Cannot be simplified   **7.** $-3\sqrt{3}$ **9.** $7\sqrt{3x}$
11. $6\sqrt{3}$ **13.** $4\sqrt{7}$ **15.** $5\sqrt{5x}$ **17.** $4\sqrt{3}$ **19.** $\sqrt{5}$ **21.** $-\sqrt{6}$
23. $11\sqrt{2}$ **25.** $2\sqrt{3}$ **27.** $2\sqrt{5}$ **29.** $4\sqrt{3}$ **31.** $4\sqrt{6}$ **33.** $15\sqrt{2}$
35. $a\sqrt{3}$ **37.** $(5x + 6)\sqrt{3x}$ **39.** 0.32 **41.** 3.97 **43.** -8.72
45. 42.07 **47.** 26 **49.** $2\sqrt{2} + 18$ **a.** $2x + 10$ **b.** $3a - 9$
c. $m^2 - 8m$ **d.** $y^2 + 7y$ **e.** $w^2 - 4$ **f.** $x^2 - 9$ **g.** $x^2 + 2xy + y^2$
h. $b^2 - 14b + 49$

9.4 Multiplying and Dividing Radicals

9.4 OBJECTIVE

Multiply and divide expressions involving radicals

The product of square roots is equal to the square root of the product of the radicands.

In Section 9.2, we stated the first property for radicals:

$$\sqrt{ab} = \sqrt{a} \cdot \sqrt{b} \qquad \text{where } a \text{ and } b \text{ are any positive real numbers}$$

That property has been used to simplify radical expressions up to this point. Suppose now that we want to find a product, such as $\sqrt{3} \cdot \sqrt{5}$.

We can use our first radical rule in the opposite manner.

$$\sqrt{a} \cdot \sqrt{b} = \sqrt{ab}$$

so

$$\sqrt{3} \cdot \sqrt{5} = \sqrt{3 \cdot 5} = \sqrt{15}$$

We may have to simplify after multiplying, as Example 1 illustrates.

• Example 1

Simplifying Radical Expressions

Multiply then simplify each expression.

(a) $\sqrt{5} \cdot \sqrt{10} = \sqrt{5 \cdot 10} = \sqrt{50}$
$$= \sqrt{25 \cdot 2} = 5\sqrt{2}$$

(b) $\sqrt{12} \cdot \sqrt{6} = \sqrt{12 \cdot 6} = \sqrt{72}$
$$= \sqrt{36 \cdot 2} = \sqrt{36} \cdot \sqrt{2} = 6\sqrt{2}$$

$$\sqrt{12} \cdot \sqrt{6} = 2\sqrt{3}\sqrt{6} = 2\sqrt{18}$$
$$= 2\sqrt{9 \cdot 2} = 2\sqrt{9}\sqrt{2}$$
$$= 2 \cdot 3\sqrt{2} = 6\sqrt{2}$$

Note: An alternative approach would be to simplify $\sqrt{12}$ first.

(c) $\sqrt{10x} \cdot \sqrt{2x} = \sqrt{20x^2} = \sqrt{4x^2 \cdot 5}$
$$= \sqrt{4x^2} \cdot \sqrt{5} = 2x\sqrt{5}$$

● ● ● CHECK YOURSELF 1

Simplify.

a. $\sqrt{3} \cdot \sqrt{6}$ **b.** $\sqrt{3} \cdot \sqrt{18}$ **c.** $\sqrt{8a} \cdot \sqrt{3a}$

If coefficients are involved in a product, we can use the commutative and associative properties to change the order and grouping of the factors. This is illustrated in Example 2.

• Example 2

Multiplying Radical Expressions

Multiply.

Note: In practice, it is not necessary to show the intermediate steps.

$$(2\sqrt{5})(3\sqrt{6}) = (2 \cdot 3)(\sqrt{5} \cdot \sqrt{6})$$
$$= 6\sqrt{5 \cdot 6}$$
$$= 6\sqrt{30}$$

● ● ● CHECK YOURSELF 2

Multiply $(3\sqrt{7})(5\sqrt{3})$.

The distributive property can also be applied in multiplying radical expressions. Consider the following.

• Example 3

Multiplying Radical Expressions

Multiply.

(a) $\sqrt{3}(\sqrt{2} + \sqrt{3})$
$$= \sqrt{3} \cdot \sqrt{2} + \sqrt{3} \cdot \sqrt{3} \qquad \text{The distributive property}$$
$$= \sqrt{6} + 3 \qquad \text{Multiply the radicals.}$$

(b) $\sqrt{5}(2\sqrt{6} + 3\sqrt{3})$
$$= \sqrt{5} \cdot 2\sqrt{6} + \sqrt{5} \cdot 3\sqrt{3} \qquad \text{The distributive property}$$
$$= 2 \cdot \sqrt{5} \cdot \sqrt{6} + 3 \cdot \sqrt{5} \cdot \sqrt{3} \qquad \text{The commutative property}$$
$$= 2\sqrt{30} + 3\sqrt{15}$$

● ● ● CHECK YOURSELF 3

Multiply.

a. $\sqrt{5}(\sqrt{6} + \sqrt{5})$ **b.** $\sqrt{3}(2\sqrt{5} + 3\sqrt{2})$

The FOIL pattern we used for multiplying binomials can also be applied in multiplying radical expressions. This is shown in Example 4.

• Example 4

Multiplying Radical Expressions

Multiply.

(a) $(\sqrt{3} + 2)(\sqrt{3} + 5)$

$= \sqrt{3} \cdot \sqrt{3} + 5\sqrt{3} + 2\sqrt{3} + 2 \cdot 5$

$= 3 + 5\sqrt{3} + 2\sqrt{3} + 10$ Combine like terms.

$= 13 + 7\sqrt{3}$

CAUTION

Note: You can use the pattern $(a + b)(a - b) = a^2 - b^2$, where $a = \sqrt{7}$ and $b = 2$, for the same result. $\sqrt{7} + 2$ and $\sqrt{7} - 2$ are called **conjugates** of each other. Note that their product is the rational number 3. The product of conjugates will *always be rational*.

Be Careful! This result *cannot* be further simplified: 13 and $7\sqrt{3}$ are *not* like terms.

(b) $(\sqrt{7} + 2)(\sqrt{7} - 2) = \sqrt{7} \cdot \sqrt{7} - 2\sqrt{7} + 2\sqrt{7} - 4$

$= 7 - 4 = 3$

(c) $(\sqrt{3} + 5)^2 = (\sqrt{3} + 5)(\sqrt{3} + 5)$

$= \sqrt{3} \cdot \sqrt{3} + 5\sqrt{3} + 5\sqrt{3} + 5 \cdot 5$

$= 3 + 5\sqrt{3} + 5\sqrt{3} + 25$

$= 28 + 10\sqrt{3}$

● ● ●   **CHECK YOURSELF 4**

Multiply.

a. $(\sqrt{5} + 3)(\sqrt{5} - 2)$ **b.** $(\sqrt{3} + 4)(\sqrt{3} - 4)$ **c.** $(\sqrt{2} - 3)^2$

We can also use our second property for radicals in the opposite manner.

The quotient of square roots is equal to the square root of the quotient of the radicands.

$$\frac{\sqrt{a}}{\sqrt{b}} = \sqrt{\frac{a}{b}}$$

One use of this property to divide radical expressions is illustrated in Example 5.

• Example 5

Simplifying Radical Expressions

Simplify.

The clue to recognizing when to use this approach is in noting that 48 is divisible by 3.

(a) $\dfrac{\sqrt{48}}{\sqrt{3}} = \sqrt{\dfrac{48}{3}} = \sqrt{16} = 4$

(b) $\dfrac{\sqrt{200}}{\sqrt{2}} = \sqrt{\dfrac{200}{2}} = \sqrt{100} = 10$

(c) $\dfrac{\sqrt{125x^2}}{\sqrt{5}} = \sqrt{\dfrac{125x^2}{5}} = \sqrt{25x^2} = 5x$

● ● ● **CHECK YOURSELF 5**

Simplify.

a. $\dfrac{\sqrt{75}}{\sqrt{3}}$ **b.** $\dfrac{\sqrt{81s^2}}{\sqrt{9}}$

There is one final quotient form that you may encounter in simplifying expressions, and it will be extremely important in our work with quadratic equations in the next chapter. This form is shown in Example 6.

● Example 6

Simplifying Radical Expressions

Simplify the expression

$$\frac{3 + \sqrt{72}}{3}$$

First, we must simplify the radical in the numerator.

CAUTION

Be Careful! Students are sometimes tempted to write

$$\frac{\cancel{3} + 6\sqrt{2}}{\cancel{3}} = 1 + 6\sqrt{2}$$

This is *not* correct. We must divide *both terms* of the numerator by the common factor.

$$\frac{3 + \sqrt{72}}{3} = \frac{3 + \sqrt{36 \cdot 2}}{3}$$ Use Property 1 to simplify $\sqrt{72}$.

$$= \frac{3 + \sqrt{36} \cdot \sqrt{2}}{3} = \frac{3 + 6\sqrt{2}}{3}$$

$$= \frac{3(1 + 2\sqrt{2})}{3} = 1 + 2\sqrt{2}$$ *Factor* the numerator—then divide by the *common* factor of 3.

● ● ● **CHECK YOURSELF 6**

Simplify $\dfrac{15 + \sqrt{75}}{5}$.

● ● ● **CHECK YOURSELF ANSWERS**

1. (a) $3\sqrt{2}$; **(b)** $3\sqrt{6}$; **(c)** $2a\sqrt{6}$.   **2.** $15\sqrt{21}$.   **3. (a)** $\sqrt{30} + 5$;
(b) $2\sqrt{15} + 3\sqrt{6}$.   **4. (a)** $-1 + \sqrt{5}$; **(b)** -13; **(c)** $11 - 6\sqrt{2}$.
5. (a) 5; **(b)** $3s$.   **6.** $3 + \sqrt{3}$.

Perform the indicated multiplication. Then simplify each radical expression.

1. $\sqrt{7} \cdot \sqrt{5}$

2. $\sqrt{3} \cdot \sqrt{7}$

3. $\sqrt{5} \cdot \sqrt{11}$

4. $\sqrt{13} \cdot \sqrt{5}$

5. $\sqrt{3} \cdot \sqrt{10m}$

6. $\sqrt{7a} \cdot \sqrt{13}$

7. $\sqrt{2x} \cdot \sqrt{15}$

8. $\sqrt{17} \cdot \sqrt{2b}$

9. $\sqrt{3} \cdot \sqrt{7} \cdot \sqrt{2}$

10. $\sqrt{5} \cdot \sqrt{7} \cdot \sqrt{3}$

11. $\sqrt{3} \cdot \sqrt{12}$

12. $\sqrt{7} \cdot \sqrt{7}$

13. $\sqrt{10} \cdot \sqrt{10}$

14. $\sqrt{5} \cdot \sqrt{15}$

15. $\sqrt{18} \cdot \sqrt{6}$

16. $\sqrt{8} \cdot \sqrt{10}$

17. $\sqrt{2x} \cdot \sqrt{6x}$

18. $\sqrt{3a} \cdot \sqrt{15a}$

19. $2\sqrt{3} \cdot \sqrt{7}$

20. $3\sqrt{2} \cdot \sqrt{5}$

21. $(3\sqrt{3})(5\sqrt{7})$

22. $(2\sqrt{5})(3\sqrt{11})$

ANSWERS
1.
2.
3.
4.
5.
6.
7.
8.
9.
10.
11.
12.
13.
14.
15.
16.
17.
18.
19.
20.
21.
22.

23. _____

24. _____

25. _____

26. _____

27. _____

28. _____

29. _____

30. _____

31. _____

32. _____

33. _____

34. _____

35. _____

36. _____

37. _____

38. _____

39. _____

40. _____

41. _____

42. _____

43. _____

44. _____

45. _____

46. _____

23. $(3\sqrt{5})(2\sqrt{10})$

24. $(4\sqrt{3})(3\sqrt{6})$

25. $\sqrt{5}(\sqrt{2} + \sqrt{5})$

26. $\sqrt{3}(\sqrt{5} - \sqrt{3})$

27. $\sqrt{3}(2\sqrt{5} - 3\sqrt{3})$

28. $\sqrt{7}(2\sqrt{3} + 3\sqrt{7})$

29. $(\sqrt{3} + 5)(\sqrt{3} + 3)$

30. $(\sqrt{5} - 2)(\sqrt{5} - 1)$

31. $(\sqrt{5} - 1)(\sqrt{5} + 3)$

32. $(\sqrt{2} + 3)(\sqrt{2} - 7)$

33. $(\sqrt{5} - 2)(\sqrt{5} + 2)$

34. $(\sqrt{7} + 5)(\sqrt{7} - 5)$

35. $(\sqrt{10} + 5)(\sqrt{10} - 5)$

36. $(\sqrt{11} - 3)(\sqrt{11} + 3)$

37. $(\sqrt{x} + 3)(\sqrt{x} - 3)$

38. $(\sqrt{a} - 4)(\sqrt{a} + 4)$

39. $(\sqrt{3} + 2)^2$

40. $(\sqrt{5} - 3)^2$

41. $(\sqrt{y} - 5)^2$

42. $(\sqrt{x} + 4)^2$

Perform the indicated division. Rationalize the denominator if necessary. Then simplify each radical expression.

43. $\dfrac{\sqrt{98}}{\sqrt{2}}$

44. $\dfrac{\sqrt{108}}{\sqrt{3}}$

45. $\dfrac{\sqrt{72a^2}}{\sqrt{2}}$

46. $\dfrac{\sqrt{48m^2}}{\sqrt{3}}$

47. $\dfrac{4 + \sqrt{48}}{4}$

48. $\dfrac{12 + \sqrt{108}}{6}$

49. $\dfrac{5 + \sqrt{175}}{5}$

50. $\dfrac{18 + \sqrt{567}}{9}$

51. $\dfrac{-8 - \sqrt{512}}{4}$

52. $\dfrac{-9 - \sqrt{108}}{3}$

53. $\dfrac{6 + \sqrt{18}}{3}$

54. $\dfrac{6 - \sqrt{20}}{2}$

55. $\dfrac{15 - \sqrt{75}}{5}$

56. $\dfrac{8 + \sqrt{48}}{4}$

57. Area of a rectangle. Find the area of the rectangle shown in the figure.

$\sqrt{3}$

$\sqrt{11}$

58. Area of a rectangle. Find the area of the rectangle shown in the figure.

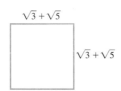

$\sqrt{3} + \sqrt{5}$

$\sqrt{3} + \sqrt{5}$

59. Complete this statement: "$\sqrt{2} \cdot \sqrt{5} = \sqrt{10}$ because . . . ."

60. Explain why $2\sqrt{3} + 5\sqrt{3} = 7\sqrt{3}$ but $7\sqrt{3} + 3\sqrt{5} \neq 10\sqrt{8}$.

61. When you look out over an unobstructed landscape or seascape, the distance to the visible horizon depends on your height above the ground. The equation

$$d = \sqrt{\dfrac{3}{2}h}$$

is a good estimate of this, where d = distance to horizon in miles and h = height of viewer above the ground. Work with a partner to make a chart of distances to the horizon given different elevations. Use the actual heights of tall buildings or prominent landmarks in your area. The local library should have a list of these. Be sure to consider the view to the horizon you get when flying in a plane. What would your elevation have to be to see from one side of your city or town to the other? From one side of your state or county to the other?

ANSWERS

47.

48.

49.

50.

51.

52.

53.

54.

55.

56.

57.

58.

59.

60.

61.

Getting Ready for Section 9.5
[Section 2.6]

Evaluate each of the following expressions.

a. $(3 - 5)^2$

b. $(-2 - 4)^2$

c. $(3 - (-2))^2$

d. $(-2 - (-3))^2$

e. $(-3 - 1)^2$

f. $(-5 - (-3))^2$

Answers

1. $\sqrt{35}$ **3.** $\sqrt{55}$ **5.** $\sqrt{30m}$ **7.** $\sqrt{30x}$ **9.** $\sqrt{42}$ **11.** 6

13. 10   **15.** $6\sqrt{3}$ **17.** $2x\sqrt{3}$ **19.** $2\sqrt{21}$ **21.** $15\sqrt{21}$

23. $30\sqrt{2}$ **25.** $\sqrt{10} + 5$ **27.** $2\sqrt{15} - 9$ **29.** $18 + 8\sqrt{3}$

31. $2 + 2\sqrt{5}$ **33.** 1   **35.** -15 **37.** $x - 9$ **39.** $7 + 4\sqrt{3}$

41. $y - 10\sqrt{y} + 25$ **43.** 7   **45.** $6a$ **47.** $1 + \sqrt{3}$ **49.** $1 + \sqrt{7}$

51. $-2 - 4\sqrt{2}$ **53.** $2 + \sqrt{2}$ **55.** $3 - \sqrt{3}$ **57.** $\sqrt{33}$ **a.** 4

b. 36   **c.** 25   **d.** 1   **e.** 16   **f.** 4

9.5 The Distance Between Two Points

9.5 OBJECTIVE

Find the distance between two points

The concept of irrational numbers was formulated by the Greeks. It was an extension of the search to find the distance between two points. If two points lie on an axis, it is a simple matter of subtraction.

● Example 1

Finding the Distance Between Two Points

Find the distance between $(-3, 0)$ and $(5, 0)$.

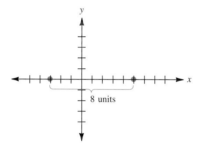

There are 8 units between the points, so the distance is 8.

● ● ●   **CHECK YOURSELF 1**

Find the distance between $(0, 7)$ and $(0, -6)$.

If two points lie on the same vertical or horizontal line, it is equally straightforward to find the distance between them.

● Example 2

Finding the Distance Between Two Points

Find the distance between $(-2, -3)$ and $(-2, 2)$.

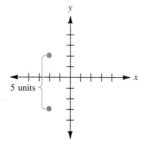

Again, by inspection we can see that there are 5 units between the two points. The distance is 5.

● ● ● **CHECK YOURSELF 2**

Find the distance between $(2, -5)$ and $(-8, -5)$.

In order to find the distance between any two points on a plane, we use a formula derived from the Pythagorean theorem.

Pythagorean Theorem

Given a right triangle, the square of the length of the hypotenuse is equal to the sum of the squares of the two sides.

We write $c^2 = a^2 + b^2$

We can rewrite the formula as

$c = \sqrt{a^2 + b^2}$

A distance is always positive, so we use only the principal square root.

We use the Pythagorean theorem in Example 3.

● **Example 3**

Finding the Distance Between Two Points

Find the distance from $(2, 3)$ to $(5, 7)$.

The distance can be seen as the hypotenuse of a right triangle.

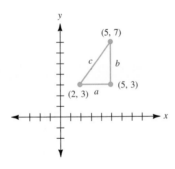

The lengths of the two legs can be found by finding the difference of the two x coordinates and the difference of the two y coordinates. So

$a = 5 - 2 = 3$ and $b = 7 - 3 = 4$

The distance, c, can then be found using the formula

$c = \sqrt{a^2 + b^2}$

or, in this case

$$c = \sqrt{3^2 + 4^2}$$
$$c = \sqrt{9 + 16}$$
$$= \sqrt{25}$$
$$= 5$$

The distance is 5 units.

● ● ● CHECK YOURSELF 3

Find the distance between $(0, 2)$ and $(5, 14)$

If we call our points (x_1, y_1) and (x_2, y_2), we can state the **distance formula.**

Distance Formula

The distance between points (x_1, y_1) and (x_2, y_2) can be found using the formula

$$d = \sqrt{(x_2 - x_1)^2 + (y_2 - y_1)^2}$$

● Example 4

Finding the Distance Between Two Points

Find the distance between $(-2, 5)$ and $(2, -3)$.
    Using the formula,

$$d = \sqrt{[2 - (-2)]^2 + [(-3) - 5]^2}$$
$$= \sqrt{(4)^2 + (-8)^2}$$
$$= \sqrt{16 + 64}$$
$$= \sqrt{80}$$
$$= 4\sqrt{5}$$

● ● ● CHECK YOURSELF 4

Find the distance between $(2, 5)$ and $(-5, 2)$

In Example 4, you were asked to find the distance between $(-2, 5)$ and $(2, -3)$.

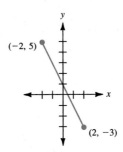

To form a right triangle, we include the point $(-2, -3)$.

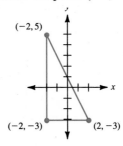

Note that the lengths of the two sides of the right triangle are 4 and 8. By the Pythagorean Theorem, the hypotenuse must have length $\sqrt{4^2 + 8^2} = \sqrt{80} = 4\sqrt{5}$. The distance formula is an application of the Pythagorean Theorem.

Using the square root key on a calculator, it is easy to estimate the length of a diagonal line. This is particularly useful in checking to see if an object is square or rectangular.

● Example 5

Estimating Length with a Calculator

Estimate the length of the diagonal of a right triangle. The diagonal forms the hypoteneuse of the triangle with legs 12.2 in. and 15.7 in. The length of the diagonal would be $\sqrt{12.2^2 + 15.7^2} = \sqrt{395.33} \approx 19.88$ in. Use your calculator to confirm the approximation.

● ● ● CHECK YOURSELF 5

Estimate the length of the diagonal of the rectangle.

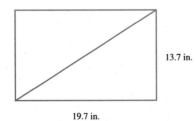

13.7 in.

19.7 in.

● ● ● CHECK YOURSELF ANSWERS

1. 13.   **2.** 10.   **3.** 13.   **4.** $\sqrt{58}$.   **5.** ≈ 24 in.

9.5 Exercises

Find the distance between each pair of points.

1. (2, 0) and (−4, 0)

2. (−3, 0) and (4, 0)

3. (0, −2) and (0, −9)

4. (0, 8) and (0, −4)

5. (2, 5) and (5, 2)

6. (3, 3) and (5, 7)

7. (5, 1) and (3, 8)

8. (2, 9) and (7, 4)

9. (−2, 8) and (1, 5)

10. (2, 6) and (−3, 4)

11. (6, −1) and (2, 2)

12. (2, −8) and (1, 0)

13. (−1, −1) and (2, 5)

14. (−2, −2) and (3, 3)

15. (−2, 9) and (−3, 3)

16. (4, −1) and (0, −5)

17. (−1, −4) and (−3, 5)

18. (−2, 3) and (−7, −1)

19. (−2, −4) and (−4, 1)

20. (−1, −1) and (4, −2)

21. (−4, −2) and (−1, −5)

22. (−2, −2) and (−4, −4)

23. (−2, 0) and (−4, −1)

24. (−5, −2) and (−7, −1)

1. _____
2. _____
3. _____
4. _____
5. _____
6. _____
7. _____
8. _____
9. _____
10. _____
11. _____
12. _____
13. _____
14. _____
15. _____
16. _____
17. _____
18. _____
19. _____
20. _____
21. _____
22. _____
23. _____
24. _____

Use the distance formula to show that each set of points describes an isosceles triangle (a triangle with two sides of equal length).

25. $(-3, 0)$, $(2, 3)$, and $(1, -1)$

26. $(-2, 4)$, $(2, 7)$, and $(5, 3)$

27. Your architecture firm just received this memo.

To:	Algebra Expert Architecture, Inc.
From:	Microbeans Coffee Company, Inc.
Re:	Design for On-Site Day Care Facility
Date:	Aug. 10, 1997

We are requesting that you submit a design for a nursery for preschool children. We are planning to provide free on-site day care for the workers at our corporate headquarters.

The nursery should be large enough to serve the needs of 20 preschoolers. There will be three child care workers in this facility. We want the nursery to be 3000 square feet in area. It needs a playroom, a small kitchen and eating space, and bathroom facilities. There should be some space to store toys and books, many of which should be accessible to children. The company plans to put this facility on the first floor on an outside wall so the children can go outside to play without disturbing workers. You are free to add to this design as you see fit.

Please send us your design drawn to a scale of 1 ft to 0.25 in., with precise measurements and descriptions. We would like to receive this design in 1 week from today. Please give us some estimate of the cost of this renovation to our building.

You decide to submit a design, but you know the design has to conform to strict design specifications for buildings designated as nurseries, including:

1. Number of exits: Two exits for the first 7 people and one exit for every additional 7 people.
2. Width of exits: The total width of exits in inches shall not be less than the total occupant load served by an exit multiplied by 0.3 for stairs and 0.2 for other exits. No exit shall be less than 3 ft wide and 6 ft 8 in. high.
3. Arrangements of exits: If two exits are required, they shall be placed a distance apart equal to but not less than one-half the length of the maximum overall diagonal dimension of the building or area to be served measured in a straight line between exits. Where three or more exits are required, two shall be placed as above and the additional exits arranged a reasonable distance apart.
4. Distance to exits: Maximum distance to travel from any point to an exterior door shall not exceed 100 ft.

Answers

1. 6   **3.** 7   **5.** $3\sqrt{2}$ **7.** $\sqrt{53}$ **9.** $3\sqrt{2}$ **11.** 5   **13.** $3\sqrt{5}$

15. $\sqrt{37}$ **17.** $\sqrt{85}$ **19.** $\sqrt{29}$ **21.** $3\sqrt{2}$ **23.** $\sqrt{5}$

25. Sides have length $\sqrt{34}$, $\sqrt{34}$, and $\sqrt{136}$

Summary

Radicals [9.1]

$\sqrt{49} = 7$

Square Roots $\sqrt{x}$ is the principal (or positive) square root of x. It is the positive number we must square to get x.
$-\sqrt{x}$ is the negative square root of x.
The square root of a negative number is not a real number.

$-\sqrt{49} = -7$
$\sqrt{-49}$ is not a real number.

$\sqrt[3]{64} = 4$ because $4^3 = 64$.

Other Roots $\sqrt[3]{x}$ is the cube root of x.
$\sqrt[4]{x}$ is the fourth root of x.

$\sqrt[4]{81} = 3$ because $3^4 = 81$.

$\dfrac{2}{3}, \dfrac{-7}{12}, 5, \sqrt{36}$, and $\sqrt[3]{64}$ are rational numbers.
$\sqrt{5}, \sqrt{37}$, and $\sqrt[3]{65}$ are irrational numbers.

Rational and Irrational Numbers Rational numbers can be expressed as the quotient of two integers with a nonzero denominator.
Irrational numbers cannot be expressed as the quotient of two integers.

Real Numbers The real numbers are the set of rational numbers and the set of irrational numbers together.

Definitions

$\sqrt{5^2} = 5 \qquad \sqrt{(-3)^2} = 3$
$\sqrt[3]{2^3} = 2 \qquad \sqrt[3]{(-3)^3} = -3$

$\sqrt{x^2} = |x| \qquad$ for any real number x
$\sqrt[3]{x^3} = x \qquad$ for any real number x

Simplifying Radical Expressions [9.2]

An expression involving square roots is in *simplest form* if

1. There are no perfect-square factors in a radical.
2. No fraction appears inside a radical.
3. No radical appears in the denominator.

$\sqrt{40} = \sqrt{4 \cdot 10}$
$\quad = \sqrt{4} \cdot \sqrt{10}$
$\quad = 2\sqrt{10}$
$\sqrt{12x^3} = \sqrt{4x^2 \cdot 3x}$
$\quad = \sqrt{4x^2} \cdot \sqrt{3x}$
$\quad = 2x \cdot \sqrt{3x}$

To simplify a radical expression, use one of the following properties. The square root of a product is the product of the square roots.

$$\sqrt{ab} = \sqrt{a} \cdot \sqrt{b}$$

$\sqrt{\dfrac{5}{16}} = \dfrac{\sqrt{5}}{\sqrt{16}} = \dfrac{\sqrt{5}}{4}$
$\sqrt{\dfrac{2y}{3}} = \dfrac{\sqrt{2y}}{\sqrt{3}} = \dfrac{\sqrt{2y} \cdot \sqrt{3}}{\sqrt{3} \cdot \sqrt{3}}$
$\quad = \dfrac{\sqrt{6y}}{\sqrt{9}} = \dfrac{\sqrt{6y}}{3}$

The square root of a quotient is the quotient of the square roots.

$$\sqrt{\dfrac{a}{b}} = \dfrac{\sqrt{a}}{\sqrt{b}}$$

Adding and Subtracting Radicals [9.3]

$3\sqrt{5}$ and $2\sqrt{5}$ are like radicals.

$$2\sqrt{3} + 3\sqrt{3} = (2 + 3)\sqrt{3}$$
$$= 5\sqrt{3}$$

$$5\sqrt{7} - 2\sqrt{7} = (5 - 2)\sqrt{7}$$
$$= 3\sqrt{7}$$

$$\sqrt{12} + \sqrt{3} = 2\sqrt{3} + \sqrt{3}$$
$$= (2 + 1)\sqrt{3}$$

$$\sqrt{7} \cdot \sqrt{5} = \sqrt{7 \cdot 5}$$
$$= \sqrt{35}$$

Like radicals have the same index and the same radicand (the expression inside the radical).

Like radicals can be added (or subtracted) in the same way as like terms. Apply the distributive law and combine the coefficients.

Certain expressions can be combined after one or more of the terms involving radicals are simplified.

Multiplying and Dividing Radicals [9.4]

Multiplying To multiply radical expressions, use the first property of radicals in the following way:

$$\sqrt{6} \cdot \sqrt{15} = \sqrt{6 \cdot 15} = \sqrt{90}$$
$$= \sqrt{9 \cdot 10}$$
$$= 3\sqrt{10}$$

$$\sqrt{a}\,\sqrt{b} = \sqrt{ab}$$

$$\sqrt{5}(\sqrt{3} + 2\sqrt{5})$$
$$= \sqrt{5} \cdot \sqrt{3} + \sqrt{5} \cdot 2\sqrt{5}$$
$$= \sqrt{15} + 10$$

The distributive property can also be applied in multiplying radical expressions.

$$(\sqrt{5} + 2)(\sqrt{5} - 1)$$
$$= \sqrt{5} \cdot \sqrt{5} - \sqrt{5} + 2\sqrt{5} - 2$$
$$= 3 + \sqrt{5}$$

The FOIL pattern allows us to find the product of binomial radical expressions.

$$(\sqrt{10} + 3)(\sqrt{10} - 3)$$
$$= 10 - 9 = 1$$

$$\frac{\sqrt{50}}{\sqrt{2}} = \sqrt{\frac{50}{2}}$$
$$= \sqrt{25}$$
$$= 5$$

Dividing To divide radical expressions, use the second property of radicals in the following way:

$$\frac{\sqrt{a}}{\sqrt{b}} = \sqrt{\frac{a}{b}}$$

$$\frac{\sqrt{3}}{\sqrt{5}} = \frac{\sqrt{3} \cdot \sqrt{5}}{\sqrt{5} \cdot \sqrt{5}}$$
$$= \frac{\sqrt{15}}{\sqrt{25}} = \frac{\sqrt{15}}{5}$$

When necessary, multiply the numerator and denominator of the expression by the same root to rationalize the denominator.

The Distance Between Two Points [9.5]

The distance between $(2, -3)$ and $(5, -4)$ is

$$d = \sqrt{(5 - 2)^2 + [(-4) - (-3)]^2}$$
$$= \sqrt{3^2 + (-1)^2}$$
$$= \sqrt{9 + 1}$$
$$= \sqrt{10}$$

Given two points (x_1, y_1) and (x_2, y_2), the distance between them can be found using the distance formula

$$d = \sqrt{(x_2 - x_1)^2 + (y_2 - y_1)^2}$$

Summary Exercises

This summary exercise set is provided to give you practice with each of the objectives of the chapter. Each exercise is keyed to the appropriate chapter section. The answers are provided in the *Instructor's Manual.* Your instructor will give you guidelines on how to best use these exercises in your instructional setting.

[9.1] Evaluate if possible.

1. $\sqrt{81}$ **2.** $-\sqrt{49}$ **3.** $\sqrt{-49}$ **4.** $\sqrt[3]{64}$

5. $\sqrt[3]{-64}$ **6.** $\sqrt[4]{81}$ **7.** $\sqrt[4]{-81}$

[9.2] Simplify each of the following radical expressions. Assume that all variables represent positive real numbers.

8. $\sqrt{50}$ **9.** $\sqrt{45}$ **10.** $\sqrt{7a^3}$ **11.** $\sqrt{20x^4}$

12. $\sqrt{49m^5}$ **13.** $\sqrt{200b^3}$ **14.** $\sqrt{147r^3s^2}$ **15.** $\sqrt{108a^2b^5}$

16. $\sqrt{\dfrac{10}{81}}$ **17.** $\sqrt{\dfrac{18x^2}{25}}$ **18.** $\sqrt{\dfrac{12m^5}{49}}$

19. $\sqrt{\dfrac{3}{7}}$ **20.** $\sqrt{\dfrac{3a}{2}}$ **21.** $\sqrt{\dfrac{8x^2}{7}}$

[9.3] Simplify by combining like terms.

22. $\sqrt{3} + 4\sqrt{3}$ **23.** $9\sqrt{5} - 3\sqrt{5}$ **24.** $3\sqrt{2} + 2\sqrt{3}$

25. $3\sqrt{3a} - \sqrt{3a}$ **26.** $7\sqrt{6} - 2\sqrt{6} + \sqrt{6}$ **27.** $5\sqrt{3} + \sqrt{12}$

28. $3\sqrt{18} - 5\sqrt{2}$ **29.** $\sqrt{32} - \sqrt{18}$ **30.** $\sqrt{27} - \sqrt{3} + 2\sqrt{12}$

31. $\sqrt{8} + 2\sqrt{27} - \sqrt{75}$ **32.** $x\sqrt{18} - 3\sqrt{8x^2}$

[9.4]   Simplify each radical expression.

33. $\sqrt{6} \cdot \sqrt{5}$

34. $\sqrt{3} \cdot \sqrt{6}$

35. $\sqrt{3x} \cdot \sqrt{2}$

36. $\sqrt{2} \cdot \sqrt{8} \cdot \sqrt{3}$

37. $\sqrt{5a} \cdot \sqrt{10a}$

38. $\sqrt{2}(\sqrt{3} + \sqrt{5})$

39. $\sqrt{7}(2\sqrt{3} - 3\sqrt{7})$

40. $(\sqrt{3} + 5)(\sqrt{3} - 3)$

41. $(\sqrt{15} - 3)(\sqrt{15} + 3)$

42. $(\sqrt{2} + 3)^2$

43. $\dfrac{\sqrt{7x^3}}{\sqrt{3}}$

44. $\dfrac{18 - \sqrt{20}}{2}$

[9.5]   Find the distance between each pair of points.

45. $(-3, 2)$ and $(-7, 2)$

46. $(2, 0)$ and $(5, 9)$

47. $(-2, 7)$ and $(-5, -1)$

48. $(5, -1)$ and $(-2, 3)$

49. $(-3, 4)$ and $(-2, -5)$

50. $(6, 4)$ and $(-3, 5)$

Self-Test
for Chapter 9

The purpose of this self-test is to help you check your progress and to review for a chapter test in class. Allow yourself about an hour to take the test. When you are done, check your answers in the back of the book. If you missed any answers, be sure to go back and review the appropriate sections in the chapter and the exercises that are provided.

Evaluate if possible.

1. $\sqrt{121}$

2. $\sqrt[3]{27}$

3. $\sqrt{-144}$

4. $-\sqrt[3]{-64}$

Simplify each of the following radical expressions.

5. $\sqrt{75}$

6. $\sqrt{24a^3}$

7. $\sqrt{\dfrac{16}{25}}$

8. $\sqrt{\dfrac{5}{9}}$

Simplify by combining like terms.

9. $2\sqrt{10} - 3\sqrt{10} + 5\sqrt{10}$

10. $3\sqrt{8} - \sqrt{18}$

11. $2\sqrt{50} - \sqrt{8} - \sqrt{50}$

12. $\sqrt{20} + \sqrt{45} - \sqrt{5}$

Simplify each of the following radical expressions.

13. $\sqrt{3x} \cdot \sqrt{6x}$

14. $(\sqrt{5} + 3)(\sqrt{5} + 2)$

15. $\dfrac{\sqrt{7}}{\sqrt{2}}$

16. $\dfrac{14 + 3\sqrt{98}}{7}$

17. $\dfrac{27 - \sqrt{243}}{9}$

ANSWERS

1. _____
2. _____
3. _____
4. _____
5. _____
6. _____
7. _____
8. _____
9. _____
10. _____
11. _____
12. _____
13. _____
14. _____
15. _____
16. _____
17. _____

Find the distance between the two points.

18. $(-3, 7)$ and $(-12, 7)$

19. $(-2, 5)$ and $(-9, -1)$

20. $(-3, -6)$ and $(-1, -2)$

Cumulative Test
for Chapters 1-9

Name

Section   Date

A N S W E R S

1. _____

2. _____

3. _____

4. _____

5. _____

6. _____

7. _____

8. _____

9. _____

10. _____

11. _____

12. _____

13. _____

14. _____

15. _____

This test covers selected topics from the first nine chapters.

Simplify the following expressions.

1. $8x^2y^3 - 5x^3y - 5x^2y^3 + 3x^3y$

2. $(4x^2 - 2x + 7) - (-3x^2 + 4x - 5)$

Evaluate each expression where $x = 2$, $y = -1$, and $z = -4$.

3. $2xyz^2 - 4x^2y^2z$

4. $-2xyz + 2x^2y^2$

Solve the following equations for x.

5. $-3x - 2(4 - 6x) = 10$

6. $5x - 3(4 - 2x) = 6(2x - 3)$

7. Solve the inequality $3x - 11 < 5x - 19$.

Perform the indicated operations.

8. $2x^2y(3x^2 - 5x + 19)$

9. $(5x + 3y)(4x - 7y)$

Factor each of the following completely.

10. $36xy - 27x^3y^2$

11. $8x^2 - 26x + 15$

Perform the indicated operations.

12. $\dfrac{2}{3x + 21} - \dfrac{3}{5x + 35}$

13. $\dfrac{x^2 - x - 6}{x^2 - x - 20} \div \dfrac{x^2 + x - 2}{x^2 + 3x - 4}$

Graph each of the following:

14. $4x + 5y = 20$

15. $5x - 4y \geq 20$

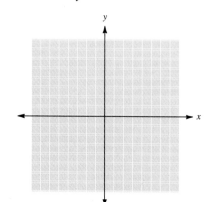

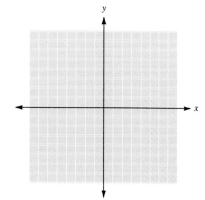

A N S W E R S

16.

17.

18.

19.

20.

21.

22.

23.

24.

25.

26.

27.

28.

29.

30.

16. Find the slope of the line through the points $(2, 9)$ and $(-1, -6)$.

17. Given that the slope of a line is $-\dfrac{3}{2}$ and the y intercept is 5, write the equation of the line.

Solve each of the following systems. If a unique solution does not exist, state whether the system is inconsistent or dependent.

18. $4x - 5y = 20$
$2x + 3y = 10$

19. $4x + 7y = 24$
$8x + 14y = 12$

Solve the following application. Be sure to show the system of equations used for your solution.

20. Amir was able to travel 80 miles (mi) downstream in 5 hours (h). Returning upstream, he took 8 h to make the trip. How fast can he travel in still water, and what was the rate of the current?

Evaluate each root, if possible.

21. $\sqrt{144}$

22. $-\sqrt{144}$

23. $\sqrt{-144}$

24. $\sqrt[3]{-27}$

Simplify each of the following radical expressions by combining like terms.

25. $a\sqrt{20} - 2\sqrt{45a^2}$

26. $\dfrac{\sqrt{8x^3}}{\sqrt{3}}$

27. $\dfrac{12 - \sqrt{72}}{3}$

28. $\sqrt{98x^2}$

29. $\sqrt{150m^3n^2}$

30. $\sqrt{\dfrac{12a^2}{25}}$

INTRODUCTION

Large cities often commission fireworks artists to choreograph elaborate displays on holidays. Such displays look like beautiful paintings in the sky, in which the fireworks seem to dance to well-known popular and classical music. The displays are feats of engineering and very accurate timing. Suppose the designer wants a second set of rockets of a certain color and shape to be released after the first set of a different color and shape reaches a specific height and explodes. She must know the strength of the initial liftoff and use a quadratic equation to determine the proper time for setting off the second round.

The equation $h = -16t^2 + 100t$ gives the height in feet t seconds after the rockets are shot into the air if the initial velocity is 100 feet per second. Using this equation, the designer knows how high the rocket will ascend and when it will begin to fall. She can time the next round to achieve the effect she wishes. Displays that involve large banks of fireworks in shows that last up to an hour are programmed using computers, but quadratic equations are at the heart of the mechanism which creates the beautiful effects.

© Kathy McLaughlin / The Image Works

10.1 Quadratic Equations

We now have more tools for solving quadratic equations. In this section and the next we will be using the ideas of Sections 9.3 and 9.4 to extend our solution techniques.

In Section 5.5 we identified all equations of the form

$$ax^2 + bx + c = 0$$

as quadratic equations in standard form. In that section, we discussed solving these equations whenever the quadratic expression was factorable. In this chapter, we want to extend our equation-solving techniques so that we can find solutions for all such quadratic equations.

Let's first review the factoring method of solution that we introduced in Chapter 5.

• Example 1

Solving Quadratic Equations by Factoring

Solve each quadratic equation by factoring.

(a) $x^2 = -7x - 12$

First, we write the equation in standard form.

Add $7x$ and 12 to both sides of the equation. The equation must be *set equal to 0.*

$$x^2 + 7x + 12 = 0$$

Once the equation is in standard form, we can factor the quadratic member.

$$(x + 3)(x + 4) = 0$$

Finally, using the zero product rule, we solve the equations $x + 3 = 0$ and $x + 4 = 0$ as follows:

These solutions can be checked as before by substitution into the original equation.

$$x = -3 \quad \text{or} \quad x = -4$$

(b) $x^2 = 16$

Again, we write the equation in standard form.

Here we factor the quadratic member of the equation as a difference of squares.

$$x^2 - 16 = 0$$

Factoring, we have

$$(x + 4)(x - 4) = 0$$

Finally, the solutions are

$$x = -4 \quad \text{or} \quad x = 4$$

666

● ● ● **CHECK YOURSELF 1**

Solve each of the following quadratic equations.

a. $x^2 - 4x = 45$ 　　　　　　　　　**b.** $w^2 = 25$

Certain quadratic equations can be solved by other methods, such as the square root method. Let's return to the equation of Example 1(*b*).

Beginning with

$$x^2 = 16$$

we can take the square root of each side, to write

$$\sqrt{x^2} = \sqrt{16}$$

From Section 9.3, we know that this is equivalent to

$$\sqrt{x^2} = 4 \tag{1}$$

or

Recall that by definition
$\sqrt{x^2} = |x|$

$$|x| = 4 \tag{2}$$

Values for x of 4 or -4 will both satisfy equation (2), and so we have the two solutions

$$x = 4 \qquad \text{or} \qquad x = -4$$

We usually write the solutions as

$x = \pm 4$ is simply a convenient "shorthand" for indicating the two solutions, and we generally will go directly to this form.

$$x = \pm 4$$

Let's look at two more equations solved by this method in Example 2.

● Example 2

Solving Equations by the Square Root Method

Solve each of the following equations by the square root method.

(*a*) $x^2 = 9$

By taking the square root of each side, we have

$$x = \pm\sqrt{9}$$

or

$$x = \pm 3$$

(*b*) $x^2 = 5$

Again, we take the square root of each side to write our two solutions as

$$x = \pm\sqrt{5}$$

●●● **CHECK YOURSELF 2**

Solve.

a. $x^2 = 100$ **b.** $t^2 = 15$

You may have to add or subtract on both sides of the equation to write an equation in the form of those in the previous example, as Example 3 illustrates.

● Example 3

Solving Equations by the Square Root Method

Solve $x^2 - 8 = 0$.

First, add 8 to both sides of the equation. We have

$$x^2 = 8$$

Now take the square root of both sides.

$$x = \pm\sqrt{8}$$

Recall that
$$\sqrt{8} = \sqrt{4 \cdot 2}$$
$$= \sqrt{4} \cdot \sqrt{2}$$
$$= 2\sqrt{2}$$

Normally, the solution should be written in the simplest form. In this case we have

$$x = \pm 2\sqrt{2}$$

●●● **CHECK YOURSELF 3**

Solve.

a. $x^2 - 18 = 0$ **b.** $x^2 + 1 = 7$

In the form
$$ax^2 = k$$
a is the coefficient of x^2 and k is some number.

To solve a quadratic equation of the form $ax^2 = k$, divide both sides of the equation by a as the first step. This is shown in Example 4.

● Example 4

Solving Equations by the Square Root Method

Solve $4x^2 = 3$.

Divide both sides of the equation by 4.

$$x^2 = \frac{3}{4}$$

Now take the square root of both sides.

$$x = \pm\sqrt{\frac{3}{4}}$$

Recall that
$$\sqrt{\frac{3}{4}} = \frac{\sqrt{3}}{\sqrt{4}}$$
$$= \frac{\sqrt{3}}{2}$$

Again write your result in the simplest form, so

$$x = \pm\frac{\sqrt{3}}{2}$$

●●● **CHECK YOURSELF 4**

Solve $9x^2 = 5$.

Equations of the form $(x - h)^2 = k$ can also be solved by taking the square root of both sides. Consider Example 5.

●Example 5

Solving Equations by the Square Root Method

Solve $(x - 1)^2 = 6$.
  Again, take the square root of both sides of the equation.

$$x - 1 = \pm\sqrt{6}$$

Now add 1 to both sides of the equation to isolate x.

$$x = 1 \pm \sqrt{6}$$

●●● **CHECK YOURSELF 5**

Solve $(x + 2)^2 = 12$.

Equations of the form $a(x - h)^2 = k$ can also be solved if each side of the equation is divided by a first, as shown in Example 6.

• Example 6

Solving Equations by the Square Root Method

Solve $3(x - 2)^2 = 5$.

$$\sqrt{\frac{5}{3}} = \frac{\sqrt{5}}{\sqrt{3}} \cdot \frac{\sqrt{3}}{\sqrt{3}} = \frac{\sqrt{15}}{3}$$

$$(x - 2)^2 = \frac{5}{3}$$

$$x - 2 = \pm\sqrt{\frac{5}{3}} = \frac{\pm\sqrt{15}}{3}$$

$$x = 2 \pm \frac{\sqrt{15}}{3}$$

$$x = \frac{6}{3} \pm \frac{\sqrt{15}}{3}$$

$$x = \frac{6 \pm \sqrt{15}}{3}$$

● ● ● **CHECK YOURSELF 6**

Solve $5(x + 3)^2 = 2$.

___

What about an equation such as the following?

$$x^2 + 5 = 0$$

If we apply the above methods, we first subtract 5 from both sides, to write

$$x^2 = -5$$

Taking the square root of both sides gives

$$x = \pm\sqrt{-5}$$

But we know there are no square roots of -5 in the real numbers, so this equation has *no real number solutions.* You'll work with this type of equation in your next algebra course.

● ● ● **CHECK YOURSELF ANSWERS**

1. (a) $-5, 9$; **(b)** $-5, 5$.   **2. (a)** ±10; **(b)** $\pm\sqrt{15}$.   **3. (a)** $\pm3\sqrt{2}$; **(b)** $\pm\sqrt{6}$.

4. $\pm\dfrac{\sqrt{5}}{3}$.   **5.** $-2 \pm 2\sqrt{3}$.   **6.** $\dfrac{-15 \pm \sqrt{10}}{5}$.

Solve each of the equations for x.

1. $x^2 = 5$

2. $x^2 = 15$

3. $x^2 = 33$

4. $x^2 = 43$

5. $x^2 - 7 = 0$

6. $x^2 - 13 = 0$

7. $x^2 - 20 = 0$

8. $x^2 = 28$

9. $x^2 = 40$

10. $x^2 - 54 = 0$

11. $x^2 + 3 = 12$

12. $x^2 - 7 = 18$

13. $x^2 + 5 = 8$

14. $x^2 - 4 = 17$

15. $x^2 - 2 = 16$

16. $x^2 + 6 = 30$

17. $9x^2 = 25$

18. $16x^2 = 9$

19. $49x^2 = 11$

20. $16x^2 = 3$

1.
2.
3.
4.
5.
6.
7.
8.
9.
10.
11.
12.
13.
14.
15.
16.
17.
18.
19.
20.

21.

22.

23.

24.

25.

26.

27.

28.

29.

30.

31.

32.

33.

34.

35.

36.

37.

38.

39.

40.

41.

42.

43.

44.

21. $4x^2 = 7$

22. $25x^2 = 13$

23. $(x - 1)^2 = 5$

24. $(x - 3)^2 = 10$

25. $(x + 1)^2 = 12$

26. $(x + 2)^2 = 32$

27. $(x - 3)^2 = 24$

28. $(x - 5)^2 = 27$

29. $(x + 5)^2 = 25$

30. $(x + 2)^2 = 16$

31. $3(x - 5)^2 = 7$

32. $2(x - 5)^2 = 3$

33. $4(x + 5)^2 = 9$

34. $16(x + 2)^2 = 25$

35. $-2(x + 2)^2 = -6$

36. $-5(x + 4)^2 = -10$

37. $-4(x - 2)^2 = -5$

38. $-9(x - 2)^2 = -11$

39. $(5x - 2)^2 = 8$

40. $(3x - 5)^2 = 14$

Solve each equation for x.

41. $x^2 - 2x + 1 = 7$
(*Hint:* Factor the left-hand side.)

42. $x^2 + 4x + 4 = 7$
(*Hint:* Factor the left-hand side.)

43. $(2x + 11)^2 + 9 = 0$

44. $(3x + 14)^2 + 25 = 0$

45. Number problem. The square of a number decreased by 2 is equal to the negative of the number. Find the number.

46. Number problem. The square of 2 more than a number is 64. Find the number.

47. Revenue. The revenue (in dollars) for selling x units of a product is given by

$$R = x\left(5 - \frac{1}{10}x\right) \qquad 0 < x < 25$$

Determine the number of units that must be sold if the revenue is to be $60.

48. Number problem. The square of the sum of a number and 5 is 36. Find the number.

49. In this section, you solved quadratic equations by "extracting roots," taking the square root of both sides after writing one side as the square of a binomial. But what if the algebraic expression cannot be written this way? Work with another student to decide what needs to be added to each expression below to make it a "perfect square trinomial." Label the dimensions of the squares and the area of each section as you did in Section 4.6.

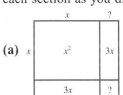

(a)

$$x^2 + 6x + \underline{\quad} = (x + ?)$$

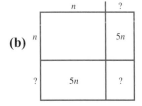

(b)

$$n^2 + 10n + \underline{\quad} = (n + ?)^2$$

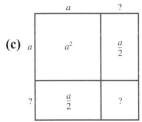

(c)

$$a^2 + a + \underline{\quad} = (a + ?)^2$$

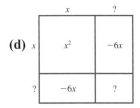

(d)

$$x^2 - 12x + \underline{\quad} = (x - ?)^2$$

(e) $x^2 + 20x + \underline{\quad} = (x + ?)^2$ **(f)** $n^2 - 16n + \underline{\quad} = (n - ?)^2$

45. _____

46. _____

47. _____

48. _____

49. _____

Getting Ready for Section 10.2
[Section 4.7]

Multiply each of the following expressions.

a. $(x + 1)^2$ **b.** $(x + 5)^2$

c. $(x - 2)^2$ **d.** $(x - 7)^2$

e. $(x + 4)^2$ **f.** $(x - 3)^2$

g. $(2x + 5)^2$ **h.** $(2x - 1)^2$

Answers

1. $\pm\sqrt{5}$ **3.** $\pm\sqrt{33}$ **5.** $\pm\sqrt{7}$ **7.** $\pm 2\sqrt{5}$ **9.** $\pm 2\sqrt{10}$

11. ± 3 **13.** $\pm\sqrt{3}$ **15.** $\pm 3\sqrt{2}$ **17.** $\pm\dfrac{5}{3}$ **19.** $\dfrac{\pm\sqrt{11}}{7}$

21. $\dfrac{\pm\sqrt{7}}{2}$ **23.** $1 \pm \sqrt{5}$ **25.** $-1 \pm 2\sqrt{3}$ **27.** $3 \pm 2\sqrt{6}$

29. $-10, 0$ **31.** $\dfrac{15 \pm \sqrt{21}}{3}$ **33.** $\dfrac{-13}{2}, \dfrac{-7}{2}$ **35.** $-2 \pm \sqrt{3}$

37. $\dfrac{4 \pm \sqrt{5}}{2}$ **39.** $\dfrac{2 \pm 2\sqrt{2}}{5}$ **41.** $1 \pm \sqrt{7}$ **43.** No real number

45. $1, -2$ **47.** $30, 20$ **a.** $x^2 + 2x + 1$ **b.** $x^2 + 10x + 25$
c. $x^2 - 4x + 4$ **d.** $x^2 - 14x + 49$ **e.** $x^2 + 8x + 16$ **f.** $x^2 - 6x + 9$
g. $4x^2 + 20x + 25$ **h.** $4x^2 - 4x + 1$

10.2 Solving Quadratic Equations by Completing the Square

10.2 OBJECTIVE

Solve a quadratic equation by completing the square

We can solve a quadratic equation such as

$$x^2 - 2x + 1 = 5$$

very easily if we notice that the expression on the left is a perfect-square trinomial. Factoring, we have

$$(x - 1)^2 = 5$$

so

$$x - 1 = \pm\sqrt{5} \quad \text{or} \quad x = 1 \pm\sqrt{5}$$

The solutions for the original equation are then $1 + \sqrt{5}$ and $1 - \sqrt{5}$.

It is true that every quadratic equation can be written in the form above (with a perfect-square trinomial on the left). That is the basis for the **completing-the-square method** for solving quadratic equations.

First, let's look at two perfect-square trinomials.

$$x^2 + 6x + 9 = (x + 3)^2 \tag{1}$$

$$x^2 - 8x + 16 = (x - 4)^2 \tag{2}$$

There is an important relationship between the coefficient of the middle term (the x term) and the constant.

In equation (1),

$$\left(\frac{1}{2} \cdot 6\right)^2 = 3^2 = 9$$

The x coefficient   The constant

In equation (2),

$$\left[\frac{1}{2}(-8)\right]^2 = (-4)^2 = 16$$

The x coefficient   The constant

It is always true that, in a perfect-square trinomial with a coefficient of 1 for x^2, the square of one-half of the x coefficient is equal to the constant term.

● Example 1

Completing the Square

(a) Find the term that should be added to $x^2 + 4x$ so that the expression is a perfect-square trinomial.

The coefficient of x^2 must be 1 before the added term is found.

To complete the square of $x^2 + 4x$, add the square of one-half of 4 (the x coefficient).

$$x^2 + 4x + \left(\frac{1}{2} \cdot 4\right)^2 \qquad \text{or} \qquad x^2 + 4x + 2^2 \qquad \text{or} \qquad x^2 + 4x + 4$$

The trinomial $x^2 + 4x + 4$ is a perfect square because

$$x^2 + 4x + 4 = (x + 2)^2$$

(*b*) Find the term that should be added to $x^2 - 10x$ so that the expression is a perfect-square trinomial.

To complete the square of $x^2 - 10x$, add the square of one-half of -10 (the x coefficient).

$$x^2 - 10x + \left[\frac{1}{2}(-10)\right]^2 \qquad \text{or} \qquad x^2 - 10x + (-5)^2 \qquad \text{or} \qquad x^2 - 10x + 25$$

Check for yourself, by factoring, that this is a perfect-square trinomial.

● ● ● **CHECK YOURSELF 1**

Complete the square and factor.

a. $x^2 + 2x$ **b.** $x^2 - 12x$

We can now use the above process along with the solution methods of Section 10.1 to solve a quadratic equation.

● Example 2

Solving a Quadratic Equation by Completing the Square

Solve $x^2 + 4x - 2 = 0$ by completing the square.

Add 2 to both sides to remove -2 from the left side.

$$x^2 + 4x = 2$$

We find the term needed to complete the square by squaring one-half of the x coefficient.

$$\left(\frac{1}{2} \cdot 4\right)^2 = 2^2 = 4$$

We now add 4 to both sides of the equation.

This *completes the square* on the left.

$$x^2 + 4x + 4 = 2 + 4$$

Now factor on the left and simplify on the right.

$$(x + 2)^2 = 6$$

Now solving as before, we have

$$x + 2 = \pm\sqrt{6}$$
$$x = -2 \pm \sqrt{6}$$

● ● ● **CHECK YOURSELF 2**

Solve by completing the square.

$$x^2 + 6x - 4 = 0$$

For the completing-the-square method to work, the coefficient of x^2 must be 1. Example 3 illustrates the solution process when the coefficient of x^2 is not equal to 1.

● Example 3

Solving a Quadratic Equation by Completing the Square

Solve $2x^2 - 4x - 5 = 0$ by completing the square.

$$2x^2 - 4x - 5 = 0 \qquad \text{Add 5 to both sides.}$$

$$2x^2 - 4x = 5 \qquad \text{Since the coefficient of } x^2 \text{ is not 1 (here it is 2), divide every term by 2. This will make the new leading coefficient equal to 1.}$$

$$x^2 - 2x = \frac{5}{2}$$

$$x^2 - 2x \boxed{+ 1} = \frac{5}{2} \boxed{+ 1} \qquad \text{Complete the square and solve as before.}$$

$$(x - 1)^2 = \frac{7}{2}$$

$$x - 1 = \pm\sqrt{\frac{7}{2}}$$

$$\sqrt{\frac{7}{2}} = \sqrt{\frac{7}{2}} \cdot \sqrt{\frac{2}{2}} \qquad x - 1 = \pm\frac{\sqrt{14}}{2} \qquad \text{Simplify the radical on the right.}$$

$$= \sqrt{\frac{14}{4}} = \sqrt{\frac{14}{2}}$$

$$x = 1 \pm \frac{\sqrt{14}}{2}$$

or

We have combined the terms on the right with the common denominator of 2.

$$x = \frac{2 \pm \sqrt{14}}{2}$$

● ● ● **CHECK YOURSELF 3**

Solve by completing the square.

$3x^2 - 6x + 2 = 0$

Let's summarize by listing the steps to solve a quadratic equation by completing the square.

Solving a Quadratic Equation by Completing the Square

STEP 1 Write the equation in the form

$$ax^2 + bx = k$$

so that the variable terms are on the left side and the constant is on the right side.

STEP 2 If the coefficient of x^2 is not 1, divide both sides of the equation by that coefficient.

STEP 3 Add the square of one-half the coefficient of x to both sides of the equation.

STEP 4 The left side of the equation is now a perfect-square trinomial. Factor and solve as before.

● ● ● **CHECK YOURSELF ANSWERS**

1. **(a)** $x^2 + 2x + 1 = (x + 1)^2$; **(b)** $x^2 - 12x + 36 = (x - 6)^2$ **2.** $-3 \pm \sqrt{13}$.

3. $\dfrac{3 \pm \sqrt{3}}{3}$.

Determine whether each of the following trinomials is a perfect square.

1. $x^2 - 14x + 49$ **2.** $x^2 + 9x + 16$

3. $x^2 - 18x - 81$ **4.** $x^2 + 10x + 25$

5. $x^2 - 18x + 81$ **6.** $x^2 - 24x + 48$

Find the constant term that should be added to make each of the following expressions a perfect-square trinomial.

7. $x^2 + 6x$ **8.** $x^2 - 8x$

9. $x^2 - 10x$ **10.** $x^2 + 5x$

11. $x^2 + 9x$ **12.** $x^2 - 20x$

Solve each of the following quadratic equations by completing the square.

13. $x^2 + 4x - 12 = 0$ **14.** $x^2 - 6x + 8 = 0$

15. $x^2 - 2x - 5 = 0$ **16.** $x^2 + 4x - 7 = 0$

ANSWERS

1.
2.
3.
4.
5.
6.
7.
8.
9.
10.
11.
12.
13.
14.
15.
16.

17. $x^2 + 3x - 27 = 0$ **18.** $x^2 + 5x - 3 = 0$

19. $x^2 + 6x - 1 = 0$ **20.** $x^2 + 4x - 4 = 0$

21. $x^2 - 5x + 6 = 0$ **22.** $x^2 - 6x - 3 = 0$

23. $x^2 + 6x - 5 = 0$ **24.** $x^2 - 2x = 1$

25. $x^2 = 9x + 5$ **26.** $x^2 = 4 - 7x$

27. $2x^2 - 6x + 1 = 0$ **28.** $2x^2 + 10x + 11 = 0$ **29.** $2x^2 - 4x + 1 = 0$

30. $2x^2 - 8x + 5 = 0$ **31.** $4x^2 - 2x - 1 = 0$ **32.** $3x^2 - x - 2 = 0$

Solve each quadratic equation by completing the square.

33. $3x^2 - 4x + 7x - 9 = 2x^2 + 5x - 4$

34. $-4x^2 - 8x + 4x + 5 = -5x^2 + 2x + 16$

Solve the following problems.

35. Number problem. If the square of 3 more than a number is 9, find the number(s).

36. Number problem. If the square of 2 less than an integer is 16, find the number(s).

37. Revenue. The revenue for selling x units of a product is given by

$$R = x\left(25 - \frac{1}{2}x\right)$$

Find the number of units sold if the revenue is $294.50

38. Number problem. Find two consecutive positive integers such that the sum of their squares is 85.

 Getting Ready for Section 10.3
[Section 2.6]

Evaluate the expression $b^2 - 4ac$ for each set of values.

a. $a = 1, b = 1, c = -3$ **b.** $a = 1, b = -1, c = -1$

c. $a = 1, b = -8, c = -3$ **d.** $a = 1, b = -2, c = -1$

e. $a = -2, b = 4, c = -2$ **f.** $a = 2, b = -3, c = 4$

ANSWERS

1. Yes   **3.** No   **5.** Yes   **7.** 9   **9.** 25   **11.** $\dfrac{81}{4}$ **13.** $-6, 2$

15. $1 \pm \sqrt{6}$ **17.** $\dfrac{-3 \pm 3\sqrt{13}}{2}$ **19.** $-3 \pm \sqrt{10}$ **21.** 2, 3

23. $-3 \pm \sqrt{14}$ **25.** $\dfrac{9 \pm \sqrt{101}}{2}$ **27.** $\dfrac{3 \pm \sqrt{7}}{2}$ **29.** $\dfrac{2 \pm \sqrt{2}}{2}$

31. $\dfrac{1 \pm \sqrt{5}}{4}$ **33.** $1 \pm \sqrt{6}$ **35.** $-6, 0$ **37.** 19, 31   **a.** 13   **b.** 5

c. 76   **d.** 8   **e.** 0   **f.** -23

10.3 The Quadratic Formula

10.3 OBJECTIVE

Solve a quadratic equation by using the quadratic formula

We are now ready to derive and use the **quadratic formula,** which will allow us to solve all quadratic equations. We derive the formula by using the method of completing the square.

To use the quadratic formula, the quadratic equation you want to solve must be in *standard form.* That form is

$$ax^2 + bx + c = 0 \qquad \text{where } a \neq 0$$

• Example 1

Writing Equations in Standard Form

Write each equation in standard form.

(*a*) $2x^2 - 5x + 3 = 0$

The equation is already in standard form.

$$a = 2 \qquad b = -5 \qquad \text{and} \qquad c = 3$$

(*b*) $5x^2 + 3x = 5$

The equation is *not* in standard form. Rewrite it by subtracting 5 from both sides.

$5x^2 + 3x - 5 = 0$ Standard form.

$$a = 5 \qquad b = 3 \qquad \text{and} \qquad c = -5$$

● ● ●   CHECK YOURSELF 1

Rewrite each quadratic in standard form.

a. $x^2 - 3x = 5$ **b.** $3x^2 = 7 - 2x$

Once a quadratic equation is written in standard form, we will be able to find both solutions to the equation. Remember that a solution is a value for *x* that will make the equation true.

What follows is the derivation of the quadratic formula, which can be used to solve quadratic equations.

683

Deriving the Quadratic Formula

Let $ax^2 + bx + c = 0$, where $a \neq 0$.

$ax^2 + bx = -c$ Subtract c from both sides.

$x^2 + \dfrac{b}{a}x = -\dfrac{c}{a}$ Divide both sides by a.

$x^2 + \dfrac{b}{a}x + \dfrac{b^2}{4a^2} = \dfrac{b^2}{4a^2} - \dfrac{c}{a}$ Add $\dfrac{b^2}{4a^2}$ to both sides.

This is the completing-the-square step that makes the left-hand side a perfect square.

$\left(x + \dfrac{b}{2a}\right)^2 = \dfrac{b^2 - 4ac}{4a^2}$ Factor on the left, and add the fractions on the right.

$x + \dfrac{b}{2a} = \pm\sqrt{\dfrac{b^2 - 4ac}{4a^2}}$ Take the square root of both sides.

$x + \dfrac{b}{2a} = \pm\dfrac{\sqrt{b^2 - 4ac}}{2a}$ Simplify the radical on the right.

$x = -\dfrac{b}{2a} \pm \dfrac{\sqrt{b^2 - 4ac}}{2a}$ Subtract $\dfrac{b}{2a}$ from both sides.

$x = \dfrac{-b \pm \sqrt{b^2 - 4ac}}{2a}$ Use the common denominator, $2a$

The Quadratic Formula

Finish the derivation, then separately box the formula.

$x = \dfrac{-b \pm \sqrt{b^2 - 4ac}}{2a}$

Let's use the quadratic formula to solve some equations.

• Example 2

Using the Quadratic Formula to Solve an Equation

The leading coefficient is 1, so $a = 1$.

Solve $x^2 - 5x + 4 = 0$ by formula.

    The equation is in standard form, so first identify a, b, and c.

$x^2 - 5x + 4 = 0$

$a = 1 \qquad b = -5 \qquad c = 4$

We now substitute the values for a, b, and c into the formula.

$$x = \dfrac{-b \pm \sqrt{b^2 - 4ac}}{2a}$$

$$= \dfrac{-(-5) \pm \sqrt{(-5)^2 - 4(1)(4)}}{2(1)}$$

Simplify the expression.

$$= \frac{5 \pm \sqrt{25 - 16}}{2}$$

$$= \frac{5 \pm \sqrt{9}}{2}$$

$$= \frac{5 \pm 3}{2}$$

Now,

Note: These results could also have been found by factoring the original equation. You should check that for yourself.

$$x = \frac{5 + 3}{2} \quad \text{or} \quad x = \frac{5 - 3}{2}$$

$$= 4 \qquad\qquad\qquad = 1$$

The solutions are 4 and 1.

● ● ● CHECK YOURSELF 2

Solve $x^2 - 2x - 8 = 0$ by formula. Check your result by factoring.

The main use of the quadratic formula is to solve equations that *cannot* be factored.

● Example 3

Using the Quadratic Formula to Solve an Equation

Solve $2x^2 = x + 4$ by formula.

First, the equation *must be written* in standard form to find *a, b,* and *c.*

$$2x^2 - x - 4 = 0$$

$$a = 2 \qquad b = -1 \qquad c = -4$$

$$x = \frac{-b \pm \sqrt{b^2 - 4ac}}{2a}$$

Substitute the values for *a, b,* and *c* into the formula.

$$= \frac{-(-1) \pm \sqrt{(-1)^2 - 4(2)(-4)}}{2(2)}$$

$$= \frac{1 \pm \sqrt{1 + 32}}{4}$$

$$= \frac{1 \pm \sqrt{33}}{4}$$

● ● ● CHECK YOURSELF 3

Solve $3x^2 = 3x + 4$ by formula.

•Example 4

Using the Quadratic Formula to Solve an Equation

Solve $x^2 - 2x = 4$ by formula.

In standard form, the equation is

$$x^2 - 2x - 4 = 0$$

$$a = 1 \qquad b = -2 \qquad c = -4$$

Again substitute the values into the quadratic formula.

$$x = \frac{-(-2) \pm \sqrt{(-2)^2 - 4(1)(-4)}}{2(1)}$$

$$= \frac{2 \pm \sqrt{20}}{2}$$

You should always write your solution in simplest form.

Since 20 has a perfect-square factor,

$\sqrt{20} = \sqrt{4 \cdot 5}$

$\quad = 2\sqrt{5}$

Now factor the numerator and divide by the common factor of 2.

$$x = \frac{2 \pm 2\sqrt{5}}{2}$$

$$= \frac{2(1 \pm \sqrt{5})}{2}$$

$$= 1 \pm \sqrt{5}$$

● ● ● CHECK YOURSELF 4

Solve $3x^2 = 2x + 4$ by formula.

Sometimes equations have common factors. Factoring first simplifies these equations, making them easier to solve. This is illustrated in Example 5.

•Example 5

Using the Quadratic Formula to Solve an Equation

Solve $3x^2 - 6x - 3 = 0$ by formula.

Since the equation is in standard form, we could use

$$a = 3 \qquad b = -6 \qquad \text{and} \qquad c = -3$$

in the quadratic formula. There is, however, a better approach.

Note the common factor of 3 in the quadratic member of the original equation. Factoring, we have

$$3(x^2 - 2x - 1) = 0$$

and dividing both sides of the equation by 3 gives

$$x^2 - 2x - 1 = 0$$

Now let $a = 1$, $b = -2$, and $c = -1$. Then

The advantage to this approach is that these values will require much less simplification after we substitute into the quadratic formula.

$$x = \frac{-(-2) \pm \sqrt{(-2)^2 - 4(1)(-1)}}{2 \cdot 1}$$

$$= \frac{2 \pm \sqrt{8}}{2}$$

$$= \frac{2 \pm 2\sqrt{2}}{2}$$

$$= \frac{2(1 \pm \sqrt{2})}{2}$$

$$= 1 \pm \sqrt{2}$$

●●● **CHECK YOURSELF 5**

Solve $4x^2 - 20x = 12$ by formula.

In applications that lead to quadratic equations, you may want to find approximate values for the solutions.

•Example 6

Using the Quadratic Formula to Solve an Equation

Solve $x^2 - 5x + 5 = 0$ by formula, and write your solutions in approximate decimal form.

Substituting $a = 1$, $b = -5$, and $c = 5$ gives

$$x = \frac{-(-5) \pm \sqrt{(-5)^2 - 4(1)(5)}}{2(1)}$$

$$= \frac{5 \pm \sqrt{5}}{2}$$

Use your calculator to find $\sqrt{5} \approx 2.236$, so

$$x \approx \frac{5 + 2.236}{2} \qquad \text{or} \qquad x \approx \frac{5 - 2.236}{2}$$

$$= \frac{7.236}{2} \qquad\qquad = \frac{2.764}{2}$$

$$= 3.618 \qquad\qquad = 1.382$$

● ● ● **CHECK YOURSELF 6**

Solve $x^2 - 3x - 5 = 0$ by formula, and approximate the solutions in decimal form.

You may be wondering whether the quadratic formula can be used to solve all quadratic equations. It can, but not all quadratic equations will have real solutions, as Example 7 shows.

● Example 7

Using the Quadratic Formula to Solve an Equation

Solve $x^2 - 3x = -5$ by formula.

Substituting $a = 1$, $b = -3$, and $c = 5$, we have

Make sure the quadratic equation is in standard form. $x^2 - 3x = -5$ is equivalent to $x^2 - 3x + 5 = 0$.

$$x = \frac{-(-3) \pm \sqrt{(-3)^2 - 4(1)(5)}}{2(1)}$$

$$= \frac{3 \pm \sqrt{-11}}{2}$$

In this case, there are no real number solutions because of the negative number in the radical.

● ● ● **CHECK YOURSELF 7**

Solve $x^2 - 3x = -3$ by formula.

Let's review the steps used for solving equations by the use of the quadratic formula.

Solving Equations with the Quadratic Formula

STEP 1 Rewrite the equation in standard form.

$ax^2 + bx + c = 0$

STEP 2 If a common factor exists, divide both sides of the equation by that common factor.

STEP 3 Identify the coefficients a, b, and c.

STEP 4 Substitute values for a, b, and c into the formula

$$x = \frac{-b \pm \sqrt{b^2 - 4ac}}{2a}$$

STEP 5 Simplify the right side of the expression formed in step 4 to write the solutions for the original equation.

Often, applied problems will lead to quadratic equations that must be solved by the methods of this or the previous section. Example 8 illustrates such an application.

•Example 8

Solving an Application from Geometry

The word "numerically" is used because we cannot compare units of area to units of length.

The perimeter of a square is numerically 6 less than its area. Find the length of one side of the square.

Step 1   You want to find the length of one side of the square.

Step 2   Let x represent the length of one side. A sketch of the problem will help.

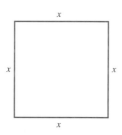

Step 3   The perimeter is $4x$. The area is x^2. So

$4x = x^2 - 6$

The perimeter   The area   "6 less than"

Step 4   Writing the equation in standard form, we solve as before.

$x^2 - 4x - 6 = 0$

The equation has the solutions

$x = 2 + \sqrt{10} \approx 5.162$

We reject the solution of -1.162; a length cannot be negative.

$x = 2 - \sqrt{10} \approx -1.162$

The length of a side is approximately 5.162.

Step 5   If you have a calculator handy, you can easily check this result. Letting x be 5.162, find the perimeter and area to verify (approximately) the result in the original problem.

● ● ●   **CHECK YOURSELF 8**

The perimeter of a square is numerically 2 more than its area. Find the length of one side.

You have now studied four methods for solving quadratic equations:

1. Factoring

2. Extracting square roots

3. Completing the square

4. The quadratic formula

The choice of which method to use depends largely on the equation you want to solve. Factoring is usually easiest and should be tried first.

Extracting roots is used only for equations in the particular form $(x - h)^2 = k$.

Both the completing-the-square method and the quadratic formula are applicable to all quadratic equations and can always be used. Many students seem to find the quadratic formula quicker and easier to apply.

For this reason, it is important that you commit the quadratic formula to memory.

● ● ● **CHECK YOURSELF ANSWERS**

1. **(a)** $x^2 - 3x - 5 = 0$; **(b)** $3x^2 + 2x - 7 = 0$.

2. $x = 4, -2$. **3.** $x = \dfrac{3 \pm \sqrt{57}}{6}$. **4.** $x = \dfrac{1 \pm \sqrt{13}}{3}$.

5. $x = \dfrac{5 \pm \sqrt{37}}{2}$. **6.** $x \approx 4.193$ or -1.193.

7. $\dfrac{3 \pm \sqrt{-3}}{2}$, no real solutions.

8. Approximately 3.414 or 0.586.

Solve each of the following quadratic equations by formula.

1. $x^2 + 9x + 20 = 0$ **2.** $x^2 - 9x + 14 = 0$

3. $x^2 - 4x + 3 = 0$ **4.** $x^2 - 13x + 22 = 0$

5. $3x^2 + 2x - 1 = 0$ **6.** $x^2 - 8x + 16 = 0$

7. $x^2 + 5x = -4$ **8.** $4x^2 + 5x = 6$

9. $x^2 = 6x - 9$ **10.** $2x^2 - 5x = 3$

11. $2x^2 - 3x - 7 = 0$ **12.** $x^2 - 5x + 2 = 0$

13. $x^2 + 2x - 4 = 0$ **14.** $x^2 - 4x + 2 = 0$

15. $2x^2 - 3x = 3$ **16.** $3x^2 - 2x + 1 = 0$

17. $3x^2 - 2x = 6$ **18.** $4x^2 = 4x + 5$

1. _____

2. _____

3. _____

4. _____

5. _____

6. _____

7. _____

8. _____

9. _____

10. _____

11. _____

12. _____

13. _____

14. _____

15. _____

16. _____

17. _____

18. _____

A N S W E R S

19. _____

20. _____

21. _____

22. _____

23. _____

24. _____

25. _____

26. _____

27. _____

28. _____

29. _____

30. _____

31. _____

32. _____

33. _____

34. _____

35. _____

36. _____

37. _____

38. _____

39. _____

40. _____

19. $3x^2 + 3x + 2 = 0$ **20.** $2x^2 - 3x = 6$

21. $5x^2 = 8x - 2$ **22.** $5x^2 - 2 = 2x$

23. $2x^2 - 9 = 4x$ **24.** $3x^2 - 6x = 2$

25. $3x - 5 = \dfrac{1}{x}$ **26.** $x + 3 = \dfrac{1}{x}$

27. $(x - 2)(x + 1) = 3$ **28.** $(x - 3)(x + 2) = 5$

Solve the following quadratic equations by factoring or by any of the techniques of this chapter.

29. $(x - 1)^2 = 7$ **30.** $(2x + 3)^2 = 5$

31. $x^2 - 5x - 14 = 0$ **32.** $3x^2 + 2x - 1 = 0$

33. $6x^2 - 23x + 10 = 0$ **34.** $x^2 + 7x - 18 = 0$

35. $2x^2 - 8x + 3 = 0$ **36.** $x^2 + 2x - 1 = 0$

37. $x^2 - 9x - 4 = 6$ **38.** $5x^2 + 10x + 2 = 2$

39. $4x^2 - 8x + 3 = 5$ **40.** $x^2 + 4x = 21$

Solve the following equations.

41. $\dfrac{3}{x} + \dfrac{5}{x^2} = 9$

42. $\dfrac{8}{x} - \dfrac{3}{x^2} = -6$

43. $\dfrac{x}{x+1} + \dfrac{10x}{x^2+4x+3} = \dfrac{15}{x+3}$

44. $x - \dfrac{9x}{x-2} = \dfrac{-10}{x-2}$

Use your calculator or a table of square roots for the following exercises.

45. Dimensions of a square. The perimeter of a square is numerically 3 less than its area. Find the length of one side.

46. Dimensions of a square. The perimeter of a square is numerically 1 more than its area. Find the length of one side.

47. Width of a picture frame. A picture frame is 15 inches (in.) by 12 in. The area of the picture that shows is 140 in². What is the width of the frame?

48. Width of a garden path. A garden area is 30 feet (ft) long by 20 ft wide. A path of uniform width is set around the edge. If the remaining garden area is 400 ft², what is the width of the path?

49. Solar frames. A solar collector is 2.5 meters (m) long by 2.0 m wide. It is held in place by a frame of uniform width around its outside edge. If the exposed collector area is 2.5 m², what is the width of the frame?

50. Solar frames. A solar collector is 2.5 m long by 2.0 m wide. It is held in place by a frame of uniform width around its outside edge. If the exposed collector is 4 m², what is the width of the frame?

51. The part of the quadratic formula, $b^2 - 4ac$, that is under the radical is called the **discriminant.** Complete the following sentences to show how this value indicates whether there are *no* solutions, *one* solution, or *two* solutions for the quadratic equation.

    (a) When $b^2 - 4ac$ is _____, there are no real number solutions because. . . .
    (b) When $b^2 - 4ac$ is _____, there is one solution because. . . .
    (c) When $b^2 - 4ac$ is _____, there are two solutions because. . . .
    (d) When $b^2 - 4ac$ is _____, there are two *rational* solutions because. . . .
    (e) When $b^2 - 4ac$ is _____, there are two *irrational* solutions because. . . .

41. _____

42. _____

43. _____

44. _____

45. _____

46. _____

47. _____

48. _____

49. _____

50. _____

51. _____

52. _____

53. _____

54. _____

a. _____

b. _____

c. _____

d. _____

e. _____

f. _____

g. _____

h. _____

52. Work with a partner to decide all values of b in the following equations that will give one or more real number solutions.
   (a) $3x^2 +$ ___ $x - 3$
   (b) $5x^2 +$ ___ $x + 1$
   (c) $-3x^2 +$ ___ $x - 3$
   (d) Write a rule for judging if an equation has solutions by looking at it in standard form.

53. Which method of solving a quadratic equation seems simplest to you? Which method do you try first?

54. Complete this statement: "You can tell an equation is quadratic and not linear by. . . ."

Getting Ready for Section 10.4 [Section 9.4]

Find the value of the expression $\sqrt{a^2 + b^2}$ for the following pairs of values. Where necessary, approximate the value by using a calculator.

a. $a = 3, b = 4$ **b.** $a = 5, b = 12$ **c.** $a = 5, b = 8$ **d.** $a = 6, b = 9$

e. $a = 7, b = 8$ **f.** $a = 1, b = 2$ **g.** $a = 7, b = 24$ **h.** $a = 10, b = 15$

ANSWERS

1. $-4, -5$ **3.** $3, 1$ **5.** $-1, \dfrac{1}{3}$ **7.** $-4, -1$ **9.** 3 **11.** $\dfrac{3 \pm \sqrt{65}}{4}$

13. $-1 \pm \sqrt{5}$ **15.** $\dfrac{3 \pm \sqrt{33}}{4}$ **17.** $\dfrac{1 \pm \sqrt{19}}{3}$ **19.** No real solutions

21. $\dfrac{4 \pm \sqrt{6}}{5}$ **23.** $\dfrac{2 \pm \sqrt{22}}{2}$ **25.** $\dfrac{5 \pm \sqrt{37}}{6}$ **27.** $\dfrac{1 \pm \sqrt{21}}{2}$

29. $1 \pm \sqrt{7}$ **31.** $-2, 7$ **33.** $\dfrac{1}{2}, \dfrac{10}{3}$ **35.** $\dfrac{4 \pm \sqrt{10}}{2}$ **37.** $10, -1$

39. $\dfrac{2 \pm \sqrt{6}}{2}$ **41.** $\dfrac{1 \pm \sqrt{21}}{6}$ **43.** 5 **45.** Approximately 4.646

47. Approximately 0.787 in. **49.** ≈ 32.5 cm **a.** 5 **b.** 13 **c.** 9.434
d. 10.817 **e.** 10.630 **f.** 2.236 **g.** 25 **h.** 18.028

Graphing Quadratic Equations

10.4 OBJECTIVE

Graph a quadratic equation of the form
$ax^2 + bx + c = 0$

In Section 7.3 you learned to graph first-degree equations. Similar methods will allow you to graph quadratic equations of the form

$$y = ax^2 + bx + c \qquad a \neq 0$$

The first thing you will notice is that the graph of an equation in this form is not a straight line. The graph is always the curve called a **parabola.**

Here are some examples:

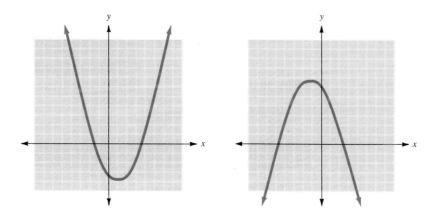

To graph quadratic equations, start by finding solutions for the equation. We begin by completing a table of values. This is done by choosing any convenient values for x. Then use the given equation to compute the corresponding values for y, as Example 1 illustrates.

• Example 1

Completing a Table of Values

If $y = x^2$, complete the ordered pairs to form solutions. Then show these results in a table of values.

$(-2,), (-1,), (0,), (1,), (2,)$

For example, to complete the pair $(-2,)$, substitute -2 for x in the given equation.

$$y = (-2)^2 = 4$$

So $(-2, 4)$ is a solution.

Substituting the other values for x in the same manner, we have the following table of values for $y = x^2$:

Remember that a solution is a pair of values that make the equation a true statement.

x	y
-2	4
-1	1
0	0
1	1
2	4

● ● ● **CHECK YOURSELF 1**

If $y = x^2 + 2$, complete the ordered pairs to form solutions and form a table of values.

$(-2, \ ), (-1, \ ), (0, \ ), (1, \ ), (2, \ )$

We can now plot points in the cartesian coordinate system that correspond to solutions to the equation.

●Example 2

Plotting Some Solution Points

Plot the points from the table of values corresponding to $y = x^2$ from Example 1.

x	y
-2	4
-1	1
0	0
1	1
2	4

Notice that the y axis acts as a mirror. Do you see that any point graphed in Quadrant I will be "reflected" in Quadrant II?

● ● ● CHECK YOURSELF 2

Plot the points from the table of values formed in Check Yourself 1.

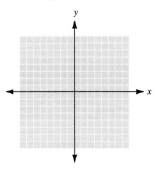

The graph of the equation can be drawn by joining the points with a smooth curve.

● Example 3

Completing the Graph of the Solution Set

Draw the graph of $y = x^2$.

  We can now draw a smooth curve between the points found in Example 2 to form the graph of $y = x^2$.

As we mentioned earlier, the graph must be the curve called a parabola.

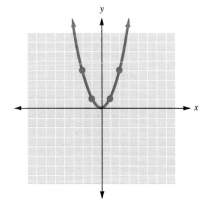

Notice that a parabola *does* **not** come to a point.

● ● ● CHECK YOURSELF 3

Draw a smooth curve between the points plotted in the Check Yourself 2 exercise.

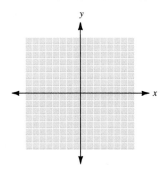

You can use any convenient values for x in forming your table of values. You should use as many pairs as are necessary to get the correct shape of the graph (a parabola).

• Example 4

Graphing the Solution Set

Graph $y = x^2 - 2x$. Use values of x between -1 and 3.

First, determine solutions for the equation. For instance, if $x = -1$,

$$y = (-1)^2 - 2(-1)$$
$$= 1 + 2$$
$$= 3$$

then $(-1, 3)$ is a solution for the given equation.

Substituting the other values for x, we can form the table of values shown below. We then plot the corresponding points and draw a smooth curve to form our graph.

Any values can be substituted for x in the original equation.

x	y
-1	3
0	0
1	-1
2	0
3	3

The graph of $y = x^2 - 2x$.

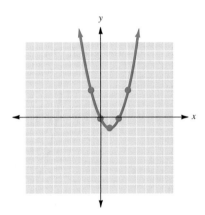

● ● ● CHECK YOURSELF 4

Graph $y = x^2 + 4x$. Use values of x between -4 and 0.

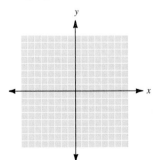

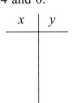

x	y

Choosing values for x is also a valid method of graphing a quadratic equation that contains a constant term.

•Example 5

Graphing the Solution Set

Graph $y = x^2 - x - 2$. Use values of x between -2 and 3. We'll show the computation for two of the solutions.

If $x = -2$:	If $x = 3$:
$y = (-2)^2 - (-2) - 2$	$y = 3^2 - 3 - 2$
$\quad = 4 + 2 - 2$	$\quad = 9 - 3 - 2$
$\quad = 4$	$\quad = 4$

You should substitute the remaining values for x into the given equation to verify the other solutions shown in the table of values below.

x	y
-2	4
-1	0
0	-2
1	-2
2	0
3	4

The graph of $y = x^2 - x - 2$.

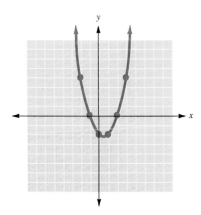

●●● **CHECK YOURSELF 5**

Graph $y = x^2 - 4x + 3$. Use values of x between -1 and 4.

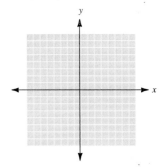

x	y

In Example 6, the graph looks significantly different from previous graphs.

•Example 6

Graphing the Solution Set

Graph $y = -x^2 + 3$. Use x values between -2 and 2.
Again we'll show two computations.

If $x = -2$:

If $x = 1$:

Note: $-(-2)^2 = -4$

$$y = -(-2)^2 + 3$$
$$= -4 + 3$$
$$= -1$$

$$y = -(1)^2 + 3$$
$$= -1 + 3$$
$$= 2$$

Verify the remainder of the solutions shown in the table of values below for yourself.

x	y
-2	-1
-1	2
0	3
1	2
2	-1

The graph of $y = -x^2 + 3$.

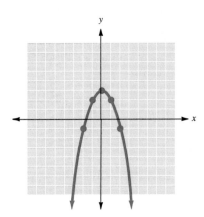

There is an important difference between this graph and the others we have seen. This time the parabola opens downward! Can you guess why? The answer is in the coefficient of the x^2 term.

If the coefficient of x^2 is *positive,* the parabola opens *upward.*

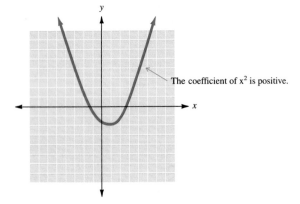

The coefficient of x^2 is positive.

If the coefficient of x^2 is *negative,* the parabola opens *downward.*

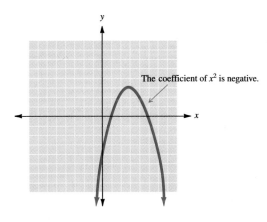

The coefficient of x^2 is negative.

●●● **CHECK YOURSELF 6**

Graph $y = -x^2 - 2x$. Use x values between -3 and 1.

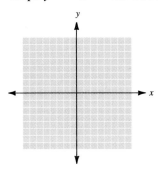

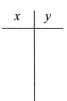

x	y

There are two other terms we would like to introduce before closing this section on graphing quadratic equations. As you may have noticed, all the parabolas that we graphed are symmetric about a vertical line. This is called the **axis of symmetry** for the parabola.

The point at which the parabola intersects that vertical line (this will be the lowest—or the highest—point on the parabola) is called the **vertex.** You'll learn more about finding the axis of symmetry and the vertex of a parabola in your next course in algebra.

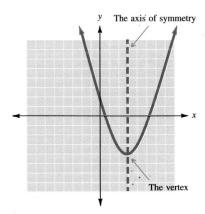

The axis of symmetry

The vertex

●●● CHECK YOURSELF ANSWERS

1.

x	y
−2	6
−1	3
0	2
1	3
2	6

2.

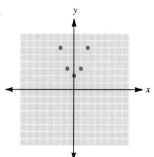

3. $y = x^2 + 2$

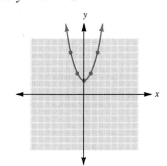

4. $y = x^2 + 4x$

x	y
−4	0
−3	−3
−2	−4
−1	−3
0	0

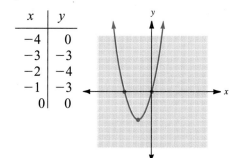

5. $y = x^2 - 4x + 3$

x	y
−1	8
0	3
1	0
2	−1
3	0
4	3

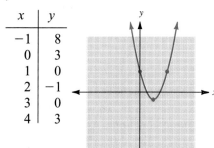

6. $y = -x^2 - 2x$

x	y
−3	−3
−2	0
−1	1
0	0
1	−3

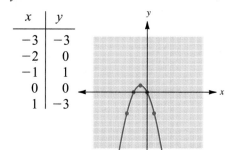

Name

Section   Date

Graph each of the following quadratic equations after completing the given table of values.

1. $y = x^2 + 1$

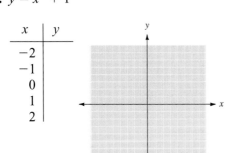

x	y
-2	
-1	
0	
1	
2	

2. $y = x^2 - 2$

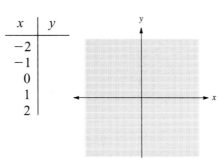

x	y
-2	
-1	
0	
1	
2	

3. $y = x^2 - 4$

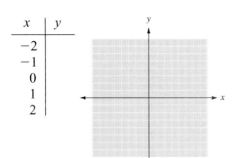

x	y
-2	
-1	
0	
1	
2	

4. $y = x^2 + 3$

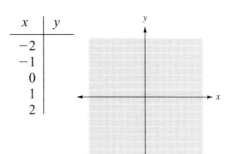

x	y
-2	
-1	
0	
1	
2	

5. $y = x^2 - 4x$

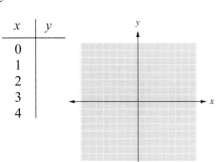

x	y
0	
1	
2	
3	
4	

6. $y = x^2 + 2x$

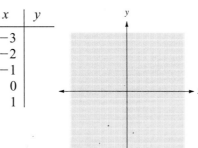

x	y
-3	
-2	
-1	
0	
1	

7. $y = x^2 + x$

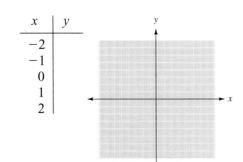

x	y
-2	
-1	
0	
1	
2	

8. $y = x^2 - 3x$

x	y
-1	
0	
1	
2	
3	

9. $y = x^2 - 2x - 3$

x	y
−1	
0	
1	
2	
3	

10. $y = x^2 - 5x + 6$

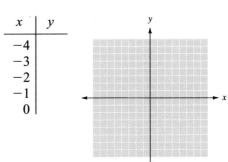

x	y
0	
1	
2	
3	
4	

11. $y = x^2 - x - 6$

x	y
−1	
0	
1	
2	
3	

12. $y = x^2 + 3x - 4$

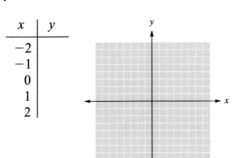

x	y
−4	
−3	
−2	
−1	
0	

13. $y = -x^2 + 2$

x	y
−2	
−1	
0	
1	
2	

14. $y = -x^2 - 2$

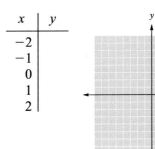

x	y
−2	
−1	
0	
1	
2	

15. $y = -x^2 - 4x$

x	y
−4	
−3	
−2	
−1	
0	

16. $y = -x^2 + 2x$

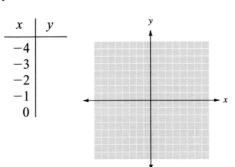

x	y
−1	
0	
1	
2	
3	

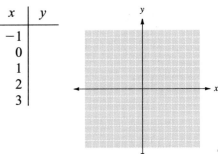

Match each graph with the correct equation on the right.

17.

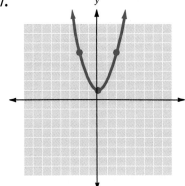

18.

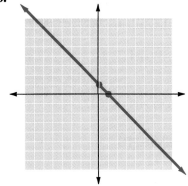

19.

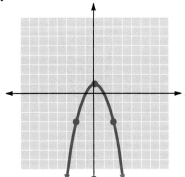

20.

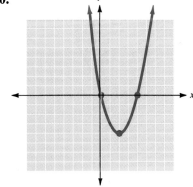

21.

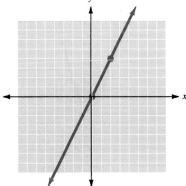

22.

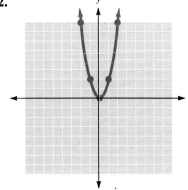

23.

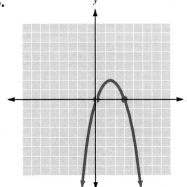

24.

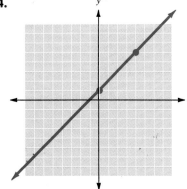

A N S W E R S

17. _____

18. _____

19. _____

20. _____

21. _____

22. _____

23. _____

24. _____

(a) $y = -x^2 + 1$

(b) $y = 2x$

(c) $y = x^2 - 4x$

(d) $y = -x + 1$

(e) $y = -x^2 + 3x$

(f) $y = x^2 + 1$

(g) $y = x + 1$

(h) $y = 2x^2$

Getting Ready for Section 10.5
[Section 9.5]

Find the distance between the two points.

a. $(0, 3)$ and $(7, 3)$ **b.** $(2, 7)$ and $(2, -3)$ **c.** $(-3, -4)$ and $(0, 0)$

d. $(0, 0)$ and $(5, -12)$ **e.** $(2, -4)$ and $(-4, 4)$

ANSWERS

1. $y = x^2 + 1$

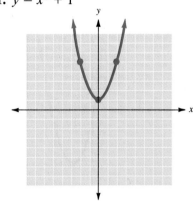

3. $y = x^2 - 4$

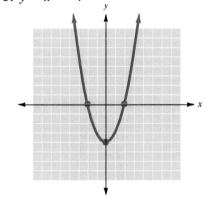

5. $y = x^2 - 4x$

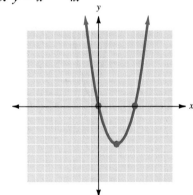

7. $y = x^2 + x$

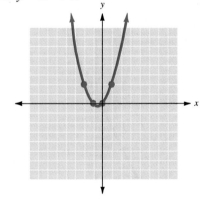

9. $y = x^2 - 2x - 3$

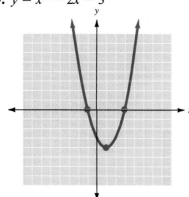

11. $y = x^2 - x - 6$

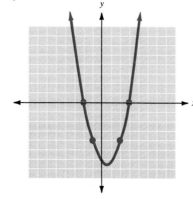

13. $y = -x^2 + 2$

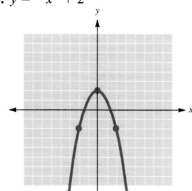

15. $y = -x^2 - 4x$

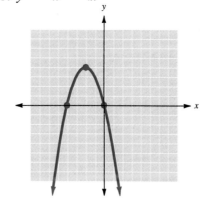

17. f **19.** a **21.** b **23.** e

a. 7   **b.** 10   **c.** 5   **d.** 13   **e.** 10

Applications of The Pythagorean Theorem

10.5 OBJECTIVE

Apply the Pythagorean theorem in solving problems

One very important application of our work with quadratic equations is the **Pythagorean theorem.** (You may recall that in Chapter 9 we used this theorem to find the distance between two points.) The theorem was named for the Greek mathematician Pythagoras, born in 572 B.C. Pythagoras was the founder of the Greek society the Pythagoreans. Although the theorem bears Pythagoras' name, his own work on this theorem is uncertain as the Pythagoreans credited new discoveries to their founder.

The Pythagorean Theorem

For every right triangle, the square of the length of the hypotenuse is equal to the sum of the squares of the lengths of the legs.

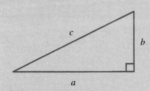

$$c^2 = a^2 + b^2$$

● Example 1

Verifying the Pythagorean Theorem

Verify the Pythagorean theorem for the given triangles.

(*a*) For the right triangle below,

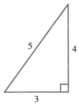

$$5^2 \stackrel{?}{=} 3^2 + 4^2$$
$$25 \stackrel{?}{=} 9 + 16$$
$$25 = 25$$

(*b*) For the right triangle below,

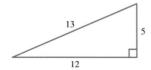

$$13^2 \stackrel{?}{=} 12^2 + 5^2$$
$$169 \stackrel{?}{=} 144 + 25$$
$$169 = 169$$

● ● ● **CHECK YOURSELF 1**

Verify the Pythagorean theorem for the right triangle shown.

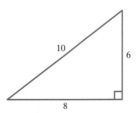

The Pythagorean theorem can be used to find the length of one side of a right triangle when the lengths of the two other sides are known.

●**Example 2**

Solving for the Length of the Hypotenuse

Find length x.

Note x will be longer than the given sides since it is the hypotenuse.

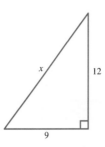

$$x^2 = 9^2 + 12^2$$
$$= 81 + 144$$
$$= 225$$

so

$$x = 15 \qquad \text{or} \qquad \underbrace{x = -15}$$

We reject this solution because a length must be positive.

● ● ● **CHECK YOURSELF 2**

Find length x.

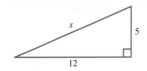

Sometimes, one or more of the lengths of the sides may be represented by an irrational number.

● Example 3

Solving for the Length of the Leg

Find length x.

Note: You can approximate $3\sqrt{3}$ (or $\sqrt{27}$) with the use of a calculator or by the table in Appendix 2.

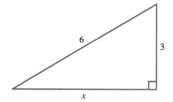

$$3^2 + x^2 = 6^2$$
$$9 + x^2 = 36$$
$$x^2 = 27$$
$$x = \pm\sqrt{27}$$

but distance cannot be negative, so

$$x = \sqrt{27} \quad \text{or} \quad x = 3\sqrt{3}$$

So x is approximately 5.2.

CHECK YOURSELF 3

Find length x.

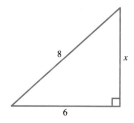

The Pythagorean theorem can be applied to solve a variety of geometric problems.

● Example 4

Solving for the Length of the Diagonal

Find the length of the diagonal of a rectangle which is 8 centimeters (cm) long and 5 cm wide. Let x be the unknown length of the diagonal:

Always draw and label a sketch showing the information from a problem when geometric figures are involved.

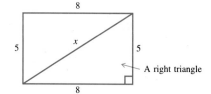

A right triangle

So

Again, distance cannot be negative, so we eliminate $x = -\sqrt{89}$.

$$x^2 = 5^2 + 8^2$$
$$= 25 + 64$$
$$= 89$$
$$x = \sqrt{89}$$

Thus

$$x \approx 9.4 \text{ cm}$$

● ● ● CHECK YOURSELF 4

The diagonal of a rectangle is 12 inches (in.) and its width is 6 in. Find its length.

The next application makes use of the Pythagorean theorem in obtaining the final solution.

● Example 5

Solving an Application

How long must a guywire be to reach from the top of a 30-foot (ft) pole to a point on the ground 20 ft from the base of the pole?

Again be sure to draw a sketch of the problem.

Always check to see if your final answer is reasonable.

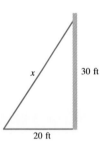

$$x^2 = 20^2 + 30^2$$
$$= 400 + 900$$
$$= 1300$$
$$x = \sqrt{1300}$$
$$= 10\sqrt{13}$$
$$\approx 36 \text{ ft}$$

● ● ● CHECK YOURSELF 5

A 16-ft ladder leans against a wall with its base 4 ft from the wall. How far off the floor is the top of the ladder?

In Example 6, one of the legs is the missing part of the triangle.

• Example 6

Solving an Application

The length of one leg of a right triangle is 2 cm more than the other. If the length of the hypotenuse is 6 cm, what are the lengths of the two legs?

Draw a sketch of the problem, labeling the known and unknown lengths. Here, if one leg is represented by *x,* the other must be represented by *x* + 2.

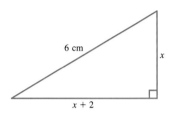

Use the Pythagorean theorem to form an equation.

The sum of the squares of the lengths of the unknown legs is equal to the square of the length of the hypotenuse.

$$x^2 + (x + 2)^2 = 6^2$$
$$x^2 + x^2 + 4x + 4 = 36$$
$$2x^2 + 4x - 32 = 0 \quad \left\{ \begin{array}{l} \text{Divide both} \\ \text{sides by 2.} \end{array} \right.$$
$$x^2 + 2x - 16 = 0$$

We apply the quadratic formula as before:

$$x = \frac{-2 \pm \sqrt{2^2 - 4(1)(-16)}}{2(1)}$$
$$= -1 \pm \sqrt{17}$$

Now,

$$x = -1 + \sqrt{17} \qquad \text{or} \qquad x = -1 - \sqrt{17}$$
$$\approx 3.123 \qquad\qquad\qquad \approx -5.123$$

Always reject the negative solution in a geometric problem.

Be sure to include the units with the final answer.

If $x \approx 3.123$, then $x + 2 \approx 5.123$. The lengths of the legs are approximately 3.123 and 5.123 cm.

● ● ● **CHECK YOURSELF 6**

The length of one leg of a right triangle is 1 in. more than the other. If the length of the hypotenuse is 3 in., what are the lengths of the legs?

● ● ● **CHECK YOURSELF ANSWERS**

1. $10^2 \overset{?}{=} 8^2 + 6^2$; $100 \overset{?}{=} 64 + 36$; $100 = 100$. **2.** 13. **3.** $2\sqrt{7}$; or approximately 5.3. **4.** Length: $6\sqrt{3}$ in. or approximately 10.4 in. **5.** The height is approximately 15.5 ft. **6.** Approximately 1.561 and 2.561 in.

Find the length *x* in each triangle.

1.

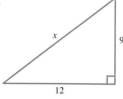

2.

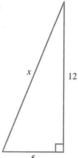

3.

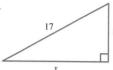

4.

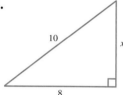

5.

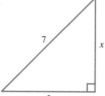

6.

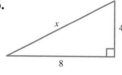

7. Length of a diagonal. Find the length of the diagonal of a rectangle with a length of 10 centimeters (cm) and a width of 7 cm.

8. Length of a diagonal. Find the length of the diagonal of a rectangle with 5 inches (in.) width and 7 in. length.

9. Width of a rectangle. Find the width of a rectangle whose diagonal is 12 feet (ft) and whose length is 10 ft.

10. Length of a rectangle. Find the length of a rectangle whose diagonal is 9 in. and whose width is 6 in.

11. Length of a wire. How long must a guywire be to run from the top of a 20-ft pole to a point on the ground 8 ft from the base of the pole?

12. Height of a ladder. The base of a 15-ft ladder is 5 ft away from a wall. How high from the floor is the top of the ladder?

13. Dimensions of a triangle. The length of one leg of a right triangle is 3 in. more than the other. If the length of the hypotenuse is 8 in., what are the lengths of the two legs?

715

A N S W E R S

14.

15.

16.

17.

18.

19.

20.

14. **Dimensions of a rectangle.** The length of a rectangle is 1 cm longer than its width. If the diagonal of the rectangle is 4 cm, what are the dimensions (the length and width) of the rectangle?

Find the altitude of each triangle.

15.

16.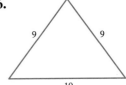

17. **Length of insulation.** A homeowner wishes to insulate her attic with fiberglass insulation in order to conserve energy. The insulation comes in 40-cm-wide rolls that are cut to fit between the rafters in the attic. If the roof is 6 meters (m) from peak to eave and the attic space is 2 m high at the peak, how long does each of the pieces of insulation need to be?

18. **Length of insulation.** For the home described in Exercise 17, if the roof is 7 m from peak to eave and the attic space is 3 m high at the peak, how long does each of the pieces of insulation need to be?

19. **Base of a triangle.** A solar collector and its stand are in the shape of a right triangle. The collector is 5.00 m long, the upright leg is 3.00 m long, and the base leg is 4.00 m long. Due to inefficiencies in the collector's position, it needs to be raised by 0.50 m on the upright leg. How long will the new base leg be?

20. **Base of a triangle.** A solar collector and its stand are in the shape of a right triangle. The collector is 5.00 m long, the upright leg is 3.00 m long, and the base leg is 4.00 m long. Due to inefficiencies in the collector's position, it needs to be lowered by 0.50 m on the upright leg. How long will the new base leg be?

ANSWERS

1. 15   **3.** 15   **5.** $2\sqrt{6}$ **7.** ≈ 12.207 cm   **9.** ≈ 6.633 ft

11. ≈ 21.541 ft   **13.** ≈ 3.954 in, 6.954 in   **15.** 4   **17.** $4\sqrt{2} \approx 5.7$ m

19. ≈ 3.6 m

Solving Quadratic Equations [10.1–10.3]

Solving Equations of the Form $ax^2 = k$

Solve $4x^2 = 13$.

$$x^2 = \frac{13}{4}$$

$$x = \sqrt{\frac{13}{4}} \text{ or } -\sqrt{\frac{13}{4}}$$

Simplifying gives

$$x = \frac{\sqrt{13}}{2} \text{ or } -\frac{\sqrt{13}}{2}$$

Divide both sides of the equation by a. The equation can then be solved by taking the square root of both sides.

$$x^2 = \frac{k}{a}$$

$$x = \sqrt{\frac{k}{a}} \qquad \text{or} \qquad x = -\sqrt{\frac{k}{a}}$$

Completing the Square To solve a quadratic equation by completing the square:

To solve:

$$2x^2 + 2x - 1 = 0$$

$$2x^2 + 2x = 1$$

$$x^2 + x = \frac{1}{2}$$

$$x^2 + x + \left(\frac{1}{2}\right)^2 = \frac{1}{2} + \left(\frac{1}{2}\right)^2$$

$$\left(x + \frac{1}{2}\right)^2 = \frac{3}{4}$$

$$x + \frac{1}{2} = \pm\sqrt{\frac{3}{4}} = \pm\frac{\sqrt{3}}{2}$$

$$x = \frac{-1 \pm \sqrt{3}}{2}$$

1. Write the equation in the form

$$ax^2 + bx = k$$

so that the variable terms are on the left side and the constant is on the right side.

2. If the leading coefficient (of x^2) is not 1, divide both sides by that coefficient.

3. Add the square of one-half the middle (x) coefficient to both sides of the equation.

4. The left side of the equation is now a perfect-square trinomial. Factor and solve as before.

To solve:

$$x^2 - 2x = 4$$

Write the equation as

$$x^2 - 2x - 4 = 0$$

$$a = 1 \quad b = -2 \quad c = -4$$

$$x =$$

$$\frac{-(-2) \pm \sqrt{(-2)^2 - 4(1)(-4)}}{2(1)}$$

$$= \frac{2 \pm \sqrt{20}}{2}$$

$$= \frac{2 \pm 2\sqrt{5}}{2} = \frac{2(1 \pm \sqrt{5})}{2}$$

$$= 1 \pm \sqrt{5}$$

The Quadratic Formula To solve an equation by formula:

1. Rewrite the equation in standard form.

$$ax^2 + bx + c = 0$$

2. If a common factor exists, divide both sides of the equation by that common factor.

3. Identify the coefficients a, b, and c.

4. Substitute the values for a, b, and c into the quadratic formula.

$$x = \frac{-b \pm \sqrt{b^2 - 4ac}}{2a}$$

5. Simplify the right side of the expression formed in step 4 to write the solutions for the original equation.

Graphing Quadratic Equations [10.4]

To graph equations of the form

$$y = ax^2 + bx + c$$

1. Form a table of values by choosing convenient values for x and finding the corresponding values for y.
2. Plot the points from the table of values.
3. Draw a smooth curve between the points.

The graph of a quadratic equation will always be a parabola. The parabola opens upward if a, the coefficient of the x^2 term, is positive.

$$y = x^2 - 4x$$

x	y
-1	5
0	0
1	-3
2	-4
3	-3
4	0
5	5

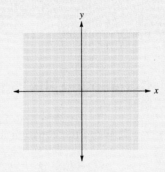

The parabola opens downward if a, the coefficient of the x^2 term, is negative.

$$y = -x^2 + 2x$$

x	y
-1	-3
0	0
1	1
2	0
3	-3

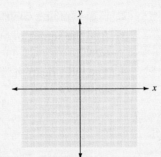

The Pythagorean Theorem [10.5]

Find length x:

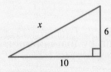

$x^2 = 10^2 + 6^2$

$\quad = 100 + 36$

$\quad = 136$

$x = \sqrt{136}$ or $2\sqrt{34}$

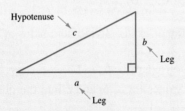

In words, given a right triangle, the square of the length of the hypotenuse is equal to the sum of the squares of the lengths of the legs.

Summary Exercises

This summary exercise set is provided to give you practice with each of the objectives of the chapter. Each exercise is keyed to the appropriate chapter section. The answers are provided in the *Instructor's Manual.* Your instructor will give you guidelines on how to best use these exercises in your instructional setting.

[10.1]   Solve each of the following equations for x by the square root method.

1. $x^2 = 10$

2. $x^2 = 48$

3. $x^2 - 20 = 0$

4. $x^2 + 2 = 8$

5. $(x - 1)^2 = 5$

6. $(x + 2)^2 = 8$

7. $(x + 3)^2 = 5$

8. $64x^2 = 25$

9. $4x^2 = 27$

10. $9x^2 = 20$

11. $25x^2 = 7$

12. $7x^2 = 3$

[10.2]   Solve each of the following equations by completing the square.

13. $x^2 - 3x - 10 = 0$

14. $x^2 - 8x + 15 = 0$

15. $x^2 - 5x + 2 = 0$

16. $x^2 - 2x - 2 = 0$

17. $x^2 - 4x - 4 = 0$

18. $x^2 + 3x = 7$

19. $x^2 - 4x = -2$

20. $x^2 + 3x = 5$

21. $x^2 - x = 7$

22. $2x^2 + 6x = 12$

23. $2x^2 - 4x - 7 = 0$

24. $3x^2 + 5x + 1 = 0$

[10.3]   Solve each of the following equations by using the quadratic formula.

25. $x^2 - 5x - 14 = 0$

26. $x^2 - 8x + 16 = 0$

27. $x^2 + 5x - 3 = 0$

28. $x^2 - 7x - 1 = 0$

29. $x^2 - 6x + 1 = 0$

30. $x^2 - 3x + 5 = 0$

31. $3x^2 - 4x = 2$

32. $2x - 3 = \dfrac{3}{x}$

33. $(x - 1)(x + 4) = 3$

34. $x^2 - 5x + 7 = 5$

35. $2x^2 - 8x = 12$

36. $5x^2 = 15 - 15x$

Solve by factoring or by any of the methods of this chapter.

37. $5x^2 = 3x$

38. $(2x - 3)(x + 5) = -11$

39. $(x - 1)^2 = 10$

40. $2x^2 = 7$

41. $2x^2 = 5x + 4$

42. $2x^2 - 4x = 30$

43. $2x^2 = 5x + 7$

44. $3x^2 - 4x = 2$

45. $3x^2 + 6x - 15 = 0$

46. $x^2 - 3x = 2(x + 5)$

47. $x - 2 = \dfrac{2}{x}$

48. The perimeter of a square is numerically 2 less than its area. Find the length of one side. (Approximate your answer to three decimal places, using a calculator or a table of square roots.)

[10.4] Graph each quadratic equation after completing the table of values.

49. $y = x^2 + 3$

x	y
-2	
-1	
0	
1	
2	

50. $y = x^2 - 2$

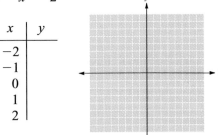

x	y
-2	
-1	
0	
1	
2	

51. $y = x^2 - 3x$

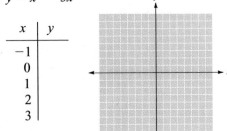

x	y
-1	
0	
1	
2	
3	

52. $y = x^2 + 4x$

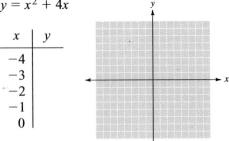

x	y
-4	
-3	
-2	
-1	
0	

53. $y = x^2 - x - 2$

x	y
-1	
0	
1	
2	
3	

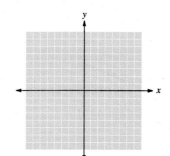

54. $y = x^2 - 4x + 3$

x	y
0	
1	
2	
3	
4	

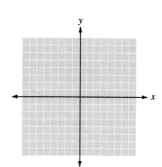

55. $y = x^2 + 2x - 3$

x	y
-3	
-2	
-1	
0	
1	

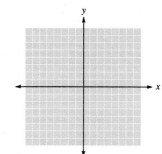

56. $y = 2x^2$

x	y
-2	
-1	
0	
1	
2	

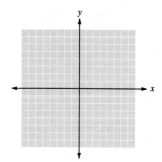

57. $y = 2x^2 - 3$

x	y
-2	
-1	
0	
1	
2	

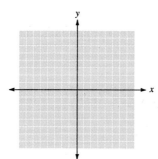

58. $y = -x^2 + 3$

x	y
-2	
-1	
0	
1	
2	

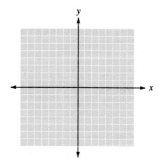

59. $y = -x^2 - 2$

x	y
-2	
-1	
0	
1	
2	

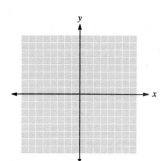

60. $y = -x^2 + 4x$

x	y
0	
1	
2	
3	
4	

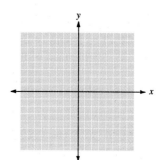

[10.5]   Find length x in each triangle.

61.

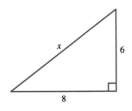

62.

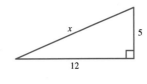

63.

64.

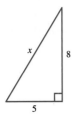

65.

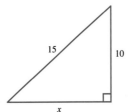

66.

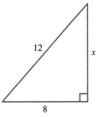

[10.5]   Solve each of the following word problems. Approximate your answer to one decimal place where necessary.

67. Find the length of the diagonal of a rectangle whose length is 12 inches (in.) and whose width is 9 in.

68. Find the length of a rectangle whose diagonal has a length of 10 centimeters (cm) and whose width is 5 cm.

69. How long must a guywire be to run from the top of an 18-foot (ft) pole to a point on level ground 16 ft away from the base of the pole?

70. The length of one leg of a right triangle is 1 in. more than the length of the other. If the length of the hypotenuse of the triangle is 6 in., what are the lengths of the two legs?

A N S W E R S

1.

2.

3.

4.

5.

6.

7.

8.

9.

10.

11.

12.

13.

14.

15.

16.

The purpose of this self-test is to help you check your progress and to review for a chapter test in class. Allow yourself about an hour to take the test. When you are done, check your answers in the back of the book. If you missed any problems, be sure to go back and review the appropriate sections in the chapter and the exercises that are provided.

Solve each of the following equations for x.

1. $x^2 = 15$

2. $x^2 - 8 = 0$

3. $(x - 1)^2 = 7$

4. $9x^2 = 10$

Solve each of the following equations by completing the square.

5. $x^2 - 2x - 8 = 0$

6. $x^2 + 3x - 1 = 0$

7. $x^2 + 2x - 5 = 0$

8. $2x^2 - 5x + 1 = 0$

Solve each of the following equations by using the quadratic formula.

9. $x^2 - 2x - 3 = 0$

10. $x^2 - 6x + 9 = 0$

11. $x^2 - 5x = 2$

12. $2x^2 = 2x + 5$

13. $2x - 1 = \dfrac{4}{x}$

14. $(x - 1)(x + 3) = 2$

Graph each quadratic equation after completing the given table of values.

15. $y = x^2 + 4$

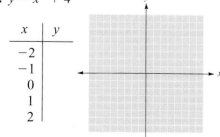

x	y
-2	
-1	
0	
1	
2	

16. $y = x^2 - 2x$

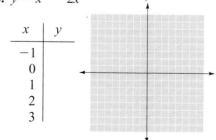

x	y
-1	
0	
1	
2	
3	

17. $y = x^2 - 3$

x	y
-2	
-1	
0	
1	
2	

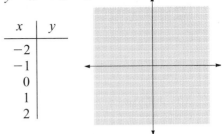

18. $y = x^2 + x - 2$

x	y
-2	
-1	
0	
1	
2	

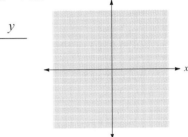

19. $y = -x^2 + 4$

x	y
-2	
-1	
0	
1	
2	

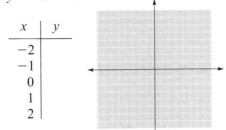

20. $y = -x^2 + 2x$

x	y
-1	
0	
1	
2	
3	

Find length x in each triangle.

21.

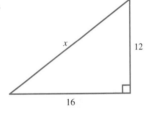

22.

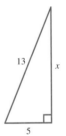

23.

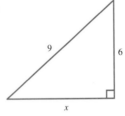

24.

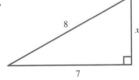

25. If the length of the diagonal of a rectangle is 12 centimeters (cm) and the width of the rectangle is 7 cm, what is the length of the rectangle?

A N S W E R S

1. _____

2. _____

3. _____

4. _____

5. _____

6. _____

7. _____

8. _____

9. _____

10. _____

11. _____

12. _____

13. _____

14. _____

15. _____

This test covers selected topics from all 10 chapters.

Simplify the following expressions.

1. $6x^2y - 4xy^2 + 5x^2y - 2xy^2$

2. $(3x^2 + 2x - 5) - (2x^2 - 3x + 2)$

Evaluate each expression where $x = 2$, $y = -3$, and $z = 4$.

3. $4x^2y - 3z^2y^2$

4. $-3x^2y^2z^2 - 2xyz$

5. Solve for x: $4x - 2(3x - 5) = 8$.

6. Solve the inequality $4x + 15 > 2x + 19$.

Perform the indicated operations.

7. $3xy(2x^2 - x + 5)$

8. $(2x + 5)(3x - 2)$

9. $(3x + 4y)(3x - 4y)$

Factor each of the following completely.

10. $16x^2y^2 - 8xy^3$

11. $8x^2 - 2x - 15$

12. $25x^2 - 16y^2$

Perform the indicated operations.

13. $\dfrac{7}{4x + 8} - \dfrac{5}{7x + 14}$

14. $\dfrac{5x + 5}{x - 2} \cdot \dfrac{x^2 - 4x + 4}{x^2 - 1}$

15. $\dfrac{3x^2 + 8x - 3}{15x^2} + \dfrac{3x - 1}{5x^2}$

A N S W E R S

16. _____

17. _____

18. _____

19. _____

20. _____

21. _____

22. _____

23. _____

24. _____

Graph the following equations.

16. $3x - 2y = 6$

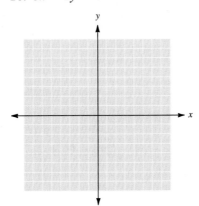

17. $y = 4x - 5$

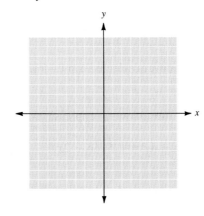

18. Find the slope of the line through the points $(2, 9)$ and $(-1, -6)$.

19. Given that the slope of a line is 2 and the y intercept is -5, write the equation of the line.

20. Graph the inequality $x + 2y < 6$.

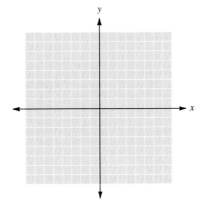

Solve each of the following systems. If a unique solution does not exist, state whether the system is inconsistent or dependent.

21. $2x - 3y = 6$
$x - 3y = 2$

22. $2x + y = 4$
$y = 2x - 8$

23. $5x + 2y = 25$
$x - 4y = 17$

24. $2x - 6y = 8$
$x = 3y + 4$

Solve each of the following applications. Be sure to show the system of equations used for your solution.

25. One number is 4 less than 5 times another. If the sum of the numbers is 26, what are the two numbers?

26. Receipts for a concert attended by 450 people were $2775. If reserved-seat tickets were $7 and general admission tickets were $4, how many of each type of ticket were sold?

27. A chemist has a 30% acid solution and a 60% solution already prepared. How much of each of the two solutions should be mixed in order to form 300 milliliters (mL) of a 50% solution?

Evaluate each root, if possible.

28. $\sqrt{169}$

29. $-\sqrt{169}$

30. $\sqrt{-169}$

31. $\sqrt[3]{-64}$

Simplify each of the following radical expressions by combining like terms.

32. $\sqrt{12} + 3\sqrt{27} - \sqrt{75}$

33. $3\sqrt{2a} \cdot 5\sqrt{6a}$

34. $(\sqrt{2} - 5)(\sqrt{2} + 3)$

35. $\dfrac{8 - \sqrt{32}}{4}$

Solve each of the following equations.

36. $x^2 - 72 = 0$

37. $x^2 + 6x - 3 = 0$

38. $2x^2 - 3x = 2(x + 1)$

Graph each of the following quadratic equations.

39. $y = x^2 - 2$

40. $y = x^2 - 4x$

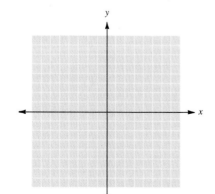

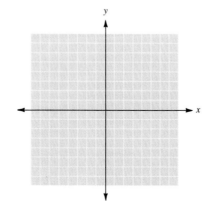

ANSWERS

25. _____

26. _____

27. _____

28. _____

29. _____

30. _____

31. _____

32. _____

33. _____

34. _____

35. _____

36. _____

37. _____

38. _____

39. _____

40. _____

Appendix The Arithmetic of Rational Numbers

This review is provided as an aid for students who wish to refresh their background in the arithmetic of fractions. You will find that much of what you will be asked to do with fractions or rational expressions in algebra has its basis in the methods you used in arithmetic.

Let's start the review with some terminology.

The Language of Fractions

Fractions name a number of equal parts of a unit or whole. A fraction is written in the form $\frac{a}{b}$, where a and b are whole numbers and b cannot be zero.

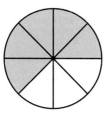

Numerator

$\frac{5}{8}$

Denominator

Denominator   The number of equal parts the whole is divided into.

Numerator   The number of equal parts of the whole that are used.

$\frac{2}{3}$ and $\frac{11}{15}$ are proper fractions.

$\frac{7}{5}, \frac{21}{20},$ and $\frac{8}{8}$ are improper fractions.

$2\frac{1}{3}$ and $5\frac{7}{8}$ are mixed numbers. Note that $2\frac{1}{3}$ means $2 + \frac{1}{3}$.

Proper fraction   A fraction whose numerator is less than its denominator. It names a number less than 1.

Improper fraction   A fraction whose numerator is greater than or equal to its denominator. It names a number greater than or equal to 1.

Mixed number   The sum of a whole number and a proper fraction.

Converting Mixed Numbers and Improper Fractions

To Change an Improper Fraction to a Mixed Number

1. Divide the numerator by the denominator. The quotient is the whole-number portion of the mixed number.
2. If there is a remainder, write the remainder over the original denominator. This gives the fractional portion of the mixed number.

●Example 1

Converting a Fraction to a Mixed Number

Change $\frac{22}{5}$ to a mixed number.

729

$$5\overline{)22} \quad \text{Quotient}$$
$$\underline{20}$$
$$2 \longleftarrow \text{Remainder}$$

$$\frac{22}{5} = 4\frac{2}{5}$$

To Change a Mixed Number to an Improper Fraction

1. Multiply the denominator of the fraction by the whole-number portion of the mixed number.
2. Add the numerator of the fraction to that product.
3. Write that sum over the original denominator to form the improper fraction.

• Example 2

Converting a Mixed Number to a Fraction

Change $5\frac{3}{4}$ to an improper fraction.

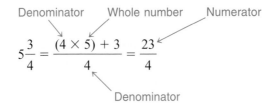

Denominator   Whole number   Numerator

$$5\frac{3}{4} = \frac{(4 \times 5) + 3}{4} = \frac{23}{4}$$

Denominator

Equivalent Fractions

Equivalent fractions   Two fractions are equivalent (have equal value) if they are different names for the same number.

Cross products

$$\frac{a}{b} = \frac{c}{d} \qquad a \times d \text{ and } b \times c \text{ are called the } \textbf{cross products.}$$

$\frac{2}{3} = \frac{4}{6}$ because $2 \times 6 = 3 \times 4$.

If their cross products are equal, two fractions are equivalent.

$\frac{1}{2} = \frac{1 \times 5}{2 \times 5} = \frac{5}{10}$

$\frac{1}{2}$ and $\frac{5}{10}$ are equivalent fractions.

The fundamental principle   For the fraction $\frac{a}{b}$, and any nonzero number c,

$$\frac{a}{b} = \frac{a \times c}{b \times c}$$

In words: We can multiply the numerator and denominator of a fraction by the same nonzero number. The result will be an equivalent fraction.

$\dfrac{2}{3}$ is in simplest form.

$\dfrac{12}{18}$ is *not* in simplest form.

The numerator and denominator have the common factor 6.

$$\frac{10}{15} = \frac{10 \div 5}{15 \div 5} = \frac{2}{3}$$

$$\frac{3}{4} = \frac{3 \times 2}{4 \times 2} = \frac{6}{8}$$

Simplest form A fraction is in simplest form, or in lowest terms, if the numerator and denominator have no common factors other than 1. This means that the fraction has the smallest possible numerator and denominator.

To Write a Fraction In Simplest Form Divide the numerator and denominator by any common factors greater than 1 to write a fraction as an equivalent fraction in simplest form.

To Build a Fraction Multiply the numerator and denominator by any whole number greater than 1 to build a fraction to an equivalent fraction with a specified denominator.

Multiplying Fractions

To Multiply Fractions

1. Multiply numerator by numerator. This gives the numerator of the product.
2. Multiply denominator by denominator. This gives the denominator of the product.
3. Simplify the resulting fraction if possible.

● Example 3

Multiplying Two Fractions

Multiply $\dfrac{5}{8} \times \dfrac{3}{7}$.

$$\frac{5}{8} \times \frac{3}{7} = \frac{5 \times 3}{8 \times 7} = \frac{15}{56}$$

In multiplying fractions, it is usually easiest to divide by any common factors in the numerator and denominator *before* multiplying.

● Example 4

Multiplying Two Fractions

Multiply $\dfrac{7}{15} \times \dfrac{10}{21}$.

We divide numerator and denominator by the common factors of 7 and 5.

$$\frac{7}{15} \times \frac{10}{21} = \frac{7 \times 10}{15 \times 21}$$

$$= \frac{\overset{1}{\cancel{7}} \times \overset{2}{\cancel{10}}}{\underset{3}{\cancel{15}} \times \underset{3}{\cancel{21}}}$$

$$= \frac{2}{9}$$

Dividing Fractions

Remember: The divisor *follows* the division sign. That is the fraction that is inverted or "turned."

To Divide Fractions Invert the divisor and multiply.

•Example 5

Dividing Two Fractions

Divide $\dfrac{3}{7} \div \dfrac{4}{5}$.

Invert

$$\frac{3}{7} \div \frac{4}{5} = \frac{3}{7} \times \frac{5}{4} = \frac{15}{28}$$

You can divide by common factors *only* after the divisor has been inverted.

•Example 6

Note: Since a fraction bar also indicates division,

$$\frac{\dfrac{3}{5}}{\dfrac{9}{10}} = \frac{3}{5} \div \frac{9}{10}$$

and the quotient is simplified as in our example.

Dividing Two Fractions

Divide $\dfrac{3}{5} \div \dfrac{9}{10}$.

$$\frac{3}{5} \div \frac{9}{10} = \frac{3}{5} \times \frac{10}{9} = \frac{\overset{1}{\cancel{3}} \times \overset{2}{\cancel{10}}}{\underset{1}{\cancel{5}} \times \underset{3}{\cancel{9}}} = \frac{2}{3}$$

Multiplying or Dividing Mixed Numbers

To Multiply or Divide Mixed Numbers Convert any mixed or whole numbers to improper fractions. Then multiply or divide the fractions as before.

• Example 7

Multiplying Mixed Numbers

Multiply $6\dfrac{2}{3} \times 3\dfrac{1}{5}$.

$$6\frac{2}{3} \times 3\frac{1}{5} = \frac{20}{3} \times \frac{16}{5} = \frac{\overset{4}{\cancel{20}} \times 16}{3 \times \underset{1}{\cancel{5}}} = \frac{64}{3} = 21\frac{1}{3}$$

• Example 8

Dividing Mixed Numbers

Divide $\dfrac{7}{8} \div 5\dfrac{1}{4}$.

$$\frac{7}{8} \div 5\frac{1}{4} = \frac{7}{8} \div \frac{21}{4} = \frac{\overset{1}{\cancel{7}}}{\underset{2}{\cancel{8}}} \times \frac{\overset{1}{\cancel{4}}}{\underset{3}{\cancel{21}}} = \frac{1}{6}$$

Finding the Least Common Denominator

To Find the LCD

1. Write the prime factorization for each of the denominators.
2. Find all the prime factors that appear in any one of the prime factorizations.
3. Form the product of those prime factors, using each factor the greatest number of times it occurs in any one factorization.

• Example 9

Finding the LCD

Find the LCD of fractions with denominators 4, 6, and 15.

$$
\begin{array}{rl}
4 = & 2 \times 2 \\
6 = & 2 \qquad \times 3 \\
\underline{15 = \qquad\qquad 3 \times 5} \\
& 2 \times 2 \times 3 \times 5
\end{array}
$$

The LCD $= 2 \times 2 \times 3 \times 5$, or 60.

To form the LCD, use two factors of 2, one of 3, and one of 5.

Adding Fractions

To Add Like Fractions

1. Add the numerators.
2. Place the sum over the common denominator.
3. Simplify the resulting fraction if necessary.

• Example 10

Adding Like Fractions

Add $\dfrac{5}{18} + \dfrac{7}{18}$.

$$\frac{5}{18} + \frac{7}{18} = \frac{12}{18} = \frac{\cancel{12}^{2}}{\cancel{18}_{3}} = \frac{2}{3}$$

To Add Unlike Fractions

1. Find the LCD of the fractions.
2. Change each fraction to equivalent fractions that have the LCD as a common denominator.
3. Add the resulting like fractions.

• Example 11

Adding Unlike Fractions

Add $\dfrac{3}{4} + \dfrac{7}{10}$.

1. The LCD for 4 and 10 is 20.

To convert to equivalent fractions with denominator 20, multiply numerator and denominator of the first fraction by 5, and of the second fraction by 2.

$$\begin{array}{cc} \times 5 & \times 2 \\ 2.\ \dfrac{3}{4} = \dfrac{15}{20} & \dfrac{7}{10} = \dfrac{14}{20} \\ \times 5 & \times 2 \end{array}$$

$$3.\ \frac{3}{4} + \frac{7}{10} = \frac{15}{20} + \frac{14}{20} = \frac{29}{20} = 1\frac{9}{20}$$

Subtracting Fractions

To Subtract Like Fractions

1. Subtract the numerators.
2. Place the difference over the common denominator.
3. Simplify the resulting fraction if necessary.

• Example 12

Subtracting Like Fractions

$$\frac{17}{20} - \frac{7}{20} = \frac{10}{20} = \frac{\overset{1}{\cancel{10}}}{\underset{2}{\cancel{20}}} = \frac{1}{2}$$

To Subtract Unlike Fractions

1. Find the LCD of the fractions.
2. Change each fraction to equivalent fractions that have the LCD as a common denominator.
3. Subtract the resulting like fractions.

• Example 13

Subtracting Unlike Fractions

Subtract $\dfrac{8}{9} - \dfrac{5}{6}$.

1. The LCD for 9 and 6 is 18.

2. $\dfrac{8}{9} = \dfrac{16}{18} \qquad \dfrac{5}{6} = \dfrac{15}{18}$

$\quad\; \times 2 \qquad\qquad \times 3$

3. $\dfrac{8}{9} - \dfrac{5}{6} = \dfrac{16}{18} - \dfrac{15}{18} = \dfrac{1}{18}$

Adding or Subtracting Mixed Numbers

To Add or Subtract Mixed Numbers

Note: Subtracting may require renaming the first mixed number.

1. Add or subtract the whole-number parts.
2. Add or subtract the fractional parts.
3. Combine the results as a mixed number.

• Example 14

Adding Mixed Numbers

Add $1\dfrac{2}{3} + 2\dfrac{3}{4}$.

First note that the LCD for the fractional portions of the mixed numbers is 12. Then convert the fractional portions of the mixed numbers to fractions with that LCD.

$$(1+2) \qquad \left(\dfrac{8}{12} + \dfrac{9}{12}\right)$$

$$1\dfrac{2}{3} + 2\dfrac{3}{4} = 1\dfrac{8}{12} + 2\dfrac{9}{12} = 3\dfrac{17}{12} = 4\dfrac{5}{12}$$

• Example 15

Subtracting Unlike Fractions

Subtract $5\dfrac{1}{2} - 3\dfrac{3}{4}$.

To rename the first fraction, borrow 1 from 5 and think of that 1 as $\dfrac{4}{4}$.

$$5\dfrac{1}{2} - 3\dfrac{3}{4} = 5\dfrac{2}{4} - 3\dfrac{3}{4}$$

Rename

$$= 4\dfrac{6}{4} - 3\dfrac{3}{4} = 1\dfrac{3}{4}$$

$$(4-3) \qquad \left(\dfrac{6}{4} - \dfrac{3}{4}\right)$$

Exercises

Name _____

Section _____ Date _____

1. Give the fractions that name the shaded portions of the following diagrams. Indicate the numerator and the denominator.

   a.

   Fraction _____

   Numerator _____

   Denominator _____

   b.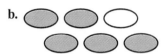

   Fraction _____

   Numerator _____

   Denominator _____

1. _____

2. _____

3. _____

4. _____

5. _____

2. If your English class has 23 students and 13 are women:

   a. What fraction names the portion that are women?

   b. What fraction names the portion that are not women?

3. You are given the following group of numbers:

   $$\frac{2}{3}, \frac{5}{4}, 2\frac{3}{7}, \frac{45}{8}, \frac{7}{7}, 3\frac{4}{5}, \frac{9}{1}, \frac{7}{10}, \frac{12}{5}, 5\frac{2}{9}$$

   a. List the proper fractions.

   b. List the improper fractions.

   c. List the mixed numbers.

4. Convert to mixed or whole numbers.

   a. $\dfrac{41}{6}$

   b. $\dfrac{32}{8}$

5. Convert to improper fractions.

   a. $3\dfrac{1}{6}$

   b. $4\dfrac{3}{8}$

6. Find out whether each pair of fractions is equivalent.

a. $\dfrac{5}{8}, \dfrac{7}{12}$
      b. $\dfrac{8}{15}, \dfrac{32}{60}$

7. Reduce each fraction to lowest terms.

a. $\dfrac{15}{18}$
  b. $\dfrac{24}{36}$
  c. $\dfrac{140}{180}$
  d. $\dfrac{210}{294}$

8. Find the missing numerators.

a. $\dfrac{5}{8} = \dfrac{?}{24}$
      b. $\dfrac{4}{5} = \dfrac{?}{40}$

9. Arrange the fractions in order from smallest to largest.

a. $\dfrac{5}{9}, \dfrac{4}{7}$
      b. $\dfrac{5}{6}, \dfrac{4}{5}, \dfrac{7}{10}$

10. Write as equivalent fractions with the LCD as a common denominator.

a. $\dfrac{1}{6}, \dfrac{7}{8}$
      b. $\dfrac{3}{10}, \dfrac{5}{8}, \dfrac{7}{12}$

11. Multiply.

a. $\dfrac{5}{8} \times \dfrac{3}{4}$
  b. $\dfrac{3}{5} \times \dfrac{4}{9}$
  c. $\dfrac{10}{27} \times \dfrac{9}{20}$
  d. $4 \times \dfrac{3}{8}$

e. $\dfrac{4}{7} \times 2\dfrac{3}{8}$
  f. $5\dfrac{1}{3} \times 1\dfrac{4}{5}$
  g. $2\dfrac{2}{5} \times 1\dfrac{7}{8}$
  h. $1\dfrac{5}{12} \times 8$

12. Divide.

a. $\dfrac{3}{5} \div \dfrac{1}{4}$
  b. $\dfrac{5}{12} \div \dfrac{5}{8}$
  c. $1\dfrac{7}{9} \div \dfrac{4}{9}$

d. $3\dfrac{3}{8} \div 2\dfrac{1}{4}$
  e. $\dfrac{9}{10} \div 3$
  f. $4 \div 2\dfrac{2}{3}$

13. A kitchen measures $5\dfrac{1}{3}$ yards (yd) by $4\dfrac{1}{4}$ yd. If you purchase linoleum that costs \$12 per square yard, what will it cost to cover the floor?

ANSWERS

14. _____

15. _____

16. _____

17. _____

18. _____

19. _____

20. _____

21. _____

14. If you drive 117 mi in $2\frac{1}{4}$ hours, what is your average speed?

15. Add.

a. $\dfrac{1}{8} + \dfrac{3}{8}$ 　　　　　　　　　　　　　**b.** $\dfrac{6}{7} + \dfrac{5}{7}$

16. Add.

a. $\dfrac{1}{5} + \dfrac{3}{4}$ 　　**b.** $\dfrac{5}{8} + \dfrac{5}{6}$ 　　**c.** $\dfrac{5}{18} + \dfrac{7}{12}$ 　　**d.** $\dfrac{3}{5} + \dfrac{1}{4} + \dfrac{5}{6}$

17. Subtract.

a. $\dfrac{5}{8} - \dfrac{3}{8}$ 　　**b.** $\dfrac{3}{5} - \dfrac{1}{6}$ 　　**c.** $\dfrac{7}{10} - \dfrac{7}{12}$ 　　**d.** $\dfrac{11}{20} - \dfrac{7}{25}$

18. Add or subtract as indicated.

a. $5\dfrac{2}{5} + 4\dfrac{1}{5}$ 　　　　**b.** $6\dfrac{5}{7} + 3\dfrac{4}{7}$ 　　　　**c.** $4\dfrac{1}{8} + 3\dfrac{5}{12}$

d. $5\dfrac{7}{10} + 3\dfrac{11}{12}$ 　　　**e.** $2\dfrac{1}{2} + 3\dfrac{5}{6} + 4\dfrac{3}{8}$ 　　　**f.** $7\dfrac{7}{9} - 3\dfrac{4}{9}$

g. $5\dfrac{1}{7} - 3\dfrac{3}{7}$ 　　　　**h.** $7\dfrac{1}{6} - 3\dfrac{1}{8}$ 　　　　**i.** $6\dfrac{5}{12} - 3\dfrac{5}{8}$

j. $4 - 2\dfrac{2}{3}$

19. Jan ran $3\dfrac{2}{3}$ mi on Monday, $1\dfrac{3}{4}$ mi on Wednesday, and $4\dfrac{1}{2}$ mi on Friday. How far did she run during the week?

20. At the beginning of a year Miguel was $51\dfrac{3}{4}$ in tall. In June he measured $53\dfrac{1}{8}$ in. How much did he grow during that period?

21. Amelia buys an 8-yd roll of wallpaper on sale. After measuring, she finds that she needs the following amounts of the paper: $2\dfrac{1}{3}$, $1\dfrac{1}{2}$, and $3\dfrac{3}{4}$ yd. Does she have enough for the job? If so, how much will be left over?

Answers

1. (a) Fraction, $\dfrac{3}{8}$; numerator, 3; denominator, 8; **(b)** fraction, $\dfrac{5}{6}$; numerator, 5; denominator, 6

3. (a) $\dfrac{2}{3}, \dfrac{7}{10}$; **(b)** $\dfrac{5}{4}, \dfrac{45}{8}, \dfrac{7}{7}, \dfrac{9}{1}, \dfrac{12}{5}$; **(c)** $2\dfrac{3}{7}, 3\dfrac{4}{5}, 5\dfrac{2}{9}$ **5. (a)** $\dfrac{19}{6}$; **(b)** $\dfrac{35}{8}$

7. (a) $\dfrac{5}{6}$; **(b)** $\dfrac{2}{3}$; **(c)** $\dfrac{7}{9}$; **(d)** $\dfrac{5}{7}$ **9. (a)** $\dfrac{5}{9}, \dfrac{4}{7}$; **(b)** $\dfrac{7}{10}, \dfrac{4}{5}, \dfrac{5}{6}$

11. (a) $\dfrac{15}{32}$; **(b)** $\dfrac{4}{15}$; **(c)** $\dfrac{1}{6}$; **(d)** $1\dfrac{1}{2}$; **(e)** $1\dfrac{5}{14}$; **(f)** $9\dfrac{3}{5}$; **(g)** $4\dfrac{1}{2}$; **(h)** $11\dfrac{1}{3}$

13. \$272   **15. (a)** $\dfrac{1}{2}$; **(b)** $1\dfrac{4}{7}$ **17. (a)** $\dfrac{1}{4}$; **(b)** $\dfrac{13}{30}$; **(c)** $\dfrac{7}{60}$; **(d)** $\dfrac{27}{100}$

19. $9\dfrac{11}{12}$ mi   **21.** Yes, $\dfrac{5}{12}$ yd

Answers to Self-Tests and Cumulative Tests

Self-Test for Chapter 1

1. $a - 5$ **2.** $6m$ **3.** $4(m + n)$ **4.** $\dfrac{a + b}{3}$ **5.** 4^4 **6.** $7b^3$ **7.** 3

8. 65 **9.** 144 **10.** Commutative property of multiplication
11. Distributive property **12.** Associative property of addition
13. 21 **14.** $20x + 12$ **15.** $15a$ **16.** $3x^2y$ **17.** $19x + 5y$
18. $8a^2$ **19.** $2x - 8$ **20.** $2x + 4$

Self-Test for Chapter 2

1. (number line with points at $-17, -12, -7, 4, 5, 18$; scale $-20, -10, 0, 10, 20$) **2.** $-6, -3, -2, 0, \dfrac{1}{2}, \dfrac{3}{4}, 2, 4, 5$

3. Max: 6; Min: -5 **4.** 7 **5.** 7 **6.** 11 **7.** 11 **8.** -13 **9.** -3
10. -21 **11.** 1 **12.** -6 **13.** -24 **14.** 9 **15.** 0 **16.** 3 **17.** 1
18. -40 **19.** 63 **20.** -27 **21.** -24 **22.** 14 **23.** -25 **24.** 3
25. -5 **26.** Undefined **27.** -4 **28.** 80 **29.** 144 **30.** 5

Self-Test for Chapter 3

1. No **2.** Yes **3.** 11 **4.** 12 **5.** 7 **6.** 7 **7.** -12 **8.** 25 **9.** 3
10. 4 **11.** $-\dfrac{2}{3}$ **12.** -5 **13.** $\dfrac{C}{2\pi}$ **14.** $\dfrac{3V}{B}$ **15.** $\dfrac{6 - 3x}{2}$ **16.** 9

17. -3 **18.** $x \le 14$ **19.** $x < -4$ **20.** $x \ge \dfrac{4}{3}$ **21.** $x > -1$ **22.** 7

23. 21, 22, 23 **24.** Juwan, 6; Jan, 12; Rick, 17 **25.** 10 in., 21 in.

Cumulative Test for Chapters 1–3

1. $3(r + s)$ **2.** $\dfrac{x - 5}{3}$ **3.** 5^5 **4.** $8x^3y^2$ **5.** Associative property of

addition **6.** Distributive property **7.** $5a^2b$ **8.** $12a^2 + 3a$
9. $-9, -6, 2, 4, 8, 9, 18$ **10.** Mean: 3 Median: 2 **11.** 2 **12.** 80
13. 7 **14.** 7 **15.** -16 **16.** 4 **17.** 63 **18.** -16 **19.** 0 **20.** -9

21. 13 **22.** 3 **23.** 5 **24.** -24 **25.** $\dfrac{5}{4}$ **26.** $-\dfrac{2}{5}$ **27.** 5

28. $\dfrac{I}{Pt}$ **29.** $\dfrac{2A}{b}$ **30.** $\dfrac{c - ax}{b}$ **31.** (graph) $x < 3$

32. (graph) $x \le -\dfrac{3}{2}$ **33.** (graph) $x > 4$

34. (graph) $x \ge \dfrac{4}{3}$ **35.** 13 **36.** 42, 43 **37.** 7

38. $420 **39.** 5 cm, 17 cm **40.** 8 in., 13 in., 16 in.

Self-Test for Chapter 4

1. a^{14} **2.** $15x^3y^7$ **3.** $2x^3$ **4.** $4ab^3$ **5.** 6 **6.** 3 **7.** $x^6y^9z^9$
8. $\dfrac{x^5y^5}{32}$ **9.** $\dfrac{b^2}{a^2}$ **10.** xz^3 **11.** $10x^2 - 12x - 7$
12. $7a^3 + 11a^2 - 3a$ **13.** $3x^2 + 11x - 12$
14. $b^2 - 7b - 5$ **15.** $7a^2 - 10a$ **16.** $4x^2 + 5x - 6$
17. $2x^2 - 7x + 5$ **18.** $15a^3b^2 - 10a^2b^2 + 20a^2b^3$
19. $3x^2 + x - 14$ **20.** $a^2 - 49b^2$ **21.** $9m^2 + 12mn + 4n^2$
22. $2x^3 + 7x^2y - xy^2 - 2y^3$ **23.** $2x^2 - 3y$ **24.** $4c^2 - 6 + 9cd$

25. $x - 6$ **26.** $x + 2 + \dfrac{10}{2x - 3}$ **27.** $2x^2 - 3x + 2 + \dfrac{7}{3x + 1}$

28. $x^2 - 4x + 5 - \dfrac{4}{x - 1}$

Cumulative Test for Chapters 1–4

1. Associative **2.** Distributive **3.** $-5, -3, 4, 6, 7, 9$; 14; 5; 3
4. 2 **5.** -3 **6.** 4 **7.** 12 **8.** 0 **9.** 65 **10.** 7 **11.** -36 **12.** 4
13. 23 **14.** $x < -15$ **15.** $x < 5$ **16.** $3x^2 + 2x - 4$

17. $x^2 - 3x - 18$ **18.** $12x^2 - 20x$ **19.** $6x^2 + x - 40$
20. $x^3 - x^2 - x + 10$ **21.** $4x^2 - 49$ **22.** $9x^2 - 30x + 25$
23. $20x^3 - 100x^2 + 125x$ **24.** $2x^2 + 9$ **25.** $5xy - 3 + 6x^2y$

26. $x - 1 + \dfrac{3}{3x + 1}$ **27.** $4x^2 + 3x + 13 + \dfrac{17}{x - 2}$ **28.** 8

29. 65, 67 **30.** 4 cm by 24 cm **31.** $\dfrac{y^2z}{x}$ **32.** $\dfrac{c^4}{a^7b^4}$

Self-Test for Chapter 5

1. $6(2b + 3)$ **2.** $3p^2(3p - 4)$ **3.** $5(x^2 - 2x + 4)$
4. $6ab(a - 3 + 2b)$ **5.** $(a + 5)(a - 5)$ **6.** $(8m + n)(8m - n)$
7. $(7x + 4y)(7x - 4y)$ **8.** $2b(4a + 5b)(4a - 5b)$ **9.** $(a - 7)(a + 2)$
10. $(b + 3)(b + 5)$ **11.** $(x - 4)(x - 7)$ **12.** $(y + 10z)(y + 2z)$
13. $(x + 2)(x - 5)$ **14.** $(2x - 3)(3x + 1)$ **15.** $(2x - 1)(x + 8)$
16. $(3w + 7)(w + 1)$ **17.** $(4x - 3y)(2x + y)$ **18.** $3x(2x + 5)(x - 2)$

19. 3, 5 **20.** $-1, 4$ **21.** $-1, \dfrac{2}{3}$ **22.** 0, 3 **23.** 5, 7

24. 3 cm by 11 cm **25.** $\dfrac{P - 2L}{2}$ **26.** $\dfrac{b}{a - 1}$ **27.** 18

Cumulative Test for Chapters 1–5

1. $2x^2y + 5xy$ **2.** $3a^4b^6$ **3.** $4x^2 + x + 3$ **4.** $x^2 + 9x - 2$ **5.** 27
6. -1 **7.** $a^2 - 9b^2$ **8.** $x^2 - 4xy + 4y^2$ **9.** $x^2 + 3x - 10$

10. $a^2 + a - 12$ **11.** $3x + 2$ **12.** $3x + 3 + \dfrac{1}{x - 1}$ **13.** 25

14. $-\dfrac{1}{3}$ **15.** 11 **16.** -33 **17.** -2 **18.** -3 **19.** 2, -3

20. $\dfrac{5}{2}, 6$ **21.** $4(3x + 5)$ **22.** $(5x + 7y)(5x - 7y)$

23. $(4x - 5)(3x + 2)$ **24.** $(x - 5)(2x - 3)$ **25.** 17 **26.** $43

27. 25 **28.** -11 or 4 **29.** $F = \dfrac{9}{5}C + 32$ **30.** 28

Self-Test for Chapter 6

1. 4 **2.** $-3, 3$ **3.** $\dfrac{-3x^4}{4y^2}$ **4.** $\dfrac{4}{a}$ **5.** $\dfrac{x + 1}{x - 2}$ **6.** $\dfrac{4p^2}{7q}$ **7.** $\dfrac{2}{x - 1}$

8. $\dfrac{3}{4y}$ **9.** $\dfrac{3}{m}$ **10.** a **11.** 2 **12.** 5 **13.** $\dfrac{17x}{15}$ **14.** $\dfrac{3s - 2}{s^2}$

15. $\dfrac{4x + 17}{(x - 2)(x + 3)}$ **16.** $\dfrac{15}{w - 5}$ **17.** $\dfrac{2}{3x}$ **18.** $\dfrac{n}{2n + m}$ **19.** 36
20. 2, 6 **21.** 4, 12 **22.** 50 mi/h, 45 mi/h **23.** 6 **24.** 20 ft, 35 ft

25. $\dfrac{2}{16}$ or .4375

Cumulative Test for Chapters 1–6

1. $-2xy$ **2.** $\dfrac{4a^2}{3}$ **3.** $2x^2 - 5x + 6$ **4.** $3a^2 - 6a - 1$ **5.** 31 **6.** 1

7. $2x^2 + xy - 6y^2$ **8.** $x^2 + 11x + 28$ **9.** $2x - 1 + \dfrac{1}{x + 2}$

10. $x + 1 - \dfrac{4}{x + 1}$ **11.** 4 **12.** -2 **13.** $(x - 7)(x + 2)$
14. $3mn(m - 2n - 3)$ **15.** $(a + 3b)(a - 3b)$ **16.** $2x(x - 6)(x - 8)$
17. 7 **18.** 4 **19.** 264 ft/s **20.** 5 in. by 7 in. **21.** $\dfrac{m}{3}$ **22.** $\dfrac{a - 7}{3a + 1}$

23. $\dfrac{3}{x}$ **24.** $\dfrac{1}{3w}$ **25.** $\dfrac{8r + 3}{6r^2}$ **26.** $\dfrac{x + 33}{3(x - 3)(x + 3)}$ **27.** $\dfrac{x - 1}{2x + 1}$

28. $\dfrac{n}{3n + m}$ **29.** $\dfrac{6}{5}$ **30.** $\dfrac{-9}{2}, 7$

Self-Test for Chapter 7

1. $(3, 6), (9, 0)$ **2.** $(4, 0), (5, 4)$ **3.** $(3, 3), (6, 2), (9, 1)$

3. $(3, 3), (6, 2), (9, 1)$ **4.** $(3, 0), (0, 4), \left(\dfrac{3}{4}, 3\right), \left(\dfrac{3}{4}, 3\right)$

5. Different answers are possible **6.** Different answers are possible

7. $(4, 2)$ **8.** $(-4, 6)$ **9.** $(0, -7)$
10–12.

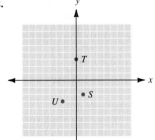

13. $x + y = 4$

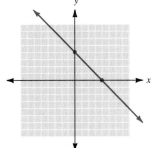

14. $y = 3x$

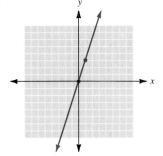

15. $y = \dfrac{3}{4}x - 4$

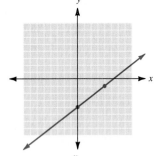

16. $x + 3y = 6$

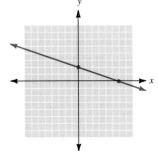

17. $2x + 5y = 10$

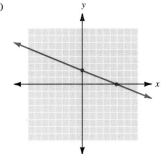

18. $y = -4$

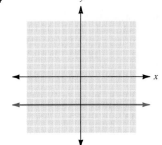

19. 1 **20.** $\dfrac{3}{4}$
21. $y = -3x + 6$

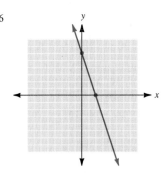

22. $y = \dfrac{2}{5}x - 3$

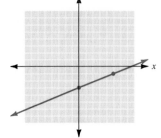

23. $x + y < 3$

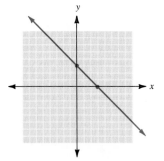

24. $3x + y \geq 9$

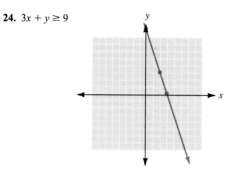

Cumulative Test for Chapters 1–7

1. $x^2y^2 - 3xy$ **2.** $\dfrac{4m^3n}{3}$ **3.** $-x + 9$ **4.** $3z^2 - 3z + 5$

5. $2x^2 + 11x - 21$ **6.** $2a^2 + 6ab - 8b^2$ **7.** $x + 6 + \dfrac{20}{x-3}$

8. $x^3 - 2x^2 + 4x - 10 + \dfrac{20}{x-2}$ **9.** $-\dfrac{4}{3}$ **10.** -2

11. $(x - 8)(x + 7)$ **12.** $2x^2y(2x - y + 4x^2)$

13. $2a(2a + 3b)(2a - 3b)$ **14.** $3(5x - 2y)(x - y)$ **15.** 1 **16.** $-\dfrac{9}{4}$

17. $x + y = 4$

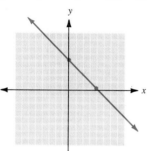

18. $y = 2x - 5$

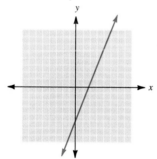

19. 4 **20.** 5 in. by 7 in.

Self-Test for Chapter 8

1. $(4, 1)$

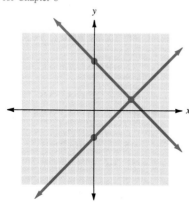

2. $(4, 2)$

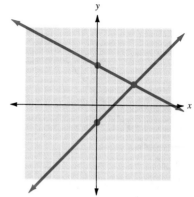

3. Inconsistent

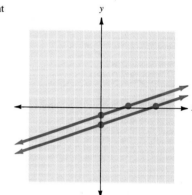

4. $(2, 4)$

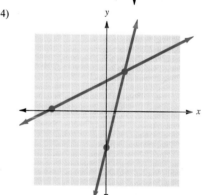

5. $(4, 1)$ **6.** $(4, 2)$ **7.** $(1, 3)$ **8.** $\left(2, \dfrac{5}{2}\right)$ **9.** Dependent

10. $\left(\dfrac{3}{4}, -1\right)$ **11.** $(6, 2)$ **12.** Inconsistent **13.** $(2, 6)$ **14.** $(6, -3)$

15. $(6, 2)$ **16.** $(5, 4)$ **17.** $(-3, 3)$ **18.** Inconsistent **19.** $(3, -5)$

20. $(3, 2)$ **21.** 12, 18 **22.** 21 m, 29 m **23.** Width 12 in., length 20 in. **24.** 12 dimes, 18 quarters **25.** Boat 15 mi/h, current 3 mi/h

Cumulative Test for Chapters 1–8

1. $8x^2 - 7x - 4$ **2.** $w^2 - 8w - 4$ **3.** $28x^3y^2 - 14x^2y^2 - 21x^2y^3$

4. $15s^2 - 23s - 28$ **5.** $-x^2 + 2xy - 3y$ **6.** $2x + 4$ **7.** 9

8. 27 $5 bills, 56 $10 bills **9.** 120 mi/h, 140 mi/h **10.** $8a^2(3a - 2)$

11. $7mn(m - 3 - 7n)$ **12.** $(a + 8b)(a - 8b)$

13. $5p(p + 4q)(p - 4q)$ **14.** $(a - 6)(a - 8)$ **15.** $2w(w - 7)(w + 3)$

16. 4, 5 **17.** $-4, 4$ **18.** 7 **19.** 5 in. by 17 in. **20.** $\dfrac{m}{3}$

21. $\dfrac{a - 7}{3a + 1}$ **22.** $\dfrac{3}{x}$ **23.** $\dfrac{1}{3w}$

24.

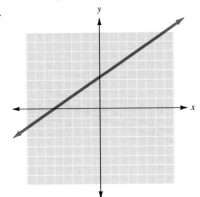

25.

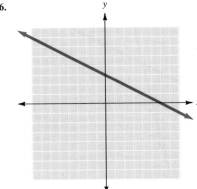

26.

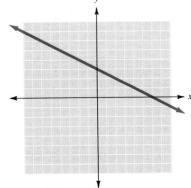

27.

28.

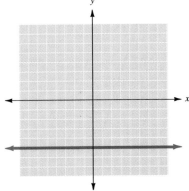

29. $\dfrac{10}{7}$ **30.** $m = \dfrac{5}{3}$, $b = -5$ **31.** $y = 2x - 5$

32.

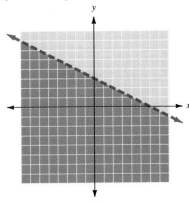

33.

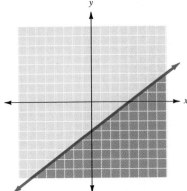

34. $(3, 1)$ **35.** $(4, -3)$ **36.** $\left(4, \dfrac{2}{3}\right)$ **37.** $(3, -2)$ **38.** $\left(7, -\dfrac{5}{2}\right)$
39. Dependent   **40.** $(5, 0)$ **41.** $(-3, -2)$ **42.** Inconsistent
43. $\left(\dfrac{3}{2}, -\dfrac{1}{3}\right)$ **44.** $\left(\dfrac{2}{5}, -3\right)$ **45.** $\left(\dfrac{3}{2}, 4\right)$ **46.** 5, 21   **47.** VHS
\$4.50, cassette \$1.50   **48.** 325 at \$7, 125 at \$4   **49.** \$5000 at 6
percent, \$7000 at 9 percent   **50.** 100 mL of 30%, 200 mL of 60%
51. Boat 20 mi/h, current 5 mi/h

Self-Test for Chapter 9
1. 11   **2.** 3   **3.** Not a real number   **4.** 4   **5.** $5\sqrt{3}$ **6.** $2a\sqrt{6a}$
7. $\dfrac{4}{5}$ **8.** $\dfrac{\sqrt{5}}{3}$ **9.** $4\sqrt{10}$ **10.** $3\sqrt{2}$ **11.** $3\sqrt{2}$ **12.** $4\sqrt{5}$
13. $3x\sqrt{2}$ **14.** $11 + 5\sqrt{5}$ **15.** $\dfrac{\sqrt{14}}{2}$ **16.** $2 + 3\sqrt{2}$
17. $3 - \sqrt{3}$ **18.** 9   **19.** $\sqrt{85}$ **20.** $\sqrt{20} = 2\sqrt{5}$

Cumulative Test for Chapters 1–9
1. $3x^2y^3 - 2x^3y$ **2.** $7x^2 - 6x + 12$ **3.** 0 **4.** 8 **5.** 2 **6.** 6
7. $x > 4$ **8.** $6x^4y - 10x^3y + 38x^2y$ **9.** $20x^2 - 23xy - 21y^2$
10. $9xy(4 - 3x^2y)$ **11.** $(4x - 3)(2x - 5)$ **12.** $\dfrac{1}{15(x - 7)}$
13. $\dfrac{x - 3}{x - 5}$ **14.**

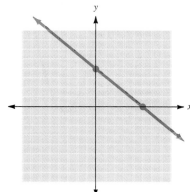

15.

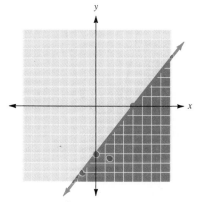

16. 5 **17.** $y = -\dfrac{3}{2}x + 5$ **18.** $(5, 0)$ **19.** Inconsistent **20.** Boat
13 mi/h, current 3 mi/h **21.** 12 **22.** -12 **23.** Not possible
24. -3 **25.** $-4a\sqrt{5}$ **26.** $\dfrac{2x\sqrt{6x}}{3}$ **27.** $4 - 2\sqrt{2}$ **28.** $7x\sqrt{2}$
29. $5mn\sqrt{6m}$ **30.** $\dfrac{2a\sqrt{3}}{5}$

Self-Test for Chapter 10
1. $\pm\sqrt{15}$ **2.** $\pm 2\sqrt{2}$ **3.** $1 \pm \sqrt{7}$ **4.** $\dfrac{\pm\sqrt{10}}{3}$ **5.** $4, -2$
6. $\dfrac{-3 \pm \sqrt{13}}{2}$ **7.** $-1 \pm \sqrt{6}$ **8.** $\dfrac{5 \pm \sqrt{17}}{4}$ **9.** $-1, 3$ **10.** 3
11. $\dfrac{5 \pm \sqrt{33}}{2}$ **12.** $\dfrac{1 \pm \sqrt{11}}{2}$ **13.** $\dfrac{1 \pm \sqrt{33}}{4}$ **14.** $-1 \pm \sqrt{6}$
15. $y = x^2 + 4$

x	y
-2	8
-1	5
0	4
1	5
2	8

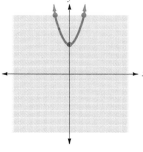

16. $y = x^2 - 2x$

x	y
-1	3
0	0
1	1
2	0
3	3

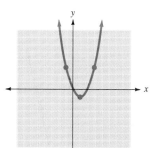

17. $y = x^2 - 3$

x	y
-2	1
-1	2
0	-1
1	-2
2	1

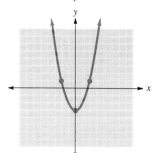

18. $y = x^2 + x - 2$

x	y
-2	0
-1	2
0	-2
1	0
2	4

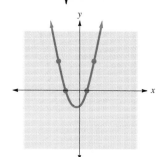

19. $y = -x^2 + 4$

x	y
-2	0
-1	3
0	4
1	3
2	0

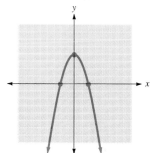

20. $y = -x^2 + 2x$

x	y
-1	-3
0	0
1	1
2	0
3	-3

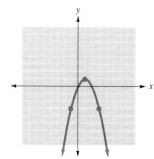

21. 20 **22.** 12 **23.** $3\sqrt{5}$ **24.** $\sqrt{15}$ **25.** Approximately 9.747 cm

Cumulative Test for Chapters 1–10
1. $11x^2y - 6xy^2$ **2.** $x^2 + 5x - 7$ **3.** -480 **4.** -1680 **5.** 1
6. $x > 2$ **7.** $6x^3 - 3x^2y - 15xy$ **8.** $6x^2 + 11x - 10$ **9.** $9x^2 - 16y^2$
10. $8xy^2(2x - y)$ **11.** $(2x - 3)(4x - 5)$ **12.** $(5x - 4y)(5x + 4y)$

13. $\dfrac{29}{28}(x + 2)$ **14.** $\dfrac{5(x - 2)}{x - 1}$ **15.** $\dfrac{(x + 3)}{3}$

16. $3x - 2y = 6$

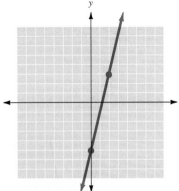

17. $y = 4x - 5$

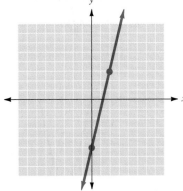

18. 5 **19.** $y = 2x - 5$ **20.** See exercise **21.** $\left(4, \dfrac{2}{3}\right)$

22. $(3, -2)$ **23.** $\left(3, \dfrac{-7}{2}\right)$ **24.** Dependent **25.** 5, 21

26. 325 reserved seat, 125 gn adm **27.** 100 mL of 30%, 200 mL of

60% **28.** 13 **29.** -13 **30.** Not possible **31.** -4 **32.** $6\sqrt{3}$

33. $30a\sqrt{3}$ **34.** $-13 - 2\sqrt{2}$ **35.** $2 - \sqrt{2}$ **36.** $\pm 6\sqrt{2}$

37. $-3 \pm 2\sqrt{3}$ **38.** $\dfrac{5 \pm \sqrt{41}}{4}$

39. $y = x^2 - 2$

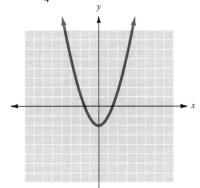

40. $y = x^2 - 4x$

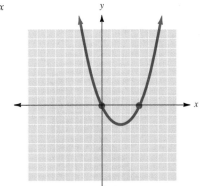

Index